ECONOMICS&
NATURAL RESOURCE
MANAGEMENT

UNIVERSITY OF
MINNESOTA

 **Learning Solutions**

Boston   Burr Ridge, IL   Dubuque, IA   New York   San Francisco   St. Louis
Bangkok   Bogotá   Caracas   Lisbon   London   Madrid   Mexico City
Milan   New Delhi   Seoul   Singapore   Sydney   Taipei   Toronto

ECONOMICS & NATURAL RESOURCE MANAGEMENT
UNIVERSITY OF MINNESOTA

This book is a McGraw-Hill Learning Solutions textbook and contains selected material from *Forest Resource Economics and Finance* by W. David Klemperer. Copyright © 1996 by W. David Klemperer. Reprinted with permission of the publisher. Many custom published texts are modified versions or adaptations of our best-selling textbooks. Some adaptations are printed in black and white to keep prices at a minimum, while others are in color.

1 2 3 4 5 6 7 8 9 0 CODE CODE 0 9 8

ISBN-13: 978-0-697-78097-3
MHID: 0-697-78097-X

Learning Solutions Specialist: Katherine Kilburg
Production Editor: Susan Culbertson
Cover Photos: © Brand X/JupiterImages; PhotoLink/Getty Images; © PhotoAlto/PunchStock; J. Luke/PhotoLink/Getty Images; © Digital Vision/PunchStock
Title Page Photo: © Brand X/JupiterImages
Cover Design: Maggie Lytle
Printer/Binder:

Primis

Contents

I have read and understand this year's class syllabus.

_____

Signature:

_____

Date:

Field: Natural Resource
Economics — An
Introduction

I. Introduction

2. Natural Resources And
The Economy

© The McGraw–Hill
Companies, 2003

CHAPTER **2**

NATURAL RESOURCES AND THE ECONOMY

An **economy** is a means by which a group of people provide themselves with adequate, and perhaps improving, levels of material and social welfare. In general, we associate economies with societies defined by national boundaries: the U.S. economy, the Japanese economy, the South African economy, and so on. Sometimes, however, we speak of the **global economy,** or of subnational economies such as one for a particular region or community.

All individuals play two roles in an economy, as producers and as consumers. In managing their economy, a society makes critical decisions about goods and services, including how much, when, and where to provide these services and the means through which this will be accomplished. They also make fundamental decisions about how these goods and services will be distributed, about who among them will have access to them and on what terms. In a market-type economy, these decisions result from the voluntary interactions of producers and consumers through **market institutions.** Such decisions are normally accompanied by varying degrees of public oversight and regulation through **governmental institutions** of different types.

Society is surrounded by, or encompassed within, a natural world. There are many ways of describing that natural system in physical terms. **Population ecology** leads us to account for it as a collection of interacting populations of organisms, subject to growth and change according to evolutionary principles and the impacts of a host of external events. A natural extension of this to

CHAPTER 2:   NATURAL RESOURCES AND THE ECONOMY

the nonbiological part of nature is to think in terms of stocks of minerals and fossil fuels, subject to chemical and physical laws. **Ecosystem ecology** puts the focus on the processes of ecosystem functioning, such as how energy flows among different trophic levels, how biophysical elements move along certain pathways, and how gases and particulates move through the atmosphere. The aim here is to clarify how various biotic and abiotic processes contribute to these ecosystem functions. Of course these two perspectives are closely related; functions are impossible without populations and vice versa.

At any point in time nature can be described by a series of variables specifying the **quantitative** and **qualitative** status of the system. The quantitative variables consist of stock variables (e.g., acres of forest, tons of marine biomass) and flow variables (e.g., energy striking the surface of the earth, wind speed), while the qualitative variables describe important features of the resources (e.g., parts per million of air pollution, salinity and temperature of water) at particular points of time. Biological and physical laws describe how these variables are transformed from one time to another.

A fruitful way of thinking about the natural resource system and its relationship to human welfare is to think of it as a **stock of natural capital** which, in conjunction with other types of inputs, yields useful **goods and services.** The word "**capital**" has been used historically in economics to refer to a stock of human-produced artifacts, such as tools, machines, and buildings.[1] The concept of "**natural capital**" is useful because it combines the notion of nature-provided inputs with the idea that their quantity and quality can be affected by human actions.

Natural capital, in conjunction with other inputs, produces a wide variety of goods and services. We can discuss these under two rubrics, as depicted in Figure 2-1: The arrow labeled (*a*) depicts the flow of **natural resource products and services** into an economy. **Natural resource economics** is the study of this flow using the analytical tools of economics. We must think of this broadly, as encompassing both traditional extractive uses and the services provided by natural resource preservation. The arrow labeled (*b*) represents the flow of

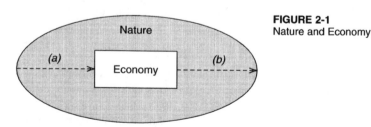

FIGURE 2-1
Nature and Economy

---

[1] There are other recognized types of capital: **working capital,** the financial assets that permit the continuity of production and consumption, and **human capital,** the capacities and capabilities of human beings.

SECTION ONE: INTRODUCTION

materials and energy **residuals** back into the natural world. This flow is the main subject of **environmental economics.**

Which particular parts of the natural world have value depends on the characteristics of the society/economy in question. At any point in time an economic system will contain a variety of **technological capabilities** (e.g., different modes of production, distribution, and communication), **economic, legal, and regulatory institutions** (e.g., private business firms, a court system, commercial law, public agencies), and an important array of **demographic factors** (e.g., tastes and preferences, population sizes, skill levels, educational institutions). It is these technological, institutional, and demographic facts that make natural resources out of arbitrary elements of nature. One-hundred years ago petroleum was not a natural resource, nor was bauxite or uranium. Sixty years ago, water resources as the provider of recreational services were almost unknown. In recent years **biological diversity** has become an important natural resource. One hundred years from now some feature of the natural world that is currently unknown may have great social value—and may be, in other words, a valuable natural resource.

So the notion of natural resources as portions of the natural world that have value must be understood in the broadest sense. We must recognize that there are dimensions of nature that may become directly utilized only at some distant time when human institutions are very different from those of today. Some of these factors are totally unknown at the present time. Thus social value also incorporates what we would regard as the future potentials of the natural world, in addition simply to those being used today.

The return flow labeled (b) in the diagram highlights services being provided by nature in the form of a "sink" for the reception of wastes. Some of these wastes may be rendered more benign through changes that are produced by the **assimilative capacity** of the environment. Some may accumulate and produce various types of negative impacts on human welfare and the health of the ecosystems comprising the natural world.

There is clearly a close relationship between natural resource economics and environmental economics. The laws of physics assure us that what is taken in by the economy, in terms of material and energy, must eventually come out. So the decisions undertaken in the context of flow (a) will have a lot to do with the problems that have to be addressed under flow (b). But convention, and the advantages of dividing the whole subject into several manageable portions, leads us to a focus in this book on the resource side of the system.[2]

Some might argue that this way of framing things tends to imply that the worth of the natural world is exclusively, or primarily, in terms of its significance for human beings:[3] Nature, it is sometimes said, has value in and of it-

---

[2] Those who would like a similar treatment of environmental economics may want to look at *Environmental Economics: An Introduction*, by Barry C. Field, 2nd ed., McGraw-Hill, New York, 1997.

[3] This is termed the "anthropocentric" point of view.

CHAPTER 2: NATURAL RESOURCES AND THE ECONOMY

self, independent of the wishes of people. We leave it to philosophers to argue about whether nonhuman organisms or entities of the natural world express values for different states of that world. This book is about how human values lead people to make decisions about natural resources. Some of these decisions may involve our preserving elements of the natural world in their undisturbed state, insofar as this can be done. We may be led to this out of a motive simply to be good **stewards** of nature, or because we are fearful of our ignorance about how nature affects human welfare. But these are as clearly the expression of human values as is the cutting down of a tree to make 2 × 4's.

SOME TERMINOLOGY

Natural resources have been critical for human welfare since people first started to walk the earth several million years ago. And conflicts over resource use have no doubt been a permanent part of this long history. In this book we take an analytical perspective on problems of natural resource use, applying somewhat formal methods and principles of social rationality to issues that engender great contention and conflict in the real world. We should be familiar with some of the main terminology that this history has produced.

Of course the primary concept is natural resource **conservation.** Battles have been fought over the meaning and application of this word.[4] It clearly has something to do with saving—or reducing—waste, but historically it has been used to cover everything from dam building, so as to reduce the "waste" implied by water runoff, to a state of moral commitment from which to launch political attacks on all the supposed villains of economic excess. Today we may say that conservation is the idea of using natural resources at a rate that is, in some sense, **socially** optimal. Of course, what is optimal for one person or group is not the same as what is correct for another, but the term does seemingly connote a course of action that finds an appropriate balance among diverse motives and avoids action that leads to waste and excessive damage.

One fault line that continues to run through public discussion is that between resource **development** and resource **preservation.** Development refers to actions that transform natural resources to a greater or lesser extent, presumably with the intent of increasing their contribution to the welfare of human beings. Preservation, on the other hand, connotes putting resources aside in a state of nonuse or in a state such that whatever use is allowed basically maintains the original status of the resource. An important modern version of this term is **scientific preservation,** in which the conflicts over development and preservation are analyzed and illuminated with sound scientific tools, especially the tools of natural science, rather than consigned solely to the emotionally charged conflicts of the political struggle. The most recent incarnation of

---

[4] See the well-known monograph of Samuel P. Hays, *Conservation and the Gospel of Efficiency. The Progressive Conservation Movement, 1890–1920,* Harvard University Press, Cambridge, MA, 1959.

SECTION ONE: INTRODUCTION

this concept is **ecosystem management,** the idea of resource management decisions based on sound principles of ecological science.

THE RANGE OF NATURAL RESOURCE SERVICES

A minimal classification of natural resources would perhaps be: land resources, water resources, and air resources. But we need to move well beyond this delineation if we are to get a more complete understanding of the number and variety of goods and services that nature provides. As a first step in this direction we distinguish between **use values** and **nonuse values.** Use value implies that attributes of nature are being utilized in some sense. This sense may be the classic one, such as when water is used to irrigate crops, which are then harvested and consumed. The sense of use may not involve traditional consumption. White-water rafting and bird watching are activities that use resources in a different sense. Scenic values involve use only in the sense that natural resources are simply present to the senses.

Nonuse values, on the other hand, are values expressed by human beings simply for the **existence** of natural resources. Existence may be related to prospects for future use, called **option value,** or the desire to leave a healthy ecosystem to future generations, called **bequest value.** People may not be using a resource at present, but may prefer actions that will ensure that the resource is available in the future, should they or future generations wish to utilize it later; in other words, it is worth something to preserve the option. But true existence values, not linked to present or possible future use, also exist. They may of course be harder to assess and measure in particular cases, but they are nonetheless real and relevant to the full set of incentives that motivate human decisions.

Table 2-1 contains a catalog of use values. These are broken down into **extractive** and **nonextractive** resources. Extractive resources are those subject to some process of physical removal from their natural surrounding and perhaps physical transformation during their use. Classic cases include the mining of ores of various types, and the harvesting of timber and its conversion to building materials. Commercial fishing, and much recreational fishing and hunting, are also extractive. It is common to use the term **natural resource products (or commodities)** to refer to quantities of physical resources that have been removed from nature and made available for use.

Nonextractive resources are those that yield valuable services without being removed from their natural setting. The classic case of a nonextractive resource is resource-based recreation, such as backpacking and river rafting. Many resources produce both extractive products and nonextractive services. Forests may produce both timber and backpacking. Water can be used for municipal and industrial water supplies and for boating.

Another important nonextractive resource service is **ecosystem protection.** One part of a resource system provides support and protection for other parts. Wetlands, for example, are usually integral parts of wider hydraulic systems,

CHAPTER 2: NATURAL RESOURCES AND THE ECONOMY

TABLE 2-1
CLASSIFICATION OF NATURAL RESOURCES

Natural resource	Natural resource products and services	
	Extractive	Nonextractive
Minerals	Nonfuel (bauxite) Fuel (coal)	Geological services (weathering)
Forests	Forest products (timber)	Recreation (backpacking) Ecosystem protection (flood control, CO_2 sequestration)
Land	Fertility	Space, scenic values
Plants	Food and fiber (agricultural crops, wild food crops) Biodiversity products (medicinal plants)	
Terrestrial animals	Food and fiber (farm animals, wild game) Biodiversity products (genetic variability)	Recreational services (bird watching, ecotourism)
Fisheries	Food (saltwater and freshwater fish)	Recreational services (recreational fishing, whale watching)
Water	Municipal and industrial supplies, irrigation	Recreation (boating)
Meteorological services	Energy sources (geothermal)	Energy sources (solar) Global radiation balances Radio spectrum Natural disasters

so their protection is important in providing protection for water resources that are subject to direct extraction, such as groundwater aquifers. Forests often provide important services in flood control and the regulation of water quality. Land and water resources in coastal areas provide important services in terms of mitigating storm damage.

The newest resource, **biological diversity,** is perhaps a special type of extractive resource. Diversity is not a feature of one ecosystem or species or gene, but of a collection of them. But the justification for preservation of diversity is often expressed in extractive terms, as a source of diversity-type products like medicines and plant characteristics. Diversity may also be important in general ecosystem maintenance. Preservation of diversity normally implies a shift away from traditional types of extractive activities.

We normally think of nature as the repository of useful goods and services, but it also supplies negative services, that is, services that may have negative value, at least to human beings. In an average year natural disasters—

SECTION ONE: INTRODUCTION

earthquakes, floods, volcano eruptions—cause enormous damage around the world. Some of these are exacerbated by human impacts on natural resources, e.g., deforestation. In all cases the need is for intelligent adjustments to manage these impacts at acceptable levels.

The dividing line between extractive and nonextractive is sometimes ambiguous. Some extractive resources are not necessarily transformed during use or are entirely lost to nature. Water that is extracted from an aquifer or river and used for irrigation may flow back into the hydraulic system at a different location, although possibly in diminished quantity and perhaps also degraded in terms of quality. The flow of zoo animals is extractive in the sense that they are removed from their natural habitats, but no physical conversion is involved. Soil fertility may be thought of as extractive in one sense, in that agricultural practices may lead to its temporary or permanent diminution. In another sense it is nonextractive, since appropriate steps can be taken for its maintenance.

MODELING RESOURCE SERVICES

There are several other ways of distinguishing among types of natural resource goods and services. In order to discuss them, however, we will adopt a slightly more formal approach. In later chapters we will be using simple analytical models to examine various natural resource problems. The material that follows in this section will give us a chance to start thinking in ways that are somewhat more formal and abstract, but that preserve the essence of the resource situations we will want to study.

Natural resource management decisions are complex because they involve connections and trade-offs between the present and the future. The connections stem from the characteristics of the resource itself, such as its biology or chemistry, and the way they are impacted by human use. Consider a situation in which there are just two time periods, period 0 and period 1. In effect period 0 could stand for today and period 1 for some time in the future, but to keep it simple think of period 0 as this year and period 1 as next year.[5]

The basic structure of a general resource use and charge problem can now be set up in the following way. Suppose that there is a certain quantity of a resource available at the beginning of period 0. During that period the resource is "used" in some amount. It is easiest to think of "use" in this case as extraction in the traditional sense. But we also interpret it in other ways. The other thing that may happen during the first period is some amount of replenishment or growth of the resource, the amount of which depends on the type of resource involved. All these factors contribute to the quantity of the resource available in period 1.

---

[5] Natural resource economics is about time, so we need a way of indexing events in different time periods. The convention that we follow throughout the book is to index today, or the present period, with a zero (e.g., q_0). Subsequent periods follow along; next year is indexed with a one (e.g., q_1), the next with a two, and so on.

CHAPTER 2:   NATURAL RESOURCES AND THE ECONOMY

We can express the basic relationship as follows:

Amount of resource available in period 1 (S_1)	=	Amount of resource available in period 0 (S_0)	−	Amount of the resource used in period 0 (Q_0)	+	Increment to the resource in period 0 (ΔS)

It is easier to write this expression in terms of the symbols shown in parentheses under each one; thus

$$S_1 = S_0 - Q_0 + \Delta S$$

The critical term is ΔS, representing the added increment of the resource that becomes available during period 0.[6] By interpreting ΔS in different ways, we can use the basic expression to describe many different types of resources.

Nonrenewable Resources

The most straightforward application of the general expression would appear to be a **nonrenewable resource.** For a **known deposit** of such a resource, we have $\Delta S = 0$; that is, there is no replenishment or increment of the resource. This being the case, the basic accounting expression becomes $S_1 = S_0 - Q_0$; the quantity available in the next period is the quantity that was available at the beginning of the present period minus the quantity used in this period. The classic example is a mineral deposit containing a given quantity of material. It is true that very long-run geological processes may be creating new deposits, but in terms of the time spans that are relevant to generations of human beings, total quantities are effectively fixed in amount.

A resource in one circumstance may be renewable; in another circumstance it may not be. Groundwater is held in underground geological formations, or aquifers. In this case, ΔS is the **recharge quantity,** the quantity that flows into the formation during a year. In some cases ΔS is essentially zero, making that aquifer a nonrenewable resource. In other cases $\Delta S > 0$, making it a renewable resource.

The basic character of nonrenewable resource changes if we move from considering a single deposit to considering **all known deposits.** Over a period of time, **exploration and development** can add to the quantity of the known stock. In this case ΔS is the quantity added to existing stocks through discovery and development. In fact this makes the situation quite complex because "new" deposits come in a variety of forms. For example, a deposit can be new in the sense of recent geological discovery, or it may be "new" in the sense that we have a new technology capable of making use of it, as compared to last year when it was geologically known but essentially beyond our reach.

---

[6] The symbol Δ is often used to denote the change in a variable of interest.

SECTION ONE: INTRODUCTION

What this tells us is that the distinction between renewable and nonrenewable resources is only partly a physical one. It is also partly an economic one. The decision to put more effort into resource exploration is an economic one; it uses resources and has certain potentials in terms of benefits. Resource development, based on human actions, can convert cases that seemingly involve nonrenewable resources into cases of renewable resources.

Recyclable Resources

Certain nonrenewable resources may be **recyclable.** A portion of the resource used in period 0 can be recycled back to add to the available supply in period 1. Here the basic expression may be rewritten as:

$$S_1 = S_0 - Q_0 + \alpha Q_0$$

where α is a percentage indicating the proportion of the first year's use that is returned via recycling. Here two basic decisions are to be made, the utilization rate Q_0 and the recycling ratio α.

Renewable Resources

A **renewable resource** is one that replenishes itself in some fashion. In this case $\Delta S > 0$, so the quantities available in period 1 are affected by the replenishment process. This may be a biological process, as for example in the case of fisheries or timber. For a forest, the amount of wood (in, e.g., cubic feet) in year 1 is what existed at the beginning, minus that which was harvested during period 0, plus the biological growth increment of the timber that was not harvested. The size of the growth increment will be related to the size of the population and also other features of the ecosystem, such as climate.

Most biological growth processes involve **accumulation** to some degree; the resource growth adds to the resource stock. Certain types of renewable resources are nonaccumulating. Consider a free-flowing river, for example. Each year a certain (no doubt fluctuating) amount of water comes down the river; this is a meteorological and geographical fact of life. But it flows by a given point and then is gone. Thus the annual replenishment does not add to any preexisting quantity. In this case our basic relationship changes to the following:

$$S_1 = \Delta S$$

The amount of the resource available in period 1 now does not depend on the rate of use during period 0.

Of course if somebody were to build a reservoir on the river, the situation would change. Now the incoming flow would augment whatever was left in the reservoir from the previous year, changing a nonaccumulating resource

CHAPTER 2: NATURAL RESOURCES AND THE ECONOMY

into an accumulating one, at least to some degree. Another example of a nonaccumulating renewable resource is the incoming stream of solar energy that strikes the earth each year. The stream itself is nonaccumulating, though of course all the biological processes it makes possible on earth represent accumulating phenomena.

This accounting expression can be applied to land resources, but it will look different according to the exact way we define the resource. If we write the formula for the total land area in a given geographical region, such as a town, the expression is simply $S_1 = S_0$. In other words, the total area is fixed and unchanging (barring political changes in town boundaries). But if we define our resource of interest as, for example, land devoted to a particular use, such as housing developments, wetlands, or land in agriculture, it would look like

$$S_1 = S_0 - Q_0 + \Delta S$$

where Q_0 is the amount of acreage taken out of that use during the year (e.g., number of acres devoted to new housing development) and ΔS is the amount of land put back into that use (e.g., wetlands restored, if our S variable of interest is acreage of wetlands).

An important feature of some natural resources is **reversibility,** expressed in terms of either quantity or quality. Usage of a natural resource is reversible if it is possible that $S_1 > S_0$. By definition, utilization of a nonrenewable resource is irreversible, at least as long as we are talking about a particular deposit. Most renewable resources are reversible; if extraction is lowered sufficiently, the natural replenishment will cause the stock to increase, at least up to some biological maximum. But many renewable resources, especially biological resources, may have **thresholds** that, once past, render the resource irreversibly changed. The classic case is a population of wildlife in which the number of adults falls below a level sufficient to support reproduction greater than mortality, and hence evolves irreversibly toward extinction. More complex cases occur, for example, where characteristics of species diversity change in an ecosystem sufficiently to set in motion forces that bring about permanent changes in many structural and functional features of that ecosystem.

SOME WORDS ABOUT ECONOMICS

This is a book about **economic analysis.** To analyze something means to examine its basic structure and the cause-and-effect relationships that govern the way it works. So to analyze the problems of saltwater fisheries, for example, we will try to understand the basic **bioeconomic** operation of the interconnected system that includes the growth and decline of fish stocks together with the human fishing effort expended on them. When we look at the role of natural resources in economic development and growth, we must try to understand the main linkages between natural resource stocks and such things as imports, exports, and rates of growth in **gross domestic product (GDP).**

SECTION ONE: INTRODUCTION

To pursue these analyses we need (1) to look at the **data** that tell us what has happened historically and what the current situation is with respect to particular natural resources, and (2) to develop simple **analytical models** with which to explore the interconnections among the important elements of each situation. A "model" in economics is an explanatory construct built up from some underlying principles and concepts, and used to examine the behavior of the economy, or some part of it. For example, the market model is built up from underlying principles of supply and of demand. The model we will use to look at issues of wildlife management contains both economic and biological concepts. A prime feature of economic models is that they are **abstract.** You got a little taste of that in the preceding section where we explored the differences among different types of resources. A model is abstract when it focuses on underlying relationships and leaves out the many factors that are not relevant to understanding those basic relationships. It is not to say that the factors left out are unimportant, only that they are not considered important in the present context. Often factors are omitted to make a model simple and easy to understand.

Natural resource problems vary over a continuum from relatively small, local issues (which are nevertheless of great importance to local communities), to larger regional problems, to all-encompassing national and global issues. The models that economics uses to study these problems must range commensurately in terms of scope and applicability. It is standard to divide economics into **microeconomics** and **macroeconomics.** Microeconomics (or just "micro" as it is often called) proceeds on the basis of detailed models of individual behavior—of consumers, producers, policy makers, and so on. These models are normally "aggregated" up so that we can derive conclusions about the performance of groups of people. Studying how individual households make choices about their use of water in and around the home—so that we might predict the affects, for example, of a tax on water use—is a problem in microeconomics. So is a study of how the logging industry in, say, Oregon, might respond to a new set of regulations on habitat preservation.

Macroeconomics, on the other hand, takes economies as a whole as the basic unit of analysis. A study on how the U.S. economy might respond to higher energy prices would probably be conducted with a macroeconomic model, one which deals directly with relationships among macro variables, such as the overall rate of unemployment, rates of economic growth, and changes in the growth patterns of major industry groupings. Another type of macroeconomic study would be one that looked at how important a role natural resource endowments have played in a country's historical pattern of economic growth. Still another would be a study to adjust commonly published measures of macroeconomic performance, gross domestic product (GDP), for example, to take into account natural resource depletion.

Many resource problems fall between these two types, and make use of both. One natural resource issue that is very common around the world is the performance of a local or regional economy that is based to some degree on

CHAPTER 2:   NATURAL RESOURCES AND THE ECONOMY

the exploitation of a natural resource (e.g., logging or mining), a resource that other groups are trying to have preserved in a natural state. A major factor in trying to determine the best course of action in such a case is knowing how the regional economy is in fact affected by changes in the availability of the resources. To get to the bottom of this we may call on both microeconomics (e.g., how will firms, workers, and consumers behave if the rates change) and macroeconomics (e.g., how will developments in the national economy affect demands for the resource). The conclusion to be drawn from this is that many resource issues call for several different types of analyses, so we need to be ready with a full array of tools to carry them out.

Another important distinction that needs to be made is that between **factual statements** and **value judgments.** In economics this is usually referred to as **positive economics** (factual) and **normative economics** (values). If somebody does an analysis of the rates at which mineral mining has grown over the last century or of the way timber prices have trended over the last few decades, they are engaged in positive economics, that is, what has actually happened in the use of these resources in these time periods. Similarly, if somebody studies how log prices and interest rates affect the rate of deforestation in some region or how fishers will respond to certain restrictions on their harvesting practices, they are also engaged in positive economics: How the world actually works, in terms of the interconnections of economic variables and the resulting rates of output, prices, and so on.

Statements as to what people **ought to do,** on the other hand, come under the heading of normative economics. If an economist recommends limiting the catch season for a certain species of fish or initiating certain policy changes to reduce the rate of soil erosion, he or she is engaging in normative economics, because the recommendations require placing value judgments on different outcomes that could result from different types of behavior.

For us to make headway in better managing the globe's natural resources, both types of economics are necessary. Policies need to be enacted and pursued, with the explicit or implicit value judgments they contain. But these policies should be based on our best understanding of how the economies and natural systems work. Activists, who are anxious to get on with doing something, are often impatient with analysts who are engaged in strictly positive analysis. The prime motivation of the latter is that better knowledge about how things actually work will allow better policies to be pursued.

THE POLITICAL UNIT PROBLEM

In the chapters that follow we will use several criteria to evaluate the performance of natural resource–using individuals and firms, and of public agencies pursuing natural resource management policies of different types. Issues of **economic efficiency** and **equity** will be encountered, as will the idea of **sustainability** in resource use. When we use such concepts, we must do it from the perspective of some specific political unit. Not political in the

SECTION ONE: INTRODUCTION

sense of bringing particular value judgments to the analyses, but in the sense of looking at things from the perspective of a given group of people. If we talk about some course of action that is economically efficient, or equitable, or sustainable, from the **social** standpoint, we have to be clear about which particular society we have in mind.

Often, economic policy and performance are evaluated from a nationalistic perspective. We will examine, for example, the policies pursued by U.S. officials to manage the stocks of fish in the coastal waters around the country. The United States has the responsibility of establishing and enforcing fisheries regulations in its own coastal waters, as other countries do in theirs. Should these policies be evaluated in terms of how well they represent the interests of the U.S. citizenry, or all of North America, or some other unit? The answers one gets may differ, depending on which perspective one takes. Exhibit 2-1 discusses a particularly interesting example of this problem in central Asia.

The problem exists also at the local and regional levels. Suppose we wish to evaluate the economic efficiency aspects of a local wetlands protection regulation. Should we evaluate this strictly from the standpoint of the one community where the wetlands is located, the region, the state, or the country? In fact

---

EXHIBIT 2-1

THE CASPIAN SEA

The Caspian Sea is a California-size body of brackish water in southeast Asia. The northern half is quite shallow, and is the main home of the Caspian sturgeon fishery, the primary world source of caviar. At various points around its borders, and within the sea itself, petroleum deposits have been exploited in the past. In recent years the pace of petroleum-related activity has heated up in the region, and many people feel that there could be a boom in oil exploration and development in the next few decades, depending on developments in the middle eastern oil fields and the building of pipelines to get the oil to export markets.

Large increases in onshore and offshore oil development and production will have huge implications for environmental quality of the region, especially through their impacts on the aquatic environment of the Caspian Sea. The people of the region will be faced with important and difficult issues about the appropriate balance between economic growth and environmental protec-

tion. Identifying and achieving this balance will be hard in light of the environmental uncertainties, political realities, and the economic aspirations of people in the region. But the Caspian Sea is bordered by five different countries (Azerbaijan, Iran, Kazakhstan, Russia, and Turkmenistan). Suppose we are trying to evaluate the performance of one of them, say Kazakhstan, regarding the use of Caspian resources and, especially, the development of petroleum resources in the Caspian basin. Suppose further that we are evaluating the cost effectiveness of Kazakhstan's planned program for protecting the water quality of the Caspian during its petroleum exploration activities. If we were to do this solely from the perspective of this one country, we might get a different answer than if we approached it from the standpoint of all the Caspian countries together. But if we do it from the standpoint of Caspian society in general, what particular group of people should we include?

CHAPTER 2: NATURAL RESOURCES AND THE ECONOMY

there is a bumper sticker that reads "Act Locally, Think Globally," which would seem to imply that we ought to evaluate all local programs like this in global terms. The upshot of this discussion is simply to make it clear that when we use criteria like efficiency, or equity, **from the social standpoint,** we need to be clear about which particular society we are talking about.

SUMMARY

Natural resource economics is the study of how the flow of goods and services derived from natural resources is, and ought to be, managed in today's world. Resource management problems derive from the underlying technological, institutional, and cultural factors that characterize an economy. **Natural resource economics** focuses on resource flows into an economy, whereas flow out of that economy back into nature is studied under **environmental economics.** There is a great variety of types of natural resource goods and services. One way of thinking about the differences among them is to take a basic accounting identity of resource use, $S_1 = S_0 - Q_0 + \Delta S$, and then alter its several terms to describe natural resources with specific characteristics. The most basic distinction between natural resources is that between **renewable** and **nonrenewable** resources. Characteristics such as **recyclability** and **reversibility** are very important. When we consider natural resource management issues, we must be very explicit about the **political unit** to which the analysis is applicable.

KEY TERMS

Natural resource
Economic, legal, and regulatory
  institutions
Natural resource services
Extractive vs. nonextractive resources
Use values vs. nonuse values
Natural resource products
  (commodities)
Ecosystem protection

Nonrenewable resources
Recyclable resources
Renewable resources
Positive and normative economic
  statements
Microeconomics and macroeconomics
Economic models
Political unit problem

QUESTIONS FOR FURTHER DISCUSSION

1 Identify several cases where certain features of the natural environment, which were not regarded as natural resources in the past, are now thought of in those terms.
2 How might the **basic resource formula** be cast so as to represent the occurrence of natural disasters (i.e., characteristics of nature that have negative values rather than positive values)? How about a natural attribute such as soil fertility?
3 Distinguish between use values and nonuse values in natural resource economics.
4 Consider a particular natural resource issue, for example the allocation of scarce water supplies among competing uses in the western United States. Give an example of a positive statement and a normative statement in the context of this problem.

SECTION ONE: INTRODUCTION

5 Suppose we are studying the extraction rates of copper ore in the United States over the last decade. There are both macro and micro factors that affect these rates. Give several possible examples of each type.

USEFUL WEB SITES

For a broad perspective on the goods and services produced by natural resources:

- International Society for Ecological Economics (http://www.isee.org).
- Sustainable Earth Exchange for Educators (links to a wide variety of web sites for resources and the environment) (http://www.class.csupomona.edu/earth.html).

For help in interpreting graphs:

- The web page for the book has a section on using and interpreting graphs. See www.mhhe.com/economics/field. Also, the main site (http://www.mhhe.com/economics) has an interactive section (called the Leading Indicator) with a graphing routine.

SELECTED READINGS

Adams, David A · *Renewable Resource Policy*, Island Press, Washington, DC, 1993.

Hays, Samuel P.: *Conservation and the Gospel of Efficiency*, Harvard University Press, Cambridge, MA, 1959.

Herfindahl, Orris C.: "What Is Conservation?" in *Three Studies in Mineral Economics*, Resources for the Future, Washington, DC, 1961.

Howe, Charles: *Natural Resource Economics*, John Wiley, New York, 1979, Chapter 1.

Poljman, Louis P. (ed.): *Environmental Ethics, Readings in Theory and Application*, Wadsworth, Belmont, CA, 1998.

Randall, Alan: *Resource Economics*, John Wiley, New York, 1987, Chapters 1 and 2.

ECONOMICS AND ECONOMIC REASONING

After reading this chapter, you should be able to:

After reading this chapter, you should be able to:

- Define economics and list three coordination problems that an economy must solve.

- Explain how to make decisions by comparing marginal costs and marginal benefits.

- Define opportunity cost and explain its relationship to economic reasoning.

- Explain real-world events in terms of economic forces, social forces, and political forces.

- Differentiate between microeconomics and macroeconomics.

- Distinguish among positive economics, normative economics, and the art of economics.

> In my vacations, I visited the poorest quarters of several cities and walked through one street after another, looking at the faces of the poorest people. Next I resolved to make as thorough a study as I could of Political Economy.
>
> —*Alfred Marshall*

When an artist looks at the world, he sees color. When a musician looks at the world, she hears music. When an economist looks at the world, she sees a symphony of costs and benefits. The economist's world might not be as colorful or as melodic as the others' worlds, but it's more practical. If you want to understand what's going on in the world that's really out there, you need to know economics.

I hardly have to convince you of this fact if you keep up with the news. Unemployment is down; the price of gas is up; interest rates are down; businesses are going bankrupt. . . . The list is endless. So let's say you grant me that economics is important. That still doesn't mean that it's worth studying. The real question then is: How much will you learn? Most of what you learn depends on you, but part depends on the teacher and another part depends on the textbook. On both these counts, you're in luck; since your teacher chose this book for your course, you must have a super teacher.[1]

WHAT ECONOMICS IS

Economics is *the study of how human beings coordinate their wants and desires, given the decision-making mechanisms, social customs, and political realities of the society.* One of the key words in the definition of the term "economics" is *coordination.* Coordination can mean many things. In the study of economics, coordination refers to how the three central problems facing any economy are solved. These central problems are:

---

[1]This book is written by a person, not a machine. That means that I have my quirks, my odd sense of humor, and my biases. All textbook writers do. Most textbooks have the quirks and eccentricities edited out so that all the books read and sound alike—professional but dull. I choose to sound like me—sometimes professional, sometimes playful, and sometimes stubborn. In my view, that makes the book more human and less dull. So forgive me my quirks—don't always take me too seriously—and I'll try to keep you awake when you're reading this book at 3 A.M. the day of the exam. If you think it's a killer to read a book this long, you ought to try writing one.

CHAPTER 1 ■ ECONOMICS AND ECONOMIC REASONING

1. What, and how much, to produce.

2. How to produce it.

3. For whom to produce it.

Three central coordination problems any economy must solve are what to produce, how to produce it, and for whom to produce it.

How hard is it to make the three decisions? Imagine for a moment the problem of living in a family: the fights, arguments, and questions that come up. "Do I have to do the dishes?" "Why can't I have piano lessons?" "Bobby got a new sweater. How come I didn't?" "Mom likes you best." Now multiply the size of the family by millions. The same fights, the same arguments, the same questions—only for society the questions are millions of time more complicated. In answering these questions, economies generally find that individuals want more than is available, given how much they're willing to work. That means that in our economy there is a problem of **scarcity**—*the goods available are too few to satisfy individuals' desires*.

The coordination questions faced by society are complicated.

Scarcity has two elements—our wants and our means of fulfilling those wants. These can be interrelated since wants are changeable and partially determined by society. The way we fulfill wants can affect those wants. For example, if you work on Wall Street you will probably want upscale and trendy clothes. Up here in Vermont, I am quite happy wearing Levi's and flannel.

The degree of scarcity is constantly changing. The quantity of goods, services, and usable resources depends on technology and human action, which underlie production. Individuals' imagination, innovativeness, and willingness to do what needs to be done can greatly increase available goods and resources. Who knows what technologies are in our future—nannites or micromachines that change atoms into whatever we want could conceivably eliminate scarcity of goods we currently consume. But they would not eliminate scarcity entirely since new wants are constantly developing.

The quantity of goods, services, and usable resources depends on technology and human action.

In all known economies, coordination has involved some type of coercion—limiting people's wants and increasing the amount of work individuals are willing to do to fulfill those wants. The reality is that many people would rather play than help solve society's problems. So the basic economic problem involves inspiring people to do things that other people want them to do, and not to do things that other people don't want them to do. Thus, an alternative definition of economics is that it is the study of how to get people to do things they're not wild about doing (such as studying) and not to do things they are wild about doing (such as eating all the lobster they like), so that the things some people want to do are consistent with the things other people want to do.

To understand an economy you need to learn:

1. *Economic reasoning.*

2. *Economic terminology.*

3. *Economic insights* economists have about issues, and theories that lead to those insights.

4. Information about *economic institutions*.

5. Information about the *economic policy options* facing society today.

Let's consider each in turn.

To understand an economy you need to learn:

1. Economic reasoning.

2. Economic terminology.

3. Economic insights.

4. Economic institutions.

5. Economic policy options.

A GUIDE TO ECONOMIC REASONING

People trained in economics think in a certain way. They analyze everything critically; they compare the costs and the benefits of every issue and make decisions based on those costs and benefits. For example, say you're trying to decide whether a policy to eliminate terrorist attacks on airlines is a good idea. Economists are trained to put their emotions aside and ask: What are the costs of the policy, and what are the benefits?

INTRODUCTION ■ THINKING LIKE AN ECONOMIST

Thus, they are open to the argument that security measures, such as conducting body searches of every passenger or scanning all baggage with bomb-detecting machinery, might not be the appropriate policy because the costs might exceed the benefits. To think like an economist is to address almost all issues using a cost/benefit approach. Economic reasoning—how to think like an economist, making decisions on the basis of costs and benefits—is the most important lesson you'll learn from this book.

Economic reasoning, once learned, is infectious. If you're susceptible, being exposed to it will change your life. It will influence your analysis of everything, including issues normally considered outside the scope of economics. For example, you will likely use economic reasoning to decide the possibility of getting a date for Saturday night, and who will pay for dinner. You will likely use it to decide whether to read this book, whether to attend class, whom to marry, and what kind of work to go into after you graduate. This is not to say that economic reasoning will provide all the answers. As you will see throughout this book, real-world questions are inevitably complicated, and economic reasoning simply provides a framework within which to approach a question. In the economic way of thinking, every choice has costs and benefits, and decisions are made by comparing them.

> **Economic reasoning is making decisions on the basis of costs and benefits.**

MARGINAL COSTS AND MARGINAL BENEFITS

The relevant costs and relevant benefits to economic reasoning are the expected *incremental*, or additional, costs incurred and the expected *incremental* benefits that result from a decision. Economists use the term *marginal* when referring to additional or incremental. Marginal costs and marginal benefits are key concepts.

A **marginal cost** is *the additional cost to you over and above the costs you have already incurred.* That means not counting **sunk costs**—*costs that have already been incurred and cannot be recovered*—in the relevant costs when making a decision. Consider, for example, attending class. You've already paid your tuition; it is a sunk cost. So the marginal (or additional) cost of going to class does not include tuition.

Similarly with marginal benefit. A **marginal benefit** is *the additional benefit above what you've already derived.* The marginal benefit of reading this chapter is the *additional* knowledge you get from reading it. If you already knew everything in this chapter before you picked up the book, the marginal benefit of reading it now is zero. The marginal benefit is not zero if by reading the chapter you learn that you are prepared for class; before, you might only have suspected you were prepared.

Comparing marginal (additional) costs with marginal (additional) benefits will often tell you how you should adjust your activities to be as well off as possible. Just follow the **economic decision rule:**

> **Web Note 1.1**
> **Costs and Benefits**

If the marginal benefits of doing something exceed the marginal costs, do it.

If the marginal costs of doing something exceed the marginal benefits, don't do it.

> **If the marginal benefits of doing something exceed the marginal costs, do it. If the marginal costs of doing something exceed the marginal benefits, don't do it.**

As an example, let's consider a discussion I might have with a student who tells me that she is too busy to attend my classes. I respond, "Think about the tuition you've spent for this class—it works out to about $30 a lecture." She answers that the book she reads for class is a book that I wrote, and that I wrote it so clearly she fully understands everything. She goes on:

> **Q-1** Say you bought a share of Sun Microsystems for $100 and a share of Cisco for $10. The price of each is currently $15. Assuming taxes are not an issue, which would you sell if you need $15?

I've already paid the tuition and whether I go to class or not, I can't get any of the tuition back, so the tuition is a sunk cost and doesn't enter into my decision. The marginal cost to me is what I could be doing with the hour instead of spending it in class. I value my time at $75 an hour [people who understand everything value their time highly], and even though I've heard that your lectures are super, I estimate that

ECONOMIC KNOWLEDGE IN ONE SENTENCE: TANSTAAFL

Knowing the Tools

Once upon a time, Tanstaafl was made king of all the lands. His first act was to call his economic advisers and tell them to write up all the economic knowledge the society possessed. After years of work, they presented their monumental effort: 25 volumes, each about 400 pages long. But in the interim, King Tanstaafl had become a very busy man, what with running a kingdom of all the lands and all. Looking at the lengthy volumes, he told his advisers to summarize their findings in one volume.

Despondently, the economists returned to their desks, wondering how they could summarize what they'd been so careful to spell out. After many more years of rewriting, they were finally satisfied with their one-volume effort, and tried to make an appointment to see the king. Unfortunately, affairs of state had become even more pressing than before, and the king couldn't take the time to see them. Instead he sent word to them that he couldn't be bothered with a whole volume, and ordered them, under threat of death (for he had become a tyrant), to reduce the work to one sentence.

The economists returned to their desks, shivering in their sandals and pondering their impossible task. Thinking about their fate if they were not successful, they decided to send out for one last meal. Unfortunately, when they were collecting money to pay for the meal, they discovered they were broke. The disgusted delivery man took the last meal back to the restaurant, and the economists started down the path to the beheading station. On the way, the delivery man's parting words echoed in their ears. They looked at each other and suddenly they realized the truth. "We're saved!" they screamed. "That's it! That's economic knowledge in one sentence!" They wrote the sentence down and presented it to the king, who thereafter fully understood all economic problems. (He also gave them a good meal.) The sentence?

There Ain't No Such Thing As A Free Lunch—
TANSTAAFL

the marginal benefit of your class is only $50. The marginal cost, $75, exceeds the marginal benefit, $50, so I don't attend class.

I congratulate her on her diplomacy and her economic reasoning, but tell her that I give a quiz every week, that students who miss a quiz fail the quiz, that those who fail all the quizzes fail the course, and that those who fail the course do not graduate. In short, she is underestimating the marginal benefits of attending my course. Correctly estimated, the marginal benefits of attending my class exceed the marginal costs. So she should attend my class.

ECONOMICS AND PASSION

Recognizing that everything has a cost is reasonable, but it's a reasonableness that many people don't like. It takes some of the passion out of life. It leads you to consider possibilities like these:

- Saving some people's lives with liver transplants might not be worth the additional cost. The money might be better spent on nutritional programs that would save 20 lives for every 2 lives you might save with transplants.
- Maybe we shouldn't try to eliminate all pollution, because the additional cost of doing so may be too high. To eliminate all pollution might be to forgo too much of some other worthwhile activity.
- Providing a guaranteed job for every person who wants one might not be a worthwhile policy goal if it means that doing so will reduce the ability of an economy to adapt to new technologies.

Economic reasoning is based on the premise that everything has a cost.

INTRODUCTION ▪ THINKING LIKE AN ECONOMIST

- It might make sense for the automobile industry to save $12 per car by not installing a safety device, even though without the safety device some people will be killed.

You get the idea. This kind of reasonableness is often criticized for being cold-hearted. But, not surprisingly, economists disagree; they argue that their reasoning leads to a better society for the majority of people.

Economists' reasonableness isn't universally appreciated. Businesses love the result; others aren't so sure, as I discovered some years back when my then-girlfriend told me she was leaving me. "Why?" I asked. "Because," she responded, "you're so, so . . . reasonable." It took me many years after she left to learn what she already knew: There are many types of reasonableness, and not everyone thinks an economist's reasonableness is a virtue. I'll discuss such issues later; for now, let me simply warn you that, for better or worse, studying economics will lead you to view questions in a cost/benefit framework.

OPPORTUNITY COST

Putting economists' cost/benefit rules into practice isn't easy. To do so, you have to be able to choose and measure the costs and benefits correctly. Economists have devised the concept of opportunity cost to help you do that. The **opportunity cost** of undertaking an activity is *the benefit forgone by undertaking that activity*. The benefit forgone is the benefit that you might have gained from choosing the next-best alternative. To obtain the benefit of something, you must give up (forgo) something else—namely, the next-best alternative. All activities that have a next-best alternative have an opportunity cost.

Let's consider some examples. The opportunity cost of going out once with Natalie (or Nathaniel), the most beautiful woman (attractive man) in the world, might well be losing your solid steady, Margo (Mike). The opportunity cost of cleaning up the environment might be a reduction in the money available to assist low-income individuals. The opportunity cost of having a child might be two boats, three cars, and a two-week vacation each year for five years.

Examples are endless, but let's consider two that are particularly relevant to you: your choice of courses and your decision about how much to study. Let's say you're a full-time student and at the beginning of the term you had to choose four or five courses to take. Taking one precluded taking some other, and the opportunity cost of taking an economics course may well have been not taking a course on theater. Similarly with studying: You have a limited amount of time to spend studying economics, studying some other subject, sleeping, or partying. The more time you spend on one activity, the less time you have for another. That's opportunity cost.

Notice how neatly the opportunity cost concept takes into account costs and benefits of all other options, and converts these alternative benefits into costs of the decision you're now making.

The relevance of opportunity cost isn't limited to your individual decisions. Opportunity costs are also relevant to government's decisions, which affect everyone in society. A common example is the guns-versus-butter debate. The resources that a society has are limited; therefore, its decision to use those resources to have more guns (more weapons) means that it must have less butter (fewer consumer goods).

Q.2 Can you think of a reason why a cost/benefit approach to a problem might be inappropriate? Can you give an example?

Opportunity cost is the basis of cost/benefit economic reasoning; it is the benefit forgone, or the cost, of the next-best alternative to the activity you've chosen. In economic reasoning, that cost is less than the benefit of what you've chosen.

Opportunity costs have always made choice difficult, as we see in the early-19th-century engraving, "One or the Other."
Bleichroeder Print Collection, Baker Library, Harvard Business School.

CHAPTER 1 ■ ECONOMICS AND ECONOMIC REASONING

Thus, when society decides to spend $50 billion more on an improved health care system, the opportunity cost of that decision is $50 billion not spent on helping the homeless, paying off some of the national debt, or providing for national defense.

The opportunity cost concept has endless implications. It can even be turned upon itself. For instance, it takes time to think about alternatives; that means that there's a cost to being reasonable, so it's only reasonable to be somewhat unreasonable. If you followed that argument, you've caught the economic bug. If you didn't, don't worry. Just remember the opportunity cost concept for now; I'll infect you with economic thinking in the rest of the book.

ECONOMIC AND MARKET FORCES

The opportunity cost concept applies to all aspects of life and is fundamental to understanding how society reacts to scarcity. When goods are scarce, those goods must be rationed. That is, a mechanism must be chosen to determine who gets what. Society must deal with the scarcity, thinking about and deciding how to allocate the scarce good.

Let's consider some specific real-world rationing mechanisms. Dormitory rooms are often rationed by lottery, and permission to register in popular classes is often rationed by a first-come, first-registered rule. Food in the United States, however, is generally rationed by price. If price did not ration food, there wouldn't be enough food to go around. All scarce goods or rights must be rationed in some fashion. These rationing mechanisms are examples of **economic forces,** *the necessary reactions to scarcity.*

One of the important choices that a society must make is whether to allow these economic forces to operate freely and openly or to try to rein them in. A **market force** is *an economic force that is given relatively free rein by society to work through the market.* Market forces ration by changing prices. When there's a shortage, the price goes up. When there's a surplus, the price goes down. Much of this book will be devoted to analyzing how the market works like an invisible hand, guiding economic forces to coordinate individual actions and allocate scarce resources. The **invisible hand** is *the price mechanism, the rise and fall of prices that guides our actions in a market.*

Societies can't choose whether or not to allow economic forces to operate—economic forces are always operating. However, societies can choose whether to allow market forces to predominate. Social, cultural, and political forces play a major role in deciding whether to let market forces operate. Economic reality is determined by a contest among these various forces.

Let's consider an example in which social forces prevent an economic force from becoming a market force: the problem of getting a date for Saturday night. If a school (or a society) has significantly more people of one gender than the other (let's say more men than women), some men may well find themselves without a date—that is, men will be in excess supply—and will have to find something else to do, say study or go to a movie by themselves. An "excess supply" person could solve the problem by paying someone to go out with him or her, but that would probably change the nature of the date in unacceptable ways. It would be revolting to the person who offered payment and to the person who was offered payment. That unacceptability is an example of the complex social and cultural norms that guides and limits our activities. People don't try to buy dates because social forces prevent them from doing so.

Now let's consider another example in which political and legal influences stop economic forces from becoming market forces. Say you decide that you can make some money delivering mail in your neighborhood. You try to establish a small business, but suddenly you are confronted with the law. The U.S. Postal Service has a legal exclusive right to deliver regular mail, so you'll be prohibited from delivering regular mail

Q-3 John, your study partner, has just said that the opportunity cost of studying this chapter is about 1/21 the price you paid for this book, since the chapter is about 1/21 of the book. Is he right? Why or why not?

Q-4 Ali, your study partner, states that rationing health care is immoral—that health care should be freely available to all individuals in society. How would you respond?

When an economic force operates through the market, it becomes a market force.

Economic reality is controlled by three forces:

1. Economic forces (the invisible hand),
2. Social and cultural forces, and
3. Political and legal forces.

Social and cultural forces can play a significant role in the economy.

Q-5 Your study partner, Joan, states that market forces are always operative. Is she right? Why or why not?

ECONOMICS IN PERSPECTIVE

All too often, students study economics out of context. They're presented with sterile analysis and boring facts to memorize, and are never shown how economics fits into the larger scheme of things. That's bad; it makes economics seem boring—but economics is not boring. Every so often throughout this book, sometimes in the appendixes and sometimes in boxes, I'll step back and put the analysis in perspective, giving you an idea from whence the analysis sprang and its historical context. In educational jargon, this is called *enrichment*.

I begin here with economics itself.

First, its history: In the 1500s there were few universities. Those that existed taught religion, Latin, Greek, philosophy, history, and mathematics. No economics. Then came the *Enlightenment* (about 1700), in which reasoning replaced God as the explanation of why things were the way they were. Pre-Enlightenment thinkers would answer the question "Why am I poor?" with "Because God wills it." Enlightenment scholars looked for a different explanation. "Because of the nature of land ownership" is one answer they found.

Such reasoned explanations required more knowledge of the way things were, and the amount of information expanded so rapidly that it had to be divided or categorized for an individual to have hope of knowing a subject. Soon philosophy was subdivided into science and philosophy. In the 1700s, the sciences were split into natural sciences and social sciences. The amount of knowledge kept increasing, and in the late 1800s and early 1900s social science itself split into subdivisions: economics, political science, history, geography, sociology, anthropology, and psychology. Many of the insights about how the economic system worked were codified in Adam Smith's *The Wealth of Nations,* written in 1776. Notice that this is before economics as a subdiscipline developed, and Adam Smith could also be classified as an anthropologist, a sociologist, a political scientist, and a social philosopher.

Throughout the 18th and 19th centuries, economists such as Adam Smith, Thomas Malthus, John Stuart Mill, David Ricardo, and Karl Marx were more than economists; they were social philosophers who covered all aspects of social science. These writers were subsequently called *classical economists.* Alfred Marshall continued in that classical tradition, and his book, *Principles of Economics,* published in the late 1800s, was written with the other social sciences much in evidence. But Marshall also changed the questions economists ask; he focused on those questions that could be asked in a graphical supply/demand framework.

This book falls solidly in the Marshallian tradition. It sees economics as a way of thinking—as an engine of analysis used to understand real-world phenomena.

Marshallian economics is primarily about policy, not theory. It sees institutions as well as political and social dimensions of reality as important, and it shows you how economics ties in to those dimensions.

---

in competition with the post office. Economic forces—the desire to make money—led you to want to enter the business, but in this case political forces squash the invisible hand.

Often political and social forces work together against the invisible hand. For example, in the United States there aren't enough babies to satisfy all the couples who desire them. Babies born to particular sets of parents are rationed—by luck. Consider a group of parents, all of whom want babies. Those who can, have a baby; those who can't have one, but want one, try to adopt. Adoption agencies ration the available babies. Who gets a baby depends on whom people know at the adoption agency and on the desires of the birth mother, who can often specify the socioeconomic background (and many other characteristics) of the family in which she wants her baby to grow up. That's the economic force in action; it gives more power to the supplier of something that's in short supply.

If our society allowed individuals to buy and sell babies, that economic force would be translated into a market force. The invisible hand would see to it that the quantity

Economic forces are always operative; society may allow market forces to operate.

Web Note 1.2
Society and Markets

CHAPTER 1 ■ ECONOMICS AND ECONOMIC REASONING

of babies supplied would equal the quantity of babies demanded at some price. The market, not the adoption agencies, would do the rationing.[2]

Most people, including me, find the idea of selling babies repugnant. But why? It's the strength of social forces reinforced by political forces.

What is and isn't allowable differs from one society to another. For example, in Cuba and North Korea, many private businesses are against the law, so not many people start their own businesses. In the United States, until the 1970s, it was against the law to hold gold except in jewelry and for certain limited uses such as dental supplies, so most people refrained from holding gold. Ultimately a country's laws and social norms determine whether the invisible hand will be allowed to work.

Social and political forces are active in all parts of your life. Political forces influence many of your everyday actions. You don't practice medicine without a license; you don't sell body parts or certain addictive drugs. These actions are against the law. But many people do sell alcohol; that's not against the law if you have a permit. Social forces also influence us. You don't make profitable loans to your friends (you don't charge your friends interest); you don't charge your children for their food (parents are supposed to feed their children); many sports and media stars don't sell their autographs (some do, but many consider the practice tacky); you don't lower the wage you'll accept in order to get a job away from someone else (you're no scab). The list is long. You cannot understand economics without understanding the limitations that political and social forces place on economic actions.

In summary, what happens in a society can be seen as the reaction to, and interaction of, these three forces: economic forces, political and legal forces, and social and historical forces. Economics has a role to play in sociology, history, and politics, just as sociology, history, and politics have roles to play in economics.

Economics is about the real world. Throughout this book I'll use the forces just described to talk about real-world events and the interrelationships of economics, history, sociology, and politics.

What happens in society can be seen as a reaction to, and interaction of, economic forces, political forces, social forces, and historical forces.
Rachel Epstein/Photoedit

ECONOMIC TERMINOLOGY

Economic terminology needs little discussion. It simply needs learning. As terms come up, you'll begin to recognize them. Soon you'll begin to understand them, and finally you'll begin to feel comfortable using them. In this book I'm trying to describe how economics works in the real world, so I introduce you to many of the terms that occur in business and in discussions of the economy. Whenever possible I'll integrate the introduction of new terms into the discussion so that learning them will seem painless. In fact I've already introduced you to a number of economic terms: *opportunity cost, the invisible hand, market forces, economic forces,* just to name a few. By the end of the book I'll have introduced you to hundreds more.

ECONOMIC INSIGHTS

Economists have thought about the economy for a long time, so it's not surprising that they've developed some insights into the way it works.

---

[2]Even though it's against the law, some babies are nonetheless "sold" on a semilegal market, also called a gray market. At the turn of the century, the "market price" for a healthy baby was about $30,000. If it were legal to sell babies (and if people didn't find it morally repugnant to have babies in order to sell them), the price would be much lower, because there would be a larger supply of babies. (It was not against the law to sell human eggs in the early 2000s, and one human egg was sold for $50,000. The average price was much lower; it varied with donor characteristics such as SAT scores and athletic accomplishments.)

INTRODUCTION ■ THINKING LIKE AN ECONOMIST

These insights are often based on generalizations, called theories, about the workings of an abstract economy. Theories tie together economists' terminology and knowledge about economic institutions. Theories are inevitably too abstract to apply in specific cases, and thus a theory is often embodied in an **economic model**—*a framework that places the generalized insights of the theory in a more specific contextual setting*—or in an **economic principle**—*a commonly held economic insight stated as a law or general assumption*. Then these theories, models, and principles are empirically tested (as best one can) to ensure that they correspond to reality. Because economics is an observational, not a laboratory, science, economists cannot test their models with controlled experiments. Instead, economists must carefully observe the economy and try to figure out what is affecting what. To do so they look for natural experiments, where something has changed in one place (say the minimum wage in New Jersey) but has not changed somewhere else (say the minimum wage in Pennsylvania) and compare the results in the two cases. But even in cases where there is a natural experiment, it is impossible to hold "other things constant," as is done in laboratory experiments, and thus the empirical results in economics are often subject to dispute.

While economic models and principles are less general than theories, they are still usually too general to apply in specific cases. Theories, models, and principles must be combined with a knowledge of real-world economic institutions to arrive at specific policy recommendations.

> Theories, models, and principles must be combined with a knowledge of real-world economic institutions to arrive at specific policy recommendations.

To see the importance of principles, think back to when you learned to add. You didn't memorize the sum of 147 and 138; instead you learned a principle of addition. The principle says that when adding 147 and 138, you first add $7 + 8$, which you memorized was 15. You write down the 5 and carry the 1, which you add to $4 + 3$ to get 8. Then add $1 + 1 = 2$. So the answer is 285. When you know just one principle, you know how to add millions of combinations of numbers.

THE INVISIBLE HAND THEORY

In the same way, knowing a theory gives you insight into a wide variety of economic phenomena, even though you don't know the particulars of each phenomenon. For example, much of economic theory deals with the *pricing mechanism* and how the market operates to coordinate *individuals' decisions*. Economists have come to the following insights:

> **Q-6** There has been a superb growing season and the quantity of tomatoes supplied exceeds the quantity demanded. What is likely to happen to the price of tomatoes?

When the quantity supplied is greater than the quantity demanded, price has a tendency to fall.

When the quantity demanded is greater than the quantity supplied, price has a tendency to rise.

Using these generalized insights, economists have developed a theory of markets that leads to the further insight that, under certain conditions, markets are efficient. That is, the market will coordinate individuals' decisions, allocating scarce resources to their best possible use. **Efficiency** means *achieving a goal as cheaply as possible*. Economists call this insight the **invisible hand theory**—*a market economy, through the price mechanism, will tend to allocate resources efficiently*.

Theories, and the models used to represent them, are enormously efficient methods of conveying information, but they're also necessarily abstract. They rely on simplifying assumptions, and *if you don't know the assumptions, you don't know the theory*. The result of forgetting assumptions could be similar to what happens if you forget that you're supposed to add numbers in columns. Forgetting that, yet remembering all the steps, can lead to a wildly incorrect answer. For example,

WINSTON CHURCHILL AND LADY ASTOR

Applying the Tools

There are many stories about Nancy Astor, the first woman elected to Britain's Parliament. A vivacious, fearless American woman, she married into the English aristocracy and, during the 1930s and 1940s, became a bright light on the English social and political scenes, which were already quite bright.

One story told about Lady Astor is that she and Winston Churchill, the unorthodox genius who had a long and distinguished political career and who was Britain's prime minister during World War II, were sitting in a pub having a theoretical discussion about morality. Churchill suggested that as a thought experiment Lady Astor ponder the following question: If a man were to promise her a huge amount of money—say a million pounds—for the privilege, would she sleep with him? Lady Astor did ponder the question for a while and finally answered, yes, she would, if the money

were guaranteed. Churchill then asked her if she would sleep with him for five pounds. Her response was sharp: "Of course not. What do you think I am—a prostitute?" This time Churchill won the battle of wits by answering, "We have already established that fact; we are now simply negotiating about price."

One moral that economists might draw from this story is that economic incentives, if high enough, can have a powerful influence on behavior. An equally important moral of the story is that noneconomic incentives can also be very strong. Why do most people feel it's wrong to sell sex for money, even if they would be willing to do so if the price were high enough? Keeping this second moral in mind will significantly increase your economic understanding of real-world events.

```
   147
+  138
```
1,608 is wrong.

Knowing the assumptions of theories and models allows you to progress beyond gut reaction and better understand the strengths and weaknesses of various economic systems. Let's consider a central economic assumption: the assumption that individuals behave rationally—that what they choose reflects what makes them happiest, given the constraints. If that assumption doesn't hold, the invisible hand theory doesn't hold.

Presenting the invisible hand theory in its full beauty is an important part of any economics course. Presenting the assumptions on which it is based and the limitations of the invisible hand is likewise an important part of the course. I'll do both throughout the book.

ECONOMIC THEORY AND STORIES

Economic theory, and the models in which that theory is presented, often developed as a shorthand way of telling a story. These stories are important; they make the theory come alive and convey the insights that give economic theory its power. In this book I present plenty of theories and models, but they're accompanied by stories that provide the context that makes them relevant.

Theory is a shorthand way of telling a story.

At times, because there are many new terms, discussing models and theories takes up much of the presentation time and becomes a bit oppressive. That's the nature of the beast. As Albert Einstein said, "Theories should be as simple as possible, but not more so." When a theory or a model becomes oppressive, pause and think about the underlying story that the theory is meant to convey. That story should make sense and be concrete. If you can't translate the theory into a story, you don't understand the theory.

MICROECONOMICS AND MACROECONOMICS

Economic theory is divided into two parts: microeconomic theory and macroeconomic theory. Microeconomic theory considers economic reasoning from the viewpoint of individuals and firms and builds up from there to an analysis of the whole economy. I define **microeconomics** as *the study of individual choice, and how that choice is influenced by economic forces.* Microeconomics studies such things as the pricing policies of firms, households' decisions on what to buy, and how markets allocate resources among alternative ends. Our discussion of opportunity cost was based on microeconomic theory. The invisible hand theory comes from microeconomics.

> Microeconomics is the study of how individual choice is influenced by economic forces.

As one builds up from microeconomic analysis to an analysis of the entire economy, everything gets rather complicated. Many economists try to uncomplicate matters by taking a different approach—a macroeconomic approach—first looking at the aggregate, or whole, and then breaking it down into components. I define **macroeconomics** as *the study of the economy as a whole.* It considers the problems of inflation, unemployment, business cycles, and growth. Macroeconomics focuses on aggregate relationships such as how household consumption is related to income and how government policies can affect growth. A micro approach would analyze a person by looking first at each individual cell and then building up. A macro approach would start with the person and then go on to his or her components—arms, legs, fingernails, feelings, and so on. Put simply, microeconomics analyzes from the parts to the whole; macroeconomics analyzes from the whole to the parts.

> Macroeconomics is the study of the economy as a whole. It considers the problems of inflation, unemployment, business cycles, and growth.

Microeconomics and macroeconomics are very much interrelated. Clearly, what happens in the economy as a whole is based on individual decisions, but individual decisions are made within an economy and can be understood only within that context. For example, whether a firm decides to expand production capacity will depend on what the owners expect will happen to the demand for their products. Those expectations are determined by macroeconomic conditions. Likewise, decisions by the federal government to change the welfare program in the mid-1990s had to be made based on how those changes would affect the decisions of millions of individuals. Because microeconomics focuses on the individual and macroeconomics focuses on the whole economy, traditionally microeconomics and macroeconomics are taught separately, even though they are interrelated.

> **Q-7** Classify the following topics as macroeconomic or microeconomic:
>
> 1. The impact of a tax increase on aggregate output.
> 2. The relationship between two competing firms' pricing behavior.
> 3. A farmer's decision to plant soy or wheat.
> 4. The effect of trade on economic growth.

ECONOMIC INSTITUTIONS

To know whether you can apply economic theory to reality, you must know about economic institutions—laws, common practices, and organizations in a society that affect the economy. Corporations, governments, and cultural norms are all examples of economic institutions. Many economic institutions have social, political, and religious dimensions. For example, your job often influences your social standing. In addition, many social institutions, such as the family, have economic functions. If any institution significantly affects economic decisions, I include it as an economic institution because you must understand that institution if you are to understand how the economy functions.

> To apply economic theory to reality, you've got to have a sense of economic institutions.

Economic institutions differ significantly among countries. For example, in Germany banks are allowed to own companies; in the United States they cannot. This contributes to a difference in the flow of resources into investment in Germany as compared to the flow in the United States. Alternatively, in the Netherlands workers are highly unionized, while in the United States they are not. Unions in the Netherlands

ECONOMISTS AND MARKET SOLUTIONS

Applying the Tools

Economic reasoning is playing an increasing role in government policy. Consider the regulation of pollution. Pollution became a policy concern in the 1960s as books such as Rachel Carson's *Silent Spring* were published. In 1970, in response to concerns about the environment, the Clean Air Act was passed. It capped the amount of pollutants (such as sulfur dioxide, carbon monoxide, nitrogen dioxides, lead, and hydrocarbons) that firms could emit. This was a "command-and-control" approach to regulation, which brought about a reduction in pollution, but also brought about lots of complaints by firms that either found the limits costly to meet or couldn't afford to meet them and were forced to close.

Enter economists. They proposed an alternative approach, called cap-and-trade, that achieved the same overall reduction in pollution, but at a lower overall cost. In the plan they proposed, government still set a pollution cap that firms had to meet, but it gave individual firms some flexibility. Firms that reduced emissions by less than the required limit could buy pollution permits from other firms that reduced their emissions by more than their limit. The price of the permits would be determined in an "emissions permit market." Thus, firms that had a low cost of reducing pollution would have a strong incentive to reduce pollution by more than their limit in order to sell these permits, or rights to pollute, to firms that had a high cost of reducing pollution and therefore reduced their pollution by less than what was required. The net reduction was the same, but the reduction was achieved at a lower cost.

In 1990 Congress adopted economists' proposal and the Clean Air Act was amended to include tradable emissions permits. An active market in emissions permits developed and it is estimated that the tradable permit program has lowered the cost of reducing sulfur dioxide emissions by $1 billion a year. Economists today are using this same argument to promote an incentive-based solution to world pollution in an agreement among some countries to reduce world pollution known as the Kyoto Protocol.

therefore have the power to agree to restrain wage demands in exchange for job creation. This means that inflation control policy is different in these two countries; recently, the Netherlands has been able to keep the unemployment rate at about 2 percent, compared to 6 percent in the United States.

Economic institutions sometimes seem to operate in ways quite different than economic theory predicts. For example, economic theory says that prices are determined by supply and demand. However, businesses say that prices are set by rules of thumb—often by what are called cost-plus-markup rules. That is, you determine what your costs are, multiply by 1.4 or 1.5, and the result is the price you set. Economic theory says that supply and demand determine who's hired; experience suggests that hiring is often done on the basis of whom you know, not by economic forces.

These apparent contradictions have two complementary explanations. First, economic theory abstracts from many issues. These issues may account for the differences. Second, there's no contradiction; economic principles often affect decisions from behind the scenes. For instance, supply and demand pressures determine what the price markup over cost will be. In all cases, however, to apply economic theory to reality—to gain the full value of economic insights—you've got to have a sense of economic institutions.

ECONOMIC POLICY OPTIONS

Economic policies are *actions (or inaction) taken by government to influence economic actions.* The final goal of the course is to present the economic policy options facing our society today. For example, should the government restrict mergers between firms?

INTRODUCTION ■ THINKING LIKE AN ECONOMIST

Should it run a budget deficit? Should it do something about the international trade deficit? Should it decrease taxes?

I saved this discussion for last because there's no sense talking about policy options unless you know some economic terminology, some economic theory, and something about economic institutions. Once you know something about them, you're in a position to consider the policy options available for dealing with the economic problems our society faces.

Policies operate within institutions, but policies can also influence the institutions within which they operate. Let's consider an example: welfare policy and the institution of the two-parent family. In the 1960s, the United States developed a variety of policy initiatives designed to eliminate poverty. These initiatives directed income to single parents with children, and assumed that family structure would be unchanged by these policies. But family structure did not remain unchanged; it changed substantially, and, very likely, these policies to eliminate poverty played a role in increasing the number of single-parent families. The result was a failure of the programs to eliminate poverty. Now this is not to say that we should not have programs to eliminate poverty, or that two-parent families are always preferable to one-parent families; it is only to say that we must build into our policies their effect on institutions.

Some policies are designed to change institutions directly. While these policies are much more difficult to implement than policies that don't, they also offer the largest potential for gain. Let's consider an example. In the 1990s, a number of Eastern and Central European countries decided to replace central planning with market economies. The result: Output in those countries fell enormously as the old institutions fell apart. While most Central European countries have rebounded from their initial losses, some countries of former Soviet Union have yet to do so. The hardships these countries continue to experience show the enormous difficulty of implementing policies involving major institutional changes.

OBJECTIVE POLICY ANALYSIS

Good economic policy analysis is objective; that is, it keeps the analyst's value judgments separate from the analysis. Objective analysis does not say, "This is the way things should be," reflecting a goal established by the analyst. That would be subjective analysis because it would reflect the analyst's view of how things should be. Instead, objective analysis says, "This is the way the economy works, and if society (or the individual or firm for whom you're doing the analysis) wants to achieve a particular goal, this is how it might go about doing so." Objective analysis keeps, or at least tries to keep, subjective views—value judgments—separate.

To make clear the distinction between objective and subjective analysis, economists have divided economics into three categories: *positive economics*, *normative economics*, and the *art of economics*. **Positive economics** is *the study of what is, and how the economy works*. It asks such questions as: How does the market for hog bellies work? How do price restrictions affect market forces? These questions fall under the heading of economic theory. **Normative economics** is *the study of what the goals of the economy should be*. Normative economics asks such questions as: What should the distribution of income be? What should tax policy be designed to achieve? In discussing such questions, economists must carefully delineate whose goals they are discussing. One cannot simply assume that one's own goals for society are society's goals.

The **art of economics** is *the application of the knowledge learned in positive economics to the achievement of the goals one has determined in normative economics*. It looks at such questions as: To achieve a certain distribution of income, how would you go about

---

To carry out economic policy effectively one must understand how institutions might change as a result of the economic policy.

Q-8 True or false? Economists should focus their policy analysis on institutional changes because such policies offer the largest gains.

 Q-9 John, your study partner, is a free market advocate. He argues that the invisible hand theory tells us that the government should not interfere with the economy. Do you agree? Why or why not?

Web Note 1.3
The Art of Economics

Positive economics is the study of what is, and how the economy works.

Normative economics is the study of what the goals of the economy should be.

The *art of economics* is the application of the knowledge learned in positive economics to the achievement of the goals determined in normative economics.

CHAPTER 1 ■ ECONOMICS AND ECONOMIC REASONING

it, given the way the economy works?[3] Most policy discussions fall under the art of economics.

In each of these three branches of economics, economists separate their own value judgments from their objective analysis as much as possible. The qualifier "as much as possible" is important, since some value judgments inevitably sneak in. We are products of our environment, and the questions we ask, the framework we use, and the way we interpret empirical evidence all embody value judgments and reflect our backgrounds.

Maintaining objectivity is easiest in positive economics, where one is working with abstract models to understand how the economy works. Maintaining objectivity is harder in normative economics. You must always be objective about whose normative values you are using. It's easy to assume that all of society shares your values, but that assumption is often wrong.

It's hardest to maintain objectivity in the art of economics because it embodies the problems of both positive and normative economics. Because noneconomic forces affect policy, to practice the art of economics we must make judgments about how these noneconomic forces work. These judgments are likely to embody our own value judgments. So we must be exceedingly careful to be as objective as possible in practicing the art of economics.

POLICY AND SOCIAL AND POLITICAL FORCES

When you think about the policy options facing society, you'll quickly discover that the choice of policy options depends on much more than economic theory. Politicians, not economists, determine economic policy. To understand what policies are chosen, you must take into account historical precedent plus social, cultural, and political forces. In an economics course, I don't have time to analyze these forces in as much depth as I'd like. That's one reason there are separate history, political science, sociology, and anthropology courses.

While it is true that these other forces play significant roles in policy decisions, specialization is necessary. In economics, we focus the analysis on the invisible hand, and much of economic theory is devoted to considering how the economy would operate if the invisible hand were the only force operating. But as soon as we apply theory to reality and policy, we must take into account political and social forces as well.

An example will make my point more concrete. Most economists agree that holding down or eliminating tariffs (taxes on imports) and quotas (numerical limitations on imports) makes good economic sense. They strongly advise governments to follow a policy of free trade. Do governments follow free trade policies? Almost invariably they do not. Politics leads society in a different direction. If you're advising a policy maker, you need to point out that these other forces must be taken into account, and how other forces should (if they should) and can (if they can) be integrated with your recommendations.

CONCLUSION

There's tons more that could be said by way of introducing you to economics, but an introduction must remain an introduction. As it is, this chapter should have:

Q-10 Tell whether the following five statements belong in positive economics, normative economics, or the art of economics.

1. We should support the market because it is efficient.

2. Given certain conditions, the market achieves efficient results.

3. Based on past experience and our understanding of markets, if one wants a reasonably efficient result, markets should probably be relied on.

4. The distribution of income should be left to markets.

5. Markets allocate income according to contributions of factors of production.

---

[3]This three-part distinction was made back in 1896 by a famous economist, John Neville Keynes, father of John Maynard Keynes, the economist who developed macroeconomics. This distinction was instilled into modern economics by Milton Friedman and Richard Lipsey in the 1950s. They, however, downplayed the art of economics, which J. N. Keynes had seen as central to understanding the economist's role in policy.

INTRODUCTION ▓ THINKING LIKE AN ECONOMIST

1. Introduced you to economic reasoning.
2. Surveyed what we're going to cover in this book.
3. Given you an idea of my writing style and approach.

We'll be spending long hours together over the coming term, and before entering into such a commitment it's best to know your partner. While I won't know you, by the end of this book you'll know me. Maybe you won't love me as my mother does, but you'll know me.

This introduction was my opening line. I hope it also conveyed the importance and relevance that belong to economics. If it did, it has served its intended purpose. Economics is tough, but tough can be fun.

SUMMARY

- The three coordination problems any economy must solve are what to produce, how to produce it, and for whom to produce it. In solving these problems economies have found that there is a problem of scarcity.

- Economic reasoning structures all questions in a cost/benefit frame: If the marginal benefits of doing something exceed the marginal costs, do it. If the marginal costs exceed the marginal benefits, don't do it.

- Sunk costs are not relevant to the economic decision rule.

- The opportunity cost of undertaking an activity is the benefit you might have gained from choosing the next-best alternative.

- "There ain't no such thing as a free lunch" (TANSTAAFL) embodies the opportunity cost concept.

- Economic forces, the forces of scarcity, are always working. Market forces, which ration by changing prices, are not always allowed to work.

- Economic reality is controlled and directed by three types of forces: economic forces, political forces, and social forces.

- Under certain conditions the market, through its price mechanism, will allocate scarce resources efficiently.

- Economics can be divided into microeconomics and macroeconomics. Microeconomics is the study of individual choice and how that choice is influenced by economic forces. Macroeconomics is the study of the economy as a whole. It considers problems such as inflation, unemployment, business cycles, and growth.

- Economics can be subdivided into positive economics, normative economics, and the art of economics. Positive economics is the study of what is, normative economics is the study of what should be, and the art of economics relates positive to normative economics.

KEY TERMS

art of economics (16)	economic principle (12)	macroeconomics (14)	opportunity cost (8)
economic decision rule (6)	economics (4)	marginal benefit (6)	positive economics (16)
economic force (9)	efficiency (12)	marginal cost (6)	scarcity (5)
economic model (12)	invisible hand (9)	market force (9)	sunk cost (6)
economic policy (15)	invisible hand theory (12)	microeconomics (14)	
		normative economics (16)	

QUESTIONS FOR THOUGHT AND REVIEW

1. What is the textbook author's reasoning for focusing the definition of economics on coordination rather than on scarcity?

2. List two recent choices you made and explain why you made those choices in terms of marginal benefits and marginal costs.

3. At times we all regret decisions. Does this necessarily mean we did not use the economic decision rule when making the decision?

4. What is the opportunity cost of buying a $20,000 car?

5. Suppose you currently earn $30,000 a year. You are considering a job that will increase your lifetime earnings by $300,000 but that requires an MBA. The job will mean also attending business school for two years at an annual cost of $25,000. You already have a bachelor's degree, for which you spent $80,000 in tuition and books. Which of the above information is relevant to your decision whether to take the job? What other information would be relevant?

6. Suppose your college has been given $5 million. You have been asked to decide how to spend it to improve your college. Explain how you would use the economic decision rule and the concept of opportunity costs to decide how to spend it.

7. Name three ways a limited number of dormitory rooms could be rationed. How would economic forces determine individual behavior in each? How would social or legal forces determine whether those economic forces become market forces?

8. Give two examples of social forces and explain how they keep economic forces from becoming market forces.

9. Give two examples of political or legal forces and explain how they might interact with the invisible hand.

10. What is an economic model? What besides a model do economists need to make policy recommendations?

11. Does economic theory prove that the free market system is best? Why?

12. List two microeconomic and two macroeconomic problems.

13. Name an economic institution and explain how it either embodies economic principles or affects economic decision making.

14. Is a good economist always objective? Why?

PROBLEMS AND EXERCISES

1. You rent a car for $29.95. The first 150 miles are free, but each mile thereafter costs 15 cents. You drive it 200 miles. What is the marginal cost of driving the car?

2. Calculate, using the best estimates you can:
   a. Your opportunity cost of attending college.
   b. Your opportunity cost of taking this course.
   c. Your opportunity cost of attending yesterday's lecture in this course.

3. Individuals have two kidneys but most of us need only one. People who have lost both kidneys through accident or disease must be hooked up to a dialysis machine, which cleanses waste from their bodies. Say a person who has two good kidneys offers to sell one of them to someone whose kidney function has been totally destroyed. The seller asks $30,000 for the kidney, and the person who has lost both kidneys accepts the offer. Who benefits from the deal? Who is hurt? Should a society allow such market transactions? Why?

4. For some years, China has had a one-child-per-family policy. For cultural reasons, there are now many more male than female children born in China. How is this likely to affect who pays the cost of dates in China in 15 or 20 years? Explain your response.

5. State whether the following are microeconomic or macroeconomic policy issues:

a. Should the U.S. government use a policy of free trade with China to encourage China to advance human rights?

b. Will the fact that more and more doctors are selling their practices to managed care networks increase the efficiency of medical providers?

c. Should the current federal income tax structure be eliminated in favor of a flat tax?

d. Should the federal minimum wage be raised?

e. Should AT&T and Verizon both be allowed to build local phone networks?

f. Should commercial banks be required to provide loans in all areas of the territory from which they accept deposits?

6. Go to two stores: a supermarket and a convenience store.
   a. Write down the cost of a gallon of milk in each.
   b. The prices are most likely different. Using the terminology used in this chapter, explain why that is the case and why anyone would buy milk in the store with the higher price.
   c. Do the same exercise with shirts or dresses in Wal-Mart (or its equivalent) and Saks (or its equivalent).

7. State whether the following statements belong in positive economics, normative economics, or the art of economics.

a. In a market, when quantity supplied exceeds quantity demanded, price tends to fall.
b. When determining tax rates, the government should take into account the income needs of individuals.
c. What society feels is fair is determined largely by cultural norms.
d. When deciding which rationing mechanism is best (lottery, price, first-come/first-served), one must take into account the goals of society.
e. California currently rations water to farmers at subsidized prices. Once California allows the trading of

water rights, it will allow economic forces to be a market force.

8. Adam Smith, who wrote *The Wealth of Nations* and is seen as the father of modern economics, also wrote *The Theory of Moral Sentiments*, in which he argued that society would be better off if people weren't so selfish and were more considerate of others. How does this view fit with the discussion of economic reasoning presented in the chapter?

WEB QUESTIONS

1. Find an employment Web page (an example is www.monster.com) and search for available jobs using "economist" as a keyword. List five jobs that economists have and write a one-sentence description of each.

2. Use an online periodical (an example is www.movingideas.org) to find two examples of political or legal forces at work. Do those forces keep economic forces from becoming market forces?

3. Using an Internet mapping page (an example is www.mapquest.com), create a map of your neighborhood and answer the following questions:

a. How is the map like a model?
b. What are the limitations of the map?
c. Could you use this map to determine change in elevation in your neighborhood? Distance from one place to another? Traffic speed? What do your answers suggest about what to consider when using a map or a model?

ANSWERS TO MARGIN QUESTIONS

The numbers in parentheses refer to the page number of each margin question.

1. Since the price of both stocks is now $15, it doesn't matter which one you sell (assuming no differential capital gains taxation). The price you bought them for doesn't matter; it's a sunk cost. Marginal analysis refers to the future gain, so what you expect to happen to future prices of the stocks—not past prices—should determine which stock you decide to sell. *(6)*

2. A cost/benefit analysis requires that you put a value on a good, and placing a value on a good can be seen as demeaning it. Consider love. Try telling an acquaintance that you'd like to buy his or her spiritual love, and see what response you get. *(8)*

3. John is wrong. The opportunity cost of reading the chapter is primarily the time you spend reading it. Reading the book prevents you from doing other things. Assuming that you already paid for the book, the original price is no longer part of the opportunity cost; it is a sunk cost. Bygones are bygones. *(9)*

4. Whenever there is scarcity, the scarce good must be rationed by some means. Free health care has an opportunity cost in other resources. So if health care is not rationed, to get the resources to supply that care, other

goods would have to be more tightly rationed than they currently are. It is likely that the opportunity cost of supplying free health care would be larger than most societies would be willing to pay. *(9)*

5. Joan is wrong. Economic forces are always operative; market forces are not. *(9)*

6. According to the invisible hand theory, the price of tomatoes will likely fall. *(12)*

7. (1) Macroeconomics; (2) Microeconomics; (3) Microeconomics; (4) Macroeconomics. *(14)*

8. False. While such changes have the largest gain, they may also have the largest cost. The policies economists should focus on are those that offer the largest net gain—benefits minus costs—to society. *(16)*

9. He is wrong. The invisible hand theory is a positive theory and does not tell us anything about policy. To do so would be to violate Hume's dictum that a "should" cannot be derived from an "is." This is not to say that government should or should not interfere; whether government should interfere is a very difficult question. *(16)*

10. (1) Normative; (2) Positive; (3) Art; (4) Normative; (5) Positive. *(17)*

SUPPLY AND DEMAND

4

Teach a parrot the terms *supply* and *demand*
and you've got an economist.

—*Thomas Carlyle*

Supply and demand. Supply and demand. Roll the phrase around in your mouth, savor it like a good wine. *Supply* and *demand* are the most-used words in economics. And for good reason. They provide a good off-the-cuff answer for any economic question. Try it.

Why are bacon and oranges so expensive this winter? *Supply and demand.*

Why are interest rates falling? *Supply and demand.*

Why can't I find decent wool socks anymore? *Supply and demand.*

The importance of the interplay of supply and demand makes it only natural that, early in any economics course, you must learn about supply and demand. Let's start with demand.

DEMAND

People want lots of things; they "demand" much less than they want because demand means a willingness and ability to pay. Unless you are willing and able to pay for it you may *want* it, but you don't *demand* it. For example, I want to own a Maserati. But, I must admit, I'm not willing to do what's necessary to own one. If I really wanted one, I'd mortgage everything I own, increase my income by doubling the number of hours I work, not buy anything else, and get that car. But I don't do any of those things, so at the going price, $240,000, I do not demand a Maserati. Sure, I'd buy one if it cost $10,000, but from my actions it's clear that, at $240,000, I don't demand it. This points to an important aspect of demand: The quantity you demand at a low price differs from the quantity you demand at a high price. Specifically, the quantity you demand varies inversely—in the opposite direction—with price.

Prices are the tool by which the market coordinates individuals' desires and limits how much people are willing to buy—how much they demand. When goods become scarce, the market reduces the quantity of those scarce goods people demand; as their prices go up, people buy fewer goods. As goods become abundant, their prices go down, and people want more of them. The invisible hand—the price mechanism—sees to it that what people demand (do what's

After reading this chapter, you should be able to:

- State the law of demand and draw a demand curve from a demand table.

- Explain the importance of substitution to the laws of supply and demand.

- Distinguish a shift in demand from a movement along the demand curve.

- State the law of supply and draw a supply curve from a supply table.

- Distinguish a shift in supply from a movement along the supply curve.

- Explain how the law of demand and the law of supply interact to bring about equilibrium.

- Show the effect of a shift in demand and supply on equilibrium price and quantity.

- State the limitations of demand and supply analysis.

INTRODUCTION ▥ THINKING LIKE AN ECONOMIST

necessary to get) matches what's available. In doing so, the invisible hand coordinates individuals' demands.

THE LAW OF DEMAND

The law of demand states that the quantity of a good demanded is inversely related to the good's price.

The ideas expressed above are the foundation of the **law of demand:**

> *Quantity demanded rises as price falls, other things constant.*

Or alternatively:

> *Quantity demanded falls as price rises, other things constant.*

When price goes up, quantity demanded goes down. When price goes down, quantity demanded goes up.

This law is fundamental to the invisible hand's ability to coordinate individuals' desires: as prices change, people change how much of a particular good they're willing to buy.

What accounts for the law of demand? Individuals' tendency to substitute other goods for goods whose relative price has gone up. If the price of music downloads from the Internet rises but the price of CDs stays the same, you're more likely to buy that new Sheryl Crow recording on CD than to download it from the Internet.

To see that the law of demand makes intuitive sense, just think of something you'd really like but can't afford. If the price is cut in half, you—and other consumers—become more likely to buy it. Quantity demanded goes up as price goes down.

Web Note 4.1
Markets without Money

Just to be sure you've got it, let's consider a real-world example: demand for vanity—specifically, vanity license plates. When the North Carolina state legislature increased the vanity plates' price from $30 to $40, the quantity demanded fell from 60,334 at $30 a year to 31,122 at $40 a year. Assuming other things remained constant, that is the law of demand in action.

THE DEMAND CURVE

A **demand curve** is *the graphic representation of the relationship between price and quantity demanded.* Figure 4-1 shows a demand curve.

Q-1
Why does the demand curve slope downward?

As you can see, in graphical terms, the law of demand states that as the price goes up, the quantity demanded goes down, other things constant. An alternative way of saying the same thing is that price and quantity demanded are inversely related, so the demand curve slopes downward to the right.

"Other things constant" places a limitation on the application of the law of demand.

Notice that in stating the law of demand, I put in the qualification "other things constant." That's three extra words, and unless they were important I wouldn't have put them in. But what does "other things constant" mean? Say that over a period of two years, both the price of cars and the number of cars purchased rise. That seems to

Figure 4-1   A Sample Demand Curve
The law of demand states that the quantity demanded of a good is inversely related to the price of that good, other things constant. As the price of a good goes up, the quantity demanded goes down, so the demand curve is downward-sloping.

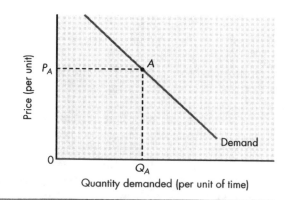

violate the law of demand, since the number of cars purchased should have fallen in response to the rise in price. Looking at the data more closely, however, we see that a third factor has also changed: Individuals' income has increased. As income increases, people buy more cars, increasing the demand for cars.

The increase in price works as the law of demand states—it decreases the number of cars bought. But in this case, income doesn't remain constant; it increases. That rise in income increases the demand for cars. That increase in demand outweighs the decrease in quantity demanded that results from a rise in price, so ultimately more cars are sold. If you want to study the effect of price alone—which is what the law of demand refers to—you must make adjustments to hold income constant. That's why the qualifying phrase "other things constant" is an important part of the law of demand.

The other things that are held constant include individuals' tastes, prices of other goods, and even the weather. Those other factors must remain constant if you're to make a valid study of the effect of an increase in the price of a good on the quantity demanded. In practice, it's impossible to keep all other things constant, so you have to be careful when you say that when price goes up, quantity demanded goes down. It's likely to go down, but it's always possible that something besides price has changed.

SHIFTS IN DEMAND VERSUS MOVEMENTS ALONG A DEMAND CURVE

To distinguish between the effects of price and the effects of other factors on how much of a good is demanded, economists have developed the following precise terminology—terminology that inevitably shows up on exams. The first distinction to make is between demand and quantity demanded.

- **Demand** refers to *a schedule of quantities of a good that will be bought per unit of time at various prices, other things constant.*
- **Quantity demanded** refers to *a specific amount that will be demanded per unit of time at a specific price, other things constant.*

In graphical terms, the term *demand* refers to the entire demand curve. Demand tells how much of a good will be bought *at various prices. Quantity demanded* tells how much of a good will be bought at a specific price; it refers to a point on a demand curve, such as point A in Figure 4-1. This terminology allows us to distinguish between *changes in quantity demanded* and *shifts in demand.* A change in the quantity demanded refers to the effect of a price change on the quantity demanded. It refers to a **movement along a demand curve**—*the graphical representation of the effect of a change in price on the quantity demanded.* A **shift in demand** refers to *the effect of anything other than price on demand.*

SHIFT FACTORS OF DEMAND

Shift factors of demand are factors that cause shifts in the demand curve. A change in anything that affects demand besides price causes a shift of the entire demand curve.

Important shift factors of demand include:

1. Society's income.
2. The prices of other goods.
3. Tastes.
4. Expectations.
5. Taxes on and subsidies to consumers.

Income From our example above of "the other things constant" qualification, we saw that a rise in income increases the demand for goods. For most goods this is true. As

Q-2 The uncertainty caused by the terrorist attacks of September 11, 2001, made consumers reluctant to spend on luxury items. This reduced _____. Should the missing words be *demand for luxury goods* or *quantity of luxury goods demanded?*

INTRODUCTION ■ THINKING LIKE AN ECONOMIST

individuals' income rises, they can afford more of the goods they want, such as steaks, computers, or clothing. These are normal goods. For other goods, called inferior goods, an increase in income reduces demand. An example is urban mass transit. A person whose income has risen tends to stop riding the bus to work because she can afford to buy a car and rent a parking space.

Price of Other Goods   Because people make their buying decisions based on the price of related goods, demand will be affected by the prices of other goods. Suppose the price of jeans rose from $25 to $35, but the price of khakis remained at $25. Next time you need pants, you're apt to try khakis instead of jeans. They are substitutes. When the price of a substitute declines, demand for the good whose price has remained the same will fall. Or consider another example. Suppose the price of movie tickets falls. What will happen to the demand for popcorn? You're likely to increase the number of times you go to the movies, so you'll also likely increase the amount of popcorn you purchase. The lower cost of a movie ticket increases the demand for popcorn because popcorn and movies are complements. When the price of a good declines, the demand for its complement rises.

Tastes   An old saying goes: "There's no accounting for taste." Of course, many advertisers believe otherwise. Changes in taste can affect the demand for a good without a change in price. As you become older, you may find that your taste for rock concerts has changed to a taste for an evening at the opera or local philharmonic.

Expectations   Finally, expectations will also affect demand. Expectations can cover a lot. If you expect your income to rise in the future, you're bound to start spending some of it today. If you expect the price of computers to fall soon, you may put off buying one until later.

Taxes and Subsidies   Taxes levied on consumers increase the cost of goods to consumers and therefore reduce demand for those goods. Subsidies to consumers have the opposite effect. When states host tax-free weeks during August's back-to-school shopping season, consumers load up on products to avoid sales taxes. Demand for retail goods rises during the tax holiday.

These aren't the only shift factors. In fact anything—except the price of the good itself—that affects demand (and many things do) is a shift factor. While economists agree these shift factors are important, they believe that no shift factor influences how much is demanded as consistently as does price of the specific item. That's what makes economists focus first on price as they try to understand the world. That's why economists make the law of demand central to their analysis.

To make sure you understand the difference between a movement along a demand curve and a shift in demand, let's consider an example. Singapore has one of the world's highest number of cars per mile of road. This means that congestion is considerable. Singapore adopted two policies to reduce road use: It increased the fee charged to use roads, and it provided an expanded public transportation system. Both policies reduced congestion. Figure 4-2(a) shows that increasing the toll charged to use roads from $1 to $2 per 50 miles of road reduces quantity demanded from 200 to 100 cars per mile every hour (a movement along the demand curve). Figure 4-2(b) shows that providing alternative methods of transportation such as buses and subways shifts the demand curve for roads. Demand for road use shifts in to the left so that at every price, demand drops by 100 cars per mile every hour (the demand curve shifts to the left).

Q-3 Explain the effect of each of the following on the demand for new computers:
1. The price of computers falls by 30 percent.
2. Total income in the economy rises.

Change in price causes a movement along a demand curve; a change in a shift factor causes a shift in demand.

36

CHAPTER 4 ■ SUPPLY AND DEMAND

Figure 4-2 Shift in Demand versus a Change in Quantity Demanded
A rise in a good's price results in a reduction in quantity demanded and is shown by a movement up along a demand curve from point A to point B in (**a**). A change in any other factor besides price that affects demand leads to a shift in the entire demand curve, as shown in (**b**).

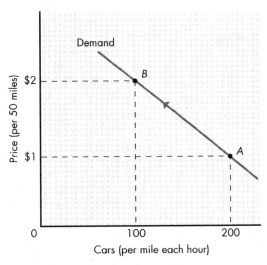

(a) Movement along a demand curve

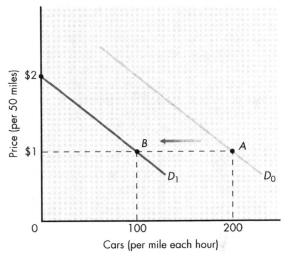

(b) Shift in demand

A REVIEW

Let's test your understanding by having you specify what happens to your demand curve for videocassettes in the following examples: First, let's say you buy a DVD player. Next, let's say that the price of videocassettes falls; and finally, say that you won $1 million in a lottery. What happens to the demand for videocassettes in each case? If you answered: It shifts in to the left; it remains unchanged; and it shifts out to the right—you've got it.

THE DEMAND TABLE

As I emphasized in Chapter 2, introductory economics depends heavily on graphs and graphical analysis—translating ideas into graphs and back into words. So let's graph the demand curve.

Figure 4-3(a), a demand table, describes Alice's demand for renting DVDs. For example, at a price of $2 Alice will rent (buy the use of) 6 DVDs per week, and at a price of 50 cents she will rent 9.

There are four points about the relationship between the number of DVDs Alice rents and the price of renting them that are worth mentioning. First, the relationship follows the law of demand: As the rental price rises, quantity demanded decreases. Second, quantity demanded has a specific *time dimension* to it. In this example demand refers to the number of DVD rentals per week. Without the time dimension, the table wouldn't provide us with any useful information. Nine DVD rentals per year is quite a different concept from 9 DVD rentals per week. Third, Alice's DVD rentals are interchangeable—the 9th DVD rental doesn't significantly differ from the 1st, 3rd, or any other DVD rental. The fourth point is already familiar to you: The schedule assumes that everything else is held constant.

Figure 4-3 (a and b) From a Demand Table to a Demand Curve

The demand table in (a) is translated into a demand curve in (b). Each combination of price and quantity in the table corresponds to a point on the curve. For example, point A on the graph represents row A in the table: Alice demands 9 DVD rentals at a price of 50 cents. A demand curve is constructed by plotting all points from the demand table and connecting the points by a line.

	Price per DVD	DVD rentals demanded per week
A	$0.50	9
B	1.00	8
C	2.00	6
D	3.00	4
E	4.00	2

(a) A demand table

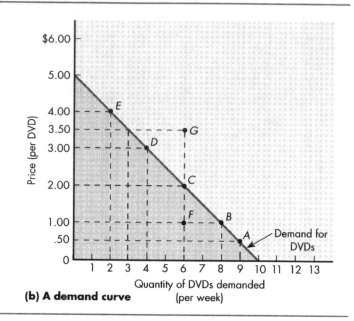

(b) A demand curve

FROM A DEMAND TABLE TO A DEMAND CURVE

Figure 4-3(b) translates the demand table in Figure 4-3(a) into a graph. Point A (quantity = 9, price = $.50) is graphed first at the (9, $.50) coordinates. Next we plot points B, C, D, and E in the same manner and connect the resulting dots with a solid line. The result is the demand curve, which graphically conveys the same information that's in the demand table. Notice that the demand curve is downward sloping (from left to right), indicating that the law of demand holds in the example.

> The demand curve represents the *maximum price* that an individual will pay for various quantities of a good; the individual will happily pay less. For example, say someone offers Alice 6 DVD rentals at a price of $1 each (point F of Figure 4-3(b)). Will she accept? Sure; she'll pay any price within the shaded area to the left of the demand curve. But if someone offers her 6 rentals at $3.50 each (point G), she won't accept. At a rental price of $3.50 apiece, she's willing to rent only 3 DVDs.

The demand curve represents the maximum price that an individual will pay.

INDIVIDUAL AND MARKET DEMAND CURVES

Normally, economists talk about market demand curves rather than individual demand curves. A **market demand curve** is *the horizontal sum of all individual demand curves*. Market demand curves are what most firms are interested in. Firms don't care whether individual A or individual B buys their goods; they only care that *someone* buys their goods.

It's a good graphical exercise to add individual demand curves together to create a market demand curve. I do that in Figure 4-4. In it I assume that the market consists of three buyers, Alice, Bruce, and Carmen, whose demand tables are given in Figure 4-4(a). Alice and Bruce have demand tables similar to the demand tables discussed previously. At a price of $3 each, Alice rents 4 DVDs; at a price of $2, she rents 6. Carmen is an all or nothing individual. She rents 1 DVD as long as the price is equal to or below $1; otherwise she rents nothing. If you plot Carmen's demand curve, it's a vertical line. However, the law of demand still holds: As price increases, quantity demanded decreases.

Q-4 Derive a market demand curve from the following two individual demand curves:

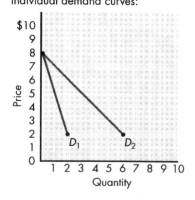

CHAPTER 4 ■ SUPPLY AND DEMAND

Figure 4-4 (a and b) From Individual Demands to a Market Demand Curve

The table (a) shows the demand schedules for Alice, Bruce, and Carmen. Together they make up the market for DVD rentals. Their total quantity demanded (market demand) for DVD rentals at each price is given in column 5. As you can see in (b), Alice's, Bruce's, and Carmen's demand curves can be added together to get the total market demand curve. For example, at a price of $2, Carmen demands 0, Bruce demands 3, and Alice demands 6, for a market demand of 9 (point D).

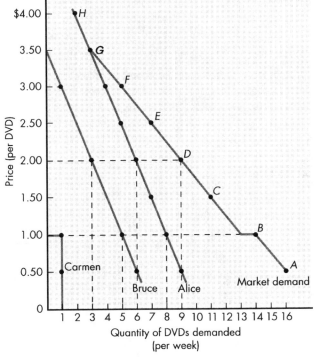

	(1)	(2)	(3)	(4)	(5)
	Price (per DVD)	Alice's demand	Bruce's demand	Carmen's demand	Market demand
A	$0.50	9	6	1	16
B	1.00	8	5	1	14
C	1.50	7	4	0	11
D	2.00	6	3	0	9
E	2.50	5	2	0	7
F	3.00	4	1	0	5
G	3.50	3	0	0	3
H	4.00	2	0	0	2

(a) A demand table

(b) Adding demand curves

The quantity demanded by each consumer is listed in columns 2, 3, and 4 of Figure 4-4(a). Column 5 shows total market demand; each entry is the horizontal sum of the entries in columns 2, 3, and 4. For example, at a price of $3 apiece (row F), Alice demands 4 DVD rentals, Bruce demands 1, and Carmen demands 0, for a total market demand of 5 DVD rentals.

Figure 4-4(b) shows three demand curves: one each for Alice, Bruce, and Carmen. The market, or total, demand curve is the horizontal sum of the individual demand curves. To see that this is the case, notice that if we take the quantity demanded at $1 by Alice (8), Bruce (5), and Carmen (1), they sum to 14, which is point B (14, $1) on the market demand curve. We can do that for each price. Alternatively, we can simply add the individual quantities demanded, given in the demand tables, prior to graphing (which we do in column 5 of Figure 4-4(a)), and graph that total in relation to price. Not surprisingly, we get the same total market demand curve.

In practice, of course, firms don't measure individual demand curves, so they don't sum them up in this fashion. Instead, they estimate total demand. Still, summing up individual demand curves is a useful exercise because it shows you how the market demand curve is the sum (the horizontal sum, graphically speaking) of the individual demand curves, and it gives you a good sense of where market demand curves come from. It also shows you that, even if individuals don't respond to small changes in price, the market demand curve can still be smooth and downward sloping. That's because, for the market, the law of demand is based on two phenomena:

1. At lower prices, existing demanders buy more.

2. At lower prices, new demanders (some all or nothing demanders like Carmen) enter the market.

For the market, the law of demand is based on two phenomena:

1. At lower prices, existing demanders buy more.

2. At lower prices, new demanders enter the market.

SIX THINGS TO REMEMBER ABOUT A DEMAND CURVE

Knowing the Tools

- A demand curve follows the law of demand: When price rises, quantity demanded falls; and vice versa.
- The horizontal axis—quantity—has a time dimension.
- The quality of each unit is the same.
- The vertical axis—price—assumes all other prices remain the same.

- The curve assumes everything else is held constant.
- Effects of price changes are shown by movements along the demand curve. Effects of anything else on demand (shift factors) are shown by shifts of the entire demand curve.

SUPPLY

In one sense, supply is the mirror image of demand. Individuals control the factors of production—inputs, or resources, necessary to produce goods. Individuals' supply of these factors to the market mirrors other individuals' demand for those factors. For example, say you decide you want to rest rather than weed your garden. You hire someone to do the weeding; you demand labor. Someone else decides she would prefer more income instead of more rest; she supplies labor to you. You trade money for labor; she trades labor for money. Her supply is the mirror image of your demand.

For a large number of goods and services, however, the supply process is more complicated than demand. For many goods there's an intermediate step in supply: individuals supply factors of production to firms.

Let's consider a simple example. Say you're a taco technician. You supply your labor to the factor market. The taco company demands your labor (hires you). The taco company combines your labor with other inputs like meat, cheese, beans, and tables, and produces tacos (production), which it supplies to customers in the goods market. For produced goods, supply depends not only on individuals' decisions to supply factors of production but also on firms' ability to produce—to transform those factors of production into usable goods.

The supply process of produced goods is generally complicated. Often there are many layers of firms—production firms, wholesale firms, distribution firms, and retailing firms—each of which passes on in-process goods to the next layer of firms. Real-world production and supply of produced goods is a multistage process.

The supply of nonproduced goods is more direct. Individuals supply their labor in the form of services directly to the goods market. For example, an independent contractor may repair your washing machine. That contractor supplies his labor directly to you.

Thus, the analysis of the supply of produced goods has two parts: an analysis of the supply of factors of production to households and to firms, and an analysis of the process by which firms transform those factors of production into usable goods and services.

> Supply of produced goods involves a much more complicated process than demand and is divided into analysis of factors of production and the transformation of those factors into goods.

THE LAW OF SUPPLY

There's a law of supply that corresponds to the law of demand. The **law of supply** states:

> *Quantity supplied rises as price rises, other things constant.*

CHAPTER 4 ■ SUPPLY AND DEMAND

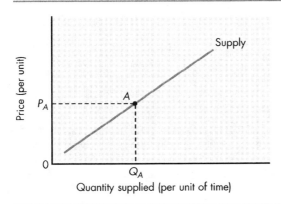

Figure 4-5   A Sample Supply Curve
The supply curve demonstrates graphically the law of supply, which states that the quantity supplied of a good is directly related to that good's price, other things constant. As the price of a good goes up, the quantity supplied also goes up, so the supply curve is upward sloping.

Or alternatively:

> *Quantity supplied falls as price falls, other things constant.*

Price regulates quantity supplied just as it regulates quantity demanded. Like the law of demand, the law of supply is fundamental to the invisible hand's (the market's) ability to coordinate individuals' actions.

What accounts for the law of supply? When the price of a good rises, individuals and firms can rearrange their activities in order to supply more of that good to the market. They want to supply more because the opportunity cost of *not* producing the goods rises as its price rises. Thus, the law of supply is based on a firm's ability to substitute production of one good for another, or vice versa. If the price of corn rises and the price of wheat has not changed, farmers will grow less wheat and more corn, other things constant.

With firms, there's a second explanation of the law of supply. Assuming firms' costs are constant, a higher price means higher profits (the difference between a firm's revenues and its costs). The expectation of those higher profits leads it to increase output as price rises, which is what the law of supply states.

> The law of supply is based on substitution and the expectation of profits.

THE SUPPLY CURVE

A **supply curve** is *the graphical representation of the relationship between price and quantity supplied.* A supply curve is shown graphically in Figure 4-5.

Notice how the supply curve slopes upward to the right. That upward slope captures the law of supply. It tells us that the quantity supplied varies *directly*—in the same direction—with the price.

As with the law of demand, the law of supply assumes other things are held constant. Thus, if the price of wheat rises and quantity supplied falls, you'll look for something else that changed—for example, a drought might have caused a drop in supply. Your explanation would go as follows: Had there been no drought, the quantity supplied would have increased in response to the rise in price, but because there was a drought, the supply decreased, which caused prices to rise.

As with the law of demand, the law of supply represents economists' off-the-cuff response to the question "What happens to quantity supplied if price rises?" If the law seems to be violated, economists search for some other variable that has changed. As was the case with demand, these other variables that might change are called shift factors.

Colander:
Microeconomics, Fifth
Edition

I. Introduction: Thinking
Like an Economist

4. Supply and Demand

© The McGraw–Hill
Companies, 2004

INTRODUCTION ■ THINKING LIKE AN ECONOMIST

SHIFTS IN SUPPLY VERSUS MOVEMENTS ALONG A SUPPLY CURVE

The same distinctions in terms made for demand apply to supply.

> **Supply** refers to *a schedule of quantities a seller is willing to sell per unit of time at various prices, other things constant.*
>
> **Quantity supplied** refers to *a specific amount that will be supplied at a specific price.*

In graphical terms, supply refers to the entire supply curve because a supply curve tells us how much will be offered for sale at various prices. "Quantity supplied" refers to a point on a supply curve, such as point A in Figure 4-5.

The second distinction that is important to make is between the effects of a change in price and the effects of shift factors on how much of a good is supplied. Changes in price cause changes in quantity supplied; such changes are represented by a **movement along a supply curve**—*the graphic representation of the effect of a change in price on the quantity supplied.* If the amount supplied is affected by anything other than price, that is, by a shift factor of supply, there will be a **shift in supply**—*the graphic representation of the effect of a change in a factor other than price on supply.*

SHIFT FACTORS OF SUPPLY

Other factors besides price that affect how much will be supplied include the price of inputs used in production, technology, expectations, and taxes and subsidies. Let's see how.

Price of Inputs   Firms produce to earn a profit. Since their profit is tied to costs, it's no surprise that costs will affect how much a firm is willing to supply. If costs rise, profits will decline, and a firm has less incentive to supply. Supply falls when the price of inputs rises. If costs rise substantially, a firm might even shut down.

Technology   Advances in technology change the production process, reducing the number of inputs needed to produce a given supply of goods. Thus, a technological advance that reduces the number of workers will reduce costs of production. A reduction in the costs of production increases profits and leads suppliers to increase production. Advances in technology increase supply.

Expectations   Supplier expectations are an important factor in the production decision. If a supplier expects the price of her good to rise at some time in the future, she may store some of today's supply in order to sell it later and reap higher profits, decreasing supply now and increasing it later.

Taxes and Subsidies   Taxes on suppliers increase the cost of production by requiring a firm to pay the government a portion of the income from products or services sold. Because taxes increase the cost of production, profit declines and suppliers will reduce supply. The opposite is true for subsidies. Subsidies to suppliers are payments by the government to produce goods; thus, they reduce the cost of production. Subsidies increase supply. Taxes on suppliers reduce supply.

These aren't the only shift factors. As was the case with demand, a shift factor of supply is anything that affects supply, other than its price.

A SHIFT IN SUPPLY VERSUS A MOVEMENT ALONG A SUPPLY CURVE

The same "movement along" and "shift of" distinction that we developed for demand exists for supply. To make that distinction clear, let's consider an example: the supply of

Q-5   In the 1980s and 1990s, as animal activists caused a decrease in the demand for fur coats, the prices of furs fell. This made _____ decline. Should the missing words be *the supply* or *the quantity supplied*?

Explain the effect of each of the following on the supply of romance novels:

1. The price of paper rises by 20 percent.

2. Government increases the sales tax on producers on all books by 5 percentage points.

CHAPTER 4 ■ SUPPLY AND DEMAND

Figure 4-6   Shift in Supply versus Change in Quantity Supplied
A change in quantity supplied results from a change in price and is shown by a movement along a supply curve like the movement from point A to point B in (**a**). A shift in supply—a shift in the entire supply curve—brought about by a change in a nonprice factor is shown in (**b**).

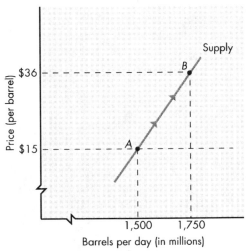

(a) Movement along a supply curve

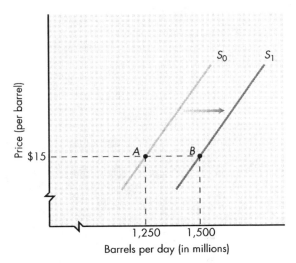

(b) Shift in supply

oil. In 1990 and 1991, world oil prices rose from $15 to $36 a barrel when oil production in the Persian Gulf was disrupted by the Iraqi invasion of Kuwait. U.S. oil producers, seeing that they could sell their oil at a higher price, increased oil production. As the price of oil rose, domestic producers increased the quantity of oil supplied. The change in domestic quantity supplied in response to the rise in world oil prices is illustrated in Figure 4-6(a) as a movement up along the U.S. supply curve from point A to point B. At $15 a barrel, producers supplied 1,500 million barrels of oil a day, and at $36 a barrel they supplied 1,750 million barrels per day.

Photodisc

Earlier, in the 1980s, technological advances in horizontal drilling more than doubled the amount of oil that could be extracted from some oil fields. Technological innovations such as this reduced the cost of supplying oil and shifted the supply of oil to the right, as shown in Figure 4-6(b). Before the innovation, suppliers were willing to provide 1,250 million barrels of oil per day at $15 a barrel. After the innovation, suppliers were willing to supply 1,500 million barrels of oil per day at $15 a barrel.

A REVIEW

To be sure you understand shifts in supply, explain what is likely to happen to your supply curve for labor in the following cases: (1) You suddenly decide that you absolutely need a new car. (2) You win a million dollars in the lottery. And finally, (3) the wage you earn doubles. If you came up with the answers: shift out to the right, shift in to the left, and no change—you've got it down. If not, it's time for a review.

Do we see such shifts in the supply curve often? Yes. A good example is computers. For the past 30 years, technological changes have continually shifted the supply curve for computers out to the right.

Figure 4-7 (a and b)   From Individual Supplies to a Market Supply

As with market demand, market supply is determined by adding all quantities supplied at a given price. Three suppliers—Ann, Barry, and Charlie—make up the market of DVD suppliers. The total market supply is the sum of their individual supplies at each price, shown in column 5 of (a).

Each of the individual supply curves and the market supply curve have been plotted in (b). Notice how the market supply curve is the horizontal sum of the individual supply curves.

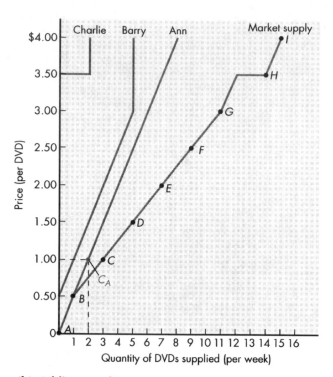

	(1)	(2)	(3)	(4)	(5)
Quantities supplied	Price (per DVD)	Ann's supply	Barry's supply	Charlie's supply	Market supply
A	$0.00	0	0	0	0
B	0.50	1	0	0	1
C	1.00	2	1	0	3
D	1.50	3	2	0	5
E	2.00	4	3	0	7
F	2.50	5	4	0	9
G	3.00	6	5	0	11
H	3.50	7	5	2	14
I	4.00	8	5	2	15

(a) A supply table

(b) Adding supply curves

THE SUPPLY TABLE

Remember Figure 4-4(a)'s demand table for DVD rentals? In Figure 4-7(a), columns 2 (Ann), 3 (Barry), and 4 (Charlie), we follow the same reasoning to construct a supply table for three hypothetical DVD suppliers. Each supplier follows the law of supply: When price rises, each supplies more, or at least as much as each did at a lower price.

FROM A SUPPLY TABLE TO A SUPPLY CURVE

Figure 4-7(b) takes the information in Figure 4-7(a)'s supply table and translates it into a graph of each supplier's supply curve. For instance, point C_A on Ann's supply curve corresponds to the information in columns 1 and 2, row C. Point C_A is at a price of $1 per DVD and a quantity of 2 DVDs per week. Notice that Ann's supply curve is upward sloping, meaning that price is positively related to quantity. Charlie's and Barry's supply curves are similarly derived.

The supply curve represents the set of *minimum* prices an individual seller will accept for various quantities of a good. The market's invisible hand stops suppliers from charging more than the market price. If suppliers could escape the market's invisible hand and charge a higher price, they would gladly do so. Unfortunately for them, and fortunately for consumers, a higher price encourages other suppliers to begin selling DVDs. Competing suppliers' entry into the market sets a limit on the price any supplier can charge.

INDIVIDUAL AND MARKET SUPPLY CURVES

The market supply curve is derived from individual supply curves in precisely the same way that the market demand curve was. To emphasize the symmetry, I've made the three suppliers quite similar to the three demanders. Ann (column 2) will supply 2 at $1; if price goes up to $2, she increases her supply to 4. Barry (column 3) begins supplying at $1, and at $3 supplies 5, the most he'll supply regardless of how high price rises. Charlie (column 4) has only two units to supply. At a price of $3.50 he'll supply that quantity, but higher prices won't get him to supply any more.

The **market supply curve** is *the horizontal sum of all individual supply curves*. In Figure 4-7(a) (column 5), we add together Ann's, Barry's, and Charlie's supplies to arrive at the market supply curve, which is graphed in Figure 4-7(b). Notice that each point on it corresponds to the information in columns 1 and 5 for each row. For example, point *H* corresponds to a price of $3.50 and a quantity of 14.

The market supply curve's upward slope is determined by two different sources: by existing suppliers supplying more and by new suppliers entering the market. Sometimes existing suppliers may not be willing to increase their quantity supplied in response to an increase in prices, but a rise in price often brings brand-new suppliers into the market. For example, a rise in teachers' salaries will have little effect on the amount of teaching current teachers do, but it will increase the number of people choosing to be teachers.

The law of supply is based on two phenomena:

1. At higher prices, existing suppliers supply more.
2. At higher prices, new suppliers enter the market.

THE INTERACTION OF SUPPLY AND DEMAND

Thomas Carlyle, the English historian who dubbed economics "the dismal science," also wrote this chapter's introductory tidbit. "Teach a parrot the terms *supply* and *demand* and you've got an economist." In earlier chapters, I tried to convince you that economics is *not* dismal. In the rest of this chapter, I hope to convince you that, while supply and demand are important to economics, parrots don't make good economists. If students think that when they've learned the terms *supply* and *demand* they've learned economics, they're mistaken. Those terms are just labels for the ideas behind supply and demand, and it's the ideas that are important. What matters about supply and demand isn't the labels but how the concepts interact. For instance, what happens if a freeze kills the blossoms on the orange trees? The quantity of oranges supplied isn't expected to equal the quantity demanded. It's in understanding the interaction of supply and demand that economics becomes interesting and relevant.

EQUILIBRIUM

Web Note 4.2
Online Markets

When you have a market in which neither suppliers nor consumers collude and in which prices are free to adjust, the forces of supply and demand interact to arrive at an equilibrium. The concept of equilibrium comes from physics—classical mechanics. **Equilibrium** is *a concept in which opposing dynamic forces cancel each other out.* For example, a hot-air balloon is in equilibrium when the upward force exerted by the hot air in the balloon equals the downward pressure exerted on the balloon by gravity. In supply/demand analysis, equilibrium means that the upward pressure on price is exactly offset by the downward pressure on price. **Equilibrium price** is *the price toward which the invisible hand drives the market.* At the equilibrium price, quantity demanded equals quantity supplied. **Equilibrium quantity** is *the amount bought and sold at the equilibrium price.*

So much for what equilibrium is. Now let's consider what it isn't.

WHAT EQUILIBRIUM ISN'T

First, equilibrium isn't a state of the world. It's a characteristic of the model—the framework you use to look at the world. The same situation could be seen as an equilibrium in one framework and as a disequilibrium in another. Say you're describing a car that's speeding along at 100 miles an hour. That car is changing position relative to objects on the ground. Its movement could be, and generally is, described as if it were in disequilibrium. However, if you consider this car relative to another car going 100 miles an hour, the cars could be modeled as being in equilibrium because their positions relative to each other aren't changing.

Equilibrium is not inherently good or bad.

Second, equilibrium isn't inherently good or bad. It's simply a state in which dynamic pressures offset each other. Some equilibria are awful. Say two countries are engaged in a nuclear war against each other and both sides are blown away. An equilibrium will have been reached, but there's nothing good about it.

What happens if the market is not in equilibrium—if quantity supplied doesn't equal quantity demanded? You get either excess supply or excess demand, and a tendency for prices to change.

EXCESS SUPPLY

Bargain hunters can get a deal when there is excess supply.
Elena Rooraid/Photoedit

If there is **excess supply** (a surplus), *quantity supplied is greater than quantity demanded,* and some suppliers won't be able to sell all their goods. Each supplier will think: "Gee, if I offer to sell it for a bit less, I'll be the lucky one who sells my goods; someone else will be stuck with not selling their goods." But because all suppliers with excess goods will be thinking the same thing, the price in the market will fall. As that happens, consumers will increase their quantity demanded. So the movement toward equilibrium caused by excess supply is on both the supply and demand sides.

EXCESS DEMAND

The reverse is also true. Say that instead of excess supply, there's **excess demand** (a shortage)—*quantity demanded is greater than quantity supplied.* There are more consumers who want the good than there are suppliers selling the good. Let's consider what's likely to go through demanders' minds. They'll likely call long-lost friends who just happen to be sellers of that good and tell them it's good to talk to them and, by the way, don't they want to sell that . . . ? Suppliers will be rather pleased that so many of their old friends have remembered them, but they'll also likely see the connection between excess demand and their friends' thoughtfulness. To stop their phones from ringing all the time,

CHAPTER 4 ■ SUPPLY AND DEMAND

they'll likely raise their price. The reverse is true for excess supply. It's amazing how friendly suppliers become to potential consumers when there's excess supply.

PRICE ADJUSTS

This tendency for prices to rise when the quantity demanded exceeds the quantity supplied and for prices to fall when the quantity supplied exceeds the quantity demanded is a central element to understanding supply and demand. So remember:

> When quantity demanded is greater than quantity supplied, prices tend to rise.
> When quantity supplied is greater than quantity demanded, prices tend to fall.

Prices tend to rise when there is excess demand and fall when there is excess supply.

Two other things to note about supply and demand are (1) the greater the difference between quantity supplied and quantity demanded, the more pressure there is for prices to rise or fall, and (2) when quantity demanded equals quantity supplied, the market is in equilibrium.

People's tendencies to change prices exist as long as there's some difference between quantity supplied and quantity demanded. But the change in price brings the laws of supply and demand into play. As price falls, quantity supplied decreases as some suppliers leave the business (the law of supply). And as some people who originally weren't really interested in buying the good think, "Well, at this low price, maybe I do want to buy," quantity demanded increases (the law of demand). Similarly, when price rises, quantity supplied will increase (the law of supply) and quantity demanded will decrease (the law of demand).

Whenever quantity supplied and quantity demanded are unequal, price tends to change. If, however, quantity supplied and quantity demanded are equal, price will stay the same because no one will have an incentive to change.

THE GRAPHICAL INTERACTION OF SUPPLY AND DEMAND

Figure 4-8 shows supply and demand curves for DVD rentals and demonstrates the force of the invisible hand. Let's consider what will happen to the price of DVD in three cases:

1. When the price is $3.50 each;
2. When the price is $1.50 each; and
3. When the price is $2.50 each.

1. When price is $3.50, quantity supplied is 7 and quantity demanded is only 3. Excess supply is 4. Individual consumers can get all they want, but most suppliers can't sell all they wish; they'll be stuck with DVDs that they'd like to rent. Suppliers will tend to offer their goods at a lower price and demanders, who see plenty of suppliers out there, will bargain harder for an even lower price. Both these forces will push the price as indicated by the A arrows in Figure 4-8.

Now let's start from the other side.

2. Say price is $1.50. The situation is now reversed. Quantity supplied is 3 and quantity demanded is 7. Excess demand is 4. Now it's consumers who can't get what they want and suppliers who are in the strong bargaining position. The pressures will be on price to rise in the direction of the B arrows in Figure 4-8.

3. At $2.50, price is at its equilibrium: quantity supplied equals quantity demanded. Suppliers offer to sell 5 and consumers want to buy 5, so there's no pressure on price to rise or fall. Price will tend to remain where it is (point E in Figure 4-8). Notice that the equilibrium price is where the supply and demand curves intersect.

INTRODUCTION ▦ THINKING LIKE AN ECONOMIST

Figure 4-8   The Interaction of Supply and Demand

Combining Ann's supply from Figure 4-7 and Alice's demand from Figure 4-4, let's see the force of the invisible hand. When there is excess demand there is upward pressure on price. When there is excess supply there is downward pressure on price. Understanding these pressures is essential to understanding how to apply economics to reality.

Price (per DVD)	Quantity supplied	Quantity demanded	Surplus (+)/ shortage (−)
$1.50	7	3	+4
$2.50	5	5	0
$3.50	3	7	−4

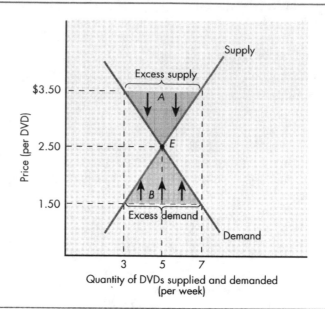

POLITICAL AND SOCIAL FORCES AND EQUILIBRIUM

When I discussed equilibrium, I emphasized that equilibrium is a characteristic of the framework of analysis, not of the real world. Understanding that idea is important in applying economic models to reality. For example, in the preceding description I said equilibrium occurs where quantity supplied equals quantity demanded. In a model where the invisible hand is the only force operating, that's true. In the real world, however, other forces—political and social forces—are operating. These will likely push price away from that supply/demand equilibrium. Were we to consider a model that included all these forces—political, social, and economic—equilibrium would be likely to exist where quantity supplied isn't equal to quantity demanded. For example:

- Farmers use political pressure to obtain prices that are higher than supply/ demand equilibrium prices.

- Social pressures often offset economic pressures and prevent unemployed individuals from accepting work at lower wages than currently employed workers receive.

- Existing firms conspire to limit new competition by lobbying Congress to pass restrictive regulations and by devising pricing strategies to scare off new entrants.

- Renters often organize to pressure local government to set caps on the rental price of apartments.

If social and political forces were included in the analysis, they'd provide a counterpressure to the dynamic forces of supply and demand. The result would be an equilibrium with continual excess supply or excess demand if the market were considered only in reference to economic forces. The invisible hand pushing toward a supply/demand equilibrium would be thwarted by social and political forces pushing in the other direction.

CHAPTER 4 ■ SUPPLY AND DEMAND

Figure 4-9 (a and b)   Shifts in Supply and Demand

When there is an increase in demand (the demand curve shifts outward), there is upward pressure on the price, as shown in (**a**). If demand increases from D_0 to D_1, the quantity of DVD rentals that was demanded at a price of $2.25, 8, increases to 10, but the quantity supplied remains at 8. This excess demand tends to cause prices to rise. Eventually, a new equilibrium is reached at the price of $2.50, where the quantity supplied and the quantity demanded is 9 (point B).

If supply of DVD rentals decreases, then the entire supply curve shifts inward to the left, as shown in (**b**), from S_0 to S_1. At the price of $2.25, the quantity supplied has now decreased to 6 DVDs, but the quantity demanded has remained at 8 DVDs. The excess demand tends to force the price upward. Eventually, an equilibrium is reached at the price of $2.50 and quantity 7 (point C).

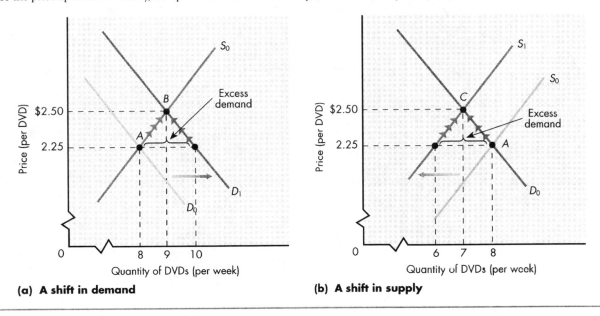

(a) A shift in demand   **(b) A shift in supply**

SHIFTS IN SUPPLY AND DEMAND

Supply and demand are most useful when trying to figure out what will happen to equilibrium price and quantity if either supply or demand shifts. Figure 4-9(a) deals with an increase in demand. Figure 4-9(b) deals with a decrease in supply.

Let's consider again the supply and demand for DVD rentals. In Figure 4-9(a), the supply is S_0 and initial demand is D_0. They meet at an equilibrium price of $2.25 per DVD and an equilibrium quantity of 8 DVDs per week (point A). Now say that the demand for DVD rentals increases from D_0 to D_1. At a price of $2.25, the quantity of DVD rentals supplied will be 8 and the quantity demanded will be 10; excess demand of 2 exists.

The excess demand pushes prices upward in the direction of the small arrows, decreasing the quantity demanded and increasing the quantity supplied. As it does so, movement takes place along both the supply curve and the demand curve.

The upward push on price decreases the gap between the quantity supplied and the quantity demanded. As the gap decreases, the upward pressure decreases, but as long as that gap exists at all, price will be pushed upward until the new equilibrium price ($2.50) and new quantity (9) are reached (point B). At point B, quantity supplied equals quantity demanded. So the market is in equilibrium. Notice that the adjustment is twofold: The higher price brings about equilibrium by both increasing the quantity supplied (from 8 to 9) and decreasing the quantity demanded (from 10 to 9).

Figure 4-9(b) begins with the same situation that we started with in Figure 4-9(a); the initial equilibrium quantity and price are 8 DVDs per week and $2.25 per DVD

Q-7 Demonstrate graphically the effect of a heavy frost in Florida on the equilibrium quantity and price of oranges.

THE SUPPLY AND DEMAND FOR CHILDREN

In Chapter 1, I distinguished between an economic force and a market force. Economic forces are operative in all aspects of our lives; market forces are economic forces that are allowed to be expressed through a market. My examples in this chapter are of market forces—of goods sold in a market—but supply and demand can also be used to analyze situations in which economic, but not market, forces operate. An economist who is adept at this is Gary Becker of the University of Chicago. He has applied supply and demand analysis to a wide range of issues, even the supply and demand for children.

Becker doesn't argue that children should be bought and sold. But he does argue that economic considerations play a large role in people's decisions on how many chil-

dren to have. In farming communities, children can be productive early in life; by age six or seven, they can work on a farm. In an advanced industrial community, children provide pleasure but generally don't contribute productively to family income. Even getting them to help around the house can be difficult.

Becker argues that since the price of having children is lower for a farming society than for an industrial society, farming societies will have more children per family. Quantity of children demanded will be larger. And that's what we find. Developing countries that rely primarily on farming often have three, four, or more children per family. Industrial societies average fewer than two children per family.

(point A). In this example, however, instead of demand increasing, let's assume supply decreases—say because some suppliers change what they like to do, and decide they will no longer supply DVDs. That means that the entire supply curve shifts inward to the left (from S_0 to S_1). At the initial equilibrium price of $2.25, the quantity demanded is greater than the quantity supplied. Two more DVDs are demanded than are supplied. (Excess demand = 2.)

Q-8 Demonstrate graphically the likely effect of an increase in the price of gas on the equilibrium quantity and price of compact cars.

This excess demand exerts upward pressure on price. Price is pushed in the direction of the small arrows. As the price rises, the upward pressure on price is reduced but will still exist until the new equilibrium price, $2.50, and new quantity, 7, are reached. At $2.50, the quantity supplied equals the quantity demanded. The adjustment has involved a movement along the demand curve and the new supply curve. As price rises, quantity supplied is adjusted upward and quantity demanded is adjusted downward until quantity supplied equals quantity demanded where the new supply curve intersects the demand curve at point C, an equilibrium of 7 and $2.50.

Here is an exercise for you to try. Demonstrate graphically how the price of computers could have fallen dramatically in the past 10 years, even as demand increased. (Hint: Supply has shifted even more, so even at lower prices, far more computers have been supplied than were being supplied 10 years ago.)

THE LIMITATIONS OF SUPPLY/DEMAND ANALYSIS

Supply and demand are tools, and, like most tools, they help us enormously when used appropriately. Used inappropriately, however, they can be misleading. Throughout the book I'll introduce you to the limitations of the tools, but let me discuss an important one here.

In supply/demand analysis other things are assumed constant. If other things change, then one cannot directly apply supply/demand analysis. Sometimes supply and demand are interconnected, making it impossible to hold other things constant. Let's take an example. Say we are considering the effect of a fall in the wage rate. In

CHAPTER 4 ■ SUPPLY AND DEMAND

supply/demand analysis, you would look at the effect that fall would have on workers' decisions to supply labor, and on business's decision to hire workers. But there are also other effects. All actions have a multitude of ripple and possible feedback effects—they create waves, like those that spread out from a stone thrown into a pool. For instance, the fall in the wage lowers people's income and thereby reduces demand. That reduction may feed back to firms and reduce the demand for their goods and that reduction might reduce the firms' demand for workers. If these effects do occur, and are important enough to affect the result, those effects have to be added to the analysis in order for you to have a complete analysis.

There is no single answer to the question of which ripples must be included, and much debate among economists involves which ripple effects to include. But there are some general rules. Supply/demand analysis, used without adjustment, is most appropriate for questions where the goods are a small percentage of the entire economy. That is when the other-things-constant assumption will most likely hold. As soon as one starts analyzing goods that are a large percentage of the entire economy, the other-things-constant assumption is likely not to hold true. The reason is found in the **fallacy of composition**—*the false assumption that what is true for a part will also be true for the whole.*

Consider the example of one supplier lowering the price of his or her good. People will substitute that good for other goods, and the quantity of the good demanded will increase. But what if all suppliers lower their prices? Since all prices have gone down, why should consumers switch? The substitution story can't be used in the aggregate. There are many such examples.

An understanding of the fallacy of composition is of central relevance to macroeconomics. In the aggregate, whenever firms produce (whenever they supply), they create income (demand for their goods). So in macro, when supply changes, demand changes. This interdependence is one of the primary reasons we have a separate macroeconomics. In macroeconomics, the other-things-constant assumption central to microeconomic supply/demand analysis cannot hold.

It is to account for these interdependencies that we separate macro analysis from micro analysis. In macro we use curves whose underlying foundations are much more complicated than the supply and demand curves we use in micro.

One final comment: The fact that there may be an interdependence between supply and demand does not mean that you can't use supply/demand analysis; it simply means that you must modify its results with the interdependency that, if you've done the analysis correctly, you've kept in the back of your head. Thus, using supply and demand analysis is generally a step in any good economic analysis, but you must remember that it may be only a step.

CONCLUSION

Throughout the book I'll be presenting examples of supply and demand. So I'll end this chapter here because its intended purposes have been served. What were those intended purposes? First, I exposed you to enough economic terminology and economic thinking to allow you to proceed to my more complicated examples. Second, I have set your mind to work putting the events around you into a supply/demand framework. Doing that will give you new insights into the events that shape all our lives. Once you incorporate the supply/demand framework into your way of looking at the world, you will have made an important step toward thinking like an economist.

Q.9 When determining the effect of a shift factor on price and quantity, in which of the following markets could you likely assume that other things will remain constant?

1. Market for eggs.
2. Labor market.
3. World oil market.
4. Market for luxury boats.

The fallacy of composition is the false assumption that what is true for a part will also be true for the whole.

Q.10 Why is the fallacy of composition relevant for macroeconomic issues?

It is to account for interdependency between aggregate supply decisions and aggregate demand decisions that we have a separate micro analysis and a separate macro analysis.

INTRODUCTION ■ THINKING LIKE AN ECONOMIST

SUMMARY

- The law of demand states that quantity demanded rises as price falls, other things constant.

- The law of supply states that quantity supplied rises as price rises, other things constant.

- Factors that affect supply and demand other than price are called shift factors. Shift factors of demand include income, prices of other goods, tastes, expectations, and taxes on and subsidies to consumers. Shift factors of supply include the price of inputs, technology, expectations, and taxes on and subsidies to producers.

- A change in quantity demanded (supplied) is a movement along the demand (supply) curve. A change in demand (supply) is a shift of the entire demand (supply) curve.

- The laws of supply and demand hold true because individuals can substitute.

- A market demand (supply) curve is the horizontal sum of all individual demand (supply) curves.

- When quantity supplied equals quantity demanded, prices have no tendency to change. This is equilibrium.

- When quantity demanded is greater than quantity supplied, prices tend to rise. When quantity supplied is greater than quantity demanded, prices tend to fall.

- When the demand curve shifts to the right (left), equilibrium price rises (declines) and equilibrium quantity rises (falls).

- When the supply curve shifts to the right (left), equilibrium price declines (rises) and equilibrium quantity rises (falls).

- In the real world, one must add political and social forces to the supply/demand model. When you do, equilibrium is likely not going to be where quantity demanded equals quantity supplied.

- In macro, small side effects that can be assumed away in micro are multiplied enormously. Thus, they can significantly change the results and cannot be ignored. To ignore them is to fall into the fallacy of composition.

KEY TERMS

demand (85)
demand curve (84)
equilibrium (96)
equilibrium price (96)
equilibrium quantity (96)
excess demand (96)
excess supply (96)

fallacy of composition (101)
law of demand (84)
law of supply (90)
market demand curve (88)
market supply curve (95)

movement along a demand curve (85)
movement along a supply curve (92)
quantity demanded (85)
quantity supplied (92)
shift in demand (85)

shift in supply (92)
supply (92)
supply curve (91)

QUESTIONS FOR THOUGHT AND REVIEW

1. State the law of demand. Why is price inversely related to quantity demanded?

2. State the law of supply. Why is price directly related to quantity supplied?

3. List four shift factors of demand and explain how each affects demand.

4. Distinguish the effect of a shift factor of demand on the demand curve from the effect of a change in price on the demand curve.

5. Mary has just stated that normally, as price rises, supply will increase. Her teacher grimaces. Why?

6. List four shift factors of supply and explain how each affects supply.

CHAPTER 4 ■ SUPPLY AND DEMAND

7. Derive the market supply curve from the following two individual supply curves.

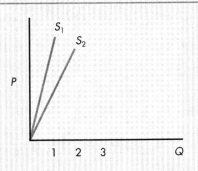

8. It has just been reported that eating red meat is bad for your health. Using supply and demand curves, demonstrate the report's likely effect on the equilibrium price and quantity of steak sold in the market.

9. Why does the price of airline tickets rise during the summer months? Demonstrate your answer graphically.

10. Why does sales volume rise during weeks when states suspend taxes on sales by retailers? Demonstrate your answer graphically.

11. What is the expected impact of increased security measures imposed by the federal government on airlines on fares and volume of travel? Demonstrate your answer graphically.

12. Explain what a sudden popularity of "Economics Professor" brand casual wear would likely do to prices of that brand.

13. In a flood, usable water supplies ironically tend to decline because the pumps and water lines are damaged. What will a flood likely do to prices of bottled water?

14. Oftentimes, to be considered for a job, you have to know someone in the firm. What does this observation tell you about the wage paid for that job?

15. In most developing countries, there are long lines of taxis at airports, and these taxis often wait two or three hours. What does this tell you about the price in that market? Demonstrate with supply and demand analysis.

16. Define the fallacy of composition. How does it affect the supply/demand model?

17. Why is a supply/demand analysis that includes only economic forces likely to be incomplete?

18. In which of the following three markets is there likely to be the greatest feedback effects: market for housing, market for wheat, market for manufactured goods?

PROBLEMS AND EXERCISES

1. You're given the following individual demand tables for comic books.

Price	John	Liz	Alex
$ 2	4	36	24
4	4	32	20
6	0	28	16
8	0	24	12
10	0	20	8
12	0	16	4
14	0	12	0
16	0	8	0

a. Determine the market demand table.
b. Graph the individual and market demand curves.
c. If the current market price is $4, what's total market demand? What happens to total market demand if price rises to $8?
d. Say that an advertising campaign increases demand by 50 percent. Illustrate graphically what will happen to the individual and market demand curves.

2. You're given the following demand and supply tables:

	Demand		
P	D_1	D_2	D_3
$37	20	4	8
47	15	2	7
57	10	0	6
67	5	0	5

	Supply		
P	S_1	S_2	S_3
$37	0	4	14
47	0	8	16
57	10	12	18
67	10	16	20

a. Draw the market demand and market supply curves.
b. What is excess supply/demand at price $37? Price $67?
c. Label equilibrium price and quantity.

INTRODUCTION ■ THINKING LIKE AN ECONOMIST

3. Draw hypothetical supply and demand curves for tea. Show how the equilibrium price and quantity will be affected by each of the following occurrences:
   a. Bad weather wreaks havoc with the tea crop.
   b. A medical report implying tea is bad for your health is published.
   c. A technological innovation lowers the cost of producing tea.
   d. Consumers' income falls. (Assume tea is a normal good.)
4. You're a commodity trader and you've just heard a report that the winter wheat harvest will be 2.09 billion bushels, a 44 percent jump, rather than an expected 35 percent jump to 1.96 billion bushels.
   a. What would you expect would happen to wheat prices?
   b. Demonstrate graphically the effect you suggested in *a*.
5. In the United States, gasoline costs consumers about $1.50 per gallon. In Italy it costs consumers about $5 per gallon. What effect does this price differential likely have on:
   a. The size of cars in the United States and in Italy?
   b. The use of public transportation in the United States and in Italy?
   c. The fuel efficiency of cars in the United States and in Italy? What would be the effect of raising the price of gasoline in the United States to $4 per gallon?
6. State whether supply/demand analysis used without significant modification is suitable to assess the following:
   a. The impact of an increase in the demand for pencils on the price of pencils.
   b. The impact of an increase in the supply of labor on the quantity of labor demanded.
   c. The impact of an increase in aggregate savings on aggregate expenditures.
   d. The impact of a new method of producing CDs on the price of CDs.

WEB QUESTIONS

1. Go to the U.S. Census Bureau's home page (www.census.gov) and navigate to the population pyramids for 2000, for 2025, and for 2050. What is projected to happen to the age distribution in the United States? Other things constant, what do you expect will happen in the next 50 years to the relative demand and supply for each of the following, being careful to distinguish between shifts of and a movement along a curve:
   a. Nursing homes.
   b. Prescription medication.
   c. Baby high chairs.
   d. College education.
2. Go to the Energy Information Administration's home page (www.eia.doe.gov) and look up its most recent "Short-Term Energy Outlook" and answer the following questions:
   a. List the factors that are expected to affect demand and supply for energy in the near term. How will each affect demand? Supply?
   b. What is the EIA's forecast for world oil prices? Show graphically how the factors listed in your answer to *a* are consistent with the EIA's forecast. Label all shifts in demand and supply.
   c. Describe and explain EIA's forecast for the price of gasoline, heating oil, and natural gas. Be sure to mention the factors that are affecting the forecast.
3. Go to the Tax Administration home page (www.taxadmin.org) and look up sales tax rates for the 50 U.S. states.
   a. Which states have no sales tax? Which state has the highest sales tax?
   b. Show graphically the effect of sales tax on supply, demand, equilibrium quantity, and equilibrium price.
   c. Name two neighboring states that have significantly different sales tax rates. How does that affect the supply or demand for goods in those states?

ANSWERS TO MARGIN QUESTIONS

1. The demand curve slopes downward because price and quantity demanded are inversely related. As the price of a good rises, people switch to purchasing other goods whose prices have not risen by as much. (84)
2. *Demand for luxury goods.* The other possibility, *quantity of luxury goods demanded*, is used to refer to movements along (not shifts of) the demand curve. (85)
3. (1) The decline in price will increase the quantity of computers demanded (movement down along the demand curve); (2) With more income, demand for computers will rise (shift of the demand curve out to the right). (86)
4. When adding two demand curves, you sum them horizontally, as in the accompanying diagram. (88)

CHAPTER 4 ▓ SUPPLY AND DEMAND

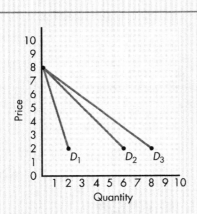

5. *The quantity supplied* declined because there was a movement along the supply curve. The supply curve itself remained unchanged. *(92)*

6. (1) The supply of romance novels declines since paper is an input to production (supply shifts in to the left); (2) the supply of romance novels declines since the tax increases the cost to the producer (supply shifts in to the left). *(92)*

7. A heavy frost in Florida will decrease the supply of oranges, increasing the price and decreasing the quantity demanded, as in the accompanying graph. *(99)*

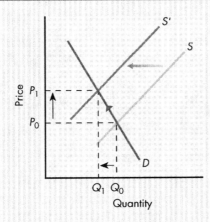

8. An increase in the price of gas will likely increase the demand for compact cars, increasing their price and increasing the quantity supplied, as in the accompanying graph. *(100)*

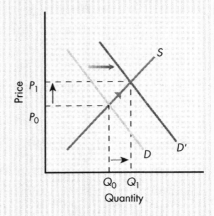

9. Other things are most likely to remain constant in the egg and luxury boat markets because each is a small percentage of the whole economy. Factors that affect the world oil market and the labor market will have ripple effects that must be taken into account in any analysis. *(101)*

10. The fallacy of composition is relevant for macroeconomic issues because it reminds us that, in the aggregate, small effects that are immaterial for micro issues can add up and be material. *(101)*

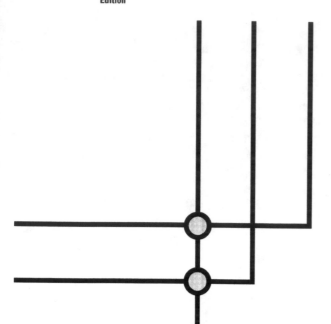

CHAPTER 4

ELASTICITY

Many illicit drug users commit crimes to finance their addiction. The connection between drugs and crime has led to calls for more vigorous efforts to stop the smuggling of illicit drugs. But can such efforts reduce the likelihood that your laptop computer will be stolen in the next month? If attempts to reduce the supply of illicit drugs are successful, their effect will be to increase the market price of drugs. (From our basic supply and demand analysis, we can see that this increase in price is caused by a leftward shift in the supply curve for drugs.) The law of demand tells us that drug users will respond by consuming a smaller quantity of drugs. But the amount of crime drug users commit depends not on the *quantity* of drugs they consume, but rather on their *total expenditure* on drugs. Depending on the specific characteristics of the demand curve for illicit drugs, a price increase might reduce total expenditure on drugs, but it could also raise total expenditure.

Suppose, for example, that extra border patrols shift the supply curve in the market for illicit drugs to the left, as shown in Figure 4.1. As a result, the equilibrium quantity of drugs would fall from 50,000 to 40,000 ounces per day, and the price of drugs would rise from $50 to $80 per ounce. The total amount spent on drugs, which was $2,500,000 per day (50,000 ounces/day × $50/ounce), would rise to $3,200,000 per day (40,000 ounces/day × $80/ounce). In this case, then, efforts to stem the supply of drugs would actually increase the likelihood of your laptop being stolen.

Other benefits from stemming the flow of illicit drugs might still outweigh the resulting increase in crime. But knowing that the policy might increase drug-related crime would clearly be useful to law-enforcement authorities.

Our task in this chapter will be to introduce the concept of elasticity, a measure of the extent to which quantity demanded and quantity supplied

CHAPTER 4 ELASTICITY

FIGURE 4.1

The Effect of Extra Border Patrols on the Market for Illicit Drugs. Extra patrols shift supply leftward and reduce the quantity demanded, but they may actually increase the total amount spent on drugs.

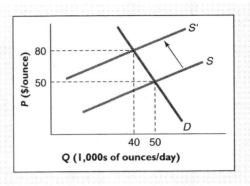

Could reducing the supply of illegal drugs cause an increase in drug-related burglaries?

respond to variations in price, income, and other factors. In the preceding chapter, we saw how shifts in supply and demand curves enabled us to predict the direction of change in the equilibrium values of price and quantity. An understanding of price elasticity will enable us to make even more precise statements about the effects of such changes. In the illicit-drug example just considered, the decrease in supply led to an increase in total spending. In many other cases, a decrease in supply will lead to a reduction in total spending. Why this difference? The underlying phenomenon that explains this pattern, we will see, is price elasticity of demand. We will explore why some goods have higher price elasticity of demand than others and the implications of that fact for how total spending responds to changes in prices. We will also discuss price elasticity of supply and examine the factors that explain why it takes different values for different goods.

PRICE ELASTICITY OF DEMAND

When the price of a good or service rises, the quantity demanded falls. But to predict the effect of the price increase on total expenditure, we must also know how much quantity falls. The quantity demanded of some goods, such as salt, is not very sensitive to changes in price. Indeed, even if the price of salt were to double, or to fall by half, most people would alter their consumption of it hardly at all. For other goods, however, the quantity demanded is extremely responsive to changes in price. For example, when a luxury tax was imposed on yachts in the early 1990s, purchases of yachts plummeted sharply.

PRICE ELASTICITY DEFINED

price elasticity of demand percentage change in quantity demanded that results from a 1 percent change in price

The **price elasticity of demand** for a good is a measure of the responsiveness of the quantity demanded of that good to changes in its price. Formally, the price elasticity of demand for a good is defined as the percentage change in the quantity demanded that results from a 1 percent change in its price. For example, if the price of beef falls by 1 percent and the quantity demanded rises by 2 percent, then the price elasticity of demand for beef has a value of −2.

Although the definition just given refers to the response of quantity demanded to a 1 percent change in price, it can also be adapted to other variations in price, provided they are relatively small. In such cases, we calculate the price elasticity of demand as the percentage change in quantity demanded divided by the corresponding percentage change in price. Thus, if a 2 percent reduction in the price of pork led to a 6 percent increase in the quantity of pork demanded, the price elasticity of demand for pork would be

Frank–Bernanke:
Principles of
Microeconomics, Second
Edition

II. Competition and the
Invisible Hand

4. Elasticity

© The McGraw–Hill
Companies, 2004

PRICE ELASTICITY OF DEMAND

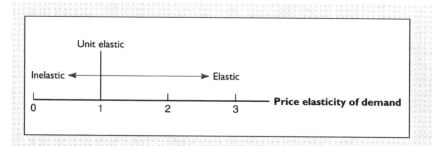

$$\frac{\text{Percentage change in quality demanded}}{\text{Percentage change in price}} = \frac{6 \text{ percent}}{-2 \text{ percent}} = -3. \quad (4.1)$$

Strictly speaking, the price elasticity of demand will always be negative (or zero), because price changes are always in the opposite direction from changes in quantity demanded. So for convenience, we can drop the negative sign and speak of price elasticities in terms of absolute value. The demand for a good is said to be **elastic** with respect to price if the absolute value of its price elasticity is greater than 1. It is said to be **inelastic** if the absolute value of its price elasticity is less than 1. Finally, demand is said to be **unit elastic** if the absolute value of its price elasticity is equal to 1. (See Figure 4.2.)

elastic demand is elastic with respect to price if price elasticity of demand is greater than 1

inelastic demand is inelastic with respect to price if price elasticity of demand is less than 1

unit elastic demand is unit elastic with respect to price if price elasticity of demand equals 1

Unit elastic

Inelastic ← → Elastic

0   1   2   3   **Price elasticity of demand**

FIGURE 4.2
Elastic and Inelastic Demand.
Demand for a good is called elastic, unit elastic, or inelastic with respect to price if the price elasticity is greater than 1, equal to 1, or less than 1, respectively.

What is the elasticity of demand for pizza?

When the price of pizza is $1 per slice, buyers wish to purchase 400 slices per day, but when price falls to $0.97 per slice, the quantity demanded rises to 404 slices per day. At the original price, what is the price elasticity of demand for pizza? Is the demand for pizza elastic with respect to price?

In response to a 3 percent reduction in the price of pizza, the quantity demanded increases by 1 percent. The price elasticity of demand for pizza is thus (1 percent)/(3 percent) = 1/3. So when the initial price of pizza is $1, the demand for pizza is not elastic with respect to price; it is inelastic.

EXAMPLE 4.1

EXERCISE 4.1

What is the elasticity of demand for season ski passes?

When the price of a season ski pass is $400, buyers wish to purchase 10,000 passes per year, but when price falls to $380, the quantity demanded rises to 12,000 passes per year. At the original price, what is the price elasticity of demand for ski passes? Is the demand for ski passes elastic with respect to price?

DETERMINANTS OF PRICE ELASTICITY OF DEMAND

What factors determine the price elasticity of demand for a good or service? To answer this question, recall that before a rational consumer buys any product, the product must first pass the cost-benefit test. For instance, consider a good (such as a dorm refrigerator) that you buy only one unit of (if you buy it at all). Suppose that, at the current price, you have decided to buy it. Now imagine that the price goes up by 10 percent. Will a price increase of this magnitude be likely to make you change your mind? The answer will depend on factors like the following.

Substitution Possibilities

When the price of a product you want to buy goes up significantly, you are likely to ask yourself, "Is there some other good that can do roughly the same job, but

Frank–Bernanke:
Principles of
Microeconomics, Second
Edition

II. Competition and the
Invisible Hand

4. Elasticity

© The McGraw–Hill
Companies, 2004

CHAPTER 4 ELASTICITY

If the price of salt were to double, would you use less of it?

for less money?" If the answer is yes, then you can escape the effect of the price increase by simply switching to the substitute product. But if the answer is no, you are more likely to stick with your current purchase.

These observations suggest that the price elasticity of demand will tend to be higher for products for which close substitutes are readily available. Salt, for example, has no close substitutes, which is one reason that the demand for it is highly inelastic. Note, however, that while the quantity of salt people demand is highly insensitive to price, the same cannot be said of the demand for any *specific brand* of salt. After all, despite what salt manufacturers say about the special advantages of their own labels, consumers tend to regard one brand of salt as a virtually perfect substitute for another. Thus, if Morton were to raise the price of its salt significantly, many people would simply switch to some other brand.

The vaccine against rabies is another product for which there are essentially no attractive substitutes. A person who is bitten by a rabid animal and does not take the vaccine faces a certain and painful death. So most people in that position would pay any price they could afford rather than do without the vaccine.

Budget Share

Suppose the price of key rings suddenly were to double. How would that affect the number of key rings you buy? If you're like most people, it would have no effect at all. Think about it—a doubling of the price of a 25-cent item that you buy only every few years is simply nothing to worry about. By contrast, if the price of the new car you were about to buy suddenly doubled, you would definitely want to check out possible substitutes, such as a used car or a smaller new model. You might also consider holding on to your current car a little longer. The larger the share of your budget an item accounts for, the greater is your incentive to look for substitutes when the price of the item rises. Big-ticket items therefore tend to have higher price elasticities of demand.

Time

Home appliances come in a variety of models, some more energy-efficient than others. As a general rule, the more efficient an appliance is, the higher its price. If you were about to buy a new air conditioner and electric rates suddenly rose sharply, it would be in your interest to buy a more efficient machine than you had originally planned. But suppose you had already bought the machine before you learned of the rate increase. In all likelihood, it would not pay you discard the machine right away and replace it with a more efficient model. Rather, you would wait until the machine wore out, or until you moved, before making the switch.

As this example illustrates, substitution of one product or service for another takes time. Some substitutions occur in the immediate aftermath of a price increase, but many others take place years or even decades later. For this reason, the price elasticity of demand for any good or service will be higher in the long run than in the short run.

RECAP **FACTORS THAT INFLUENCE PRICE ELASTICITY**

The price elasticity of demand for a good or service tends to be larger when substitutes for the good are more readily available, when the good's share in the consumer's budget is larger, and when consumers have more time to adjust to a change in price.

SOME REPRESENTATIVE ELASTICITY ESTIMATES

As the entries in Table 4.1 show, the price elasticities of demand for different products often differ substantially—in this sample, ranging from a high of 2.8 for green peas to a low of 0.18 for theater and opera tickets. This variability is explained in part by the determinants of elasticity just discussed. Patrons of theater and opera, for example, tend to have high incomes, implying that the shares of their budgets devoted to these items are likely to be small. What is more, theater and opera patrons are often highly knowledgeable and enthusiastic about these art forms; for many of them, there are simply no acceptable substitute forms of entertainment.

TABLE 4.1
Price Elasticity Estimates for Selected Products

Good or service	Price elasticity
Green peas	2.80
Restaurant meals	1.63
Automobiles	1.35
Electricity	1.20
Beer	1.19
Movies	0.87
Air travel (foreign)	0.77
Shoes	0.70
Coffee	0.25
Theater, opera	0.18

SOURCE: These short-run elasticity estimates are taken from the following sources: Ronald Fisher, *State and Local Public Finance,* Chicago: Irwin, 1996; H. S. Houthakker and Lester Taylor, *Consumer Demand in the United States: Analyses and Projections,* 2nd ed., Cambridge, MA: Harvard University Press, 1970; L. Taylor, "The Demand for Electricity: A Survey," *Bell Journal of Economics,* Spring 1975; K. Elzinga, "The Beer Industry," in *The Structure of American Industry,* Walter Adams, ed., New York: Macmillan, 1977.

Why is the price elasticity of demand more than 14 times larger for green peas than for theater and opera performances? The answer cannot be that income effects loom any larger for green peas than for theater tickets. Even though the average consumer of green peas earns much less than the average theater or opera patron, the share of a typical family's budget devoted to green peas is surely very small. What differentiates green peas from theater and opera performances is that there are so many more close substitutes for peas than for opera and theater. The lowly green pea, which is mostly found in the canned goods or frozen foods sections of supermarkets, just does not seem to have inspired a loyal consumer following.

USING PRICE ELASTICITY OF DEMAND

An understanding of the factors that govern price elasticity of demand is necessary not only to make sense of consumer behavior, but also to design effective public policy. Consider, for example, the debate about how taxes affect smoking among teenagers.

Will a higher tax on cigarettes curb teenage smoking?

Consultants hired by the tobacco industry have testified in Congress against higher cigarette taxes aimed at curbing teenage smoking. The main reason teenagers smoke is that their friends smoke, these consultants testified, and they concluded that higher taxes would have little effect. Does the consultants' testimony make economic sense?

The consultants are almost certainly right that peer influence is the most important determinant of teen smoking. But that does not imply that a higher tax

ECONOMIC NATURALIST 4.1

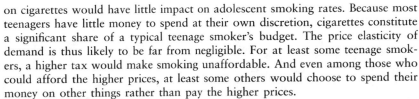

on cigarettes would have little impact on adolescent smoking rates. Because most teenagers have little money to spend at their own discretion, cigarettes constitute a significant share of a typical teenage smoker's budget. The price elasticity of demand is thus likely to be far from negligible. For at least some teenage smokers, a higher tax would make smoking unaffordable. And even among those who could afford the higher prices, at least some others would choose to spend their money on other things rather than pay the higher prices.

Given that the tax would affect at least *some* teenage smokers, the consultants' argument begins to unravel. If the tax deters even a small number of smokers directly through its effect on the price of cigarettes, it will also deter others indirectly, by reducing the number of peer role models who smoke. And those who refrain because of these indirect effects will in turn no longer influence others to smoke, and so on. So even if the direct effect of higher cigarette taxes on teen smoking is small, the cumulative effects may be extremely large. The mere fact that peer pressure may be the primary determinant of teen smoking therefore does not imply that higher cigarette taxes will have no significant impact on the number of teens who smoke.

Why was the luxury tax on yachts such a disaster?

Under the Omnibus Budget Reconciliation Act of 1990, Congress imposed a luxury tax on yachts costing more than $100,000, along with similar taxes on a handful of other luxury goods. Before these taxes were imposed, the Joint Committee on Taxation estimated that they would yield more than $31 million in revenue in 1991. But in fact their yield was little more than half that amount, $16.6 million. Several years later, the Joint Economic Committee estimated that the tax on yachts had led to a loss of 7,600 jobs in the U.S. boating industry. Taking account of lost income taxes and increased unemployment benefits, the U.S. government actually came out $7.6 million behind in fiscal 1991 as a result of its luxury taxes—almost $39 million worse than the initial projection. What went wrong?

The 1990 law imposed no luxury taxes on yachts built and purchased outside the United States. What Congress failed to consider was that such yachts are almost perfect substitutes for yachts built and purchased in the United States. And, no surprise, when prices on domestic yachts went up because of the tax, yacht buyers switched in droves to foreign models. A tax imposed on a good with high elasticity of demand stimulates large rearrangements of consumption but yields little revenue. Had Congress done the economic analysis properly, it would have predicted that this particular tax would be a big loser. Facing angry protests from unemployed New England shipbuilders, Congress repealed the luxury tax on yachts in 1993.

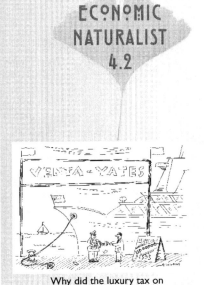

Why did the luxury tax on yachts backfire?

A GRAPHICAL INTERPRETATION OF PRICE ELASTICITY

For small changes in price, price elasticity of demand is the proportion by which quantity demanded changes divided by the corresponding proportion by which price changes. This formulation enables us to construct a simple expression for the price elasticity of demand for a good using only minimal information about its demand curve.

To illustrate, suppose we let P represent the current price of the good and Q the quantity demanded at that price. Similarly, let ΔP represent a small change in the current price and ΔQ the resulting change in quantity demanded. (See Figure 4.3.) The expression $\Delta P/P$ will then stand for the proportion by which price changes when P changes by ΔP; and $\Delta Q/Q$ will stand for the corresponding

Frank–Bernanke:
Principles of
Microeconomics, Second
Edition

II. Competition and the
Invisible Hand

4. Elasticity

© The McGraw–Hill
Companies, 2004

A GRAPHICAL INTERPRETATION OF PRICE ELASTICITY

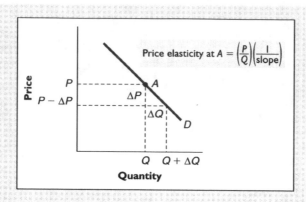

Price elasticity at $A = \left(\dfrac{P}{Q}\right)\left(\dfrac{1}{\text{slope}}\right)$

FIGURE 4.3
**A Graphical
Interpretation of Price
Elasticity of Demand.**
Price elasticity of demand at
any point along a straight-line
demand curve is the ratio of
price to quantity at that
point times the reciprocal of
the slope of the demand
curve.

proportion by which quantity changes. The formula for price elasticity may then
be written as

$$\text{Price elasticity} = \epsilon = \frac{\Delta Q/Q}{\Delta P/P}. \tag{4.2}$$

Suppose, for example, that 20 units were sold at the original price of 100,
and that when price rose to 105, quantity demanded fell to 15 units. Neglecting
the negative sign of the quantity change, we would then have $\Delta Q/Q = 5/20$ and
$\Delta P/P = 5/100$, which yields $\epsilon = (5/20)/(5/100) = 5$.

One attractive feature of this formula is that it has a straightforward graphical interpretation. Thus, if we want to calculate the price elasticity of demand
at point A on the demand curve shown in Figure 4.3, we can begin by rewriting
the right-hand side of equation (4.2) as $(P/Q) \times (\Delta Q/\Delta P)$. And since the slope of
the demand curve is equal to $\Delta P/\Delta Q$, $\Delta Q/\Delta P$ is the reciprocal of that slope:
$\Delta Q/\Delta P = 1/\text{slope}$. So the price elasticity of demand at point A, denoted ϵ_A, has
the following simple formula:

$$\epsilon_A = \frac{P}{Q} \times \frac{1}{\text{slope}}. \tag{4.3}$$

To demonstrate how convenient this graphical interpretation of elasticity can
be, suppose we want to find the price elasticity of demand at point A on the demand
curve in Figure 4.4. The slope of this demand curve is the ratio of its vertical intercept to its horizontal intercept: $20/5 = 4$. So $1/\text{slope} = 1/4$. (Actually, the slope is
-4, but we again ignore the minus sign for convenience, since price elasticity of

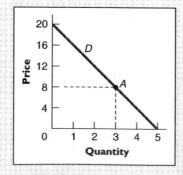

FIGURE 4.4
**Calculating Price
Elasticity of Demand.**
The price elasticity of
demand at A is given by
$(P/Q) \times (1/\text{slope}) = (8/3)$
$\times (1/4) = 2/3$.

CHAPTER 4   ELASTICITY

demand always has the same sign.) The ratio P/Q at point A is 8/3, so the price elasticity at point A is equal to $(P/Q) \times (1/\text{slope}) = (8/3) \times (1/4) = 2/3$. This means that when the price of the good is 8, a 3 percent reduction in price will lead to a 2 percent increase in quantity demanded.

EXERCISE 4.2

What is the price elasticity of demand when $P = 4$ on the demand curve in Figure 4.4?

EXAMPLE 4.2

For the demand curves D_1 and D_2 shown in Figure 4.5, calculate the price elasticity of demand when $P = 4$. What is the price elasticity of demand on D_2 when $P = 1$?

FIGURE 4.5

Price Elasticity and the Steepness of the Demand Curve.

When price and quantity are the same, price elasticity of demand is always greater for the less steep of two demand curves.

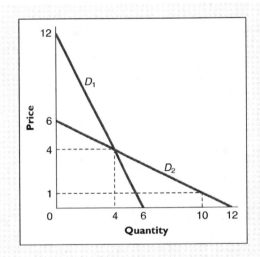

These elasticities can be calculated easily using the formula $\epsilon = (P/Q) \times (1/\text{slope})$. The slope of D_1 is the ratio of its vertical intercept to its horizontal intercept: $12/6 = 2$. So $(1/\text{slope})$ is 1/2 for D_1. Similarly, the slope of D_2 is the ratio of its vertical intercept to its horizontal intercept: $6/12 = 1/2$. So the reciprocal of the slope of D_2 is 2. For both demand curves, $Q = 4$ when $P = 4$, so $(P/Q) = 4/4 = 1$ for each. Thus the price elasticity of demand when $P = 4$ is $(1) \times (1/2) = 1/2$ for D_1 and $(1) \times (2) = 2$ for D_2. When $P = 1$, $Q = 10$ on D_2, so $(P/Q) = 1/10$. Thus price elasticity of demand $= (1/10) \times (2) = 1/5$ when $P = 1$ on D_2.

Example 4.2 illustrates the general rule that if two demand curves have a point in common, the steeper curve must be the less elastic of the two with respect to price at that point. But note carefully that this does not mean that the steeper curve is less elastic at *every* point. Thus we saw that at $P = 1$, price elasticity of demand on D_2 was only 1/5, or less than half the corresponding elasticity on the steeper D_1 at $P = 4$.

PRICE ELASTICITY CHANGES ALONG A STRAIGHT-LINE DEMAND CURVE

As a glance at our elasticity formula makes clear, price elasticity has a different value at every point along a straight-line demand curve. The slope of a straight-line demand curve is constant, which means that 1/slope is also constant. But the

A GRAPHICAL INTERPRETATION OF PRICE ELASTICITY

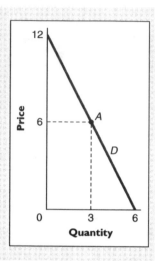

FIGURE 4.6
Elasticity at the Midpoint of a Straight-Line Demand Curve.
The price elasticity of demand at the midpoint of any straight-line demand curve always takes the value 1.

price-quantity ratio, P/Q, declines as we move down the demand curve. The elasticity of demand thus declines steadily as we move downward along a straight-line demand curve.

Since price elasticity is the percentage change in quantity demanded divided by the corresponding percentage change in price, this pattern makes sense. After all, a price movement of a given absolute size is small in percentage terms when it occurs near the top of the demand curve, where price is high, but large in percentage terms when it occurs near the bottom of the demand curve, where price is low. Likewise, a quantity movement of a given absolute value is large in percentage terms when it occurs near the top of the demand curve, where quantity is low, and small in percentage terms when it occurs near the bottom of the curve, where quantity is high.

The graphical interpretation of elasticity also makes it easy to see why the price elasticity of demand at the midpoint of any straight-line demand curve must always be 1. Consider, for example, the price elasticity of demand at point A on the demand curve D shown in Figure 4.6. At that point, the ratio P/Q is equal to $6/3 = 2$. The slope of this demand curve is the ratio of its vertical intercept to its horizontal intercept, $12/6 = 2$. So (1/slope) = 1/2 (again, we neglect the negative sign for simplicity). Inserting these values into the graphical elasticity formula yields $\epsilon_A = (P/Q) \times (1/\text{slope}) = (2) \times (1/2) = 1$.

This result holds not just for the particular demand curve shown, but also for any other straight-line demand curve.[1] A glance at the formula also tells us that since P/Q declines as we move downward along a straight-line demand curve, price elasticity of demand must be less than 1 at any point below the midpoint. By the same token, price elasticity must be greater than 1 for any point above the midpoint. Figure 4.7 summarizes these findings by denoting the elastic, inelastic, and unit elastic portions of any straight-line demand curve.

TWO SPECIAL CASES

There are actually two important exceptions to the general rule that elasticity declines along straight-line demand curves. Note that the horizontal demand

[1]To see why, note that at the midpoint of any such curve, P is exactly half the vertical intercept of the demand curve and Q is exactly half the horizontal intercept. Since the ratio of the vertical intercept to the horizontal intercept is the slope of the demand curve, the ratio (P/Q) must also be equal to the slope of the demand curve. And this means that (1/slope) will always be equal to (Q/P). Thus the product $(P/Q) \times (1/\text{slope}) = (P/Q) \times (Q/P)$ will always be exactly 1 at the midpoint of any straight-line demand curve.

CHAPTER 4 ELASTICITY

FIGURE 4.7
Price Elasticity Regions along a Straight-Line Demand Curve.
Demand is elastic on the top half, unit elastic at the midpoint, and inelastic on the bottom half of a straight-line demand curve.

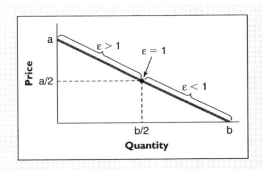

FIGURE 4.8
Perfectly Elastic and Perfectly Inelastic Demand Curves.
The horizontal demand curve (a) is perfectly elastic, or infinitely elastic, at every point. Even the slightest increase in price leads consumers to desert the product in favor of substitutes. The vertical demand curve (b) is perfectly inelastic at every point. Consumers do not, or cannot, switch to substitutes even in the face of large increases in price.

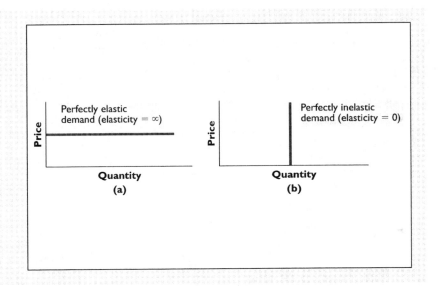

perfectly elastic demand
demand is perfectly elastic with respect to price if price elasticity of demand is infinite

perfectly inelastic demand
demand is perfectly inelastic with respect to price if price elasticity of demand is zero

curve in Figure 4.8(a) has a slope of zero, which means that the reciprocal of its slope is infinite. Price elasticity of demand is thus infinite at every point along a horizontal demand curve. Such demand curves are said to be **perfectly elastic**.

In contrast, the demand curve in Figure 4.8(b) is vertical, which means that its slope is infinite. The reciprocal of its slope is thus equal to zero. Price elasticity of demand is thus exactly zero at every point along the curve. For this reason, vertical demand curves are said to be **perfectly inelastic**.

THE MIDPOINT FORMULA

Suppose you encounter a question like the following on a standardized test in economics:

> At a price of 3, quantity demanded of a good is 6, while at a price of 4, quantity demanded is 4. What is the price elasticity of demand for this good?

Let's attempt to answer this question by using the formula $\epsilon = (\Delta Q/Q)/(\Delta P/P)$. In Figure 4.9 we first plot the two price–quantity pairs given in the question and then draw the straight-line demand curve that connects them. From the graph, it is clear that $\Delta P = 1$ and $\Delta Q = 2$. But what values do we use for P and Q? If we use $P = 4$ and $Q = 4$ (point A), we get an elasticity of 2. But if we use $P = 3$ and

A GRAPHICAL INTERPRETATION OF PRICE ELASTICITY

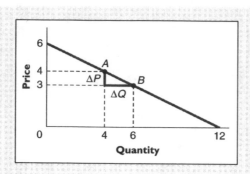

FIGURE 4.9
Two Points on a Demand Curve.

$Q = 6$ (point B), we get an elasticity of 1. Thus, if we reckon price and quantity changes as proportions of their values at point A we get one answer, but if we compute them as proportions of their values at point B we get another. Neither of these answers is incorrect. The fact that they differ is merely a reflection of the fact that the elasticity of demand differs at every point along a straight-line demand curve.

Strictly speaking, the original question ("What is the price elasticity of demand for this good?") was not well posed. To have elicited a uniquely correct answer, it should have been "What is the price elasticity of demand at point A?" or "What is the price elasticity of demand at point B?" Economists have nonetheless developed a convention, which we call the *midpoint formula,* for answering ambiguous questions like the one originally posed. If the two points in question are (Q_A, P_A) and (Q_B, P_B), this formula is given by

$$\epsilon = \frac{\Delta Q/[(Q_A + Q_B)/2]}{\Delta P/[(P_A + P_B)/2]}. \tag{4.4}$$

The midpoint formula thus sidesteps the question of which price–quantity pair to use by using averages of the new and old values. The formula reduces to

$$\epsilon = \frac{\Delta Q/(Q_A + Q_B)}{\Delta P/(P_A + P_B)}. \tag{4.5}$$

For the two points shown in Figure 4.9, the midpoint formula yields $\epsilon = [2/(4 + 6)]/[1/(4 + 3)] = 1.4$, which lies between the values for price elasticity at A and B.

We will not employ the midpoint formula again in this text. Hereafter, all questions concerning elasticity will employ the measure discussed earlier, which is called *point elasticity.*

RECAP   **CALCULATING PRICE ELASTICITY OF DEMAND**

The price elasticity of demand for a good is the percentage change in the quantity demanded that results from a 1 percent change in its price. Mathematically, the elasticity of demand at a point along a demand curve is equal to $(P/Q) \times (1/\text{slope})$, where P and Q represent price and quantity and $(1/\text{slope})$ is the reciprocal of the slope of the demand curve at that point. Demand is elastic with respect to price if the absolute value of its price elasticity exceeds 1; inelastic if price elasticity is less than 1; and unit elastic if price elasticity is equal to 1.

Frank–Bernanke:
Principles of
Microeconomics, Second
Edition

II. Competition and the
Invisible Hand

4. Elasticity

© The McGraw–Hill
Companies, 2004

CHAPTER 4 ELASTICITY

ELASTICITY AND TOTAL EXPENDITURE

Sellers of goods and services will often have a strong interest in being able to answer questions like "Will consumers spend more on my product if I sell more units at a lower price or fewer units at a higher price?" As it turns out, the answer to this question depends critically on the price elasticity of demand. To see why, let us first examine how the total amount spent on a good varies with the price of the good.

The total daily expenditure on a good is simply the daily number of units bought times the price for which it sells. The market demand curve for a good tells us the quantity that will be sold at each price. We can thus use the information on the demand curve to show how the total amount spent on a good will vary with its price.

To illustrate, let's calculate how much moviegoers will spend on tickets each day if the demand curve is as shown in Figure 4.10 and the price is $2 per ticket (a). The demand curve tells us that at a price of $2 per ticket, 500 tickets per day will be sold, so total expenditure at that price will be $1,000 per day. If tickets sell not for $2 but for $4 apiece, 400 tickets will be sold each day (b), so total expenditure at the higher price will be $1,600 per day.

FIGURE 4.10

The Demand Curve for Movie Tickets.

An increase in price from $2 to $4 per ticket increases total expenditure on tickets.

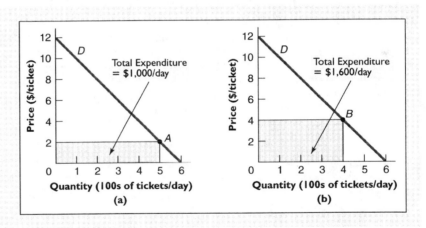

Note that the total amount consumers spend on a product each day must equal the total amount sellers of the product receive. That is to say, the terms **total expenditure** and **total revenue** are simply two sides of the same coin:

> **Total Expenditure = Total Revenue:** The dollar amount that consumers spend on a product ($P \times Q$) is equal to the dollar amount that sellers receive.

It might seem that an increase in the market price of a product should always result in an increase in the total revenue received by sellers. But although that happened in the case we just saw, it needn't always be so. The law of demand tells us that when the price of a good rises, people will buy less of it. The two factors that govern total revenue—price and quantity—will thus always move in opposite directions. When price goes up and quantity goes down, the product of the two may go either up or down.

Note, for example, that for the demand curve shown in Figure 4.11 (which is the same as the one in Figure 4.10), a rise in price from $8 per ticket (a) to $10 per ticket (b) will cause total expenditure on tickets to go down. Thus people will spend $1,600 per day on tickets at a price of $8, but only $1,000 per day at a price of $10.

The general rule illustrated by Figures 4.10 and 4.11 is that a price increase will produce an increase in total revenue whenever it is greater, in percentage

Frank–Bernanke:
Principles of
Microeconomics, Second
Edition

II. Competition and the
Invisible Hand

4. Elasticity

© The McGraw–Hill
Companies, 2004

ELASTICITY AND TOTAL EXPENDITURE

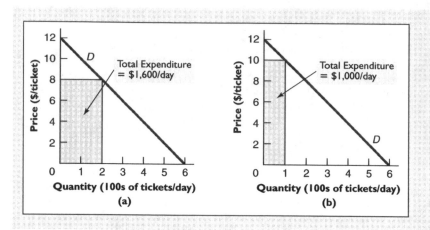

FIGURE 4.11
**The Demand Curve for
Movie Tickets.**
An increase in price from $8
to $10 per ticket results in a
fall in total expenditure on
tickets.

terms, than the corresponding percentage reduction in quantity demanded. Although the two price increases (from $2 to $4 and from $8 to $10) were of the same absolute value—$2 in each case—they are much different when expressed as a percentage of the original price. An increase from $2 to $4 represents a 100 percent increase in price, whereas an increase from $8 to $10 represents only a 25 percent increase in price. And although the quantity reductions caused by the two price increases were also equal in absolute terms, they too are very different when expressed as percentages of the quantities originally sold. Thus, although the decline in quantity demanded was 100 tickets per day in each case, it was just a 20 percent reduction in the first case (from 500 units to 400 in Figure 4.10) but a 50 percent reduction in the second (from 200 units to 100 in Figure 4.11). In the second case, the negative effect on total expenditure of the 50 percent quantity reduction outweighed the positive effect of the 25 percent price increase. The reverse happened in the first case: the 100 percent increase in price (from $2 to $4) outweighed the 20 percent reduction in quantity (from 5 units to 4 units).

The following example provides further insight into the relationship between total revenue and price.

For the demand curve shown in Figure 4.12, draw a separate graph showing how total expenditure varies with the price of movie tickets.

EXAMPLE 4.3

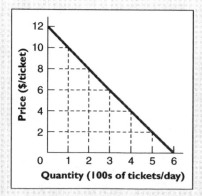

FIGURE 4.12
**The Demand Curve for
Movie Tickets.**

The first step in constructing this graph is to calculate total expenditure for a sample of price points on the demand curve and record the results, as in Table 4.2. The

CHAPTER 4   ELASTICITY

next step is to plot total expenditure at each of the price points on a graph, as in Figure 4.13. Finally, sketch the curve by joining these points. (If greater accuracy is required, you can use a larger sample of points than the one shown in Table 4.2.)

TABLE 4.2
Total Expenditure as a Function of Price

Price ($/ticket)	Total expenditure ($/day)
12	0
10	1,000
8	1,600
6	1,800
4	1,600
2	1,000
0	0

FIGURE 4.13

Total Expenditure as a Function of Price.
For a good whose demand curve is a straight line, total expenditure reaches a maximum at the price corresponding to the midpoint of the demand curve.

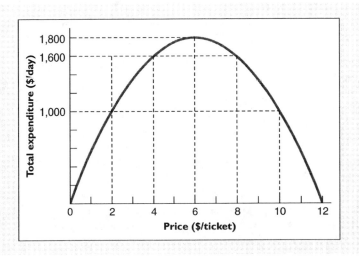

Note in Figure 4.13 that as the price per ticket increases from 0 to $6, total expenditure increases. But as the price rises from $6 to $12, total expenditure decreases. Total expenditure reaches a maximum of $1,800 per day at a price of $6.

The pattern observed in Example 4.3 holds true in general. For a straight-line demand curve, total expenditure is highest at the price that lies on the midpoint of the demand curve.

Bearing in mind these observations about how expenditure varies with price, let's return to the question of how the effect of a price change on total expenditure depends on the price elasticity of demand. Suppose, for example, that the business manager of a rock band knows he can sell 5,000 tickets to the band's weekly summer concerts if he sets the price at $20 per ticket. If the elasticity of demand for tickets is equal to 3, will total ticket revenue go up or down in response to a 10 percent increase in the price of tickets?

Total revenue from tickets sold is currently ($20/ticket) × (5,000 tickets/week) = $100,000 per week. The fact that the price elasticity of demand for tickets is 3 implies that a 10 percent increase in price will produce a 30 percent reduction in the number of tickets sold, which means that quantity will fall to 3,500 tickets per week. Total expenditure on tickets will therefore fall to (3,500

Frank–Bernanke:
Principles of
Microeconomics, Second
Edition

II. Competition and the
Invisible Hand

4. Elasticity

© The McGraw–Hill
Companies, 2004

tickets/week) $\times$ ($22/ticket) = $77,000 per week, which is significantly less than the current spending total.

What would have happened to total expenditure if the band manager had *reduced* ticket prices by 10 percent, from $20 to $18? Again assuming a price elasticity of 3, the result would have been a 30 percent increase in tickets sold—from 5,000 per week to 6,500 per week. The resulting total expenditure would have been ($18/ticket) $\times$ (6,500 tickets/week) = $117,000 per week, significantly more than the current total.

These examples illustrate the following important rule about how price changes affect total expenditure for an elastically demanded good:

> **When price elasticity is greater than 1, changes in price and changes in total expenditure always move in opposite directions.**

Let's look at the intuition behind this rule. Total expenditure is the product of price and quantity. For an elastically demanded product, the percentage change in quantity will be larger than the corresponding percentage change in price. Thus the change in quantity will more than offset the change in revenue per unit sold.

Now let's see how total spending responds to a price increase when demand is *inelastic* with respect to price. Consider a case like the one just considered except that the elasticity of demand for tickets is not 3 but 0.5. How will total expenditure respond to a 10 percent increase in ticket prices? This time the number of tickets sold will fall by only 5 percent to 4,750 tickets per week, which means that total expenditure on tickets will rise to (4,750 tickets/week) $\times$ ($22/ticket) = $104,500 per week, or $4,500 per week more than the current expenditure level.

In contrast, a 10 percent price reduction (from $20 to $18 per ticket) when price elasticity is 0.5 would cause the number to tickets sold to grow by only 5 percent, from 5,000 per week to 5,250 per week, resulting in total expenditure of ($18/ticket) $\times$ (5,250 tickets/week) = $94,500 per week, significantly less than the current total.

As these examples illustrate, the effect of price changes on total expenditure when demand is inelastic is precisely the opposite of what it was when demand was elastic:

> **For a product whose price elasticity of demand is less than 1, price changes and total expenditure changes always move in the same direction.**

Again, the intuition behind this rule is straightforward. For a product whose demand is inelastic with respect to price, the percentage change in quantity demanded will be smaller than the corresponding percentage change in price. The change in revenue per unit sold (price) will thus more than offset the change in the number of units sold.

The relationship between elasticity and the effect of a price change on total revenue are summarized in Table 4.3, where the symbol ϵ is used to denote elasticity.

Recall that in the example with which we began this chapter, an increase in the price of drugs led to an increase in the total amount spent on drugs. That will happen whenever the demand for drugs is inelastic with respect to price, as it was in that example. Had the demand for drugs instead been elastic with respect to price, the drug supply interruption would have led to a reduction in total expenditure on drugs.

INCOME ELASTICITY AND CROSS-PRICE ELASTICITY OF DEMAND

The elasticity of demand for a good can be defined not only with respect to its own price but also with respect to the prices of substitutes or complements, or even to income. For example, the elasticity of demand for peanuts with respect to the

CHAPTER 4 ELASTICITY

TABLE 4.3
Elasticity and the Effect of a Price Change on Total Expenditure

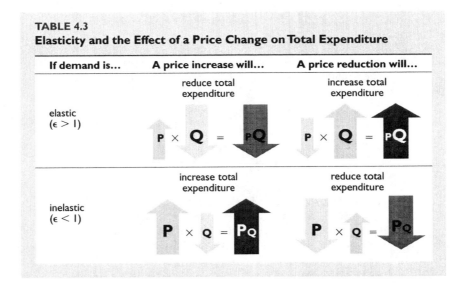

cross-price elasticity of demand the percentage by which quantity demanded of the first good changes in response to a 1 percent change in the price of the second

income elasticity of demand the percentage by which quantity demanded changes in response to a 1 percent change in income

price of cashews—also known as the **cross-price elasticity of demand** for peanuts with respect to cashew prices—is the percentage by which the quantity of peanuts demanded changes in response to a 1 percent change in the price of cashews. The **income elasticity of demand** for peanuts is the percentage by which the quantity demanded of peanuts changes in response to a 1 percent change in income.

Unlike the elasticity of demand for a good with respect to its own price, these other elasticities may be either positive or negative, so it is important to note their algebraic signs carefully. The income elasticity of demand for inferior goods, for example, is negative, whereas the income elasticity of demand for normal goods is positive. When the cross-price elasticity of demand for two goods is positive— as in the peanuts/cashews example—the two goods are substitutes. When it is negative, the two goods are complements. The elasticity of demand for tennis racquets with respect to court rental fees, for example, is less than zero.

EXERCISE 4.3

If a 10 percent increase in income causes the number of students who choose to attend private universities to go up by 5 percent, what is the income elasticity of demand for private universities?

 RECAP CROSS-PRICE AND INCOME ELASTICITIES

When the elasticity of demand for one good with respect to the price of another good is positive, the two goods are substitutes; when this cross-price elasticity of demand is negative, the two goods are complements. A normal good has positive income elasticity of demand and an inferior good has negative income elasticity of demand.

THE PRICE ELASTICITY OF SUPPLY

price elasticity of supply the percentage change in quantity supplied that occurs in response to a 1 percent change in price

On the buyer's side of the market, we use price elasticity of demand to measure the responsiveness of quantity demanded to changes in price. On the seller's side of the market, the analogous measure is **price elasticity of supply**. It is defined as the percentage change in quantity supplied that occurs in response to a 1 percent

Frank–Bernanke:
Principles of
Microeconomics, Second
Edition

II. Competition and the
Invisible Hand

4. Elasticity

© The McGraw–Hill
Companies, 2004

THE PRICE ELASTICITY OF SUPPLY

change in price. For example, if a 1 percent increase in the price of peanuts leads to a 2 percent increase in the quantity supplied, the price elasticity of supply of peanuts would be 2.

The mathematical formula for price elasticity of supply at any point is the same as the corresponding expression for price elasticity of demand:

$$\text{Price elasticity of supply} = \frac{\Delta Q/Q}{\Delta P/P}. \qquad (4.6)$$

where P and Q are the price and quantity at that point, ΔP is a small change in the initial price, and ΔQ the resulting change in quantity.

As with the corresponding expression for price elasticity of demand, Equation 4.6 can be rewritten as $(P/Q) \times (\Delta Q/\Delta P)$. And since $(\Delta Q/\Delta P)$ is the reciprocal of the slope of the supply curve, the right-hand side of Equation 4.6 is equal to $(P/Q) \times (1/\text{slope})$—the same expression we saw for price elasticity of demand. Price and quantity are always positive, as is the slope of the typical supply curve, which implies that price elasticity of supply will be a positive number at every point.

Consider the supply curve shown in Figure 4.14. The slope of this supply curve is 1/3, so the reciprocal of this slope is 3. Using the formula, this means that the price elasticity of supply at A is $(4/12) \times (3) = 1$. The corresponding expression at B, $(5/15) \times (3)$, yields exactly the same value. Indeed, because the ratio P/Q is the same at every point along the supply curve shown, price elasticity of supply will be exactly 1 at every point along this curve. Note the contrast between this result and our earlier finding that price elasticity of demand declines as we move downward along any straight-line demand curve.

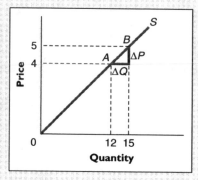

FIGURE 4.14
Calculating the Price Elasticity of Supply Graphically.
Price elasticity of supply is $(P/Q) \times (1/\text{slope})$, which at A is $(4/12) \times (12/4) = 1$, exactly the same as at B. The price elasticity of supply is equal to 1 at any point along a straight-line supply curve that passes through the origin.

Why price elasticity equals 1 at every point in this illustration is explained by one special property: The supply curve was a straight line through the origin. For movements along any such line, both price and quantity always change in exactly the same proportion.

Elasticity is not constant, however, along straight-line supply curves like the one in Figure 4.15, which does not pass through the origin. Although the slope of this supply curve is equal to 1 at every point, the ratio P/Q declines as we move to the right along the curve. Elasticity at A is equal to $(4/2) \times (1) = 2$ and declines to $(5/3) \times (1) = 5/3$ at B.

EXERCISE 4.4

For the supply curve shown in Figure 4.15, calculate the elasticity of supply when $P = 3$.

CHAPTER 4   ELASTICITY

FIGURE 4.15

A Supply Curve for which Price Elasticity Declines as Quantity Rises.

For the supply curve shown, (1/slope) is the same at every point, but the ratio P/Q declines as Q increases. So elasticity = $(P/Q) \times (1/\text{slope})$ declines as quantity increases.

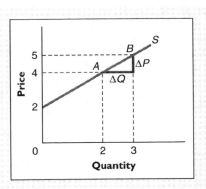

On the buyer's side of the market, two important polar cases were demand curves with infinite price elasticity and zero price elasticity. As the next two examples illustrate, analogous polar cases exist on the seller's side of the market.

EXAMPLE 4.4

What is the elasticity of supply of land within the borough limits of Manhattan?

Land in Manhattan sells in the market for a price, just like aluminum or corn or automobiles or any other product. And the demand for land in Manhattan is a downward-sloping function of its price. For all practical purposes, however, its supply is completely fixed. No matter whether its price is high or low, the same amount of it is available in the market. The supply curve of such a good is vertical, and its price elasticity is zero at every price. Supply curves like the one shown in Figure 4.16 are said to be **perfectly inelastic**.

perfectly inelastic supply
supply is perfectly inelastic with respect to price if elasticity is zero

FIGURE 4.16

A Perfectly Inelastic Supply Curve.

Price elasticity of supply is zero at every point along a vertical supply curve.

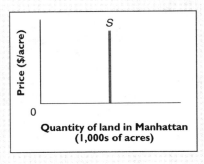

EXAMPLE 4.5

What is the elasticity of supply of lemonade?

Suppose that the ingredients required to bring a cup of lemonade to market and their respective costs are as follows:

Paper cup	2.0 cents
Lemon	3.8 cents
Sugar	2.0 cents
Water	0.2 cents
Ice	1.0 cents
Labor (30 seconds @ $6/hour)	5.0 cents

THE PRICE ELASTICITY OF SUPPLY

If these proportions remain the same no matter how many cups of lemonade are made, and the inputs can be purchased in any quantities at the stated prices, draw the supply curve of lemonade and compute its price elasticity.

Since each cup of lemonade costs exactly 14¢ to make, no matter how many cups are made, the marginal cost of lemonade is constant at 14¢ per cup. And since each point on a supply curve is equal to marginal cost (see Chapter 3), this means that the supply curve of lemonade is not upward-sloping but is instead a horizontal line at 14¢ per cup (Figure 4.17). The price elasticity of supply of lemonade is infinite.

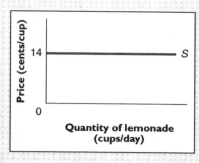

FIGURE 4.17
A Perfectly Elastic Supply Curve.
The elasticity of supply is infinite at every point along a horizontal supply curve.

Whenever additional units of a good can be produced by using the same combination of inputs, purchased at the same prices, as have been used so far, the supply curve of that good will be horizontal. Such supply curves are said to be **perfectly elastic**.

perfectly elastic supply supply is perfectly elastic with respect to price if elasticity of supply is infinite

DETERMINANTS OF SUPPLY ELASTICITY

The two preceding examples suggest some of the factors that govern the elasticity of supply of a good or service. The lemonade case was one whose production process was essentially like a cooking recipe. For such cases, we can exactly double our output by doubling each ingredient. If the price of each ingredient remains fixed, the marginal cost of production for such goods will be constant—and hence their horizontal supply curves.

The Manhattan land example is a contrast in the extreme. The inputs that were used to produce land in Manhattan—even if we knew what they were—could not be duplicated at any price.

The key to predicting how elastic the supply of a good will be with respect to price is to know the terms on which additional units of the inputs involved in producing that good can be acquired. In general, the more easily additional units of these inputs can be acquired, the higher price elasticity of supply will be. The following factors (among others) govern the ease with which additional inputs can be acquired by a producer.

Flexibility of Inputs

To the extent that production of a good requires inputs that are also useful for the production of other goods, it is relatively easy to lure additional inputs away from their current uses, making supply of that good relatively elastic with respect to price. Thus the fact that lemonade production requires labor with only minimal skills means that a large pool of workers could shift from other activities to lemonade production if a profitable opportunity arose. Brain surgery, by contrast, requires elaborately trained and specialized labor, which means that even a large price increase would not increase available supplies, except in the very long run.

Frank–Bernanke:
Principles of
Microeconomics, Second
Edition

II. Competition and the
Invisible Hand

4. Elasticity

© The McGraw–Hill
Companies, 2004

Mobility of Inputs

If inputs can be easily transported from one site to another, an increase in the price of a product in one market will enable a producer in that market to summon inputs from other markets. For example, the supply of agricultural products is made more elastic with respect to price by the fact that thousands of farm workers are willing to migrate northward during the growing season. The supply of entertainment is similarly made more elastic by the willingness of entertainers to hit the road. Circus performers, lounge singers, comedians, and even exotic dancers often spend a substantial fraction of their time away from home. For instance, according to a 1996 *New York Times* article, the top exotic dancers "basically follow the action, so the same entertainers who worked the Indianapolis 500 now head to Atlanta for the Olympics."

For most goods, the price elasticity of supply increases each time a new highway is built; or when the telecommunications network improves, or indeed when any other development makes it easier to find and transport inputs from one place to another.

Ability to Produce Substitute Inputs

The inputs required to produce finished diamond gemstones include raw diamond crystal, skilled labor, and elaborate cutting and polishing machinery. In time, the number of people with the requisite skills can be increased, as can the amount of specialized machinery. The number of raw diamond crystals buried in the earth is probably fixed in the same way that Manhattan land is fixed, but unlike Manhattan land, rising prices will encourage miners to spend the effort required to find a larger proportion of those crystals. Still, the supply of natural gemstone diamonds tends to be relatively inelastic because of the difficulty of augmenting the number of diamond crystals.

The day is close at hand, however, when gemstone makers will be able to produce synthetic diamond crystals that are indistinguishable from real ones. Indeed, there are already synthetic crystals that fool even highly experienced jewelers. The introduction of a perfect synthetic substitute for natural diamond crystals would increase the price elasticity of supply of diamonds (or, at any rate, the price elasticity of supply of gemstones that look and feel just like diamonds).

Time

Because it takes time for producers to switch from one activity another, and because it takes time to build new machines and factories and train additional skilled workers, the price elasticity of supply will be higher for most goods in the long run than in the short run. In the short run, a manufacturer's inability to augment existing stocks of equipment and skilled labor may make it impossible to expand output beyond a certain limit. But if a shortage of managers was the bottleneck, new MBAs can be graduated in only two years. Or if a shortage of legal staff is the problem, new lawyers can be trained in three years. In the long run, firms can always buy new equipment, build new factories, and hire additional skilled workers.

The conditions that gave rise to the perfectly elastic supply curve for lemonade in the example we discussed earlier are also satisfied for many other products in the long run. If a product can be copied (in the sense that any company can acquire the design and other technological information required to produce it), and if the inputs needed for its production are used in roughly fixed proportions and are available at fixed market prices, then the long-run supply curve for that product will be horizontal. But many products do not satisfy these conditions, and their supply curves remain steeply upward-sloping, even in the very long run.

THE PRICE ELASTICITY OF SUPPLY

"In six more weeks, these M.B.A.s will be ready for market."

Why are gasoline prices so much more volatile than car prices?

Automobile price changes in the United States usually occur just once a year, when manufacturers announce an increase of only a few percentage points. In contrast, gasoline prices often fluctuate wildly from day to day. As shown in Figure 4.18, for example, the highest daily gasoline prices in California's two largest cities were three times higher than the lowest daily prices during a recent year. Why this enormous difference in volatility?

With respect to price volatility, at least two important features distinguish the gasoline market from the market for cars. One is that the short-run price elasticity of demand for gasoline is much smaller than the corresponding elasticity for

ECONOMIC NATURALIST 4.3

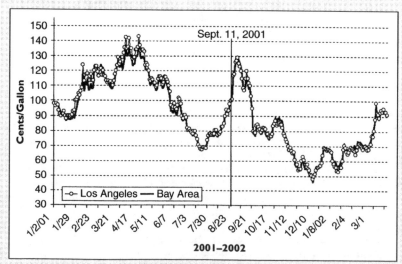

FIGURE 4.18
Gasoline Prices in Two California Cities.

SOURCE: Oil Price Information Service (http://www.opisnet.com).

CHAPTER 4 ELASTICITY

FIGURE 4.19

Greater Volatility in Gasoline Prices than in Car Prices.

Gasoline prices are more volatile prices because supply shifts are larger and more frequent in the gasoline market (a) than in the car market (b), and also because supply and demand are less elastic in the short run in the gasoline market.

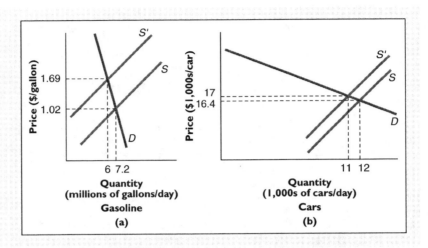

cars. The other is that supply shifts are much more pronounced and frequent in the gasoline market than in the car market. (See Figure 4.19.)

Why are the two markets different in these ways? Consider first the difference in price elasticities of demand. The quantity of gasoline we demand depends largely on the kinds of cars we own and the amounts we drive them. In the short run, car ownership and commuting patterns are almost completely fixed, so even if the price of gasoline were to change sharply, the quantity we demand would not change by much. In contrast, if there were a sudden dramatic change in the price of cars, we could always postpone or accelerate our next car purchases.

To see why the supply curve in the gasoline market experiences larger and more frequent shifts than the supply curve in the car market, we need only examine the relative stability of the inputs employed by sellers in these two markets. Most of the inputs used in producing cars—steel, glass, rubber, plastics, electronic, components, labor, and others—are reliably available to car makers. In contrast, the key input used in making gasoline—crude oil—is subject to profound and unpredictable supply interruptions.

This is so in part because much of the world's supply of crude oil is controlled by OPEC, a group of oil-exporting countries that has sharply curtailed its oil shipments to the United States on several previous occasions. Even in the absence of formal OPEC action, however, large supply curtailments often occur in the oil market—for example, whenever producers fear that political instability might engulf the major oil-producing countries of the Middle East.

Note in Figure 4.18 the sharp spike in gasoline prices that occurred just after the terrorist attacks on the World Trade Center and Pentagon on September 11, 2001. Because many believed that the aim of these attacks was to provoke large-scale war between Muslim societies and the West, fears of an impending oil supply interruption were perfectly rational. And such fears alone can trigger a temporary supply interruption, even if war is avoided. The prospect of war creates the expectation of oil supply cutbacks that would cause higher prices in the future, which leads producers to withdraw some of their oil from current markets (in order to sell it at higher prices later). But once the fear of war recedes, the supply curve of gasoline reverts with equal speed to its earlier position. Given the low short-run price elasticity of demand for gasoline, that's all it takes to generate the considerable price volatility we see in this market.

Price volatility is also common in markets in which demand curves fluctuate sharply and supply curves are highly inelastic. One such market was California's unregulated market for wholesale electricity during the summer of 2000. The supply of electrical generating capacity was essentially fixed in the short run. And because air conditioning accounts for a large share of demand, several spells of unusually warm weather caused demand to shift sharply to the right. Price at one point reached more than four times its highest level from the previous summer.

UNIQUE AND ESSENTIAL INPUTS: THE ULTIMATE SUPPLY BOTTLENECK

Fans of professional basketball are an enthusiastic bunch. Directly through their purchases of tickets and indirectly through their support of television advertisers, they spend literally billions of dollars each year on the sport. But these dollars are not distributed evenly across all teams. A disproportionate share of all revenues and product endorsement fees accrue to the people associated with consistently winning teams, and at the top of this pyramid generally stands the National Basketball Association's championship team.

Consider the task of trying to produce a championship team in the NBA. What are the inputs you would need? Talented players, a shrewd and dedicated coach and assistants, trainers, physicians, an arena, practice facilities, means for transporting players to away games, a marketing staff, and so on. And whereas some of these inputs can be acquired at reasonable prices in the marketplace, many others cannot. Indeed, the most important input of all—highly talented players—is in extremely limited supply. *This is so because the very definition of talented player is inescapably relative—simply put, such a player is one who is better than most others.*

Given the huge payoff that accrues to the NBA championship team, it is no surprise that the bidding for the most talented players has become so intense. If there were a long list of 7-foot, 3-inch, 325-pound centers, the Los Angeles Lakers wouldn't have had to pay Shaquille O'Neal $120 million over a seven-year contract. But, of course, the supply of such players is extremely limited. There are many hungry organizations that would like nothing better than to claim the NBA championship each year, yet no matter how much each is willing to spend, only one can succeed. The supply of NBA championship teams is perfectly inelastic with respect to price even in the very long run.

Sports champions are by no means the only important product whose supply elasticity is constrained by the inability to reproduce unique and essential inputs. In the movie industry, for example, although the supply of movies starring Jim Carrey is not perfectly inelastic, there are only so many films he can make each year. Because his films consistently generate huge box office revenues, scores of film producers want to sign him for their projects. But because there isn't enough of him to go around, his salary per film is more than $20 million.

In the long run, unique and essential inputs are the only truly significant supply bottleneck. If it were not for the inability to duplicate the services of such inputs, most goods and services would have extremely high price elasticities of supply in the long run.

■ SUMMARY ■

- The price elasticity of demand is a measure of how strongly buyers respond to changes in price. It is the percentage change in quantity demanded that occurs in response to a 1 percent change in price. The demand for a good is called elastic with respect to price if its price elasticity is more than 1; inelastic if its price elasticity is less than 1; and unit elastic if its price elasticity is equal to 1.

- Goods such as salt, which occupy only a small share of the typical consumer's budget and have few or no good substi-

tutes, tend to have low price elasticity of demand. Goods like new cars of a particular make and model, which occupy large budget shares and have many attractive substitutes, tend to have high price elasticity of demand. Price elasticity of demand is higher in the long run than in the short run because people often need time to adjust to price changes.

- The price elasticity of demand at a point along a demand curve can also be expressed as the formula $\epsilon = (\Delta Q/Q)/(\Delta P/P)$. Here, P and Q represent price and quantity at that

CHAPTER 4 ELASTICITY

point, and ΔQ and ΔP represent small changes in price and quantity. For straight-line demand curves, this formula can also be expressed as $\epsilon = (P/Q) \times (1/\text{slope})$. These formulations tell us that price elasticity declines in absolute terms as we move down a straight-line demand curve.

• A cut in price will increase total spending on a good if demand is elastic but reduce it if demand is inelastic. An increase in price will increase total spending on a good if demand is inelastic but reduce it if demand is elastic. Total expenditure on a good reaches a maximum when price elasticity of demand is equal to 1.

• Analogous formulas are used to define the elasticity of demand for a good with respect to income and the prices of other goods. In each case, elasticity is the percentage change in quantity demanded divided by the corresponding percentage change in income or price.

• Price elasticity of supply is defined as the percentage change in quantity supplied that occurs in response to a 1 percent change in price. The mathematical formula for the price elasticity of supply at any point is $(\Delta Q/Q)/(\Delta P/P)$, where P and Q are the price and quantity at that point, ΔP is a small change in the initial price, and ΔQ is the resulting change in quantity. This formula can also be expressed as $(P/Q) \times (1/\text{slope})$, where $(1/\text{slope})$ is the reciprocal of the slope of the supply curve.

• The price elasticity of supply of a good depends on how difficult or costly it is to acquire additional units of the inputs involved in producing that good. In general, the more easily additional units of these inputs can be acquired, the higher price elasticity of supply will be. It is easier to expand production of a product if the inputs used to produce that product are similar to inputs used to produce other products, if inputs are relatively mobile, or if an acceptable substitute for existing inputs can be developed. And like the price elasticity of demand, the price elasticity of supply is greater in the long run than in the short run.

■ KEY TERMS ■

cross-price elasticity of demand (106)
elastic (93)
income elasticity of demand (106)
inelastic (93)
perfectly elastic demand (100)

perfectly elastic supply (109)
perfectly inelastic demand (100)
perfectly inelastic supply (108)
price elasticity of demand (92)

price elasticity of supply (106)
total expenditure (102)
total revenue (102)
unit elastic (93)

■ REVIEW QUESTIONS ■

1. Why does a consumer's price elasticity of demand for a good depend on the fraction of the consumer's income spent on that good?

2. Why does the elasticity of demand for a good with respect to its own price decline as we move down along a straight-line demand curve?

3. Under what conditions will an increase in the price of a product lead to a reduction in total spending for that product?

4. Why do economists pay little attention to the algebraic sign of the elasticity of demand for a good with respect to its own price, yet pay careful attention to the algebraic sign of the elasticity of demand for a good with respect to another good's price?

5. Why is supply elasticity higher in the long run than in the short run?

■ PROBLEMS ■

1. On the accompanying demand curve, calculate the price elasticity of demand at points A, B, C, D, and E.

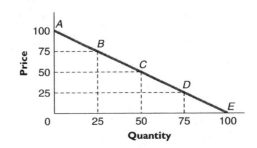

Frank–Bernanke:
Principles of
Microeconomics, Second
Edition

II. Competition and the
Invisible Hand

4. Elasticity

© The McGraw–Hill
Companies, 2004

PROBLEMS

2. The schedule below shows the number of packs of bagels bought in Davis, California, each day at a variety of prices.

Price of bagels ($/pack)	Number of packs purchased per day
6	0
5	3,000
4	6,000
3	9,000
2	12,000
1	15,000
0	18,000

a. Graph the daily demand curve for packs of bagels in Davis.
b. Calculate the price elasticity of demand at the point on the demand curve at which the price of bagels is $3 per pack.
c. If all bagel shops increased the price of bagels from $3 per pack to $4 per pack, what would happen to total revenues?
d. Calculate the price elasticity of demand at a point on the demand curve where the price of bagels is $2 per pack.
e. If bagel shops increased the price of bagels from $2 per pack to $3 per pack, what would happen to total revenues?

3. Suppose, while rummaging through your uncle's closet, you found the original painting of *Dogs Playing Poker,* a valuable piece of art. You decided to set up a display in your uncle's garage. The demand curve to see this valuable piece of art is as shown in the diagram. What price should you charge if your goal is to maximize your revenues from tickets sold? On a graph, show the inelastic and elastic regions of the demand curve.

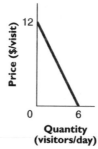

4. Is the demand for a particular brand of car, like a Chevrolet, likely to be more or less price-elastic than the demand for all cars? Explain.

5. Among the following groups—senior executives, junior executives, and students—which is likely to have the most and which is likely to have the least price-elastic demand for membership in the Association of Business Professionals?

6. A 2 percent increase in the price of milk causes a 4 percent reduction in the quantity demanded of chocolate syrup. What is the cross-price elasticity of demand for milk with respect to the price of chocolate syrup? Are the two goods complements or substitutes?

7. What are the respective price elasticities of supply at *A* and *B* on the supply curve shown in the accompanying figure?

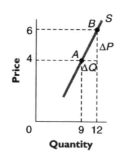

CHAPTER 4   ELASTICITY

8. Suppose that the ingredients required to bring a slice of pizza to market and their respective costs are as listed in the table:

Paper plate	2 cents
Flour	8 cents
Tomato sauce	20 cents
Cheese	30 cents
Labor (3 minutes @ $12/hour)	60 cents

If these proportions remain the same no matter how many slices are made, and the inputs can be purchased in any quantities at the stated prices, draw the supply curve of pizza slices and compute its price elasticity.

9.* At point A on the demand curve shown, by what percentage will a 1 percent increase in the price of the product affect total expenditure on the product?

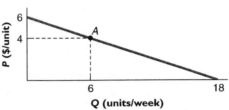

10.* In an attempt to induce citizens to conserve energy, the government enacted regulations requiring that all air conditioners be more efficient in their use of electricity. After this regulation was implemented, government officials were then surprised to discover that people used even more electricity than before. Using the concept of price elasticity, explain how this

*Problems marked with an asterisk (*) are more difficult.

■ ANSWERS TO IN-CHAPTER EXERCISES ■

4.1 In response to a 5 percent reduction in the price of ski passes, the quantity demanded increased by 20 percent. The price elasticity of demand for ski passes is thus (20 percent)/(5 percent) = 4, and that means that at the initial price of $400, the demand for ski passes is elastic with respect to price.

4.2 At point A in the accompanying diagram, $P/Q = 4/4 = 1$. The slope of this demand curve is $20/5 = 4$, so $\epsilon = 1(1/\text{slope}) = 1/4$.

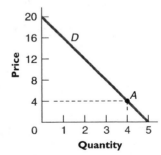

4.3 Income elasticity = percentage change in quantity demanded/percentage change in income = 5 percent/10 percent = 0.5.

4.4 For this supply curve, $Q = 1$ when $P = 3$, so elasticity of supply = $(P/Q) \times (1/\text{slope}) = (3) \times (1) = 3$.

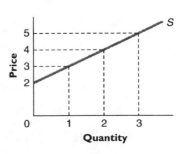

8

THE LOGIC OF INDIVIDUAL CHOICE: THE FOUNDATION OF SUPPLY AND DEMAND

After reading this chapter, you should be able to:

- Discuss the principle of diminishing marginal utility.

- Summarize the principle of rational choice.

- Explain the relationship between marginal utility and price when a consumer is maximizing total utility.

- Explain how the principle of rational choice accounts for the laws of demand and supply.

- Explain why economists can believe there are many explanations of individual choice but nonetheless focus on self-interest.

> The theory of economics must begin with
> a correct theory of consumption.
>
> —*Stanley Jevons*

The analysis of how individuals make choices is central to microeconomics. It is the foundation of economic reasoning and it gives economics much of its power. The first part of this chapter shows you that foundation and leads you through some exercises to make sure you understand the reasoning. The second part of the chapter relates that analysis to the real world, giving you a sense of when the model is useful and when it's not.

As you go through this chapter, think back to Chapter 1, which set out the goals for this book. One goal was to get you to think like an economist. This chapter, which formally develops the reasoning process behind economists' cost/benefit approach to problems, examines the underpinnings of how to think like an economist.

UTILITY THEORY AND INDIVIDUAL CHOICE

Different sciences have various explanations for why people do what they do. For example, Freudian psychology tells us we do what we do because of an internal fight between the id, ego, and superego plus some hangups we have about our bodies. Other psychologists tell us it's a search for approval by our peers; we want to be OK. Economists agree that these are important reasons but argue that if we want an analysis that's simple enough to apply to problems, these heavy psychological explanations are likely to get us all mixed up. At least to start with, we need an easier underlying psychological foundation. And economists have one—self-interest. People do what they do because it's in their self-interest.

Economists' analysis of individual choice doesn't deny that most of us have our quirks. That's obvious in what we buy. On certain items we're penny-pinchers; on others we're big spenders. For example, how many of you or your parents clip coupons to save 40 cents on cereal but then spend $40 on a haircut? How many save 50 cents a pound by buying a low grade of meat but then spend $20 on a bottle of wine, $75 on dinner at a restaurant, or $60 for a concert ticket?

But through it all comes a certain rationality. Much of what people do reflects their rational self-interest. That's why economists start their analysis of individual choice with a relatively simple, but powerful, underlying psychological foundation.

CHAPTER 8 ■ THE LOGIC OF INDIVIDUAL CHOICE: THE FOUNDATION OF SUPPLY AND DEMAND

Using that simple theory, two things determine what people do: the pleasure people get from doing or consuming something, and the price of doing or consuming that something. Price is the tool the market uses to bring the quantity supplied equal to the quantity demanded. Changes in price provide incentives for people to change what they're doing. Through those incentives the invisible hand guides us all. To understand economics you must understand how price affects our choices. That's why we focus on the effect of price on the quantity demanded. We want to understand the way in which a change in price will affect what we do.

In summary, economists' theory of rational choice is a simple, but powerful, theory that shows how these two things—pleasure and price—are related.

MEASURING PLEASURE

Let's start with an analysis of what we buy. Why do we buy what we buy? Economists' analysis of individual choice starts with the proposition that individuals try to get as much pleasure as possible out of life. To analyze the choice formally we must measure pleasure.

How does one measure pleasure? I don't know the answer to that, but back in the 1800s economists such as Jeremy Bentham thought that eventually they would be able to measure pleasure by measuring brain waves. In the expectation of this discovery they even developed a measure of pleasure they called a *util*. They predicted that someday a machine that could measure utils would be developed. Not surprisingly they called this machine a *utilometer*. This utilometer was to be connected to people's heads and an economist would read it as people went through their daily activities. Eating broccoli might give 10 utils; eating a hot fudge sundae might give 10,000 utils.

Eventually these 19th-century economists gave up hope of developing a utilometer, but economists still use a quaint shorthand term, **utility,** for *the pleasure or satisfaction that one expects to get from consuming a good or service.* (And you thought that economists didn't have a sense of humor.) Utility serves as the basis of economists' analysis of individual choice.

Economists initially used actual numbers to represent utility. But no economist today believes that the actual numbers given to utility have meaning. Economists have gone to great lengths to show that all you need is a relative ranking of goods that people reveal when they choose one good over another.

It's important to keep in the back of your mind that economists don't need actual numbers to discuss utility, especially if you're going on in economics. In introductory economics there's nothing quite as useful as a unit of utility. It gives us real numbers to work with rather than all kinds of fancy measure theories. So here's the deal: I'll use real numbers in discussing utility and you promise that you'll remember they're not really needed. (If you don't accept this deal, see Appendix A, where I go through the same analysis without using actual numbers.)

TOTAL UTILITY AND MARGINAL UTILITY

In thinking about utility, it's important to distinguish between *total utility* and *marginal utility*. **Total utility** refers to *the total satisfaction one gets from consuming a product.* **Marginal utility** refers to *the satisfaction one gets from consuming one additional unit of a product above and beyond what one has consumed up to that point.* For example, eating a whole pound of Beluga caviar might give you 4,700 units of utility.[1] Consuming the first 15

Web Note 8.1
Pleasure and Pain

Utility refers to the satisfaction one gets from consuming a good or service.

Q-1 One of the assumptions of economists' theory of choice is that utility must be measured. True or false? Why?

It is important to distinguish between marginal and total utility.

---

[1]Throughout the book I choose specific numbers to make the examples more understandable and to make the points I want to make. A useful exercise is for you to choose different numbers and reason your way through the same analysis.

MICROECONOMICS ▉ FOUNDATIONS OF SUPPLY AND DEMAND

ounces may have given you 4,697 units of utility. Consuming the last ounce of caviar might give you an additional 3 units of utility. The 4,700 is total utility; the 3 is the marginal utility of eating that last ounce of caviar.

An example of the relationship between total utility and marginal utility is given in Figure 8-1. Let's say that the marginal utility of the 1st slice of pizza is 14, and since you've eaten only 1 slice, the total utility is also 14. Let's also say that the marginal utility of the 2nd slice of pizza is 12, which means that the total utility of 2 slices of pizza is 26 (14 + 12). Similarly for the 3rd, 4th, and 5th slices of pizza, whose marginal utilities are 10, 8, and 6, respectively. The total utility of your eating those 5 pieces of pizza is the sum of the marginal utilities you get from eating each of the 5 slices. The fifth row of column 2 of Figure 8-1(a) shows that sum.

Notice that marginal utility shows up between the lines. It is the utility of changing consumption levels. For example, the marginal utility of changing from 1 to 2 slices of pizza is 12. The relationship between total and marginal utility can also be seen graphically. In Figure 8-1(b) we graph total utility (column 2 of the utility table) on the vertical axis, and the number of slices of pizza (column 1 of the utility table) on the horizontal axis. As you can see, total utility increases up to 7 slices of pizza; after 8 slices it starts decreasing—after 8 pieces of pizza you're so stuffed that you can't stand to look at another slice.

In Figure 8-1(c) we graph marginal utility (column 3 of the utility table) on the vertical axis and slices of pizza (column 1) on the horizontal axis. Notice how marginal utility decreases while total utility increases. When total utility stops increasing (between 7 and 8 slices), marginal utility is zero. Beyond this point total utility decreases and marginal utility is negative. An additional slice of pizza will actually make you worse off.

DIMINISHING MARGINAL UTILITY

Now let's consider the shapes of these curves a bit more carefully: What are they telling us about people's choices? As we've drawn the curves, the marginal utility that a person gets from each additional slice of pizza decreases with each slice of pizza eaten. Economists believe that the shapes of these curves is generally a reasonable description of the pattern of people's enjoyment. They call that pattern the **principle of diminishing marginal utility:**

> As you consume more of a good, after some point the marginal utility received from each additional unit of a good decreases with each additional unit consumed, other things equal.

As individuals increase their consumption of a good, at some point consuming another unit of the product will simply not yield as much additional pleasure as did consuming the preceding unit.

Consider, for example, that late-night craving for a double-cheese-and-pepperoni pizza. You order one and bite into it. Ah, pleasure! But if you've ordered a large pizza and you're eating it all by yourself, eventually you'll get less additional enjoyment from eating additional slices. In other words, the marginal utility you get is going to decrease with each additional slice of pizza you consume. That's the principle of diminishing marginal utility.

Notice that the principle of diminishing marginal utility does not say that you don't enjoy consuming more of a good; it simply states that as you consume more of the good, you enjoy the additional units less than you did the initial units. A fourth slice of pizza still tastes good, but it doesn't match the taste of the third slice. At some point, however, marginal utility can become negative. Say you had two large pizzas and only two hours in which to eat them. Eating the last slice could be pure torture. But in most

Q-2 If the total utility curve is a straight line—that is, does not exhibit diminishing marginal utility—what will the marginal utility curve look like?

The principle of diminishing marginal utility states that, after some point, the marginal utility received from each additional unit of a good decreases with each additional unit consumed, other things equal.

Q-3 Consuming more of a good generally increases its marginal utility. True or false? Why?

Figure 8-1 (a, b, and c)   Marginal and Total Utility
Marginal utility tends to decrease as consumption of a good increases. Notice how the information in the table (**a**) can be presented graphically in two different ways. The two different ways are, however, related. The downward slope of the marginal utility curve (**c**) is reflected in the total utility curve bowed downward in (**b**). Notice that marginal utility relates to changes in quantity so the marginal utility line is graphed at the halfway point. For example, in (**c**), between 7 and 8, marginal utility becomes zero.

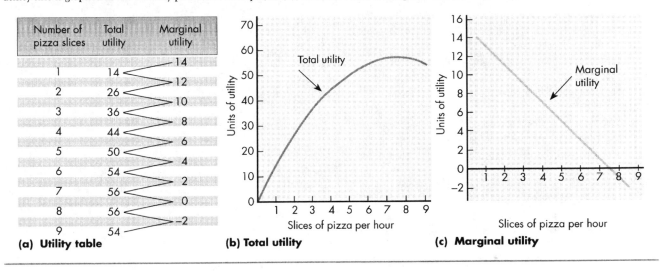

Number of pizza slices	Total utility	Marginal utility
1	14	14
2	26	12
3	36	10
4	44	8
5	50	6
6	54	4
7	56	2
8	56	0
9	54	−2

(a) Utility table   **(b) Total utility**   **(c) Marginal utility**

situations you have the option *not* to consume any more of a good. When consuming a good becomes torture (meaning its utility is negative), you simply don't consume any more of it. If you eat a slice of pizza (or consume an additional unit of a good), that's a good indication that its marginal utility is still positive.

RATIONAL CHOICE AND MARGINAL UTILITY

The analysis of rational choice is the analysis of how individuals choose goods within their budget in order to maximize total utility, and how maximizing total utility can be accomplished by considering marginal utility. That analysis begins with the premise that rational individuals want as much satisfaction as they can get from their available resources. The term *rational* in economics means, specifically, that people prefer more to less and will make choices that give them as much satisfaction as possible. The problem is that people face a budget constraint. They must choose among the alternatives. How do they do that?

Because people face a budget constraint, they must choose among alternatives.

SOME CHOICES

Let's start by considering three choices. (Answer each choice as you read it.)[2]

   Choice 1:   Between spending another dollar on a slice of pizza that gives you an additional 41 units of utility or spending another dollar on a hero sandwich that gives you an additional 30 units of utility.

   Choice 2:   Between reading an additional chapter in this book that gives you an additional 200 units of utility at a cost of one hour of your time, or reading an

Web Note 8.2
Tastes and Choices

---

[2]To keep the analysis simple in this example, I consider either/or decisions. Below, I show how to extend the analysis to marginal choices.

PSYCHOLOGY AND ECONOMICS

More and more psychology is being integrated into economics and economic reasoning. Instead of just assuming that individuals act rationally, modern economists are conducting experiments to determine how individuals act. In 2002 the Nobel Prize Committee recognized this change when it awarded the Nobel Prize in Economics to a professor of psychology, Danny Kahneman, and to an economist, Vernon Smith.

Smith was given the award for being a leader in experimental economics. He has played a central role in getting economists to test their theories with laboratory experiments, in which one can observe, rather than assume, how people behave. In these experiments economists have found that individuals have a sense of fairness along with economic rationality that guides their decisions.

Kahneman, together with Amos Tversky (who died in 1996), developed the theory of behavioral economics and argued that people aren't as calculating as economists often assume and that they repeatedly make errors in judgment that can be predicted and categorized. For example, a principle of economic rationality is that a sunk cost is a sunk cost, and should not be taken into account in decisions. But consistently individuals take sunk costs into account. He found that people are far less likely to sell a share of stock that they bought for $90 for $70 than they are to sell a share of stock for $70 that they bought for $50, even though economic rationality says that a rational person will not take into account the purchase price of a stock when deciding whether to sell it; they will only take into account future stock prices. Such insights are changing the face of modern economics, but they should be seen as complements to, rather than substitutes for, standard economic reasoning.

---

additional chapter in psychology that gives you an additional 100 units of utility at a cost of 40 minutes of your time.

Choice 3: Between having your next date with that awesome guy Jerry, which gives you an additional 2,000 units of utility and costs you $70, or taking out plain Jeff on your next date, which gives you an additional 200 units of utility and costs you $10.

The correct choices, in terms of marginal utility, are (1) the pizza, (2) a chapter of this book, and (3) Jerry.

If you answered all three correctly, either you're lucky or you have a good intuitive understanding of the principle of rational choice. Now let's explore the principle of rational choice more thoroughly by considering each of the three examples.

Choice 1 Since the slice of pizza and the hero sandwich both cost $1, and the pizza gives you more units of utility than the hero, the pizza is the rational choice. If you spend $1 on the hero rather than the pizza, you're losing 11 units of utility and not making yourself as happy as you could be. You're being irrational. Any choice (for the same amount of money) that doesn't give you as much utility as possible is an irrational choice.

But now let's say that the price of heroes falls to 50 cents so that you can buy two heroes for the same price you previously had to pay for only one. Let's also say that two heroes would give you 56 units of utility (not $2 \times 30 = 60$—remember the principle of diminishing marginal utility). Which would now be the more rational choice? The two heroes, because their 56 units of utility are 15 more than you would get from that dollar spent on one slice of pizza.

Another way of thinking about your choice is to recognize that essentially what you're doing is buying units of utility. Obviously you want to get the most for your

CHAPTER 8 ■ THE LOGIC OF INDIVIDUAL CHOICE: THE FOUNDATION OF SUPPLY AND DEMAND

money, so you choose goods that have the highest units of utility per unit of cost. Let's see how this way of thinking about a decision works by considering our second choice.

Choice 2   Here the two alternatives have a cost in time, not money. The analysis, however, is the same. You calculate the marginal utility (additional units of utility) of the choice facing you, and divide that by the costs of the activity; that gives you the marginal utility per unit of cost. Then choose the activity that has the highest marginal utility per unit of cost or lowest cost per unit of utility. When you do that, you see that this chapter gives you 3⅓ units of utility per minute (200/60 = 3⅓), while the psychology chapter gives you 2½ units of utility per minute. So you choose to read another chapter in this book.[3]

Choice 3   Taking out Jerry gives you 28½ units of utility per dollar (2,000/$70), while taking out Jeff gives you 20 units of utility per dollar (200/$10). So you choose to take out Jerry.[4]

THE PRINCIPLE OF RATIONAL CHOICE

The **principle of rational choice** is as follows: *Spend your money on those goods that give you the most marginal utility (MU) per dollar.* The principle of rational choice is important enough for us to restate.

If $\dfrac{MU_x}{P_x} > \dfrac{MU_y}{P_y}$, choose to consume an additional unit of good *x*.

If $\dfrac{MU_x}{P_x} < \dfrac{MU_y}{P_y}$, choose to consume an additional unit of good *y*.

By substituting the marginal utilities and prices of goods into these formulas, you can always decide which good it makes more sense to consume. Consume the one with the highest marginal utility per dollar.

SIMULTANEOUS DECISIONS

So far in discussing our examples, we've considered the choices separately. But in real life, choices aren't so neatly separated. Say you were presented with all three choices simultaneously. If you make all three of the decisions given in the examples, are you being rational? The answer is no. Why? The pizza gives you 41 units of utility per dollar; taking out Jerry gives you 28½ units of utility per dollar. You aren't being rational; you aren't maximizing your utility. It would clearly make sense to eat more pizza, paying for it by cutting the date with Jerry short. (Skip the coffee at the end of the meal.)

But what about the other choice: studying psychology or economics? We can't compare the costs of studying to the costs of the other goods because, as I noted earlier, the costs of both studying alternatives are expressed in terms of time, not money. If we can assign a money value to the time, however, we can make the comparison. Let's say you can earn $6 per hour, so the value of your time is 10 cents per minute. This allows us to think about both alternatives in terms of dollars and cents. Since a chapter in economics takes an hour to read, the cost in money of reading a chapter is

Q-4 Which is the rational choice—watching one hour of MTV that gives you 20 units of utility or watching a two-hour movie that gives you 30 units of utility?

The principle of rational choice tells us to spend our money on those goods that give us the most marginal utility per dollar.

---

[3]As I've pointed out before, I choose the numbers to make the points I want to make. A good exercise for you is to choose different numbers that reflect your estimate of the marginal utility you get from choice, and see what your rational choices are. And remember our deal.

[4]In these examples I am implicitly assuming that the "goods" are divisible. Technically, this assumption is needed for marginal utilities to be fully specified.

60 minutes × 10 cents = $6. Similarly, the cost of the 40 minutes you'd take to read the psychology chapter is $4.

With these values we can compare our studying decisions with our other decisions. The value in units of utility per dollar of reading a chapter of this book is:

$$\frac{200}{\$6} = 33\tfrac{1}{3} \text{ units of utility per dollar}$$

So forget about dating Jerry with its 28½ units of utility per dollar. Your rational choice is to study this chapter while stuffing yourself with pizza.

But wait. Remember that, according to the principle of diminishing marginal utility, as you consume more of something, the marginal utility you get from it falls. So as you consume more pizza and spend more time reading this book, the marginal utilities of these activities will fall. Thus, as you vary your consumption, the marginal utilities you get from the goods are changing.

MAXIMIZING UTILITY AND EQUILIBRIUM

When do you stop changing your consumption? The principle of rational choice says you should keep adjusting your spending within your budget if the marginal utility per dollar (MU/P) of two goods differs. The only time you don't adjust your spending is when there is no clear winner. *When the ratios of the marginal utility to price of the two goods are equal*, you're maximizing utility; this is the **utility-maximizing rule:**

$$If \frac{MU_x}{P_x} = \frac{MU_y}{P_y}, \text{ you're maximizing utility.}$$

When you're maximizing utility, you're in equilibrium. To understand how, by adjusting your spending, you can achieve equilibrium, it's important to remember the principle of diminishing marginal utility. As we consume more of an item, the marginal utility we get from the last unit consumed decreases. Conversely, as we consume *less* of an item, the marginal utility we get from the last unit consumed *increases*. (The principle of diminishing marginal utility operates in reverse.)

Achieving equilibrium by maximizing utility (juggling your choices, adding a bit more of one and choosing a bit less of another) requires more information than I've so far presented. We need to know the marginal utility of alternative amounts of consumption for each choice and how much we have to spend on all those items. With that information we can choose among alternatives, given our available resources.

AN EXAMPLE OF MAXIMIZING UTILITY

Table 8-1 offers an example in which we have the necessary information to make simultaneous decisions and maximize utility. In this example, we have $7 to spend on ice cream cones and Big Macs. The choice is between ice cream at $1 a cone and Big Macs at $2 apiece. In the table you can see the principle of diminishing marginal utility in action. The marginal utility (MU) we get from either good decreases as we consume more of it. Marginal utility (MU) becomes negative after 5 Big Macs or 6 ice cream cones.

The key columns for your decision are the MU/P columns. They tell you the MU per dollar spent on each of the items. By following the rule that we choose the good with the higher marginal utility per dollar, we can quickly determine the optimal choice.

Let's start by considering what we'd do with our first $2. Clearly we'd only eat ice cream. Doing so would give us 29 + 17 = 46 units of utility, compared to 20 units of utility if we spent the $2 on a Big Mac. How about our next $2? Again the choice is

---

Q.5 True or false? You are maximizing total utility only when the marginal utility of all goods is zero. Explain your answer.

The utility maximizing rule:
$$\frac{MU_x}{P_x} = \frac{MU_y}{P_y}$$

Table 8-1 Maximizing Utility

This table provides the information needed to make simultaneous decisions. Notice that the marginal utility we get from another good declines as we consume more of it. To maximize utility, adjust your choices until the marginal utility of all goods is equal.

Big Macs (P = $2)				Ice Cream (P = $1)			
Q	TU	MU	MU/P	Q	TU	MU	MU/P
0	0			0	0		
		20	10			29	29
1	20			1	29		
		14	7			17	17
2	34			2	46		
		10	5			7	7
3	44			3	53		
		3	1.5			2	2
4	47			4	55		
		0	0			1	1
5	47			5	56		
		−5	−2.5			0	0
6	42			6	56		
		−10	−5			−4	−4
7	32			7	52		

clear; the 10 units of utility per dollar from the Big Mac are plainly better than the 7 units of utility per dollar we can get from ice cream cones. So we buy 1 Big Mac and 2 ice cream cones with our first $4.

Now let's consider our fifth and sixth dollars. The MU/P for a second Big Mac is 7. The MU/P for a third ice cream cone is also 7, so we could spend the fifth dollar on either—if McDonald's will sell us half a Big Mac. We ask them if they will, and they tell us no, so we must make a choice between either two additional ice cream cones or another Big Mac for our fifth and sixth dollars. Since the marginal utility per dollar of the fourth ice cream cone is only 2, it makes sense to spend our fifth and sixth dollars on another Big Mac. So now we're up to 2 Big Macs and 2 ice cream cones and we have one more dollar to spend.

Now how about our last dollar? If we spend it on a third ice cream cone we get 7 additional units of utility. If McDonald's maintains its position and only sells whole Big Macs, this is our sole choice since we only have a dollar and Big Macs sell for $2. But let's say that McDonald's wants the sale and this time offers to sell us half a Big Mac for $1. Would we take it? The answer is no. One-half of the next Big Mac gives us only 5 units of utility per dollar whereas the third ice cream cone gives us 7 units of utility per dollar. So we spend the seventh dollar on a third ice cream cone.

With these choices and $7 to spend we've arrived at equilibrium—the marginal utilities per dollar are the same for both goods and we're maximizing total utility. Our total utility is 34 from 2 Big Macs and 53 units of utility from the 3 ice cream cones, making a total utility of 87.

Why do these two choices make sense? Because they give us the most total utility for the $7 we have to spend. We've followed the utility-maximizing rule: Maximize utility by adjusting your choices until the marginal utilities per dollar are the same. These choices make the marginal utility per dollar between the last Big Mac and the last ice cream cone equal. The marginal utility per dollar we get from our last Big Mac is:

Colander:
Microeconomics, Fifth
Edition

II. Microeconomics

8. The Logic of Individual
Choice: The Foundation of
Supply and Demand

© The McGraw–Hill
Companies, 2004

MICROECONOMICS ▪ FOUNDATIONS OF SUPPLY AND DEMAND

$$\frac{MU}{P} = \frac{14}{\$2} = 7$$

The marginal utility per dollar we get from our last ice cream cone is:

$$\frac{MU}{P} = \frac{7}{\$1} = 7$$

The marginal utility per dollar of each choice is equal, so we know we can't do any better. For any other choice we would get less total utility, so we could increase our total utility by switching to one of these two choices.

EXTENDING THE PRINCIPLE OF RATIONAL CHOICE

Our example involved only two goods, but the reasoning can be extended to the choice among many goods. Our analysis has shown us that the principle of rational choice among many goods is simply an extension of the principle of rational choice applied to two goods. That general principle of rational choice is to consume more of the good that provides a higher marginal utility per dollar.

When $\frac{MU_x}{P_x} > \frac{MU_z}{P_z}$, consume more of good x.

When $\frac{MU_y}{P_y} > \frac{MU_z}{P_z}$, consume more of good y.

Stop adjusting your consumption when the marginal utilities per dollar are equal.

So the general utility-maximizing rule is that you are maximizing utility when the marginal utilities per dollar of the goods consumed are equal.

When $\frac{MU_x}{P_x} = \frac{MU_y}{P_y} = \frac{MU_z}{P_z}$ you are maximizing utility.

When this rule is met, the consumer is in equilibrium; the cost per additional unit of utility is equal for all goods and the consumer is as well off as it is possible to be.

Notice that the rule does not say that the rational consumer should consume a good until its marginal utility reaches zero. The reason is that consumers don't have enough money to buy all they want. They face a budget constraint and do the best they can under that constraint—that is, they maximize utility. To buy more goods a person has to work more, so she should work until the marginal utility of another dollar earned just equals the marginal utility of goods purchased with another dollar. According to economists' analysis of rational choice, a person's choice of how much to work is made simultaneously with the person's decision of how much to consume. So when you say you want a Porsche but can't afford one, economists ask whether you're working two jobs and saving all your money to buy a Porsche. If you aren't, you're demonstrating that you don't really want a Porsche, given what you would have to do to get it.

Q-6 If you are initially in equilibrium and the price of one good rises, how would you adjust your consumption to return to equilibrium?

RATIONAL CHOICE AND THE LAWS OF DEMAND AND SUPPLY

Now that you know the rule for maximizing utility, let's see how it relates to the laws of demand and supply. We begin with demand. The law of demand says that the quantity demanded of a good is inversely related to its price. That is, when the price of a good goes up, the quantity we consume of it goes down.

INCOME AND SUBSTITUTION EFFECTS

In the discussion of the law of demand I didn't say precisely how much the quantity demanded would decrease with an increase in the price of an ice cream cone from $1 to $2. I didn't because of a certain ambiguity that arises when one talks about changes in nominal prices. To understand the cause of this ambiguity, notice that if the price of an ice cream cone has risen to $2, with $7 we can no longer consume 2 Big Macs and 3 ice cream cones. We've got to cut back for two reasons: First, we're poorer due to the rise in price. The reduction in quantity demanded because we're poorer is called the *income effect*. Second, the *relative* prices have changed. The price of ice cream has risen relative to the price of Big Macs. The reduction in quantity demanded because relative price has risen is called a *substitution effect*. Technically the law of demand is based only on the substitution effect.

To separate the two effects, let's assume that somebody compensates us for the rise in price of ice cream cones. Since it would cost $10 [(2 × $2 = $4) + (3 × $2 = $6)] to buy what $7 bought previously, we'll assume that someone gives us an extra $3 to compensate us for the rise in price. Since we are not any poorer because of the price change, this eliminates the income effect. We now have $10, so we can buy 2 Big Macs and the 3 ice cream cones as we did before. If we do so, our total utility is once again 87 (34 units of utility from 2 Big Macs and 53 units of utility from 3 ice cream cones.) But will we do so? We can answer that with the table.

We see that Big Macs give us more *MU* per dollar. What happens if we exchange an ice cream cone for an

Big Macs (P = $2)				Ice Cream (P = $2)			
Q	TU	MU	MU/P	Q	TU	MU	MU/P
0	0			0	0		
		20	10			29	14.5
1	20			1	29		
		14	7			17	8.5
2	34			2	46		
		10	5			7	3.5
3	44			3	53		

additional Big Mac, so instead of buying 3 ice cream cones and 2 Big Macs, we buy 3 Big Macs and 2 ice cream cones? The *MU* per dollar of Big Macs falls from 7 to 5 and the *MU* per dollar of the ice cream cone (whose price is now $2) rises from 3.5 to 8.5. Our total utility rises to 44 from 3 Big Macs and 46 from 2 ice cream cones, for a total of 90 units of utility rather than the previous 87. We've increased our total utility by shifting our consumption out of ice cream, the good whose price has risen. The price of ice cream went up and, even though we were given more money so we could buy the same amount as before, we did not; we bought fewer ice cream cones. That's the substitution effect in action: It tells us that when the relative price of a good goes up, the quantity purchased of that good decreases, *even if you're given money to compensate you for the rise.*

Now let's consider the law of demand in relation to our principle of rational choice. When the price of a good goes up, the marginal utility *per dollar* we get from that good goes down. So when the price of a good goes up, if we were initially in equilibrium, we no longer are. Therefore, we choose to consume less of that good. The principle of rational choice shows us formally that following the law of demand is the rational thing to do.

Let's see how. If:

$$\frac{MU_x}{P_x} = \frac{MU_y}{P_y}$$

and the price of good y goes up, then:

$$\frac{MU_x}{P_x} > \frac{MU_y}{P_y}$$

According to the principle of rational choice, if there is diminishing marginal utility and the price of a good goes up, we consume less of that good. Hence, the principle of rational choice leads to the law of demand.

MICROECONOMICS ▪ FOUNDATIONS OF SUPPLY AND DEMAND

Our utility-maximizing rule is no longer satisfied. Consider the preceding example, in which we were in equilibrium with 87 units of utility (34 from 2 Big Macs and 53 from 3 ice cream cones) with the utility-maximizing rule fulfilled:

$$\underset{\text{Big Mac}}{\frac{14 \text{ units of utility}}{\$2}} = \underset{\text{Ice cream}}{\frac{7 \text{ units of utility}}{\$1}} = 7$$

If the price of an ice cream cone rises from $1 to $2, the marginal utility per dollar for Big Macs (whose price hasn't changed) exceeds the marginal utility per dollar of ice cream cones:

Big Mac > Ice cream

$$\frac{14}{\$2} > \frac{7}{\$2}$$

To satisfy our utility-maximizing rule so that our choice will be rational, we must somehow raise the marginal utility we get from the good whose price has risen. Following the principle of diminishing marginal utility, we can increase marginal utility only by *decreasing* our consumption of the good whose price has risen. As we consume fewer ice cream cones and more Big Macs, the marginal utility of ice cream rises and the marginal utility of a Big Mac falls.

This example can be extended to a general rule: If the price of a good rises, you'll increase your total utility by consuming less of it. When the price of a good goes up, consumption of that good will go down. Our principle of rational choice underlies the law of demand:

Quantity demanded rises as price falls, other things constant.

Or alternatively:

Quantity demanded falls as price rises, other things constant.

This discussion of marginal utility and rational choice shows the relationship between marginal utility and the price we're willing to pay. When marginal utility is high, as it is with diamonds, the price we're willing to pay is high. When marginal utility is low, as it is with tap water, the price we're willing to pay is low. Since our demand for a good is an expression of our willingness to pay for it, quantity demanded is related to marginal utility.

THE LAW OF SUPPLY

According to the principle of rational choice, if there is diminishing marginal utility and the price of supplying a good goes up, you supply more of that good.

The above discussion focused on demand and goods we consume, but this analysis of choice holds for the law of supply of factors of production, such as labor, that individuals supply to the market, as well as for demand. In supply decisions you are giving up something—your time, land, or some other factor of production—and getting money in return. To show you how this works, let's consider one final example—how much labor you should supply to the market.

Say that working another hour at your part-time job pays you another $5 and that you currently work 20 hours per week. That additional income from the final hour of work gives you an additional 24 units of utility. Also assume that your best alternative use of that hour—studying economics—gives you another 24 units of utility. (You didn't know economics gave you so much pleasure, did you?) So what should you do when your boss asks you to work an extra hour? Tell her no, you are already satisfying the utility-maximum rule $MU_w/W = MU_s/W$.

CHAPTER 8 ■ THE LOGIC OF INDIVIDUAL CHOICE: THE FOUNDATION OF SUPPLY AND DEMAND

$$\frac{\text{Studying}}{24 \text{ units of utility}}{\$5} = \frac{\text{Working}}{24 \text{ units of utility}}{\$5}$$

The price of studying an additional hour is also your wage per hour because that wage is the opportunity cost of studying.

But now say that your boss offers to raise your wage to $5.50 per hour for work you do over 20 hours. That means that both your wage at work and the price of studying have increased. But now you can get more goods for working that additional hour. Let's say that those additional goods raise the marginal utility you get from an additional hour of work to 32 additional units of utility. Now the marginal utility of working an additional hour exceeds the marginal utility of studying an additional hour:

$$\frac{\text{Studying}}{24 \text{ units of utility}}{\$5.50} < \frac{\text{Working}}{32 \text{ units of utility}}{\$5.50}$$

So you work the extra hour.

Now say your boss comes to you and asks what it would take to get you to work five hours more per week. After running the numbers through your computer-mind, you solve the utility-maximizing rule and tell her, "$8.00 an hour for overtime work and you've got your worker." Combining these hours and wages gives you the supply curve shown in Figure 8-2, which demonstrates the law of supply.

To see that you have the reasoning down, say that an exam is coming, and you haven't studied. This will likely raise the marginal utility of studying sufficiently, so you will choose to work less, if you have a choice. What will that change do to the supply curve?

If you answered that it will shift it to the left, you're in good shape.

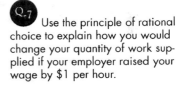 Q.7 Use the principle of rational choice to explain how you would change your quantity of work supplied if your employer raised your wage by $1 per hour.

OPPORTUNITY COST

Before we leave the principle of rational choice, let's consider how it relates to the opportunity cost concept that I presented in earlier chapters. *Opportunity cost* was the benefit forgone of the next-best alternative. Now that you've been through the principle of rational choice, you have a better sense of what is meant by opportunity cost of a forgone opportunity—it is essentially the marginal utility per dollar you forgo from the consumption of the next-best alternative.

To say $MU_x/P_x > MU_y/P_y$ is to say that the opportunity cost of not consuming good x is greater than the opportunity cost of not consuming good y. So you consume x.

The principle of rational choice states that, to maximize utility, choose goods until the opportunity costs of all alternatives are equal.

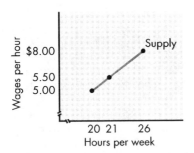

Figure 8-2   Deriving Labor Supply from Marginal Utility
Factor supply curves can be derived from a comparison of marginal utilities for various activities in relation to work. In this example the higher the wage, the higher the marginal utility of the goods you can get for the wage relative to the next-best alternative, giving you an upward-sloping labor supply curve.

When the marginal utilities per dollar spent are equal, the opportunity cost of the alternatives are equal. In reality people don't use the utility terminology, and, indeed, a specific measure of utility doesn't exist. But the choice based on the price of goods relative to the benefit they provide is used all the time. Instead of utility terminology, people use the "really need" terminology. They say they will work the extra hour rather than study because they *really need* the money. To say you are working because you "really need" the money is the equivalent of saying the marginal utility of working is higher than the opportunity cost of other choices. So the general rule fits decisions about supply, even if most people don't use the word *utility*. The more you "really, really need" something, the higher its marginal utility.

APPLYING ECONOMISTS' THEORY OF CHOICE TO THE REAL WORLD

Understanding a theory involves more than understanding how a theory works; it also involves understanding the limits the assumptions underlying the theory place on the use of the theory. So let's consider some of the assumptions on which economists' analysis of choice is based. The first assumption we'll consider is the implicit assumption that decisions can be made costlessly.

THE COST OF DECISION MAKING

The principle of rational choice makes reasonably good intuitive sense when we limit our examples to two or three choices, as I did in this chapter. But in reality, we make hundreds of thousands of choices simultaneously. It simply doesn't make intuitive sense that we're going to apply rational choice to all those choices at once—that would exceed our decision-making abilities. This cost of decision making means that it is only rational to be somewhat irrational—to do things without applying the principle of rational choice. Thinking about decisions is one of the things we all economize on.

How real-world people make decisions in real-world situations is an open question that modern economists are spending a lot of time researching. Following the work of Nobel Prize winner Herbert Simon, a number of economists have come to believe that, to make real-world decisions, most people use *bounded rationality*—rationality based on rules of thumb—rather than using the principle of rational choice. They argue that many of our decisions are made with our minds on automatic pilot. This view of rationality has significant implications for interpreting and predicting economic events. For example, one rule of thumb is "You get what you pay for," which means that something with a high price is better than something with a low price. Put technically, we rely on price to convey information about quality. This reliance on price for information changes the inferences one can draw from the analysis, and can lead to upward-sloping demand curves.

A second rule of thumb that people sometimes use is "Follow the leader." If you don't know what to do, do what you think smart people are doing. Consider the clothes you're wearing. I suspect many of your choices of what to wear reflect this and the previous rules of thumb. Suppliers of clothing certainly think so and spend enormous amounts of money to exploit these rules of thumb. They try to steer your automatic pilot toward their goods. The suppliers emphasize these two rules ("You get what you pay for" and "Follow the leader") to convince people their product is the "in" thing to buy. If they succeed, they've got a gold mine; if they fail, they've got a flop. Advertising is designed to mine these rules of thumb.

In technical terms, the "Follow the leader" rule leads to *focal point equilibria,* in which a set of goods is consumed, not because the goods are objectively preferred to all

Q-8 If the opportunity cost of consuming good *x* is greater than the opportunity cost of consuming good *y*, which good has the higher marginal utility per dollar?

Q-9 Bounded rationality violates the principle of rational choice. True or false?

Advertising is designed to mine rules of thumb.

other goods, but simply because, through luck, or advertising, they have become focal points to which people have gravitated. Once some people started consuming a good, others followed.

GIVEN TASTES

A second assumption implicit in economists' theory of rational choice is that our preferences are given, and are not shaped by society. In reality our preferences are determined not only by nature but also by our experiences—by nurture. Let's consider an example: Forty percent of major league baseball players chew tobacco, but close to zero percent of college professors chew tobacco. Why? Are major league baseball players somehow born with a tobacco-chewing gene while college professors are not? I doubt it. Tastes often are significantly influenced by society.

CONSPICUOUS CONSUMPTION

Another aspect of taste that has been described by economists is **conspicuous consumption**—*the consumption of goods not for one's direct pleasure, but simply to show off to others*. The term was created approximately 100 years ago by Thornstein Veblen. Veblen argued that, just as some animals strut around to show their abilities, humans consume to show that they can "afford it." For Veblen, mansions, designer clothing, and $300 appetizers were all examples of conspicuous consumption. He further argued that male industrialists (which were all industrialists at the time) were so busy with business that they didn't have time to show off enough, so they married a trophy spouse whose purpose was to show off for them in the most ostentatious manner possible.

TASTES AND INDIVIDUAL CHOICE

One way in which economists integrate the above insights into economics is by emphasizing that the analysis is conducted on the assumption of "given tastes." As discussed above, in reality, economists agree that often forces besides price and marginal utility play a role in determining what people demand. They fully recognize that a whole other analysis is necessary to supplement theirs—an analysis of what determines taste.

 Web Note 8.3
Veblen Goods

Ask yourself what you ate today. Was it health food? Pizza? Candy? Whatever it was, it was probably not the most efficient way to satisfy your nutritional needs. The most efficient way to do that would be to eat only soybean mush and vitamin supplements at a cost of about $300 per year. That's less than one-tenth of what the average individual today spends on food per year. Most of us turn up our noses at soybean mush. Why? Because tastes are important.

I emphasize this point because some economists have been guilty of forgetting their simplifying assumption. Some economists in the 1800s thought that society's economic needs eventually would be fully met and that we would enter a golden age of affluence where all our material wants would be satisfied. They thought there would be surpluses of everything. Clearly that hasn't happened. Somehow it seems that whenever a need is met, it's replaced by a want, which soon becomes another need.

Somehow, whenever a need is met, it's replaced by a want, which soon becomes another need.

There are, of course, examples of wants being temporarily satisfied, as a U.S. company on a small island in the Caribbean is reported to have discovered. Employees weren't showing up for work. The company sent in a team of efficiency experts who discovered the cause of their problem: The firm had recently raised wages, and workers had decided they could get all they wanted (warm weather, a gorgeous beach, plenty of food, and a little bit of spending money) by showing up for work once, maybe twice, a week. Such a situation was clearly not good for business, but the firm found a solution. It sent

MAKING STUPID DECISIONS

Applying the Tools

It is hard to make good decisions. You need lots of training—in math, in economics, in logic. Think of kids—do five-year-olds make rational decisions? Some dyed-in-the-wool utilitarians might argue that whatever decision one makes must, by definition, be rational, but such usage makes the concept tautological—true by definition.

When applying the theory of rational choice, most economists agree that some decisions people make can be irrational. For example, they will concede that five-year-olds make a lot of what most parents would call stupid (or irrational) decisions. By a stupid decision they mean a decision with expected consequences that, if the child had logically thought about them, would have caused the child not to make that particular decision. But five-year-olds often haven't learned how to think logically about expected consequences, so economists don't assume decisions made by five-year-olds reflect the rational choice model.

In the real world, parents and teachers spend enormous effort to teach children what is rational, reasonable, and

"appropriate." Children's decision-making process reflects that teaching. But parents and teachers teach more than a decision-making process; they also teach children a moral code that often includes the value of honor and the value of selflessness. These teachings shape their children's decision-making process (although not always in the way that parents or teachers think or hope) and modify their preferences. So our decision-making process and our preferences are, to some degree, taught to us.

Recognizing that preferences and decision-making processes are, to some degree, taught, not inherent, eliminates the fixed point by which to judge people's decisions: Are they making decisions that reflect their true needs, or are they simply reflecting what they have been taught? Eliminating that fixed point makes it difficult to draw unambiguous policy implications from economists' model of rational choice.

---

in thousands of Sears catalogs (back when Sears sent catalogs), and suddenly the workers were no longer satisfied with what they already had. They wanted more and went back to work to get it. When they were presented with new possibilities, their wants increased. Companies know that tastes aren't constant, and they spend significant amounts of money on advertising to make consumers have a taste for their goods. It works, too.

Tastes are also important in explaining differences in consumption between countries. For example, a Japanese person wouldn't consider having a meal without rice. Rice has a ceremonial, almost mystical value in Japan. In many parts of the United States supper means meat and potatoes. In Germany, carp (a large goldfish) is a delicacy; in the United States many people consider carp inedible. In the United States corn is a desirable vegetable; in parts of Europe, until recently, it was considered pig food.

To say we don't analyze tastes in the core of economic theory doesn't mean that we don't take them into account. Think back to Chapter 4, when we distinguished shifts in demand (the entire demand schedule shifts) from movements along the demand curve. Those movements along the demand curve were the effect of price. Tastes were one of the shift factors of demand. So economists do include tastes in their analysis; a change in tastes makes the demand curve shift.

Q-10 Using the principle of rational choice, explain why a change in tastes will shift a demand curve.

Economists take into account changes in tastes as shift factors of demand.

CONCLUSION

We began this chapter with a discussion of the simplifying nature of the economists' analysis of rational choice. Now that you've been through it, you may be wondering if it's all that simple. In any case, I'm sure most of you would agree that it's complicated enough. When we're talking about formal analysis, I'm in total agreement.

But if you're talking about informal analysis and applying the analysis to the real world, most economists would also agree that this theory of choice is in no way acceptable. Economists believe that there's more to life than maximizing utility. We believe in love, anger, and doing crazy things just for the sake of doing crazy things. We're real people.

But, we argue, simplicity has its virtue, and often people hide their selfish motivations. Few people like to go around and say, "I did this because I'm a self-interested, calculating person who cares primarily about myself." Instead they usually emphasize other motives. "Society conditioned me to do it"; "I'm doing this to achieve fairness"; "It's my upbringing." And they're probably partially right, but often they hide and obscure their self-interested motives in their psychological explanations. The beauty of economists' simple psychological assumption is that it cuts through many obfuscations (that's an obfuscating word meaning "smokescreens") and, in doing so, often captures a part of reality that others miss. Let's consider a couple of examples.

> Economists use their simple self-interest theory of choice because it cuts through many obfuscations, and in doing so, often captures a part of reality that others miss.

Why does government have restrictions on who's allowed to practice law? The typical layperson's answer is that these restrictions exist to protect the public. The economists' answer is that many of the restrictions do little to protect the public. Instead their primary function is to restrict the number of lawyers and thereby increase the marginal utility of existing lawyers and the price they can charge.

Why do museum directors almost always want to increase the size of their collections? The layperson's (and museum directors') answer is that they're out to preserve our artistic heritage. The economists' answer is that it often has more to do with maximizing the utility of the museum staff. (Economist William Grampp made this argument in a book about the economics of art. He supported his argument by pointing out that more than half of museums' art is in storage and not accessible to the public. Acquiring more art will simply lead to more art going into storage.)

Now in no way am I claiming that the economic answer based on pure self-interest is always the correct one. But I am arguing that approaching problems by asking the question "What's in it for the people making the decisions?" is a useful approach that will give you more insight into what's going on than many other approaches. It gets people to ask tough, rather than easy, questions. After you've asked the tough questions, then you can see how to modify the conclusions by looking deeply into the real-world institutions.

> Approaching problems by asking the question "What's in it for the people making the decision?" is a useful approach that will give you more insight than many other approaches.

All too often students think of economics and economic reasoning as establishment reasoning. That's not true. Economic reasoning can be extremely subversive to existing establishments. But whatever it is, it is not subversive in order to be subversive, or proestablishment to be proestablishment. It's simply a logical application of a simple idea—individual choice theory—to a variety of problems.

SUMMARY

- Total utility is the satisfaction obtained from consuming a product; marginal utility is the satisfaction obtained from consuming one additional unit of a product.

- The principle of diminishing marginal utility states that after some point, the marginal utility of consuming more of the good will fall.

MICROECONOMICS ■ FOUNDATIONS OF SUPPLY AND DEMAND

- The principle of rational choice is:

  If $\dfrac{MU_x}{P_x} > \dfrac{MU_y}{P_y}$, choose to consume more of good x.

  If $\dfrac{MU_x}{P_x} < \dfrac{MU_y}{P_y}$, choose to consume more of good y.

- The utility-maximizing rule says:

  If $\dfrac{MU_x}{P_x} = \dfrac{MU_y}{P_y}$, you're maximizing utility; you're indifferent between good x and good y.

- Unless $MU_x/P_x = MU_y/P_y$, an individual can rearrange his or her consumption to increase total utility.

- Opportunity cost is essentially the marginal utility per dollar one forgoes from the consumption of the next-best alternative.

- The law of demand can be derived from the principle of rational choice.

- If you're in equilibrium and the price of a good rises, you'll reduce your consumption of that good to reestablish equilibrium.

- The law of supply can be derived from the principle of rational choice.

- If your wage rises, the marginal utility of the goods you can buy with that wage will rise and you will work more to satisfy the utility-maximizing rule.

- To apply economists' analysis of choice to the real world, we must carefully consider, and adjust for, the underlying assumptions, such as costlessness of decision making and given tastes.

Key Terms

conspicuous
consumption (*191*)
marginal utility (*179*)

principle of diminishing
marginal utility (*180*)

principle of rational
choice (*183*)
total utility (*179*)

utility (*179*)
utility-maximizing
rule (*184*)

Questions for Thought and Review

1. Explain how marginal utility differs from total utility.
2. According to the principle of diminishing marginal utility, how does marginal utility change as more of a good is consumed? As less of a good is consumed?
3. How would the world be different than it is if the principle of diminishing marginal utility seldom held true?
4. It is sometimes said that an economist is a person who knows the price of everything but the value of nothing. Is this statement true or false? Why?
5. Assign a measure of utility to your studying for various courses. Do your study habits follow the principle of rational choice?
6. What key psychological assumptions do economists make in their theory of individual choice?
7. Explain your motivation for four personal decisions you have made in the past year, using economists' model of individual choice.
8. State the law of demand and explain how it relates to the principle of rational choice.

9. State the law of supply and explain how it relates to opportunity cost.
10. If the supply curve is perfectly inelastic, what is the opportunity cost of the supplier?
11. There is a small but growing movement known as "voluntary simplicity," which is founded on the belief in a simple life of working less and spending less. Do Americans who belong to this movement follow the principle of rational choice?
12. Although the share of Americans who say they are "very happy" hasn't changed much in the last five decades, the number of products produced and consumed per person has risen tremendously. How can this be?
13. Early Classical economists found the following "diamond/water" paradox perplexing: "Why is water, which is so useful and necessary, so cheap, when diamonds, which are so useless and unnecessary, so expensive?" Using the utility concept, explain why it is not really a paradox.

CHAPTER 8 ■ THE LOGIC OF INDIVIDUAL CHOICE: THE FOUNDATION OF SUPPLY AND DEMAND

14. Give an example of a recent purchase for which you used a rule of thumb in your decision-making process. Did your decision follow the principle of rational choice? Explain.

15. According to Thorstein Veblen what is the purpose of conspicuous consumption? Does the utility derived from the consumption of these goods come from their price or functionality? Give an example of such a good.

PROBLEMS AND EXERCISES

1. Complete the following table of Scout's utility from drinking cans of soda and answer the questions below.

Cans of Soda	Total Utility	Marginal Utility
0	——	
		10
1	——	
		12
2	22	
		——
3	32	
		8
4	——	
		4
5	——	
		——
6	44	
		——
7	42	

a. At what point does marginal utility begin to fall?
b. Will Scout consume the 7th can of soda? Explain your answer.
c. True or false? Scout will be following the utility-maximizing rule by consuming 2 cans of soda. Explain your answer.

2. The following table gives the price and total units of three goods: A, B, and C.

Good	Price				Total Utility				
		1	2	3	4	5	6	7	8
A	$10	200	380	530	630	680	700	630	430
B	2	20	34	46	56	64	72	78	82
C	6	50	60	70	80	90	100	90	80

As closely as possible, determine how much of the three goods you would buy with $20. Explain why you chose what you did.

3. The following table gives the marginal utility of John's consumption of three goods: A, B, and C.

Units of Consumption	MU of A	MU of B	MU of C
1			
	20	25	45
2			
	18	20	30
3			
	16	15	24
4			
	14	10	18
5			
	12	8	15
6			
	10	6	12

a. Good A costs $2 per unit, good B costs $1, and good C costs $3. How many units of each should a consumer with $12 buy to maximize his or her utility?
b. How will the answer change if the price of B rises to $2?
c. How about if the price of C is 50 cents but the other prices are as in a?

4. The total utility of your consumption of widgets is 40; it changes by 2 with each change in widgets consumed. The total utility of your consumption of wadgets is also 40 but changes by 3 with each change in wadgets consumed. The price of widgets is $2 and the price of wadgets is $3. How many widgets and wadgets should you consume?

5. Nobel Prize–winning economist George Stigler explains how the famous British economist Phillip Wicksteed decided where to live. His two loves were fresh farm eggs, which were more easily obtained the farther from London he was, and visits from friends, which decreased the farther he moved away from London. Given these two loves, describe the decision rule that you would have expected Wicksteed to follow.

6. You are buying your spouse, significant other, or close friend a ring. You decide to show your reasonableness, and buy a cubic zirconium ring that sells at ⅟₆₀ the cost of a mined diamond and that any normal person could not tell from a mined diamond just by looking at it. In fact, the zirconium will have more brilliance and fewer occlusions (imperfections) than a mined diamond.

a. How will your spouse (significant other, close friend) likely react?

b. Why?

c. Is this reaction justified?

7. Suppose Charlie Parker CDs cost $10 apiece and Lester Young CDs cost $5 apiece. You have $40 to spend on CDs. The marginal utility that you derive from additional CDs is as follows:

Number of CDs	Charlie Parker	Lester Young
0		30
	60	
1		28
	40	
2		24
	30	
3		20
	20	
4		10
	10	
5		

How many of each CD would you buy? Suppose the price of a Lester Young CD rises to $10. How many of each CDs would you buy? Use this to show how the principle of rational choice leads to the law of demand.

WEB QUESTIONS

1. Go to www.travelocity.com.
   a. Find a selection of prices of airline fares between two cities for a period of one month ahead of time and staying over a Saturday night. If there are differences in the prices explain why they likely differ.
   b. Now shorten your stay, and do not include a Saturday-night stay. What happens to the prices? Explain why.
   c. Now find the price of the same flight you had in a, only this time booking only three days ahead. What happens to prices? Explain why.

2. Go to www.iwon.com.
   a. What does this site do?
   b. Why do they give out a $10,000 daily prize and a $25 million yearly prize for using the site?
   c. What advertisements were shown there?
   d. What does the existence of these advertisements suggest about economists' assumption that tastes are fixed?

ANSWERS TO MARGIN QUESTIONS

1. False. Economists' theory of choice does not require them to measure utility. It only requires that the marginal utility of one good be compared to the marginal utility of another. (179)

2. If the total utility curve is a straight line, the marginal utility curve will be flat with a slope of zero since marginal utility would not change with additional units. (180)

3. False. The principle of diminishing marginal utility is that as one increases consumption of a good, the good's marginal utility decreases. (180)

4. Given a choice between the two, the rational choice is to watch MTV for one hour since it provides the highest marginal utility per hour. (183)

5. False. You are maximizing total utility when the marginal utilities per dollar are the same for all goods. This does not have to be where marginal utility is zero. (184)

6. If I am currently in equilibrium, then $MU_x/P_x = MU_y/P_y = MU_z/P_z$ for all goods I consume. If the price of one good goes up, I will decrease my consumption of that good and increase the consumption of other goods until the equilibrium is met again where $MU_x/P_x = MU_y/P_y = MU_z/P_z$. (186)

7. If offered one more dollar per hour, I would choose to substitute labor for leisure since the price of leisure (pay per hour of work) has increased. Following the principle of rational choice, I would work more to lower the marginal utility of work so that $MU_w/P_w = MU_l/P_l$. (189)

8. Good y has the higher marginal utility per dollar since the opportunity cost of consuming good x is the marginal utility per dollar of consuming good y. (190)

9. This could be true or false. It depends on how you interpret bounded rationality. If it is interpreted within a costless decision-making environment, it does violate the principle of rational choice since there is no reason to be less than rational. If, however, it is interpreted within a costly decision-making environment, then you can be making decisions within a range because the marginal

cost of increasing the range of choices exceeds the marginal benefit of doing so, and in that case bounded rationality is consistent with the principle of rational choice. Information is not costless. (190)

10. If a person is in equilibrium and a change in tastes leads to an increase in the marginal utility for one good, he will increase consumption of that good to reestablish equilibrium. A change in tastes will shift a demand curve because it will cause a change in quantity consumed without a change in the good's price. (192)

APPENDIX A

Indifference Curve Analysis

As I stated in the chapter, analyzing individual choice using actual numbers is unnecessary. In the chapter, I asked you to make a deal with me: You'd remember that actual numbers are unnecessary and I'd use them anyway. This appendix is for those who didn't accept my deal (and for those whose professors want them to get some practice in Graphish). It presents an example of a more formal analysis of individual choice.

SOPHIE'S CHOICE

Sophie is a junk food devotee. She lives on two goods: chocolate bars, which cost $1 each, and cans of soda, which sell for 50 cents apiece. Sophie is trying to get as much pleasure as possible, given her resources. Alternatively expressed, Sophie is trying to maximize her utility, given a budget constraint.

By translating this statement of Sophie's choice into graphs, I can demonstrate the principle of rational choice without ever mentioning any specific amount of utility.

The graph we'll use will have chocolate bars on the vertical axis and cans of soda on the horizontal axis, as in Figure A8-1.

GRAPHING THE BUDGET CONSTRAINT

Let's begin by asking: How can we translate her budget constraint (the $10 maximum she has to spend) into Graphish? The easiest way to do that is to ask what would happen if she spends her $10 all on chocolate bars or all on cans of soda. Since a chocolate bar costs $1, if she

Figure A8-1 Graphing the Budget Constraint

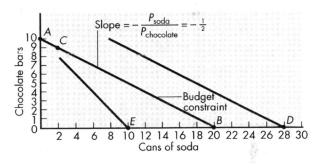

$$\text{Slope} = -\frac{P_{soda}}{P_{chocolate}} = -\frac{1}{2}$$

spends it all on chocolate bars she can get 10 bars (point A in Figure A8-1). If she spends it all on cans of soda, she can get 20 cans of soda (point B). This gives us two points.

But what if she wants some combination of soda and chocolate bars? If we draw a line between points A and B, we'll have a graphical picture of her budget constraint and can answer that question because a **budget constraint** is *a curve that shows us the various combinations of goods an individual can buy with a given amount of money.* The line is her budget constraint in Graphish.

To see that it is, say Sophie is spending all her money on chocolate bars. She then decides to buy one fewer chocolate bar. That gives her $1 to spend on soda, which, since those cans cost 50 cents each, allows her to buy 2 cans. Point C (9 chocolate bars and 2 cans of soda) represents that decision. Notice how point C is on the budget constraint. Repeat this exercise from various starting points until you're comfortable with the fact that the line does indeed represent the various combinations of soda

MICROECONOMICS ▥ FOUNDATIONS OF SUPPLY AND DEMAND

and chocolate bars Sophie can buy with the $10. It's a line with a slope of −½ and intersects the chocolate-bars-axis at 10 and the cans-of-soda axis at 20.

To be sure that you've got it, ask yourself what would happen to the budget constraint if Sophie got another $4 to spend on the two goods. Going through the same reasoning should lead you to the conclusion that the budget constraint will shift to the right so that it will intersect the cans-of-soda axis at 28 (point D), but its slope won't change. (I started the new line for you.) Make sure you can explain why.

Now what if the price of a can of soda goes up to $1? What happens to the budget line? (This is a question many people miss.) If you said the budget line becomes steeper, shifting in along the cans-of-soda axis to point E while remaining anchored along the chocolate-bars-axis until the slope equals −1, you've got it. If you didn't say that, go through the same reasoning we went through at first (if Sophie buys only cans of soda . . .) and then draw the new line. You'll see it becomes steeper. Put another way, the absolute value of the slope of the curve is the ratio of the price of cans of soda to the price of chocolate bars; the absolute value of the slope becomes greater with a rise in the price of cans of soda.

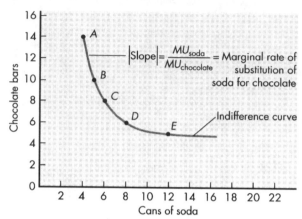

Figure A8-2 Sophie's Indifference Curve

$$|\text{Slope}| = \frac{MU_{soda}}{MU_{chocolate}} = \text{Marginal rate of substitution of soda for chocolate}$$

Chocolate bars	Cans of soda	
14	4	A
10	5	B
8	6	C
6	8	D
5	12	E

GRAPHING THE INDIFFERENCE CURVE

Now let's consider the second part of Sophie's choice: the pleasure part. Sophie is trying to get as much pleasure as she can from her $10. How do we deal with this in Graphish?

To see, let's go through a thought experiment. Say Sophie had 14 chocolate bars and 4 cans of soda (point A in Figure A8-2). Let's ask her, "Say you didn't know the price of either good and we took away 4 of those chocolate bars (so you had 10). How many cans of soda would we have to give you so that you would be just as happy as before we took away the 4 chocolate bars?"

Since she's got lots of chocolate bars and few cans of soda, her answer is probably "Not too many; say, 1 can of soda." This means that she would be just as happy to have 10 chocolate bars and 5 cans of soda (point B) as she would to have 14 chocolate bars and 4 cans of soda (point A). Connect those points and you have the beginning of a "just-as-happy" curve. But that doesn't sound impressive enough, so, following economists' terminology, we'll call it an **indifference curve**—*a curve that shows combinations of goods among which an individual is indifferent.* She's indifferent between points A and B.

If you continue our thought experiment, you'll get a set of combinations of chocolate bars and cans of soda like that shown in the table in Figure A8-2.

If you plot each of these combinations of points on the graph in Figure A8-2 and connect all these points, you have one of Sophie's indifference curves: a curve representing combinations of cans of soda and chocolate bars among which Sophie is indifferent.

Let's consider the shape of this curve. First, it's downward-sloping. That's reasonable; it simply says that if you take something away from Sophie, you've got to give her something in return if you want to keep her indifferent between what she had before and what she has now. The absolute value of the slope of an indifference curve is the **marginal rate of substitution**—*the rate at which one good must be added when the other is taken away in order to keep the individual indifferent between the two combinations.*

Second, it's bowed inward. That's because as Sophie gets more and more of one good, it takes fewer and fewer of another good to compensate for the loss of the good she incurred in order to get more of the other good. The underlying reasoning is similar to that in our discussion of the law of diminishing marginal utility, but notice we haven't even mentioned utility. Technically the reasoning for the indifference curve being bowed inward is called the

CHAPTER 8 ▪ THE LOGIC OF INDIVIDUAL CHOICE: THE FOUNDATION OF SUPPLY AND DEMAND

Figure A8-3   A Group of Indifference Curves

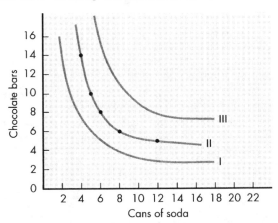

Figure A8-4   Why Indifference Curves Cannot Cross

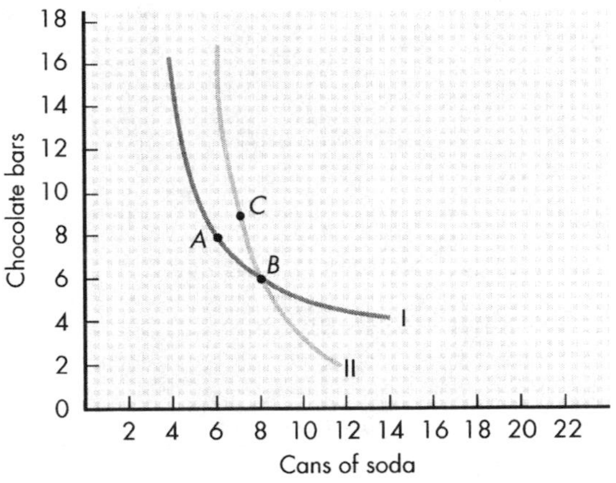

law of diminishing marginal rate of substitution—which tells us that *as you get more and more of a good, if some of that good is taken away, then the marginal addition of another good you need to keep you on your indifference curve gets less and less*.

Even more technically we can say that the absolute value of the slope of the indifference curve equals the ratio of the marginal utility of cans of soda to the marginal utility of chocolate bars:

$$\left| \text{ Slope } \right| = \frac{MU_{soda}}{MU_{chocolate}} = \text{Marginal rate of substitution}$$

That ratio equals the marginal rate of substitution of cans of soda for chocolate bars. Let's consider an example. Say that in Figure A8-2 Sophie is at point A and that the marginal utility she gets from an increase from 4 to 5 cans of soda is 10. Since we know that she was willing to give up 4 chocolate bars to get that 1 can of soda (and thereby move from point A to point B), that 10 must equal the loss of utility she gets from the loss of 4 chocolate bars out of the 14 she originally had. So the marginal rate of substitution of cans of soda for chocolate bars between points A and B must be 4. That's the absolute value of the slope of that curve. Therefore, her MU of a chocolate bar must be about 2.5 (10 for 4 chocolate bars).

You can continue this same reasoning, starting with various combinations of goods. If you do so, you can get a whole group of indifference curves like that in Figure A8-3. Each curve represents a different level of happiness. Assuming she prefers more to less, Sophie is better off if she's on Curve II than if she's on Curve I, and even better off if she's on Curve III. Her goal in life is to get out to the furthest indifference curve she can.

To see whether you've followed the reasoning, ask yourself the following question: "Assuming Sophie prefers more of a good to less (which seems reasonable), can any two of Sophie's indifference curves cross each other as the ones in Figure A8-4 do?"

The answer is no, no, no! Why? Because they're indifference curves. If the curves were to cross, the "prefer-more-to-less" principle would be violated. Say we start at point A: Sophie has 8 chocolate bars and 6 cans of soda. We know that since A (8 chocolate bars and 6 sodas) and B (6 chocolate bars and 8 cans of soda) are on the same indifference curve, Sophie is indifferent between A and B. Similarly with points B and C: Sophie would just as soon have 9 chocolate bars and 7 cans of soda as she would 6 chocolate bars and 8 cans of soda.

It follows by logical deduction that point A must be indifferent to C. But consider points A and C carefully. At point C, Sophie has 7 cans of soda and 9 chocolate bars. At point A she has 6 cans of soda and 8 chocolate bars. At point C she has more of both goods than she has at point A, so to say she's indifferent between these two points violates the "prefer-more-to-less" criterion. Ergo (that's Latin, meaning "therefore"), two indifference curves cannot intersect. That's why we drew the group of indifference curves in Figure A8-3 so that they do not intersect.

COMBINING INDIFFERENCE CURVES AND BUDGET CONSTRAINTS

Now let's put the budget constraint and the indifference curves together and ask how many chocolate bars and cans of soda Sophie will buy if she has $10, given the

MICROECONOMICS ▦ FOUNDATIONS OF SUPPLY AND DEMAND

Figure A8-5   Combining Indifference Curves and Budget Constraint

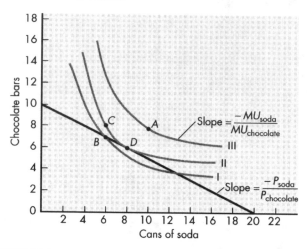

psychological makeup described by the indifference curves in Figure A8-3.

To answer that question, we must put the budget line of Figure A8-1 and the indifference curves of Figure A8-3 together, as we do in Figure A8-5.

As we discussed, Sophie's problem is to get to as high an indifference curve as possible, given her budget constraint. Let's first ask if she should move to point A (8 chocolate bars and 10 cans of soda). That looks like a good point. But you should quickly recognize that she can't get to point A; her budget line won't let her. (She doesn't have enough money.) Well then, how about point B (7 chocolate bars and 6 cans of soda)? She can afford that combination; it's on her budget constraint. The problem with point B is the following: She'd rather be at point C since point C has more chocolate bars and the same amount of soda (8 chocolate bars and 6 cans of soda). But, you say, she can't reach point C. Yes, that's true, but she can reach point D. And, by the definition of indifference curve, she's indifferent between point C and point D, so point D (6 chocolate bars and 8 cans of soda), which she can reach given her budget constraint, is preferred to point B.

The same reasoning holds for all other points. The reason is that the combination of chocolate bars and cans of soda represented by point D is the best she can do. It is the point where the indifference curve and the budget line are tangent—the point at which the slope of the

budget line ($-P_s/P_c$) equals the slope of the indifference curve ($-MU_s/MU_c$). Equating those slopes gives $P_s/P_c = (MU_s/MU_c)$, or:

$$MU_c/P_c = MU_s/P_s$$

This equation, you may remember from the chapter, is the equilibrium condition of our principle of rational choice. So by our Graphish analysis we arrived at the same conclusion we arrived at in the chapter, only this time we did it without using actual numbers. This means that even without a utilometer, economists' principle of rational choice is internally logical.

DERIVING A DEMAND CURVE FROM THE INDIFFERENCE CURVE

Not only can we derive the principle of rational choice with indifference curve/budget line analysis, we can also derive a demand curve. To do so, ask yourself what a demand curve is. It's the quantity of a good that a person will buy at various prices. Since the budget line gives us the relative price of a good, and the point of tangency of the indifference curve gives us the quantity that a person would buy at that price, we can derive a demand curve from the indifference curves and budget lines. To derive a demand curve we go through a set of thought experiments asking how many cans of soda Sophie would buy at various prices. We'll go through one of those experiments.

We start with the analysis we used before when Sophie started with $10 and chose to buy 8 cans of soda when the price of a can of soda was 50 cents (point A in Figure A8-6(a)). That analysis provides us with one point on the demand curve. I represent that by point A in Figure A8-6(b). At a price of 50 cents, Sophie buys 8 cans of soda.

Now say the price of a can of soda rises to $1. That rotates the budget line in, from budget line 1 to budget line 2 as in Figure A8-6(a). She can't buy as much as she could before. But we can determine how much she'll buy by the same reasoning we used previously. She'll choose a point at which her lower indifference curve is tangent to her new budget line. As you can see, she'll choose point B, which means that she buys 6 cans of soda when the price of a can of soda is $1. Graphing that point (6 cans of soda at $1 each) on our price/quantity axis in Figure A8-6(b), we have another point on our demand curve, point B. Connect these two together and you can see we're getting a downward-sloping demand curve, just as the law of

CHAPTER 8 ■ THE LOGIC OF INDIVIDUAL CHOICE: THE FOUNDATION OF SUPPLY AND DEMAND

Figure A8-6 (a and b)   From Indifference Curves to Demand Curves

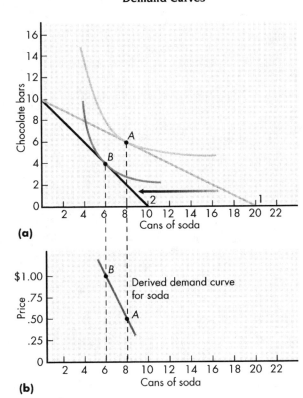

demand said we would. To make sure you understand, continue the analysis for a couple of additional price changes. You'll see that the demand curve you derive will be downward-sloping.

There's much more we can do with indifference curves. We can distinguish income effects and substitution effects. (Remember, when the price of a can of soda rose, Sophie was worse off. So to be as well off as before, as is required by the substitution effect, she'd have to be compensated for that rise in price by an offsetting fall in the price of chocolate bars.) But let's make a deal. You tentatively believe me when I say that all kinds of stuff can be done with indifference curves and budget constraints, and I'll leave the further demonstration and the proofs for you to experience in the intermediate microeconomics courses.

KEY TERMS

budget constraint (*197*)
indifference curve (*198*)

law of diminishing marginal rate of
    substitution (*199*)

marginal rate of substitution (*198*)

QUESTIONS FOR THOUGHT AND REVIEW

1. Zachary has $5 to spend on two goods: video games and hot dogs. Hot dogs cost $1 apiece while video games cost 50 cents apiece.
   a. Draw a graph of Zachary's budget constraint, placing videos on the Y axis.
   b. Suppose the price of hot dogs falls to 50 cents apiece. Draw the new budget constraint.

   c. Suppose Zachary now has $8 to spend. Draw the new budget constraint using the prices from *b*.

2. Zachary's indifference curves are shown in the following graph. Determine on which indifference curve Zachary will be, given the budget constraints and prices in *a*, *b*, and *c* from problem 1.

MICROECONOMICS ▪ FOUNDATIONS OF SUPPLY AND DEMAND

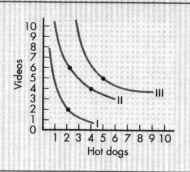

a. Given a choice, which budget constraint would Zachary prefer most? Least?

b. What is the marginal rate of substitution of hot dogs for videos at each of the combinations chosen with budget constraints *a*, *b*, and *c* in problem 1?

3. What would an indifference curve look like if the marginal rate of substitution were zero? If it were constant?

4. What might an indifference curve look like if the law of diminishing marginal utility did not hold?

PRODUCTION AND COST ANALYSIS I

9

Production is not the application of tools
to materials, but logic to work.

—*Peter Drucker*

After reading this chapter, you should be able to:

• Differentiate economic profit from accounting profit.

• Distinguish between long-run and short-run production.

• State the law of diminishing marginal productivity.

• Calculate fixed costs, variable costs, marginal costs, total costs, average fixed costs, average variable costs, and average total costs, given the appropriate information.

• Distinguish the various kinds of cost curves and describe the relationships among them.

• Explain why the marginal and average cost curves are U-shaped.

• Explain why the marginal cost curve always goes through the minimum point of an average cost curve.

The ability of market economies to supply material goods and services to members of their societies makes them the envy of many other societies and is one of the strongest arguments for using the market as a means of organizing society. Somehow markets are able to channel individuals' imagination, creativity, and drive into the production of material goods and services that other people want. They do this by giving people incentives to supply goods and services to the market.

Ultimately all supply comes from individuals. Individuals control the factors of production such as land, labor, and capital. Why do individuals supply these factors to the market? Because they want something in return. This means that industry's ability to supply goods is dependent on individuals' willingness to supply the factors of production they control. This connection became obvious in the formerly socialist countries in the late 1980s and early 1990s when consumer goods were often unavailable. People in those countries stopped working (supplying their labor). They reasoned: Why supply our labor if there's nothing to get in return?

The analysis of supply is more complicated than the analysis of demand. In the supply process, people first offer their factors of production to the market. Then the factors are transformed by firms, such as GM or IBM, into goods that consumers want. **Production** is the name given to that *transformation of factors into goods and services*.

To make it simple for you, I separate out the analysis of the supply of factors of production (considered in detail in later chapters) from the supply of produced goods. This allows us to assume that the prices of factors of production are constant, which simplifies the analysis of the supply of produced goods enormously. There's no problem with doing this as long as you remember that behind any produced good are individuals' factor supplies. Ultimately people, not firms, are responsible for supply.

Even with the analysis so simplified, there's still a lot to cover—so much, in fact, that we devote two chapters (this chapter and the next) to considering production, costs, and supply. In this chapter I introduce you to the production

MICROECONOMICS ■ FOUNDATIONS OF SUPPLY AND DEMAND

process and short-run cost analysis. Then, in the next chapter, I focus on long-run costs and how cost analysis is used in the real world.

THE ROLE OF THE FIRM

Web Note 9.1
Virtual Firms

With goods that already exist, like housing and labor, the law of supply is rather intuitive. Their supply to the market depends on people's opportunity costs of keeping them for themselves and of supplying them to the market. But many of the things we buy (such as VCRs, cars, and jackets) don't automatically exist; they must be produced. The supply of such goods depends on production.

A key concept in production is the firm. A **firm** is *an economic institution that transforms factors of production into goods and services.* A firm (1) organizes factors of production; and/or (2) produces goods; and/or (3) sells produced goods to individuals, businesses, or government.

Firms:

1. Organize factors of production,

2. produce goods and services, and/or

3. sell produced goods and services.

Which combination of activities a firm will undertake depends on the cost of undertaking each activity relative to the cost of subcontracting the work out to another firm. When the firm only organizes production, it is called a *virtual firm.* Virtual firms organize the factors of production and subcontract out all production. Let's consider an example—a "psychic superline" that provides super psychic advice to individuals. If it is a virtual firm, it hires individuals to act as psychics, an advertising company to convince gullible people to call in, a phone routing company to route incoming calls, and a billing company to bill callers (the telephone company does this for them). The firm's sole role is organization. While most firms are not totally virtual, more and more of the organizational structure of businesses is being separated from the production process. As cost structures change because of technological advances such as the Internet, an increasing number of well-known firms will likely concentrate on organizational instead of production activities.

More and more of the organizational structure of business is being separated from the production process.

THE FIRM AND THE MARKET

The firm operates within a market, but, simultaneously, it is a negation of the market in the sense that it replaces the market with command and control. How an economy operates—which activities are organized through markets, and which activities are organized through firms—depends on *transactions costs* (costs of undertaking trades through the market) and the rent or command over resources that organizers can appropriate to themselves by organizing production in a certain way. Ronald Coase won a Nobel Prize in 1991 for pathbreaking work on the nature of the firm and transactions costs.

Firms replace the market with command and control.

In Chapter 3 we discussed the types of firms that exist in real life. They include sole proprietorships, partnerships, corporations, for-profit firms, nonprofit firms, and cooperatives. These various firms are the production organizations that translate factors of production into consumer goods.

FIRMS MAXIMIZE PROFIT

The firm plays the same role in the theory of supply that the individual does in the theory of demand. The difference is that whereas individuals maximize utility, firms maximize profit. Profit is defined as follows:

Profit = *Total revenue − Total cost*

In accounting, total revenue equals total sales times price; if a firm sells 1,000 pairs of earrings at $5 each, its total revenue is $5,000. For an accountant, total costs are the

VALUE ADDED AND THE CALCULATION OF TOTAL PRODUCTION

Applying the Tools

This book (like all economics textbooks) treats production as if it were a one-stage process—as if a single firm transformed a factor of production into a consumer good. Economists write like that to keep the analysis manageable. (Believe me, it's complicated enough.) But you should keep in mind that reality is more complicated. Most goods go through a variety of stages of production.

For example, consider the production of desks. One firm transforms raw materials into usable raw materials (iron ore into steel); another firm transforms usable raw materials into more usable inputs (steel into steel rods, bolts, and nuts); another firm transforms those inputs into desks, which it sells wholesale to a general distributor, which then sells them to a retailer, which sells them to consumers. Many goods go through five or six stages of production and distribution. As a result, if you added up all the sales of all the firms you would overstate how much total production was taking place.

To figure out how much total production is actually taking place, economists use the concept *value added*. Value added is the contribution that each stage of production makes to the final value of a good. A firm's value added is determined by subtracting from the firm's total output the cost of the inputs bought from other firms. For example, if a desk assembly firm spends $4,000 of its revenue on component parts and sells its output for $6,000, its value added is $2,000, or 33⅓ percent of its revenue.

When you add up all the stages of production, the value added of all the firms involved must equal 100 percent, and no more, of the total output. When I discuss "a firm's" production of a good in this book, to relate that discussion to reality, you should think of that firm as a composite firm consisting of all the firms contributing to the production and distribution of that product.

Why is it important to remember that there are various stages of production? Because it brings home to you how complicated producing a good is. If any one stage gets messed up, the good doesn't get to the consumer. Producing a better mousetrap isn't enough. The firm must also be able to get it out to consumers and let them know that it's a better mousetrap. The standard economic model doesn't bring home this point. But if you're ever planning to go into business for yourself, you'd better remember it. Many people's dreams of supplying a better product to the market have been squashed by this reality.

---

wages paid to labor, rent paid to owners of capital, interest paid to lenders, and actual payments to other factors of production. If the firm paid $2,000 to employees to make the earrings and $1,000 for the materials, total cost is $3,000.

In determining what to include in total revenue and total costs, accountants focus on such explicit revenues and explicit costs. That's because they must have quantifiable measures that go into a firm's income statement. For this reason, you can think of *accounting profit* as explicit revenue less explicit cost. The accounting profit for the earring firm is $2,000.

Economists have different measures of revenues and costs and hence have a different measure of profit. Economists include in revenue and costs both explicit and implicit costs and revenues. Their measure of profit is both explicit and implicit revenue less both explicit and implicit costs.

What are implicit costs and implicit revenue? Implicit costs include the opportunity costs of the factors of production provided by the owners of the business. Say that the owner of our earring firm could have earned $1,500 working elsewhere if he did not own the earring firm. The opportunity cost of working in his own business is $1,500. It is an implicit cost of doing business and would be included as a cost. For economists, **total cost** is *explicit payments to the factors of production plus the opportunity cost of the factors provided by the owners of the firm.* Total cost of the earring firm is $3,000 in explicit cost and $1,500 in implicit cost, or $4,500. Generally implicit costs must be estimated and are not directly measurable, which is why accountants do not include them.

Accounting focuses on explicit costs and revenues; economics focuses on both explicit and implicit costs and revenues.

ENRON, ACCOUNTING GIMMICKS, AND THE THEORY OF THE FIRM

ENRON, ACCOUNTING GIMMICKS, AND THE THEORY OF THE FIRM

Applying the Tools

Issues of accounting were much in the news in 2002 when Enron Corporation went into bankruptcy and its accounting practices were questioned. What Enron did was to use accounting gimmicks to record implicit revenue on its books while keeping implicit costs off its books, thereby inflating profits. (Its accounting firm, Arthur Andersen, should have disallowed the practice, but did not and was convicted for failing to do so.) To understand why Enron wanted to overstate profits requires us to go beyond the standard theory of the firm. Standard theory assumes that the owner of the firm is the person making the decisions, so

he gets the profit he maximizes. It is economic profit that he wants to maximize; accounting, for him, is simply a way of figuring out what he is earning.

As discussed in Chapter 3, corporations do the great majority of business in the real world. In corporations owners of the business (whose interest is in economic profits) do not make decisions; instead corporate managers, whose compensation is often tied to accounting profits, not economic profits, do. This can give managers an incentive to overstate accounting profits, which is what Enron did. The result, in this case, was bankruptcy.

Implicit revenues include the increase in the value of assets. Say the earring firm owns a kiosk whose market value rises from $10,000 to $11,000. The economic concept of revenue would include the $1,000 increase in the value of the kiosk as part of total revenue. For economists, **total revenue** is *the amount a firm receives for selling its product or service plus any increase in the value of the assets owned by the firm.* Total revenue of the earring firm is $5,000 in explicit revenue plus $1,000 in implicit revenue, or $6,000. For economists,

Economic profit = *(Explicit and implicit revenue)* − *(Explicit and implicit cost)*

So in this case, economic profit is ($5,000 + $1,000) − ($3,000 + $1,500) = $1,500. The difference really has to do with measurability. Implicit costs must be estimated, and the estimations can sometimes be inexact. General accounting rules do not permit such inexactness because it might allow firms to misstate their profit, something accounting rules are designed to avoid.

THE PRODUCTION PROCESS

As I stated at the beginning of the chapter, supply is the key to the market's ability to provide the goods people want. Underlying supply is production; firms are important because they control the production process.

THE LONG RUN AND THE SHORT RUN

The production process is generally divided into a *long-run* planning decision, in which a firm chooses the least expensive method of producing from among all possible methods, and a *short-run* adjustment decision, in which a firm adjusts its long-run planning decision to reflect new information.

In a **long-run decision** *a firm chooses among all possible production techniques.* This means that it can choose the size of the plant it wants, the type of machines it wants, and the location it wants. The firm has fewer options in a **short-run decision,** in which *the firm is constrained in regard to what production decisions it can make.*

The terms *long run* and *short run* do not necessarily refer to specific periods of time independent of the nature of the production process. They refer to the degree of flexibility the firm has in changing the level of output. In the long run, by definition, the

A long-run decision is a decision in which the firm can choose among all possible production techniques.

A short-run decision is a decision in which the firm is constrained in regard to what production decisions it can make.

CHAPTER 9 ■ PRODUCTION AND COST ANALYSIS I

firm can vary the inputs as much as it wants. In the short run some of the flexibility that existed in the long run no longer exists. In the short run some inputs are so costly to adjust that they are treated as fixed. *So in the long run all inputs are variable; in the short run some inputs are fixed.*

PRODUCTION TABLES AND PRODUCTION FUNCTIONS

How a firm combines factors of production to produce goods and services can be presented in a **production table** *(a table showing the output resulting from various combinations of factors of production or inputs)*.

Real-world production tables are complicated. They often involve hundreds of inputs, hundreds of outputs, and millions of possible combinations of inputs and outputs. Studying these various combinations and determining which is best requires expertise and experience. Business schools devote entire courses to it (operations research and production analysis); engineering schools devote entire specialties to it (industrial engineering).

Studying the problems and answering the questions that surround production make up much of what a firm does: What combination of outputs should it produce? What combination of inputs should it use? What combination of techniques should it use? What new techniques should it explore? To answer these questions, the managers of a firm look at a production table.

Production tables are so complicated that in introductory economics we concentrate on short-run production analysis in which one of the factors is fixed. Doing so allows us to capture some important technical relationships of production without getting too tied up in numbers. The relevant part of a production table of earrings appears in Figure 9-1(c). In it the number of the assumed fixed inputs (machines) has already been determined. Columns 1 and 2 of the table tell us how output of earrings varies as the variable input (the number of workers) changes. For example, you can see that with 3 workers the firm can produce 17 pairs of earrings. Column 3 tells us workers' **marginal product** *(the additional output that will be forthcoming from an additional worker, other inputs constant)*. Column 4 tells us workers' **average product** *(output per worker)*.

It is important to distinguish marginal product from average product. Workers' average product is the total output divided by the number of workers. For example, let's consider the case of 5 workers. Total output is 28, so average product is 5.6 (28 divided by 5). To find the marginal product we must ask how much additional output will be forthcoming if we change the number of workers. For example, if we change from 4 to 5 workers, the additional worker's marginal product will be 5; if we change from 5 to 6, the additional worker's marginal product will be 3. That's why the marginal products are written between each level of output.

The information in a production table is often summarized in a production function. A **production function** is *the relationship between the inputs (factors of production) and outputs*. Specifically, the production function tells the maximum amount of output that can be derived from a given number of inputs. Figure 9-1(a) is the production function that displays the information in the production table in Figure 9-1(c). The number of workers is on the horizontal axis and the output of earrings is on the vertical axis.

THE LAW OF DIMINISHING MARGINAL PRODUCTIVITY

Figure 9-1(b) graphs the workers' average and marginal productivities from the production function in Figure 9-1(a). (Alternatively you can determine those graphs by plotting columns 3 and 4 from the table in Figure 9-1(c).) Notice that both marginal and average productivities are initially increasing, but that eventually they both

The marginal product is the additional output forthcoming from an additional input, other inputs constant; the average product is the total output divided by the quantity of the input.

MICROECONOMICS ■ FOUNDATIONS OF SUPPLY AND DEMAND

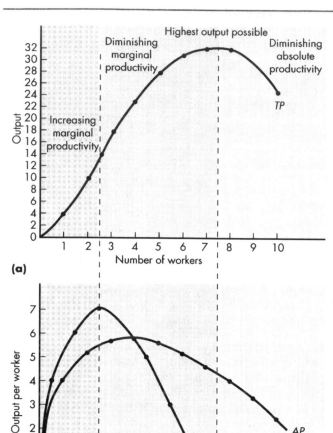

(a)

(b)

Figure 9-1 (a, b, and c)   A Production Table and Production Function

The production function in (a) is a graph of the production table in (c). Its shape reflects the underlying production technology. The graph in (b) shows the marginal and average product. Notice that when marginal product is increasing, the production function is bowed upward; when marginal product is decreasing, the production function is bowed downward, and when marginal product is zero, the production function is at its highest point. Firms are interested in producing where both average product and marginal product are positive and falling, which starts at 4 workers and ends at 7.5 workers.

Number of workers	Total output	Marginal product (change in total output)	Average product (total product/ number of workers)	
1	4	4	4	Increasing
2	10	6	5	marginal
3	17	7	5.7	productivity
4	23	6	5.8	Diminishing
5	28	5	5.6	marginal
6	31	3	5.2	productivity
7	32	1	4.6	
8	32	0	4.0	Diminishing
9	30	-2	3.3	absolute
10	25	-5	2.5	productivity

(c)

Q-1 What are the normal shapes of marginal productivity and average productivity curves?

decrease. Between 7 and 8 workers, the marginal productivity of workers actually becomes negative.

This means that initially this production function exhibits increasing marginal productivity and then it exhibits *diminishing marginal productivity*. Eventually it exhibits negative marginal productivity.

The same information can be gathered from Figure 9-1(a), but it's a bit harder to interpret.[1] Notice that initially the production function is bowed upward. Where it's bowed upward there is increasing marginal productivity, as you can see if you extend a line down to Figure 9-1(b). Then, between 2.5 and 7.5 workers, the production function is bowed downward but is still rising. In this range there's diminishing marginal productivity, as you can see by extending a line down to Figure 9-1(b). Finally marginal productivity is negative.

---

[1]Technically the marginal productivity curve is a graph of the slope of the total product curve.

CHAPTER 9 ▧ PRODUCTION AND COST ANALYSIS I

The most important area of these relationships is the area of diminishing marginal productivity and falling average product (between 4 and 7.5 workers). Why? Because that's the most likely area for a firm to operate in. For example, if it's in the first range and marginal productivity is increasing, a firm can increase its existing workers' output by hiring more workers; it will have a strong incentive to do so and get out of that range. Similarly, if hiring an additional worker actually cuts total output (as it does when marginal productivity is negative), the firm would be crazy to hire that worker. So it stays out of that range.

This range of the relationship between fixed and variable inputs is so important that economists have formulated a law that describes what happens in production processes when firms reach this range—when more and more of one input is added to a fixed amount of another input. The **law of diminishing marginal productivity** states that *as more and more of a variable input is added to an existing fixed input, eventually the additional output one gets from that additional input is going to fall.*

As I stated in Chapter 2, the law of diminishing marginal productivity is sometimes called the *flowerpot law* because if it didn't hold true, the world's entire food supply could be grown in one flowerpot. In the absence of diminishing marginal productivity, we could take a flowerpot and keep adding seeds to it, getting more and more food per seed until we had enough to feed the world. In reality, however, a given flowerpot is capable of producing only so much food no matter how many seeds we add to it. At some point, as we add more and more seeds, each additional seed will produce less food than did the seed before it. Eventually the pot reaches a stage of diminishing absolute productivity, in which the total output, not simply the output per unit of input, decreases as inputs are increased.

> **Q-2** Firms are likely to operate on what portion of the marginal productivity curve?

> The law of diminishing marginal productivity states that as more and more of a variable input is added to an existing fixed input, after some point the additional output one gets from the additional input will fall.

THE COSTS OF PRODUCTION

In any given firm, owners and managers probably discuss costs far more than anything else. Invariably costs are too high and the firm is trying to figure out ways to lower them. But the concept *costs* is ambiguous; there are many different types of costs and it's important to know what they are. Let's consider some of the most important categories of costs in reference to Table 9-1, which shows costs associated with making between 3 and 32 pairs of earrings.

FIXED COSTS, VARIABLE COSTS, AND TOTAL COSTS

Fixed costs are *costs that are spent and cannot be changed in the period of time under consideration*. There are no fixed costs in the long run since all inputs are variable and hence their costs are variable. In the short run, however, a number of costs will be fixed. For example, say you make earrings. You buy a machine for working with silver, but suddenly there's no demand for silver earrings. Assuming that machine can't be modified and used for other purposes, the money you spent on it is a fixed cost. So within the model, all fixed costs are assumed to be sunk costs.

Web Note 9.2
What's Fixed? What's Variable?

Fixed costs are shown in column 2 of Table 9-1. Notice that fixed costs remain the same ($50) regardless of the level of production. As you can see, it doesn't matter whether output is 15 or 20; fixed costs are always $50.

Besides buying the machine, the silversmith must also hire workers. These workers are the earring firm's **variable costs**—*costs that change as output changes*. The earring firm's variable costs are shown in column 3. Notice that as output increases, variable costs increase. For example, when the firm produces 10 pairs of earrings, variable costs are $108; when it produces 16, variable costs rise to $150.

MICROECONOMICS ■ FOUNDATIONS OF SUPPLY AND DEMAND

Table 9-1 The Cost of Producing Earrings

1	2	3	4	5	6	7	8
Output	Fixed Costs (*FC*)	Variable Costs (*VC*)	Total Costs (*TC*) (*FC* + *VC*)	Marginal Costs (*MC*) (Change in total costs/ Change in output)	Average Fixed Costs (*AFC*) (*FC*/Output)	Average Variable Costs (*AVC*) (*VC*/Output)	Average Total Costs (*ATC*) (*AFC* + *AVC*)
3	$50	$ 38	$ 88	$12	$16.67	$12.66	$29.33
4	50	50	100		12.50	12.50	25.00
9	50	100	150	8	5.56	11.11	16.67
10	50	108	158		5.00	10.80	15.80
16	50	150	200	7	3.13	9.38	12.50
17	50	157	207		2.94	9.24	12.18
22	50	200	250	10	2.27	9.09	11.36
23	50	210	260		2.17	9.13	11.30
27	50	255	305	15	1.85	9.44	11.30
28	50	270	320		1.79	9.64	11.43
32	50	400	450		1.56	12.50	14.06

All costs are either fixed or variable in the standard model, so the *total cost* is the sum of the fixed and variable costs:

$TC = FC + VC$

$$TC = FC + VC$$

The earring firm's total costs are presented in column 4. Each entry in column 4 is the sum of the entries in columns 2 and 3 in the same row. For example, to produce 16 pairs of earrings, fixed costs are $50 and variable costs are $150, so total cost is $200.

AVERAGE TOTAL COST, AVERAGE FIXED COST, AND AVERAGE VARIABLE COST

Total cost, fixed cost, and variable cost are important, but much of a firm's discussion is about average cost. So the next distinction we want to make is between total cost and average cost. To arrive at the earring firm's average cost, we simply divide the total amount of whatever cost we're talking about by the quantity produced. Each of the three costs we've discussed has a corresponding average cost.

For example, **average total cost** (often called average cost) equals *total cost divided by the quantity produced*. Thus:

Average cost equals total cost divided by quantity.

$$ATC = TC/Q$$

Average fixed cost equals *fixed cost divided by quantity produced*:

$$AFC = FC/Q$$

Average variable cost equals *variable cost divided by quantity produced*:

Q-3 If total costs are 400, fixed costs are 0, and output is 10, what are average variable costs?

$$AVC = VC/Q$$

Average fixed cost and average variable cost are shown in columns 6 and 7 of Table 9-1. The most important average cost concept, average total cost, is shown in column 8. Average total cost can also be thought of as the sum of average fixed cost and average variable cost:

$$ATC = AFC + AVC$$

As you can see, the average total cost of producing 16 pairs of earrings is $12.50. It can be calculated by dividing total cost ($200) by output (16).

MARGINAL COST

All these costs are important to our earring firm, but they are not the most important cost it considers when deciding how many pairs of earrings to produce. That distinction goes to marginal cost, which appears in column 5.[2] **Marginal cost** is *the increase (decrease) in total cost from increasing (or decreasing) the level of output by one unit.* Let's find marginal cost by considering what happens if our earring firm increases production by one unit—from 9 to 10. Looking again at Table 9-1, we see that the total cost rises from $150 to $158. In this case the marginal cost of producing the 10th unit is $8.

GRAPHING COST CURVES

Let's say that the owner of the earring firm is a visually oriented person who asks you (an economic consultant) to show her what all those numbers in Table 9-1 mean. To do so, you first draw a graph, putting quantity on the horizontal axis and a dollar measure of various costs on the vertical axis.

TOTAL COST CURVES

Figure 9-2(a) graphs the total cost, total fixed cost, and total variable costs of all the levels of output given in Table 9-1.[3] The total cost curve is determined by plotting the entries in column 1 and the corresponding entries in column 4. For example, point L corresponds to a quantity of 10 and a total cost of $158. Notice that the curve is upward-sloping: Increasing output increases total cost.

The total fixed cost curve is determined by plotting column 1 and column 2 on the graph. The total variable cost curve is determined by plotting column 1 and column 3.

As you can see, the total variable cost curve has the same shape as the total cost curve: Increasing output increases variable cost. This isn't surprising, since the total cost curve is the vertical summation of total fixed cost and total variable cost. For example, at output 10, total fixed cost equals $50 (point M); total variable cost equals $108 (point O); and total cost equals $158 (point L).

AVERAGE AND MARGINAL COST CURVES

Figure 9-2(b) presents the average fixed cost curve, average total cost curve (or average cost curve, as it's generally called), average variable cost curve, and marginal cost curve associated with the cost figures in Table 9-1. Each point on the four curves represents a combination of two corresponding entries in Table 9-1. Points on the average variable cost curve are determined by plotting the entries in column 1 and the corresponding entries in column 7. Points on the average fixed cost curve are determined by entries in column 1 and the corresponding entries in column 6. Points on the average total cost curve are determined by entries in column 1 and the corresponding entries in column 8. Finally, the marginal cost curve is determined by plotting the entries in column 1 and the corresponding entries in column 5. As was the case with the total cost curves, all

The marginal cost curve goes through the minimum point of the average total cost curve and average variable cost curve; each of these curves is U-shaped. The average fixed cost curve slopes down continuously.

---

[2]Since only selected output levels are shown, not all entries have marginal costs. For a marginal cost to exist, there must be a marginal change, a change by only one unit.

[3]To keep the presentation simple, we focus only on the most important part of the total cost curve, that part that follows the simplest rules. Other areas of the total cost curve can be bowed downward rather than bowed upward.

MICROECONOMICS ▪ FOUNDATIONS OF SUPPLY AND DEMAND

Figure 9-2 (a and b) Total and per Unit Output Cost Curves

Total fixed costs, shown in (a), are always constant; they don't change with output. All other total costs increase with output. As output gets high, the rate of increase has a tendency to increase. The average fixed cost curve shown in (b), is downward-sloping; the average variable cost curve and average total cost curve are U-shaped. The U-shaped MC curve goes through the minimum points of the AVC and ATC curves. (The AFC curve is often not drawn since AFC is also represented by the distance between the AVC and ATC.)

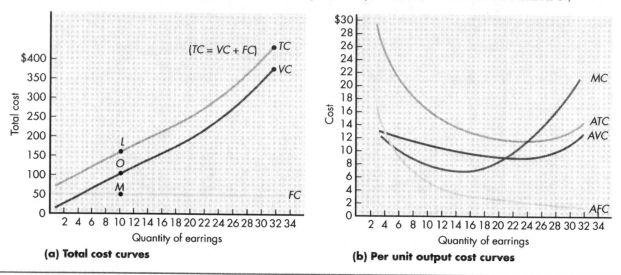

(a) Total cost curves

(b) Per unit output cost curves

the firm's owner need do is look at this graph to find the various costs associated with different levels of output.

One reason the graphical visualization of cost curves is important is that the graphs of the curves give us a good sense of what happens to costs as we change output.

DOWNWARD-SLOPING SHAPE OF THE AVERAGE FIXED COST CURVE

Let's start our consideration with average fixed cost. Average fixed cost is decreasing throughout. The average fixed cost curve looks like a child's slide: It starts out with a steep decline; then it becomes flatter and flatter. What this tells us about production is straightforward: As output increases, the same fixed cost can be spread over a wider range of output, so average fixed cost falls. Average fixed cost initially falls quickly but then falls more and more slowly. As the denominator gets bigger while the numerator stays the same, the increase has a smaller and smaller effect.

THE U SHAPE OF THE AVERAGE AND MARGINAL COST CURVES

Q-4 Draw a graph of both the marginal cost curve and the average cost curve.

Let's now move on to the average and marginal cost curves. Why do they have the shapes they do? Or, expressed another way, how does our analysis of production relate to our analysis of costs? You may have already gotten an idea of how production and costs relate if you remembered Figure 9-1 and recognized the output numbers that we presented there were similar output numbers to those that we used in the cost analysis. Cost analysis is simply another way of considering production analysis. The laws governing costs are the same laws governing productivity that we just saw in our consideration of production.

CHAPTER 9 ■ PRODUCTION AND COST ANALYSIS I

In the short run, output can be raised only by increasing the variable input. But as more and more of a variable input is added to a fixed input, the law of diminishing marginal productivity enters in. Marginal and average productivities fall. The key insight here is that when marginal productivity falls, marginal cost must rise, and when average productivity of the variable input falls, average variable cost must rise. So to say that productivity falls is equivalent to saying that cost rises.

It follows that if eventually the law of diminishing marginal productivity holds true, then eventually both the marginal cost curve and the average cost curve must be upward-sloping. And, indeed, in our examples they are. It's also generally held that at low levels of production, marginal and average productivities are increasing. This means that marginal cost and average variable cost are initially falling. If they're falling initially and rising eventually, at some point they must be neither rising nor falling. This means that both the marginal cost curve and the average variable cost curve are U-shaped.

As you can see in Figure 9-2(b), the average total cost curve has the same general U shape as the average variable cost curve. It has the same U shape because it is the vertical summation of the average fixed cost curve and the average variable cost curve. Its minimum, however, is to the right of the minimum of the average variable cost curve. We'll discuss why after we cover the shape of the average variable cost curve.

Average total cost initially falls faster and then rises more slowly than average variable cost. If we increased output enormously, the average variable cost curve and the average total cost curve would almost meet. Average total cost is of key importance to the firm's owner. She wants to keep it low.

THE RELATIONSHIP BETWEEN THE MARGINAL PRODUCTIVITY AND MARGINAL COST CURVES

Let's now consider the relationship between marginal product and marginal cost. In Figure 9-3(a), I draw a marginal cost curve and average variable cost curve. Notice their U shape. Initially costs are falling. Then there's some minimum point. After that, costs are rising.

In Figure 9-3(b), I graph the average and marginal productivity curves similar to those that I presented in Figure 9-1(b), although this time I relate average and marginal productivities to output, rather than to the number of workers. This allows us to relate output per worker and output. Say, for example that we know that the average product of 2 workers is 5, and that 2 workers can produce an output of 10. This means that when output is 10, the workers' average productivity is 5. By continuing this reasoning we can construct the curves. Point A corresponds to an output of 10 and average productivity of 5.

Now let's compare the graphs in Figure 9-3 (a and b). If you look at the two graphs carefully, you'll see that one is simply the mirror image of the other. The minimum point of the average variable cost curve (output = 21) is the same level of output as the maximum point of the average productivity curve; the minimum point of the marginal cost curve (output = 12) is at the same level of output as the maximum point on the marginal productivity curve. When the productivity curves are falling, the corresponding cost curves are rising. Why is that the case? Because as productivity falls, costs per unit increase; and as productivity increases, costs per unit decrease.

THE RELATIONSHIP BETWEEN THE MARGINAL COST AND AVERAGE COST CURVES

Now that we've considered the shapes of each cost curve, let's consider some of the important relationships among them—specifically the relationships between the marginal

As more and more of a variable input is added to a fixed input, the law of diminishing marginal productivity causes marginal and average productivities to fall. As these fall, marginal and average costs rise.

Q.5 What determines the distance between the average total cost and the average variable cost?

Q.6 If you increase output enormously, what two cost curves would almost meet?

If MP > AP, then AP is rising.
If MP < AP, then AP is falling.

When the marginal cost equals the minimum point of the average variable cost, what is true about the average productivity and marginal productivity of workers?

When the productivity curves are falling, the corresponding cost curves are rising.

Web Note 9.3
Marginal Costs in the
Information Economy

117

MICROECONOMICS ■ FOUNDATIONS OF SUPPLY AND DEMAND

Figure 9-3 (a and b)   The Relationship between Productivity and Costs

The shapes of the cost curves are mirror-image reflections of the shapes of the corresponding productivity curves. (The corresponding productivity curve is an implicit function in which marginal productivity is related to output rather than inputs. At each output there is an implicit number of workers who would supply that output.) When one is increasing, the other is decreasing; when one is at a minimum, the other is at a maximum.

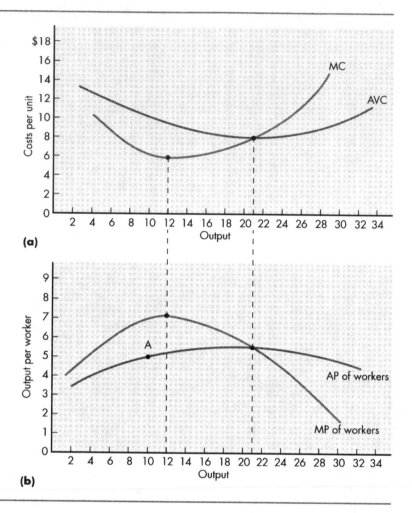

(a)

(b)

cost curve on the one hand and the average variable cost and average total cost curves on the other. These relationships are shown graphically for a different production process in Figure 9-4.

Let's first look at the relationship between marginal cost and average total cost. In areas A and B at output below 5, even though marginal cost is rising, average total cost is falling. Why? Because in areas A and B the marginal cost curve is below the average total cost curve. At point B, where average total cost is at its lowest, the marginal cost curve intersects the average total cost curve. In area C, above output 5, where average total cost is rising, the marginal cost curve is above the ATC curve.

The positioning of the marginal cost curve is not happenstance. The position of marginal cost relative to average total cost tells us whether average total cost is rising or falling.

If $MC > ATC$, then ATC is rising.

If $MC = ATC$, then ATC is at its low point.

If $MC < ATC$, then ATC is falling.

To understand why this is, think of it in terms of your grade point average. If you have a B average and you get a C on the next test (that is, your marginal grade is a C),

REVIEW OF COSTS

We've covered a lot of costs and cost curves quickly, so a review is in order. First, let's list the cost concepts and their definitions.

1. Marginal cost: the additional cost resulting from a one-unit increase in output.
2. Total cost: the sum of all costs.
3. Average total cost: total cost divided by total output (TC/Q).
4. Fixed cost: cost that is already spent and cannot be recovered. (It exists only in the short run.)
5. Average fixed cost: fixed cost divided by total output (FC/Q).
6. Variable cost: cost of variable inputs. Variable cost does not include fixed cost.
7. Average variable cost: variable cost divided by total output (VC/Q).

Each of these costs can be represented by a curve. A number of these curves have specific relationships to the other cost curves.

1. MC: MC intersects AVC and ATC at their minimum points.
2. If $MC > AVC$, then AVC is rising. If $MC < AVC$, then AVC is falling.
3. If $MC > ATC$, then ATC is rising. If $MC < ATC$, then ATC is falling.
4. ATC: a U-shaped curve higher than the AVC.
5. AVC: a U-shaped curve lower than the ATC, with the minimum point slightly to the left.
6. AFC: a downward-sloping curve that starts high, initially decreases rapidly, and then decreases slowly.

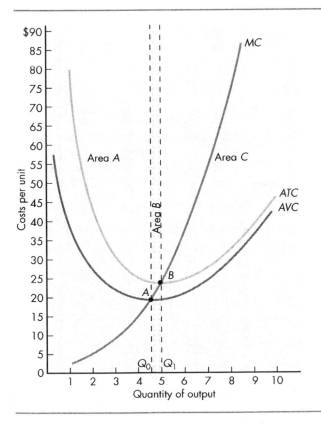

Figure 9-4   The Relationship of Marginal Cost Curve to Average Variable Cost and Average Total Cost Curves

The marginal cost curve goes through the minimum point of both the average variable cost curve and the average total cost curve. Thus, there is a small range where average total costs are falling and average variable costs are rising.

MICROECONOMICS ■ FOUNDATIONS OF SUPPLY AND DEMAND

Q.8 If marginal costs are increasing, what is happening to average total costs?

Q.9 If marginal costs are decreasing, what must be happening to average variable costs?

your grade point average will fall below a B. Your marginal grade is below your average grade, so your average grade is falling. If you get a C+ on the next exam (that is, your marginal grade is a C+), *even though your marginal grade has risen from a C to a C+*, your grade point average will fall. Why? Because your marginal grade is still below your average grade. To make sure you understand the concept, explain the next two cases:

1. If your marginal grade is above your average grade, your average grade will rise.
2. If your marginal grade and average grade are equal, the average grade will remain unchanged.

Marginal and average reflect a general relationship that also holds for marginal cost and average variable cost.

If MC > AVC, then AVC is rising.

If MC = AVC, then AVC is at its low point.

If MC < AVC, then AVC is falling.

This relationship is best seen in area B of Figure 9-4, when output is between Q_0 and Q_1. In this area the marginal cost curve is above the average variable cost curve, so average variable cost is rising; but the MC curve is below the average total cost curve, so average total cost is falling.

Q.10 Why does the marginal cost curve intersect the average total cost curve at the minimum point?

The intuitive explanation for what is represented in this area is that average total cost includes average variable cost, but it also includes average fixed cost, which is falling. As long as short-run marginal cost is only slightly above average variable cost, the average total cost will continue to fall. Put another way: Once marginal cost is above average variable cost, as long as average variable cost doesn't rise by more than average fixed cost falls, average total cost will still fall.

Dr. Seuss books are often more interesting than economics books. From HORTON HATCHES THE EGG by Dr. Seuss, TM & Copyright © by Dr. Seuss Enterprises, L. P. 1940. Renewed 1968. Used by permission of Random House Children's Books, a Division of Random House, Inc.

INTERMISSION

At this point I'm going to cut off the chapter, not because we're finished with the subject, but because there's only so much that anyone can absorb in one chapter. It's time for a break.

Those of you with significant others, go out and do something significant. Those of you with parents bearing the cost of this education, give them a call and tell them that you appreciate their expenditure on your education. Think of the opportunity cost of that education to them; it's not peanuts. Those of you who are married should go out and give your spouse a big kiss; tell him or her that the opportunity cost of being away for another minute was so high that you couldn't control yourself. Those of you with kids, go out and read them a Dr. Seuss book. (My favorite is about Horton.) Let's face it—Seuss is a better writer than I, and if you've been conscientious about this course, you may not have paid your kids enough attention. We'll return to the grind in the next chapter.

SUMMARY

- Accounting profit is explicit revenue less explicit cost. Economists include implicit revenue and cost in their determination of profit.

- Implicit revenue includes the increases in the value of assets owned by the firm. Implicit costs include opportunity cost of time and capital provided by the owners of the firm.

- In the long run a firm can choose among all possible production techniques; in the short run it is constrained in its choices.

- The law of diminishing marginal productivity states that as more and more of a variable input is added to a fixed input, the additional output the firm gets will eventually be decreasing.

- Costs are generally divided into fixed costs, variable costs, and total costs.

- $TC = FC + VC$; MC = change in TC; $AFC = FC/Q$; $AVC = VC/Q$; $ATC = AFC + AVC$.

- The average variable cost curve and marginal cost curve are mirror images of the average product curve and the marginal product curve, respectively.

- The law of diminishing marginal productivity causes marginal and average costs to rise.

- If $MC > ATC$, then ATC is rising.
  If $MC = ATC$, then ATC is constant.
  If $MC < ATC$, then ATC is falling.

- The marginal cost curve goes through the minimum points of the average variable cost curve and average total cost curve.

KEY TERMS

average fixed cost (210)
average product (207)
average total cost (210)
average variable cost (210)
economic profit (206)

firm (204)
fixed costs (209)
law of diminishing marginal productivity (209)
long-run decision (206)

marginal cost (211)
marginal product (207)
production (203)
production function (207)
production table (207)

profit (204)
short-run decision (206)
total cost (205)
total revenue (206)
variable costs (209)

QUESTIONS FOR THOUGHT AND REVIEW

1. What costs and revenues do economists include when calculating profit that accountants don't include? Give an example of each.

2. "There is no long run; there are only short and shorter runs." Evaluate that statement.

3. What is the difference between marginal product and average product?

4. If average product is falling, what is happening to short-run average variable cost?

5. If marginal cost is increasing, what do we know about average cost?

6. If average productivity falls, will marginal cost necessarily rise? How about average cost?

7. Say that neither labor nor machines are fixed but that there is a 50 percent quick-order premium paid to both workers and machines for delivery of them in the short run. Once you buy them, they cannot be returned, however. What do your short-run marginal cost and short-run average total cost curves look like?

8. If machines are variable and labor fixed, how will the general shapes of the short-run average cost curve and marginal cost curve change?

9. If you increase production to an infinitely large level, the average variable cost and the average total cost will merge. Why?

10. Explain whether the following statements are true or false: Supplying labor depends on opportunity costs because labor already exists. Supplying goods that need to be produced does not depend on opportunity costs since they do not already exist.

11. Explain how studying for an exam is subject to the law of diminishing marginal productivity.

12. Labor costs are 17.5 percent of revenue per vehicle for General Motors. In union negotiations in the late 1990s, GM attempted to cut its workforce to increase productivity. Together with the reductions they expected in jobs, GM officials hoped to make its North American operations fully competitive with its U.S. and Japanese rivals on total costs. Why are productivity gains so important to GM?

13. It is obvious that all for-profit businesses in the United States will maximize profit. True or false? Why? (Requires reading "Applying the Tools: Enron, Accounting Gimmicks, and the Theory of the Firm")

MICROECONOMICS ■ FOUNDATIONS OF SUPPLY AND DEMAND

PROBLEMS AND EXERCISES

1. Peggy-Sue's cookies are the best in the world, or so I hear. She has been offered a job by Cookie Monster, Inc., to come to work for them at $125,000 per year. Currently, she is producing her own cookies, and she has revenues of $260,000 per year. Her costs are $40,000 for labor, $10,000 for rent, $35,000 for ingredients, and $5,000 for utilities. She has $100,000 of her own money invested in the operation, which, if she leaves, can be sold for $40,000 that she can invest at 10 percent per year.
   a. Calculate her accounting and economic profits.
   b. Advise her as to what she should do.

2. Economan has been infected by the free enterprise bug. He sets up a firm on extraterrestrial affairs. The rent of the building is $4,000, the cost of the two secretaries is $40,000, and the cost of electricity and gas comes to $5,000. There's a great demand for his information, and his total revenue amounts to $100,000. By working in the firm, though, Economan forfeits the $50,000 he could earn by working for the Friendly Space Agency and the $4,000 he could have earned as interest had he saved his funds instead of putting them in this business. Is he making a profit or loss by an accountant's definitions of profit and loss? How about by an economist's definition?

3. Find and graph the TC, AFC, AVC, AC, and MC from the following table.

Units	FC	VC
0	$100	$ 0
1	100	40
2	100	60
3	100	70
4	100	85
5	100	130

4. An economic consultant is presented with the following total product table and asked to derive a table for average variable costs. The price of labor is $15 per hour.

Labor	TP
1	5
2	15
3	30
4	36
5	40

a. Help him do so.
b. Show that the graph of the average productivity curve and average variable cost curve are mirror images of each other.
c. Show the marginal productivity curve for labor inputs between 1 and 5.
d. Show that the marginal productivity curve and marginal cost curve are mirror images of each other.

5. A firm has fixed costs of $100 and variable costs of the following:

Output	1	2	3	4	5	6	7	8	9
Variable costs	$35	75	110	140	175	215	260	315	390

a. Graph the AFC, ATC, AVC, and MC curves.
b. Explain the relationship between the MC curve and the two average cost curves.
c. Say fixed costs dropped to $50. Graph the new AFC, ATC, AVC, and MC curves.
d. Which curves shifted in c? Why?

6. Say that a firm has fixed costs of $100 and constant average variable costs of $25.
   a. Graph the AFC, ATC, AVC, and MC curves.
   b. Explain why the curves have the shapes they do.
   c. What law is not operative for this firm?
   d. Say that instead of remaining a constant $25, average variable costs increase by $5 for each unit, so that the cost of 1 is $25, the cost of 2 is $30, the cost of 3 is $35, and so on. Graph the AFC, ATC, AVC, and MC curves associated with these costs.
   e. Explain how costs would have to increase in d in order for the curves to have the "normal" shapes of the curves presented in the text.

7. Explain how each of the following will affect the average fixed cost, average variable cost, average total cost, and marginal cost curves faced by a steel manufacturer:
   a. New union agreement increases hourly pay.
   b. Local government imposes an annual lump-sum tax per plant.
   c. Federal government imposes a "stack tax" on emission of air pollutants by steel mills.
   d. New steel-making technology increases productivity of every worker.

CHAPTER 9 ■ PRODUCTION AND COST ANALYSIS I

WEB QUESTIONS

1. Go to the Avis Rent A Car, Inc., home page at www.avis.com, and find out how much it costs to rent a car for a week, driving from your city to a city in another state.
   a. Fill in the following cost table:

Miles	Total Cost	Marginal Cost	Average Fixed Cost	Average Variable Cost
0	———	———	———	———
500	———	———	———	———
1,000	———	———	———	———
1,500	———	———	———	———
2,500	———	———	———	———

   b. How does average fixed cost change as total number of miles driven increases?
   c. How does marginal cost change as total number of miles driven increases?

2. Go to www.ers.usda.gov. Click on the "data" button, look for cost data on corn, and answer the following questions:
   a. What is the cost of producing an acre of corn?
   b. State two major components of the variable (operating) costs of corn production.
   c. State two major components of fixed (allocated overhead) costs of corn production.
   d. What price of corn was needed to cover operating costs?
   e. What price of corn was needed to cover corn's total operating costs?

ANSWERS TO MARGIN QUESTIONS

1. Normally the marginal productivity curve and average productivity curve are both inverted U shapes. (208)

2. Firms are likely to operate on the downward-sloping portion of the marginal productivity curve because on the upward-sloping portion, firms could increase workers' output by hiring more workers. It will continue to hire more workers at least to the point where diminishing marginal productivity sets in. (209)

3. Average variable costs would be 40. (210)

4. As you can see in the graph, both these curves are U-shaped and the marginal cost curve goes through the average cost curve at the minimum point of the average cost curve. (212)

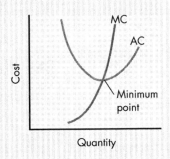

5. The distance between the average total cost and the average variable cost is determined by the average fixed cost at that quantity. As quantity increases, the average fixed cost decreases, so the two curves get closer and closer together. (213)

6. As output increases, the average total costs and average variable costs come closer and closer together. (213)

7. Since the average productivity and marginal productivity of workers are the mirror images of average costs and marginal costs, and when the marginal costs and average costs intersect the two are equal, it follows that the average productivity and marginal productivity of workers must be equal at that point. (213)

8. It is impossible to say what is happening to average total costs on the basis of what is happening to marginal costs. It is the magnitude of marginal costs relative to average total costs that is important. (216)

9. It is impossible to say because it is the magnitude of marginal cost relative to average variable cost that determines what is happening to average variable cost. (216)

10. The marginal cost curve intersects the average total cost curve at the minimum point because once the marginal cost exceeds average total costs, the average total costs must necessarily begin to rise, and vice versa. (216)

PERFECT COMPETITION

11

There's no resting place for an enterprise
in a competitive economy.

—*Alfred P. Sloan*

The concept *competition* is used in two ways in economics. One way is as a process. *Competition as a process* is a rivalry among firms and is prevalent throughout our economy. It involves one firm trying to figure out how to take away market share from another firm. An example is my publishing firm giving me a contract to write a great book like this in order for the firm to take market share away from other publishing firms that are also selling economics textbooks. The other use of *competition* is as a *perfectly competitive market structure*. It is this use that is the subject of this chapter. Although perfect competition has highly restrictive assumptions, it provides us with a reference point we can use to think about various market structures and competitive processes. Why is such a reference point important? Think of the following analogy.

In physics when you study the laws of gravity, you initially study what would happen in a vacuum. Perfect vacuums don't exist, but talking about what would happen if you dropped an object in a perfect vacuum makes the analysis easier. So too with economics. Our equivalent of a perfect vacuum is perfect competition. In perfect competition the invisible hand of the market operates unimpeded. In this chapter we'll consider how perfectly competitive markets work and see how to apply the cost analysis developed in Chapters 9 and 10.

A PERFECTLY COMPETITIVE MARKET

A **perfectly competitive market** is *a market in which economic forces operate unimpeded*. For a market to be called *perfectly competitive*, it must meet some stringent conditions:

1. Both buyers and sellers are price takers.
2. The number of firms is large.
3. There are no barriers to entry.
4. Firms' products are identical.
5. There is complete information.
6. Selling firms are profit-maximizing entrepreneurial firms.

After reading this chapter, you should be able to:

- List the six conditions for a perfectly competitive market.

- Explain why producing an output at which marginal cost equals price maximizes total profit for a perfect competitor.

- Demonstrate why the marginal cost curve is the supply curve for a perfectly competitive firm.

- Determine the output and profit of a perfect competitor graphically and numerically.

- Construct a market supply curve by adding together individual firms' marginal cost curves.

- Explain why perfectly competitive firms make zero economic profit in the long run.

- Explain the adjustment process from short-run equilibrium to long-run equilibrium.

Colander:
Microeconomics, Fifth
Edition

II. Microeconomics

11. Perfect Competition

© The McGraw–Hill
Companies, 2004

MICROECONOMICS ■ MARKET STRUCTURE AND POLICY

These conditions are needed to ensure that economic forces operate instantaneously and are unimpeded by political and social forces. For example, if there weren't a large number of firms, the few firms in the industry would have an incentive to get together and limit output so they could get a higher price. They would stop the invisible hand from working. Similarly for the other conditions, although the reasoning why they're necessary can get rather complicated.

THE NECESSARY CONDITIONS FOR PERFECT COMPETITION

To give you a sense of these conditions, let's consider each a bit more carefully.

1. *Both buyers and sellers are price takers.* A **price taker** is *a firm or individual who takes the price determined by market supply and demand as given.* When you buy, say, toothpaste, you go to the store and find that the price of toothpaste is, say, $2.33 for the medium-size tube; you're a price taker. The firm, however, is a price maker since it set the price at $2.33. So even though the toothpaste industry is highly competitive, it's not a perfectly competitive market. In a perfectly competitive market, market supply and demand determine the price; both firms and consumers take the market price as given.

2. *The number of firms is large.* This is almost self-explanatory. *Large* means sufficiently large so that any one firm's output compared to the market output is imperceptible, and what one firm does has no influence on what other firms do.

Q.1 Why is the assumption of no barriers to entry necessary for the existence of perfect competition?

3. *There are no barriers to entry.* **Barriers to entry** are *social, political, or economic impediments that prevent firms from entering a market.* They might be legal barriers such as exist when firms acquire a patent to produce a certain product. Barriers might be technological, such as when the minimum efficient scale of production allows only one firm to produce at the lowest average total cost. Or barriers might be created by social forces, such as when bankers will lend only to individuals with specific racial characteristics. Perfect competition can have no barriers to entry.

4. *Firms' products are identical.* This requirement means that each firm's output is indistinguishable from any other firm's output. Corn bought by the bushel is relatively homogeneous. One kernel is indistinguishable from any other kernel. In contrast, you can buy 30 different brands of many goods—soft drinks, for instance: Pepsi, Coke, 7UP, and so on. They are all slightly different from one another and thus not identical.

5. *There is complete information.* In a perfectly competitive market, firms and consumers know all there is to know about the market—prices, products, and available technology, to name a few aspects. If any firm experiences a technological breakthrough, all firms know about it and are able to use the same technology instantaneously. No firm or consumer has a competitive edge over another.

6. *Selling firms are profit-maximizing entrepreneurial firms.* Firms can have many goals and be organized in a variety of ways. For perfect competition to exist, firms must seek maximum profit and only profit, and the people who make the decisions must receive only profits and no other form of income from the firms.

THE DEFINITION OF SUPPLY AND PERFECT COMPETITION

These are enormously strong conditions and are seldom met simultaneously. But they are necessary for a perfectly competitive market to exist. Combined, they create an

THE INTERNET AND THE PERFECTLY COMPETITIVE MODEL

Applying the Tools

Recent technological developments are making the perfectly competitive model more directly relevant to our economy. Specifically, the Internet has eliminated the spatial dimension of competition (except for shipping), allowing individuals to compete globally rather than locally. When you see a bid on the Internet, you don't care where the supplier is (as long as you do not have to pay shipping fees). Because it allows access to so many buyers and sellers, the Internet reduces the number of seller-set posted price markets (such as found in retail stores), and replaces them with auction markets.

The Internet has had its biggest impact in firms' buying practices. Today, when firms want to buy standardized products, they will often post their technical requirements for desired components on the Net and allow suppliers from all over the world to bid to fill their orders. Firms have found that buying in this fashion over the Internet has on average lowered the prices they pay by over 10 percent.

Similar changes are occurring in consumer markets. With sites like Priceline.com, individuals can set the price they are willing to pay for goods and services (such as hotel rooms and airline tickets) and see if anyone wants to supply them. (Recently, I successfully bid $120 for a $460 retail price hotel room in New York City.) With sites such as eBay you can buy and sell almost anything. The Internet is even developing its own payment systems, such as PayPal.

In short, with the Internet, entry and exit are much easier than in traditional brick-and-mortar business, and that makes the market more like a perfectly competitive market. As Internet search engines become better designed for commerce, and as more people become Internet savvy, the economy will more and more closely resemble the perfectly competitive model.

environment in which each firm, following its own self-interest, will offer goods to the market in a predictable way. If these conditions hold, we can talk formally about the supply of a produced good and how it relates to costs. This follows from the definition of supply we gave in Chapter 4:

Supply is a schedule of quantities of goods that will be offered to the market at various prices.

This definition requires the supplier to be a price taker (our first condition). In almost all other market structures (frameworks within which firms interact economically), firms are not price takers; they are price makers. They don't ask, "How much should I supply, given the market price?" Instead they ask, "Given a demand curve, how much should I produce and what price should I charge?" In other market structures, the supplier sets the quantity and price, based on costs, at whatever level is best for it.[1]

The second condition—that the number of firms is large—is necessary so that firms have no ability to *collude* (to operate in concert so that they can get more for themselves). Conditions 3 through 5 are closely related to the first two; they make it impossible for any firm to forget about the hundreds of other firms out there just waiting to replace their supply. Condition 6 tells us a firm's goals. If we didn't know the goals, we wouldn't know how firms would react when faced with the given price.

What's nice about these conditions is that they allow us to formally relate supply to the cost concept we developed in Chapters 9 and 10: marginal cost. If the conditions

---

[1]A firm's ability to set price doesn't mean that it can choose just any price it pleases. Other market structures can be highly competitive, so the range of prices a firm can charge and still stay in business is often limited. Such highly competitive firms are not perfectly competitive—they still set price rather than supply a certain quantity and accept whatever price they get.

Figure 11-1 (a and b)   Market Demand Curve versus Individual Firm Demand Curve
Even though the demand curve for the market is downward-sloping, the perceived demand curve of an individual firm is perfectly elastic because each firm is so small relative to the market.

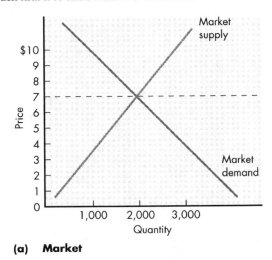

(a)   Market

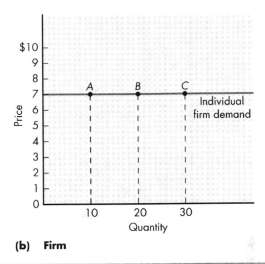

(b)   Firm

Web Note 11.1
Barriers to Entry

Even if we can't technically specify a supply curve, supply forces are still strong and many of the insights of the competitive model carry over.

Q-2 How can the demand curve for the market be downward-sloping but the demand curve for a competitive firm be perfectly elastic?

hold, a firm's supply curve will be that portion of the firm's short-run marginal cost curve above the average variable cost curve, as we'll see shortly.

If the conditions for perfect competition aren't met, then we can't use our formal concept of supply and how it relates to cost; we can still talk informally about the supply of produced goods and cost conditions. We generally talk informally about perfect competition, keeping in the back of our minds which conditions aren't met and modifying the analysis accordingly. Even if the conditions for perfect competition don't fully exist, supply forces are still strong and many of the insights of the competitive model can be applied to firm behavior in other market structures.

DEMAND CURVES FOR THE FIRM AND THE INDUSTRY

Now that we've considered the competitive supply curve for the firm, let's turn our attention to the competitive demand curve for the firm. Here we must recognize that the demand curve for the industry is downward-sloping as in Figure 11-1(a), but the perceived demand curve for the firm is horizontal (perfectly elastic), as in Figure 11-1(b).

Why the difference? It's a difference in perception. Each firm in a competitive industry is so small that it perceives that its actions will not affect the price it can get for its product. Price is the same no matter how much the firm produces. Think of an individual firm's actions as removing one piece of sand from a beach. Does that lower the level of the beach? For all practical, and even most impractical, purposes, we can assume it doesn't. Similarly for a perfectly competitive firm. That is why we consider the demand curve facing the firm to be horizontal.

The price the firm can get is determined by the market supply and demand curves shown in Figure 11-1(a). Market price is $7, and the firm represented in Figure 11-1(b) will get $7 for each unit of its product whether it produces 10 units (point A), 20 units (point B), or 30 units (point C). Its demand curve is perfectly elastic even though the demand curve for the market is downward sloping.

This difference in perception is extremely important. It means that firms will increase their output in response to an increase in market demand even though that

CHAPTER 11 ■ PERFECT COMPETITION

Figure 11-2 (a and b) Marginal Cost, Marginal Revenue, and Price
The profit-maximizing output for a firm occurs where marginal cost equals marginal revenue. Since for a competitive firm $P = MR$, its profit-maximizing output is where $MC = P$. At any other output it is forgoing profit.

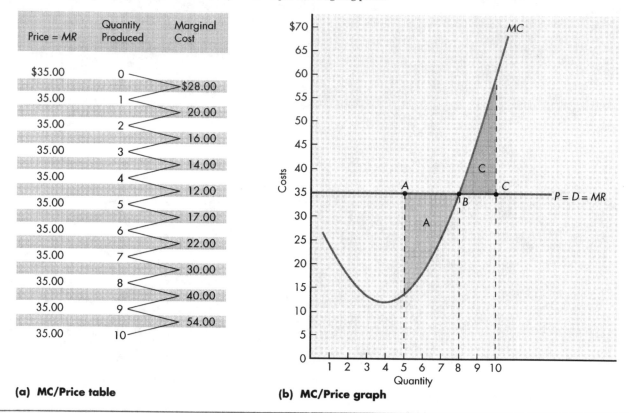

Price = MR	Quantity Produced	Marginal Cost
$35.00	0	
		$28.00
35.00	1	
		20.00
35.00	2	
		16.00
35.00	3	
		14.00
35.00	4	
		12.00
35.00	5	
		17.00
35.00	6	
		22.00
35.00	7	
		30.00
35.00	8	
		40.00
35.00	9	
		54.00
35.00	10	

(a) MC/Price table

(b) MC/Price graph

increase in output will cause price to fall and can make all firms collectively worse off. But since, by the assumptions of perfect competition, they don't act collectively, each firm follows its self-interest. Let's now consider that self-interest in more detail.

THE PROFIT-MAXIMIZING LEVEL OF OUTPUT

The goal of a firm is to maximize profits—to get as much for itself as possible. So when it decides what quantity to produce, it will continually ask the question "What will changes in how much I produce do to profit?" Since profit is the difference between total revenue and total cost, what happens to profit in response to a change in output is determined by **marginal revenue (MR),** *the change in total revenue associated with a change in quantity,* and **marginal cost (MC),** *the change in total cost associated with a change in quantity.* That's why marginal revenue and marginal cost are key concepts in determining the profit-maximizing or loss-minimizing level of output of any firm.

To emphasize the importance of *MR* and *MC,* those are the only cost and revenue figures shown in Figure 11-2. Notice that we don't illustrate profit at all. We'll calculate profit later. All we want to determine now is the profit-maximizing level of output. To do this you need only know *MC* and *MR.* Specifically, a firm maximizes profit when $MC = MR$. To see why, let's first look at *MC* and *MR* more closely.

To determine the profit-maximizing output, all you need to know is *MC* and *MR.*

MICROECONOMICS ▪ MARKET STRUCTURE AND POLICY

MARGINAL REVENUE

Let's first consider marginal revenue. Since a perfect competitor accepts the market price as given, marginal revenue is simply the market price. In the example shown in Figure 11-2, if the firm increases output from 2 to 3, its revenue rises by $35 (from $70 to $105). So its marginal revenue is $35, the price of the good. Since at a price of $35 it can sell as much as it wants, for a competitive firm, $MR = P$.

For a competitive firm, $MR = P$.

Marginal revenue is given in column 1 of Figure 11-2(a). As you can see, MR equals $35 for all levels of output. But that's what we saw in Figure 11-1, which showed that the demand curve for a perfect competitor is perfectly elastic at the market price. For a perfect competitor, the marginal revenue curve and demand curve it faces are the same.

MARGINAL COST

Now let's move on to marginal cost. I'll be brief since I discussed marginal cost in detail in Chapter 9. Marginal cost is that change in total cost that accompanies a change in output. Figure 11-2(a) shows marginal cost in column 3. Notice that initially in this example, marginal cost is falling, but by the fifth unit of output, it's increasing. This is consistent with our discussion in earlier chapters.

Notice also that the marginal cost figures are given for movements from one quantity to another. That's because marginal concepts tell us what happens when there's a change in something, so marginal concepts are best defined between numbers. The numbers in the shaded rows are the marginal costs. So the marginal cost of increasing output from 1 to 2 is $20, and the marginal cost of increasing output from 2 to 3 is $16. The marginal cost right at 2 (which the marginal cost graph shows) would be between $20 and $16 at approximately $18.

PROFIT MAXIMIZATION: MC = MR

As I noted above, to maximize profit, a firm should produce where marginal cost equals marginal revenue. Looking at Figure 11-2(b), we see that a firm following that rule should produce at an output of 8, where $MC = MR = \$35$. Now let me try to convince you that 8 is indeed the profit-maximizing output. To do so, let's consider three different possible quantities the firm might look at.

Q-3 *What are the two things you must know to determine the profit-maximizing output?*

Let's say that initially the firm decides to produce 5 widgets, placing it at point A in Figure 11-2(b). At output A, the firm gets $35 for each widget but its marginal cost of increasing output is $17. We don't yet know the firm's total profit, but we do know how changing output will affect profit. For example, say the firm increases production from 5 to 6. Its revenue will rise by $35. (In other words, its marginal revenue is $35.) Its marginal cost of increasing output is $17. Since profit increases by $18 (the difference between MR, $35, and MC, $17), it makes sense (meaning the firm can increase its profit) to increase output from 5 to 6 units. It makes sense to increase output as long as the marginal cost is below the marginal revenue. The blue shaded area (A) represents the entire increase in profit the firm can get by increasing output.

Now let's say that the firm decides to produce 10 widgets, placing it at point C. Here the firm gets $35 for each widget. The marginal cost of producing that 10th unit is $54. So, $MC > MR$. If the firm decreases production by one unit, its cost decreases by $54 and its revenue decreases by $35. Profit increases by $19 ($54 − $35 = $19), so at point C, it makes sense to decrease output. This reasoning holds true as long as the marginal cost is above the marginal revenue. The red shaded area (C) represents the increase in profits the firm can get by decreasing output.

CHAPTER 11 ■ PERFECT COMPETITION

At point B (output = 8) the firm gets $35 for each widget, and its marginal cost is $35, as you can see in Figure 11-2(b). The marginal cost of increasing output by one unit is $40 and the marginal revenue of selling one more unit is $35, so its profit falls by $5. If the firm decreases output by one unit, its MC is $30 and its MR is $35, so its profit falls by $5. Either increasing or decreasing production will decrease profit, so at point B, an output of 8, the firm is maximizing profit.

Since MR is just market price, we can state the **profit-maximizing condition** of a competitive firm as $MC = MR = P$.

You should commit this profit-maximizing condition to memory. You should also be sure that you understand the intuition behind it. If marginal revenue isn't equal to marginal cost, a firm obviously can increase profit by changing output. If that isn't obvious, the marginal benefit of an additional hour of thinking about this condition will exceed the marginal cost (whatever it is), meaning that you should . . . right, you guessed it . . . study some more.

> Profit-maximizing condition for a competitive firm: $MC = MR = P$.

> If marginal revenue does not equal marginal cost, a firm can increase profit by changing output.

THE MARGINAL COST CURVE IS THE SUPPLY CURVE

Now let's consider again the definition of the supply curve as a schedule of quantities of goods that will be offered to the market at various prices. Notice that the marginal cost curve fits that definition. It tells how much the firm will supply at a given price. Figure 11-3 shows the various quantities the firm will supply at different market prices. If the price is $35, we showed that the firm would supply 8 (point A). If the price had been $19.50, the firm would have supplied 6 (point B); if the price had been $61, the firm would have supplied 10 (point C). Because the marginal cost curve tells us how much of a produced good a firm will supply at a given price, *the marginal cost curve is the firm's supply curve*. The MC curve tells the competitive firm how much it should produce at a given price. (As you'll see later, there's an addendum to this statement. Specifically, the marginal cost curve is the firm's supply curve only if price exceeds average variable cost.)

> Because the marginal cost curve tells us how much of a produced good a firm will supply at a given price, the marginal cost curve is the firm's supply curve.

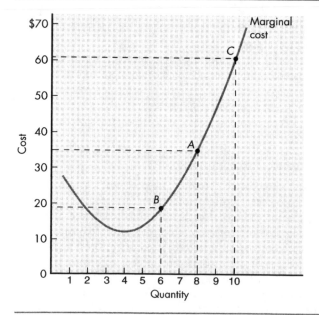

Figure 11-3   The Marginal Cost Curve Is a Firm's Supply Curve

Since the marginal cost curve tells the firm how much to produce, the marginal cost curve is the perfectly competitive firm's supply curve. This exhibit shows three points on a firm's supply curve; as you can see the quantity the firm chooses to supply depends on the price. For example, if market price is $19.50 the firm produces 6 units.

THE BROADER IMPORTANCE OF THE $MR = MC$ EQUILIBRIUM CONDITION

Applying the Tools

This Marginal revenue = Marginal cost equilibrium condition is simple, but it's enormously powerful. As we'll see, it carries over to other market structures. If you replace revenue with benefits, it also forms the basis of economic reasoning. With whom should you go out? What's the marginal benefit? What's the marginal cost? Should you marry Pat? What's the marginal benefit? What's the marginal cost? As we discussed in Chapter 1, thinking like an economist requires thinking in these marginal terms and applying this marginal reasoning to a wide variety of activities. Understanding this condition is to economics what understanding gravity is to physics. It gives you a sense of if, how, and why prices and quantities will move.

FIRMS MAXIMIZE TOTAL PROFIT

Q-4 Why do firms maximize total profit rather than profit per unit?

Notice that when you talk about maximizing profit, you're talking about maximizing *total profit*, not profit per unit. Profit per unit would be maximized at a much lower output level than is total profit. Firms don't care about profit per unit; as long as an increase in output will increase total profits, a profit-maximizing firm should increase output. That's difficult to grasp, so let's consider a concrete example.

Say two people are selling T-shirts that cost $4 each. One sells 2 T-shirts at a price of $6 each and makes a profit per shirt of $2. His total profit is $4. The second person sells 8 T-shirts at $5 each, making a profit per unit of only $1 but selling 8. Her total profit is $8, twice as much as the fellow who had the $2 profit per unit. In this case, $5 (the price with the lower profit per unit), not $6, yields more total profit.

PROFIT MAXIMIZATION USING TOTAL REVENUE AND TOTAL COST

An alternative method of determining the profit-maximizing level of output is to look at the total revenue and total cost curves directly. Figure 11-4 shows total cost and total revenue for the firm we're considering so far. The table in Figure 11-4(a) shows total revenue in column 2, which is just the number of units sold times market price. Total cost is in column 3. Total cost is the cumulative sum of the marginal costs from Figure 11-2(a) plus a fixed cost of $40. Total profit (column 4) is the difference between total revenue and total cost. The firm is interested in maximizing total profit. Looking down column 4 of Figure 11-4(a), you can quickly see that the profit-maximizing level of output is 8, as it was using the $MR = MC$ rule, since total profit is highest at an output of 8.

In Figure 11-4(b) we plot the firm's total revenue and total cost curves from the table in Figure 11-4(a). The total revenue curve is a straight line; each additional unit sold increases revenue by the same amount, $35. The total cost curve is bowed upward at most quantities, reflecting the increasing marginal cost at different levels of output. The firm's profit is represented by the distance between the total revenue curve and the total cost curve. For example, at output 5, the firm makes $45 in profit.

Total profit is maximized where the vertical distance between total revenue and total cost is greatest. In this example total profit is maximized at output 8, just as in the alternative approach. At that output, marginal revenue (the slope of the total revenue curve) and marginal cost (the slope of the total cost curve) are equal.

CHAPTER 11 ■ PERFECT COMPETITION

Figure 11-4 (a and b)   Determination of Profits by Total Cost and Total Revenue Curves

The profit-maximizing output level can also be seen by considering the total cost curve and the total revenue curve. Profit is maximized at the output where total revenue exceeds total cost by the largest amount. This occurs at an output of 8.

Quantity	Total Revenue	Total Cost	Total Profit
0	$ 0	$ 40	$−40
1	35	68	−33
2	70	88	−18
3	105	104	1
4	140	118	22
5	175	130	45
6	210	147	63
7	245	169	76
8	280	199	81
9	315	239	76
10	350	293	57

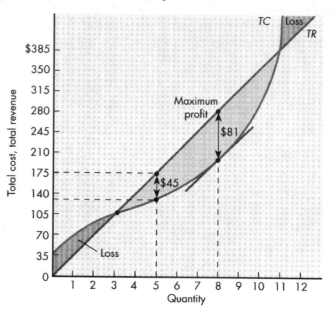

(a) Total revenue and total cost table   **(b) Total revenue and total cost curves**

TOTAL PROFIT AT THE PROFIT-MAXIMIZING LEVEL OF OUTPUT

In the initial discussion of the firm's choice of output, given price, I carefully presented only marginal cost and price. We talked about maximizing profit, but nowhere did I mention what profit, average total cost, average variable cost, or average fixed cost is. I mentioned only marginal cost and price to emphasize that marginal cost is all that's needed to determine a competitive firm's supply curve (and a competitive firm is the only firm that has a supply curve) and the output that will maximize profit. Now that you know that, let's turn our attention more closely to profit.

Marginal cost is all that is needed to determine a competitive firm's supply curve.

DETERMINING PROFIT FROM A TABLE OF COSTS AND REVENUE

The $P = MR = MC$ condition tells us how much output a competitive firm should produce to maximize profit. It does not tell us the profit the firm makes. Profit is determined by total revenue minus total cost. Table 11-1 expands Figure 11-2(a) and presents a table of all the costs relevant to the firm. Going through the columns and reminding yourself of the definition of each is a good review of Chapters 9 and 10. If the definitions don't come to mind immediately, you need a review. If you don't know the definitions of MC, AVC, ATC, FC, and AFC, go back and reread Chapters 9 and 10.

The firm is interested in maximizing profit. Looking at Table 11-1, you can quickly see that the profit-maximizing position is 8, as it was before, since at an output of 8, total profit is highest.

MICROECONOMICS ■ MARKET STRUCTURE AND POLICY

Table 11-1 Costs Relevant to a Firm

Price = Marginal Revenue	1 Quantity Produced	2 Total Fixed Cost	3 Average Fixed Cost	4 Total Variable Cost	5 Average Variable Cost	6 Total Cost	7 Marginal Cost	8 Average Total Cost	9 Total Revenue	10 Total Profit
$35.00	0	$40.00	—	0	—	$ 40.00		—	0	$−40.00
							$28.00			
35.00	1	40.00	$40.00	$ 28.00	$28.00	68.00		$68.00	$ 35.00	−33.00
							20.00			
35.00	2	40.00	20.00	48.00	24.00	88.00		44.00	70.00	−18.00
							16.00			
35.00	3	40.00	13.33	64.00	21.33	104.00		34.67	105.00	1.00
							14.00			
35.00	4	40.00	10.00	78.00	19.50	118.00		29.50	140.00	22.00
							12.00			
35.00	5	40.00	8.00	90.00	18.00	130.00		26.00	175.00	45.00
							17.00			
35.00	6	40.00	6.67	107.00	17.83	147.00		24.50	210.00	63.00
							22.00			
35.00	7	40.00	5.71	129.00	18.43	169.00		24.14	245.00	76.00
							30.00			
35.00	8	40.00	5.00	159.00	19.88	199.00		24.88	280.00	81.00
							40.00			
35.00	9	40.00	4.44	199.00	22.11	239.00		26.56	315.00	76.00
							54.00			
35.00	10	40.00	4.00	253.00	25.30	293.00		29.30	350.00	57.00

Using the $MC = MR = P$ rule, you can also see that the profit-maximizing level of output is 8. Increasing output from 7 to 8 has a marginal cost of $30, which is less than $35, so it makes sense to do so. Increasing output from 8 to 9 has a marginal cost of $40, which is more than $35, so it does not make sense to do so. The output 8 is the profit-maximizing output. At that profit-maximizing level of output, the profit the firm earns is $81, which is calculated by subtracting total cost of $199 from total revenue of $280. Notice also that average total cost is lowest at an output of about 7, and the average variable cost is lowest at an output of about 6.[2] Thus, the profit-maximizing position (which is 8) is *not* necessarily a position that minimizes either average variable cost or average total cost. It is only the position that maximizes total profit.

DETERMINING PROFIT FROM A GRAPH

The profit-maximizing output can be determined in a table (as in Table 11-1) or in a graph (as in Figure 11-5).

These relationships can be seen in a graph. In Figure 11-5(a) I add the average total cost and average variable cost curves to the graph of marginal cost and price first presented in Figure 11-2. Notice that the marginal cost curve goes through the lowest points of both average cost curves. (If you don't know why, it would be a good idea to go back and review Chapter 9.)

---

[2]I say "about 6" and "about 7" because the table gives only whole numbers. The actual minimum point occurs at 5.55 for average variable cost and 6.55 for average total cost. The nearest whole numbers to these are 6 and 7.

CHAPTER 11 ■ PERFECT COMPETITION

Figure 11-5 (a, b, and c)   Determining Profits Graphically

The profit-maximizing output depends *only* on where the MC and MR curves intersect. The total amount of profit or loss that a firm makes depends on the price it receives and its average total cost of producing the profit-maximizing output. This exhibit shows the case of (a) a profit, (b) zero profit, and (c) a loss.

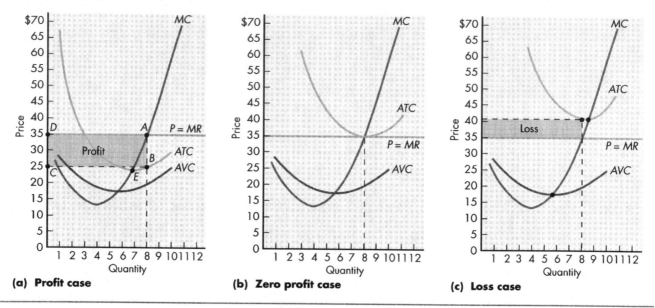

(a) Profit case   **(b) Zero profit case**   **(c) Loss case**

Find Output Where MC = MR   The way you find profit graphically is first to find the point where MC = MR (point A). That intersection determines the quantity the firm will produce if it wants to maximize profit. Why? Because the vertical distance between a point on the marginal cost curve and a point on the marginal revenue curve represents the additional profit the firm can make by changing output. For example, if it increases production from 6 to 7, its marginal cost is $22 and its marginal revenue is $35. By increasing output it can increase profit by $13 (from $63 to $76). The same reasoning holds true for any output less than 8. For outputs higher than 8, the opposite reasoning holds true. Marginal cost exceeds marginal revenue, so it pays to decrease output. So, to maximize profit, the firm must see that there is no distance between the two curves—it must see where they intersect.

Find Profit per Unit Where MC = MR   After having determined the profit-maximizing quantity, drop a vertical line down to the horizontal axis and see what average total cost is at that output level (point B). Doing so determines the profit per unit at the profit-maximizing output because it's the difference between the price the firm receives (its average revenue) and its average cost. Since the firm will earn that profit on each unit sold, you next extend a line back to the vertical axis (point C). That tells us that the average total costs per unit are $25. Next go up the price axis to the price that the firm receives (point D). For a competitive firm, that price is the marginal revenue. Connecting these points gives us the shaded rectangle, ABCD, which is the total profit earned by the firm (the total quantity times the profit per unit).

Notice that at the profit-maximizing position, the profit per unit isn't at its highest because average total cost is *not* at its minimum point. Profit per unit of output would be highest at point E. A common mistake that students make is to draw a line up from point E when they are finding profits. That is wrong. It is important to remember: *To*

Q.5   If the firm described in Figure 11-5 is producing 4 units, what would you advise it to do, and why?

When the *ATC* curve is below the marginal revenue curve, the firm makes a profit. When the *ATC* curve is above the marginal revenue curve, the firm incurs a loss.

PROFIT MAXIMIZATION AND REAL-WORLD FIRMS

Applying the Tools

Most real-world firms do not have profit as their only goal. The reason is that, in the real world, the decision maker's income is part of the cost of production. For example, a paid manager has an incentive to hold down costs, but has little incentive to hold down his income which, for the firm, is a cost. Alternatively, say that a firm is a worker-managed firm. If workers receive a share of the profits, they'll push for higher profits, but they'll also see to it that in the process of maximizing profits they don't hurt their own interest—maximizing their wages.

A manager-managed firm will push for high profits but will see to it that it doesn't achieve those profits by hurting the manager's interests. Managers' pay will be high. In

short, real-world firms will hold down the costs of factors of production *except* the cost of the decision maker.

In real life, this problem of the lack of incentives to hold down costs is important. For example, firms' managerial expenses often balloon even as firms are cutting "costs." Similarly, CEOs and other high-ranking officers of the firm often have enormously high salaries. How and why the lack of incentives to hold down costs affects the economy is best seen by first considering the nature of an economy with incentives to hold down all costs. That's why we use as our standard model the profit-maximizing firm. (*Standard model* means the model that economists use as our basis of reasoning; from it, we branch out.)

To determine maximum profit, you must first determine what output the firm will choose to produce by seeing where *MC* equals *MR*, and then dropping a line down to the *ATC* curve.

Q-6 What is wrong with the following diagram?

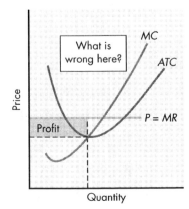

determine maximum profit you must first determine what output the firm will choose to produce by seeing where MC equals MR and then determine the average total cost at that quantity by dropping a line down to the ATC curve. Only then can you determine what maximum profit will be.

Zero Profit or Loss Where MC = MR   Notice also that as the curves in Figure 11-5(a) are drawn, ATC at the profit-maximizing position is below the price, and the firm makes a profit per unit of a little over $10. The choice of short-run average total cost curves was arbitrary and doesn't affect the firm's profit-maximizing condition: MC = MR. It could have been assumed that fixed cost was higher, which would have shifted the ATC curve up. In Figure 11-5(b) it's assumed that fixed cost is $81 higher than in Figure 11-5(a). Instead of $40, it's $121. The appropriate average total cost curve for a fixed cost of $121 is drawn in Figure 11-5(b). Notice that in this case economic profit is zero and the marginal cost curve intersects the minimum point of the average total cost curve at an output of 8 and a price of $35. In this case, the firm is making zero economic profit. (Remember from Chapter 10 that even though economic profit is zero, all resources, including entrepreneurs, are being paid their opportunity cost.)

In Figure 11-5(c), fixed cost is much higher—$169. Profit-maximizing output is still 8, but now at an output of 8, the firm is making an economic loss of $6 on each unit sold, since its average total cost is $41. The loss is given by the shaded rectangle. In this case, the profit-maximizing condition is actually a loss-minimizing condition. So MC = MR = P is both a *profit-maximizing condition* and a *loss-minimizing condition*.

I draw these three cases to emphasize to you that determining the profit-maximizing output level doesn't depend on fixed cost or average total cost. It depends only on where marginal cost equals price.

THE SHUTDOWN POINT

Earlier I stated the supply curve of a competitive firm is its marginal cost curve. More specifically, the supply curve is the part of the marginal cost curve that is above the

CHAPTER 11 ■ PERFECT COMPETITION

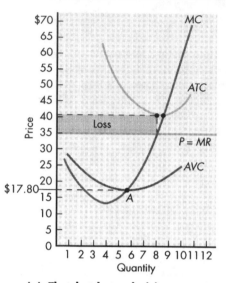

(a) The shutdown decision

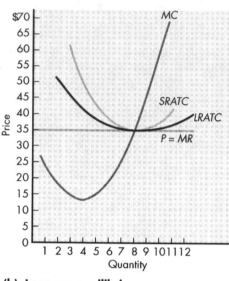

(b) Long-run equilibrium

Figure 11-6 The Shutdown Decision and Long-Run Equilibrium

A firm should continue to produce as long as price exceeds average variable cost. Once price falls below that, it will do better by temporarily shutting down and saving the variable costs. This occurs at point A in (a). In (b), the long-run equilibrium position for a marginal firm in an industry is shown. In that long-run equilibrium, only normal profits are made.

average variable cost curve. Considering why this is the case should help the analysis stick in your mind.

Let's consider Figure 11-6(a)—a reproduction of Figure 11-5(c)—and the firm's decision at various prices. At a price of $35, it's incurring a loss of $6 per unit. If it's making a loss, why doesn't it shut down? The answer lies in the fixed costs. There's no use crying over spilt milk. In the short run a firm knows these fixed costs are sunk costs; it must pay them regardless of whether or not it produces. The firm considers only the costs it can save by stopping production, and those costs are its variable costs. As long as a firm is covering its variable costs, it pays to keep on producing. By producing, its loss is $48; if it stopped producing, its loss would be all the fixed costs ($169). So it makes a smaller loss by producing.

However, once the price falls below average variable costs (below $17.80), it will pay to shut down (point A in Figure 11-6(a)). In that case the firm's loss from producing would be more than $169, and it would do better to simply stop producing temporarily and avoid paying the variable cost. Thus, the point at which price equals AVC is the **shutdown point** (*that point at which the firm will be better off if it temporarily shuts down than it will if it stays in business*). When price falls below the shutdown point, the average variable costs the firm can avoid paying by shutting down exceed the price it would get for selling the good. When price is above average variable cost, in the short run a firm should keep on producing even though it's making a loss. As long as a firm's total revenue is covering its total variable cost, temporarily producing at a loss is the firm's best strategy because it's making a smaller loss than it would make if it were to shut down.

SHORT-RUN MARKET SUPPLY AND DEMAND

Most of the preceding discussion has focused on supply and demand analysis of a firm. Now let's consider supply and demand in an industry. We've already discussed industry

Q-7 In the early 2000s, many airlines were making losses, yet they continued to operate. Why?

The shutdown point is the point at which the firm will be better off if it shuts down than it will if it stays in business.

If P > minimum of AVC, the firm will continue to produce in the short run. If P < minimum of AVC, the firm will shut down.

FINDING OUTPUT, PRICE, AND PROFIT

To find a competitive firm's price, level of output, and profit given a firm's marginal cost curve and average total cost curve, use the following three steps:

1. Determine the market price at which market supply and demand curves intersect. This is the price the competitive firm accepts for its products. Draw the horizontal marginal revenue (MR) curve at the market price.

2. Determine the profit-maximizing level of output by finding the level of output where the MR and MC curves intersect.

3. Determine profit by subtracting average total costs at the profit-maximizing level of output from the price and multiplying by the firm's output.

If you are demonstrating profit graphically, find the point at which MC = MR. Extend a line down to the ATC curve. Extend a line from this point to the vertical axis. To complete the box indicating profit, go up the vertical axis to the market price.

---

demand. Even though the demand curve faced by the firm is perfectly elastic, the industry demand curve is downward sloping.

How about the industry supply curve? We previously demonstrated that the supply curve for a competitive firm is that firm's marginal cost curve (above the average variable cost curve). To discuss the industry supply curve, we must use a market supply curve. In the short run when the number of firms in the market is fixed, the **market supply curve** is just the *horizontal sum of all the firms' marginal cost curves, taking account of any changes in input prices that might occur.* To move from individual firms' marginal cost curves or supply curves to the market supply curve we add the quantities all firms will supply at each possible price. Since all firms have identical marginal cost curves, a quick way of summing the quantities is to multiply the quantities from the marginal cost curve of a representative firm at each price by the number of firms in the market. As the short run evolves into the long run, the number of firms in the market can change. As more firms enter the market, the market supply curve shifts to the right because more firms are supplying the quantity indicated by the representative marginal cost curve. Likewise, as the number of firms in the market declines, the market supply curve shifts to the left. Knowing how the number of firms in the market affects the market supply curve is important to understanding long-run equilibrium in perfectly competitive markets.

The market supply curve is the horizontal sum of all the firms' marginal cost curves, taking account of any changes in input prices that might occur.

LONG-RUN COMPETITIVE EQUILIBRIUM

The analysis of the competitive firm consists of two parts: the short-run analysis just presented and the long-run analysis. In the short run the number of firms is fixed and the firm can either earn economic profit or incur economic loss. In the long run, firms enter and exit the market and neither economic profits nor economic losses are possible. In the long run, firms make zero economic profit. Thus, in the long run, only the zero profit equilibrium shown in Figure 11-6(b) is possible. As you can see, at that long-run equilibrium, the firm is at the minimum of both the short-run and the long-run average total cost curves.

Why can't firms earn economic profit or make economic losses in the long run? Because of the entry and exit of firms: If there are economic profits, firms will enter the

THE SHUTDOWN DECISION AND THE RELEVANT COSTS

Applying the Tools

Chapters 9 and 10 emphasized that it is vital to choose the relevant costs to the decision at hand. Discussing the shutdown decision gives us a chance to demonstrate the importance of those choices. Say the firm leases a large computer it needs to operate. The rental cost of that computer is a fixed cost for most decisions, if, as long as the firm keeps the computer, the rent must be paid whether or not the computer is used. However, if the firm can end the rental contract at any time, and thereby save the rental cost, the computer is not a fixed cost. But neither is it your normal variable cost. Since the firm can end the rental contract and save the cost only if it shuts down, that rental cost of the computer is an *indivisible setup cost*. For the shutdown decision, the computer cost is a variable cost. For other decisions about changing quantity, it's a fixed cost.

The moral: The relevant cost can change with the decision at hand, so when you apply the analysis to real-world situations, be sure to think carefully about what the *relevant cost* is.

---

market, shifting the market supply curve to the right. As market supply increases, the market price will decline and reduce profits for each firm. Firms will continue to enter the market and the market price will continue to decline until the incentive of economic profits is eliminated. At that price, all firms are earning zero profit. Similarly, if the price is lower than the price necessary to earn a profit, firms incurring losses will leave the market and the market supply curve will shift to the left. As market supply shifts to the left, market price will rise. Firms will continue to exit the market and market price will continue to rise until all remaining firms no longer incur losses and earn zero profit. Only at zero profit do entry and exit stop.

> Since profits create incentives for new firms to enter, output will increase, and the price will fall until zero profits are being made.

Zero profit does not mean that entrepreneurs don't get anything for their efforts. The entrepreneur is an input to production just like any other factor of production. In order to stay in the business the entrepreneur must receive the opportunity cost, or **normal profit** (*the amount the owners of business would have received in the next-best alternative*). That normal profit is built into the costs of the firm; economic profits are profits above normal profits.

Web Note 11.2
Barriers to Exit

Another aspect of the zero profit position deserves mentioning. What if one firm has superefficient workers or machinery? Won't the firm make a profit in the long run? The answer is, again, no. In a long-run competitive market, other firms will see the value of those workers and machines and will compete to get them for themselves. As firms compete for the superefficient factors of production, the price of those specialized inputs will rise until all profits are eliminated. Those factors will receive what are called rents to their specialized ability. For example, say the average worker receives $400 per week, but Sarah, because she's such a good worker, receives $600. So $200 of the $600 she receives is a rent to her specialized ability. Either her existing firm matches that $600 wage or she will change employment.

> Q-8 If a competitive firm makes zero profit, why does it stay in business?

The zero profit condition is enormously powerful; it makes the analysis of competitive markets far more applicable to the real world than can a strict application of the assumption of perfect competition. If economic profit is being made, firms will enter and compete that profit away. Price will be pushed down to the average total cost of production as long as there are no barriers to entry. As we'll see in later chapters, in their analysis of whether markets are competitive, many economists focus primarily on whether barriers to entry exist.

> The zero profit condition is enormously powerful; it makes the analysis of competitive markets far more applicable to the real world than would otherwise be the case.

MICROECONOMICS ▪ MARKET STRUCTURE AND POLICY

Figure 11-7 (a and b)   Market Response to an Increase in Demand
Faced with an increase in demand, which it sees as an increase in price and hence profits, a competitive firm will respond by increasing output (from A to B) in order to maximize profit. The market response is shown in (a); the firm's response is shown in (b). As all firms increase output and as new firms enter, price will fall until all profit is competed away. Thus the long-run market supply curve will be perfectly elastic, as is S_{LR} in (a). The final equilibrium will be the original price but a higher output. The original firms return to their original output (A), but since there are more firms in the market, the market output increases to C.

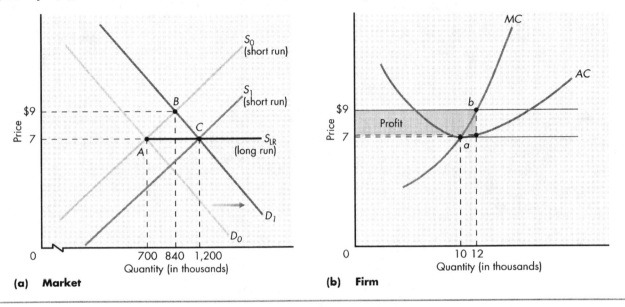

(a)   **Market**   (b)   **Firm**

ADJUSTMENT FROM THE SHORT RUN TO THE LONG RUN

Now that we've been through the basics of the perfectly competitive supply and demand curves, we're ready to consider the two together and to see how the adjustment to long-run equilibrium will likely take place in the firm and in the market.

AN INCREASE IN DEMAND

Q.9 If berets suddenly became the "in" thing to wear, what would you expect to happen to the price in the short run? In the long run?

First, in Figure 11-7(a and b), let's consider a market that's in equilibrium but that suddenly experiences an increase in demand. Figure 11-7(a) shows the market reaction. Figure 11-7(b) shows a representative firm's reaction. Originally market equilibrium occurs at a price of $7 and market quantity supplied of 700 thousand units (point A in (a)), with each of 70 firms producing 10 thousand units (point a in (b)). Firms are making zero profit because they're in long-run equilibrium. If demand increases from D_0 to D_1, the firms will see the market price increasing and will increase their output until they're once again at a position where MC = P. This occurs at point B at a market output of 840 thousand units in (a) and at point b at a firm output of 12 in (b). In the short run the 70 existing firms each make an economic profit (the shaded area in Figure 11-7(b)). Price has risen to $9, but average cost is only $7.10, so if the price remains $9 each firm is making a profit of $1.90 per unit. But price cannot remain at $9 since each firm will have an incentive to expand output and new firms will have an incentive to enter the market.

As existing firms expand and new firms enter, if input prices remain constant, the short-run market supply curve shifts from S_0 to S_1 and the market price returns to $7.

A SUMMARY OF A PERFECTLY COMPETITIVE INDUSTRY

Knowing the Tools

Four things to remember when considering a perfectly competitive industry are

1. The profit-maximizing condition for perfectly competitive firms is $MC = MR = P$.

2. To determine profit or loss at the profit-maximizing level of output, subtract the average total cost at that level of output from the price and multiply the result by the output level.

3. Firms will shut down production if price is equal to or falls below the minimum of their average variable costs.

4. A perfectly competitive firm is in long-run equilibrium only when it is earning zero economic profit, or when price equals the minimum of long-run average total costs.

The entry of 50 new firms provides the additional output in this example, bringing market output to 1.2 million units sold for $7 apiece. The final equilibrium will be at a higher market output but the same price.

LONG-RUN MARKET SUPPLY

The long-run market supply curve is a schedule of quantities supplied when firms are no longer entering or exiting the market. This occurs when firms are earning zero profit. In this case, the long-run supply curve is created by extending to the right the line connecting points A and C. Since equilibrium price remains at $7, the long-run supply curve is perfectly elastic. The long-run supply curve is horizontal because factor prices are constant. That is, factor prices do not increase as industry output increases. Economists call this market a *constant-cost industry*. Two other possibilities exist: an *increasing-cost industry* (in which factor prices rise as more firms enter the market and existing firms expand production) and a *decreasing-cost industry* (in which factor prices fall as industry output expands).

Factor prices are likely to rise when industry output increases if the factors of production are specialized. An increase in the demand for the factors of production that accompanies an increase in output, in this case, will bid up factor prices. The effect on long-run supply is the following: The rise in factor prices forces costs up for each individual firm and increases the price at which firms earn zero profit. Firms will stop entering the market and expanding production at a higher equilibrium price since the price at which zero profit is made has risen. Therefore, in increasing-cost industries, the long-run supply curve is upward sloping. In the extreme case, in which all firms in an industry are competitively supplying a perfectly inelastic resource or factor input, the long-run market supply curve is perfectly inelastic (vertical). Any increase in demand would increase the price of that factor. Costs would rise in response to the increase in demand; output would not. Input costs would also rise if there are diseconomies of scale. In both cases, the long-run equilibrium price would have been higher and output would have been lower than if input prices remained constant.[3]

In the long run firms earn zero profits.

Q-10 In 2001, demand for burkhas (the garment the Taliban required all Afghani women to wear) declined when the Taliban was ousted. In the short run, what would you expect to happen to the price of burkhas? How about in the long run?

---

[3]To check your understanding, ask yourself the following question: What if there had been economies of scale? If you answered, "There couldn't have been," you're really into economic thinking. (For those of you who aren't all that heavily into economic thinking, the reason is that if there had been economies of scale, the market structure would not have been perfectly competitive. One firm would have kept expanding and expanding and, as it did, its costs would have kept falling.)

MICROECONOMICS ▪ MARKET STRUCTURE AND POLICY

The other possibility is a decreasing-cost industry. If factor prices decline when industry output expands, individual firms' cost curves shift down. As they do, the price at which the zero profit condition falls and the price at which firms cease to enter the market also falls. In this case, the long-run market supply curve is downward sloping. Factor prices may decline as output rises when new entrants make it more cost-effective for other firms to provide services to all firms in the area. The supply of factors of production expands and reduces the price of inputs to production.

Notice that in the long-run equilibrium, once again zero profit is being made. Long-run equilibrium is defined by zero economic profit. Notice also that the long-run supply curve is more elastic than the short-run supply curve. That's because output changes are much less costly in the long run than in the short run. *In the short run, the price does more of the adjusting. In the long run, more of the adjustment is done by quantity.*

In the short run, the price does more of the adjusting. In the long run, more of the adjustment is done by quantity.

AN EXAMPLE IN THE REAL WORLD

The perfectly competitive model and the reasoning underlying it are extremely powerful. With them you have a simple model to use as a first approach to predict the effect of an event, or to explain why an event occurred. For example, consider the decision of the owners of the Kmart chain of department stores to close nearly 300 stores after experiencing two years of losses.

Figure 11-8 shows what happened. Initially, Kmart saw the losses it was suffering as temporary. In the two years prior to the shutdown decision, Kmart's cost curves looked like those in Figure 11-8. Since price exceeded average variable cost, Kmart continued to produce even though it was making a loss.

But after two years of losses Kmart's perspective changed. The company moved from the short run to the long run. Kmart began to believe that the demand wasn't temporarily low but rather permanently low. It began to ask: What costs are truly fixed and what costs are simply indivisible costs that we can save if we close down completely, selling our buildings and reducing our overhead? Since in the long run all costs are variable, the ATC became its relevant AVC. Kmart recognized that demand had fallen below these long-run average costs. At that point, it shut down those stores for which $P < AVC$.

There are hundreds of other real-world examples to which the perfectly competitive model adds insight. That's one reason why it's important to keep it in the back of your mind.

Tim Boyle/Getty Images.

Figure 11-8   A Real-World Example: A Shutdown Decision
Supply/demand analysis can be applied to a wide variety of real-world examples. This exhibit shows one, but there are many more. As you experience life today, a good exercise is to put on your supply/demand glasses and interpret everything you see in a supply/demand framework.

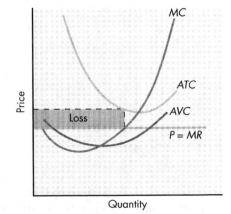

CHAPTER 11 ▓ PERFECT COMPETITION

CONCLUSION

We've come to the end of the presentation of perfect competition. It was tough going, but if you went through it carefully, it will serve you well, both as a basis for later chapters and as a reference point for how real-world economies work. But like many good things, a complete understanding of the chapter doesn't come easy.

SUMMARY

- The necessary conditions for perfect competition are that buyers and sellers be price takers, the number of firms be large, there be no barriers to entry, firms' products be identical, there be complete information, and sellers be profit-maximizing entrepreneurial firms.

- The profit-maximizing position of a competitive firm is where marginal revenue equals marginal cost.

- The supply curve of a competitive firm is its marginal cost curve. Only competitive firms have supply curves.

- To find the profit-maximizing level of output for a perfect competitor, find that level of output where MC = MR. Profit is price less average total cost times output at the profit-maximizing level of output.

- In the short run, competitive firms can make a profit or loss. In the long run, they make zero profits.

- The shutdown price for a perfectly competitive firm is a price below the minimum point of the average variable cost curve.

- The short-run market supply curve is the horizontal summation of the marginal cost curves for all firms in the market. An increase in the number of firms in the market shifts the market supply curve to the right, while a decrease shifts it to the left.

- Perfectly competitive firms make zero profit in the long run because if profit were being made, new firms would enter and the market price would decline, eliminating the profit. If losses were being made, firms would exit and the market price would rise, eliminating the loss.

- The long-run supply curve is a schedule of quantities supplied where firms are making zero profit. The slope of the long-run supply curve depends on what happens to factor prices when output increases. Constant-cost industries have horizontal long-run supply curves. Increasing-cost industries have upward-sloping long-run supply curves, and decreasing-cost industries have downward-sloping long-run supply curves.

KEY TERMS

barriers to entry (242)
marginal cost (MC) (245)

marginal revenue (MR) (245)
market supply curve (254)

normal profit (255)
perfectly competitive market (241)
price taker (242)

profit-maximizing condition (247)
shutdown point (253)

QUESTIONS FOR THOUGHT AND REVIEW

1. Why must buyers and sellers be price takers for a market to be perfectly competitive?

2. Draw marginal cost, marginal revenue, and average total cost curves for a typical perfectly competitive firm and indicate the profit-maximizing level of output and total profit for that firm. Is the firm in long-run equilibrium? Why or why not?

3. Draw marginal cost, marginal revenue, and average total cost curves for a typical perfectly competitive firm in long-run equilibrium and indicate the profit-maximizing level of output and total profit for that firm.

4. What portion of the marginal cost curve is the firm's supply curve? How is a firm's marginal cost curve related to the market supply curve?

MICROECONOMICS ▪ MARKET STRUCTURE AND POLICY

5. Draw the ATC, AVC, and MC curves for a typical firm. Label the price at which the firm would shut down temporarily and the price at which the firm would exit the market in the long run.

6. Under what cost condition is the shutdown point the same as the point at which a firm exits the market?

7. Why is long-run market supply curve upward-sloping in an increasing-cost industry, downward-sloping in a decreasing-cost industry, and horizontal in a constant-cost industry?

8. What will be the effect of a technological development that reduces marginal costs in a competitive market on short-run price, quantity, and profit?

9. If a firm is owned by its workers but otherwise meets all the qualifications for a perfectly competitive firm, will its price and output decisions differ from the price and output decisions of a perfectly competitive firm? Why?

10. You're thinking of buying one of two firms. One has a profit margin of $8 per unit; the other has a profit margin of $4 per unit. Which should you buy? Why?

11. If marginal cost is four times the quantity produced and the price is $20, how much should the firm produce? Why?

12. Find three events in the newspaper that can be explained or interpreted with supply/demand analysis.

13. State what is *wrong* with each of the graphs.

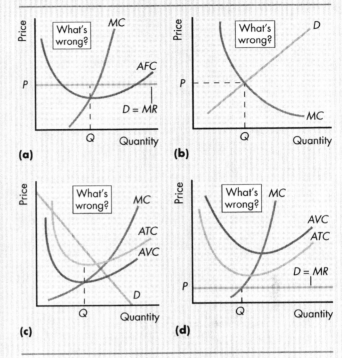

(a)

(b)

(c)

(d)

14. In the late 1990s and early 2000s, hundreds of music stores closed in the face of stagnant demand for CDs and new competitors—online music vendors and discount retailers. Explain how price competition from these new sources would cause a retail store to close. In the long run, what effect will new entrants have on the price of CDs?

PROBLEMS AND EXERCISES

1. a. Based on the following table, what is the profit-maximizing output?

Output	Price	Total Costs
0	$10	$ 31
1	10	40
2	10	45
3	10	48
4	10	55
5	10	65
6	10	80
7	10	100
8	10	140
9	10	220
10	10	340

b. How would your answer change if, in response to an increase in demand, the price of the good increased to $15?

2. A profit-maximizing firm has an average total cost of $4, but it gets a price of $3 for each good it sells.
   a. What would you advise the firm to do?
   b. What would you advise the firm to do if you knew average variable costs were $3.50?

3. Say that half of the cost of producing wheat is the rental cost of land (a fixed cost) and half is the cost of labor and machines (a variable cost). If the average total cost of producing wheat is $8 and the price of wheat is $6, what would you advise the farmer to do? ("Grow something else" is not allowed.)

Colander:
Microeconomics, Fifth
Edition

II. Microeconomics

11. Perfect Competition

© The McGraw–Hill
Companies, 2004

CHAPTER 11 ■ PERFECT COMPETITION

4. Use the accompanying graph, which shows the marginal cost and average total cost curves for the shoe store Zapateria, a perfectly competitive firm.
   a. How many pairs of shoes will Zapateria produce if the market price of shoes is $70 a pair?
   b. What is the total profit Zapateria will earn if the market price of shoes is $70 a pair?
   c. Should Zapateria expect more shoe stores to enter this market? Why or why not?

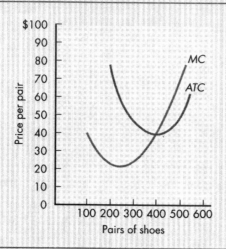

Price per pair / Pairs of shoes

d. What is the long-run equilibrium price in the shoe market assuming it is a constant-cost industry?

5. Each of 10 firms in a given industry has the costs given in the left-hand table. The market demand schedule is given in the right-hand table.

Quantity	Total Cost		Price	Quantity Demanded
0	12		2	110
1	24		4	100
2	27		6	90
3	31		8	80
4	39		10	70
5	53		12	60
6	73		14	50
7	99		16	40

   a. What is the market equilibrium price and the price each firm gets for its product?
   b. What is the equilibrium market quantity and the quantity each firm produces?
   c. What profit is each firm making?
   d. Below what price will firms begin to exit the market?

6. Suppose an increasing-cost industry is in both long-run and short-run equilibrium. Explain what will happen to the following in the long run if the demand for that product declines:
   a. Price.
   b. Quantity.
   c. Number of firms in the market.
   d. Profit.

7. Graphically demonstrate the quantity and price of a perfectly competitive firm.
   a. Explain why a slightly larger quantity would not be preferred.
   b. Explain why a slightly lower quantity would not be preferred.
   c. Label the shutdown point in your diagram.
   d. You have just discovered that shutting down means that you would lose your land zoning permit which is required to start operating again. How does that change your answer to c?

8. A California biotechnology firm submitted a tomato that will not rot for weeks to the U.S. Food and Drug Administration. It designed such a fruit by changing the genetic structure of the tomato. What effect will this technological change have:
   a. On the price of tomatoes?
   b. On farmers who grow tomatoes?
   c. On the geographic areas where tomatoes are grown?
   d. On where tomatoes are generally placed on salad bars in winter?

9. Currently central banks (banks of governments) hold 35,000 tons of gold—one-third of the world's supply. This is the equivalent of 17 years' production. In the 1990s there was discussion about the central banks selling off their gold, since it is no longer tied to money supplies. Assuming they did sell it:
   a. Demonstrate, using supply/demand analysis, the effect on the price of gold in the long run and the short run.
   b. If you were an economist advising the central banks and you believed that selling off the gold made sense, would you advise them to do it quickly or slowly? Why?

10. The milk industry has a number of interesting aspects. Provide economic explanations for the following:
    a. Fluid milk is 87 percent water. It can be dried and reconstituted so that it is almost indistinguishable from fresh milk. What is a likely reason that such reconstituted milk is not produced?
    b. The United States has regional milk-marketing regulations whose goals are to make each of the regions self-sufficient in milk. What is a likely reason for this?
    c. A U.S. senator from a milk-producing state has been quoted as saying, "I am absolutely convinced . . . that simply bringing down dairy price supports is not a way to cut production." Is it likely that he is correct? What is a probable reason for his statement?

MICROECONOMICS ▪ MARKET STRUCTURE AND POLICY

11. Subtle changes in the tax laws often mean enormous amounts of money to individuals and groups. Consider the case of whiskey, as did economists Jack High and Clayton Coppin. Whiskey is distilled grain. The distilling process produces poisonous impurities, called fusel oil, that must be removed before the whiskey is drinkable. One way to remove these impurities is by aging the whiskey in wooden barrels. Whiskey produced in this manner is "straight whiskey." The second method is distillation—removing the fusel oil through additional distilling. The latter method removes more impurities and is cheaper, but it results in a whiskey with little taste. However, taste can be added back through flavorings or blending with aged whiskey. Up until 1868 distilled or blended whiskey predominated, but in that year a law was passed that allowed straight-whiskey producers who stored their whiskey in government warehouses to defer their taxes on it until it was fully aged.

   a. What advantage would this law have for straight-whiskey producers?
   b. After the tax was paid the whiskey received a tax stamp, certifying that its producers had paid the tax and that their straight whiskey had been stored in a "bonded government warehouse." If you were a straight-whiskey producer, how might you try to use that tax stamp to your advantage in advertising?
   c. How might competing producers of distilled whiskey certify the quality of their product?

WEB QUESTIONS

1. A number of markets are developing on the Internet. One of those markets is eBay. Check out eBay at www.ebay.com and explain whether you believe that the eBay Internet auction market is perfectly competitive. Be sure to explain which of the six conditions are met and how.

2. Find 60-month new auto loans in five different states using a loan information center on the Internet such as www.rates.net and answer the following questions:

   a. By how much did the interest rates differ among those institutions you sampled?
   b. Which of the six conditions for perfect competition does the auto loan market meet?
   c. Is your answer to b consistent with your answer to a? Why or why not?

ANSWERS TO MARGIN QUESTIONS

1. Without the assumption of no barriers to entry, firms could make a profit by raising price; hence, their demand curve would not be perfectly elastic and, hence, perfect competition would not exist. (242)

2. The competitive firm is such a small portion of the total market that it can have no effect on price. Consequently it takes the price as given, and hence its perceived demand curve is perfectly elastic. (244)

3. To determine the profit-maximizing output of a competitive firm, you must know price and marginal cost. (246)

4. Firms are interested in getting as much for themselves as they possibly can. Maximizing total profit does this. Maximizing profit per unit might yield very small total profits. (248)

5. If the firm in Figure 11-5 were producing 4 units, I would explain to it that the marginal cost of increasing output is only $12 and the marginal revenue is $35, so it should significantly expand output until 8, where the marginal cost equals the marginal revenue, or price. (251)

6. The diagram is drawn with the wrong profit-maximizing output and hence the wrong profit. Output is determined where marginal cost equals price and profit is the difference between the average total cost and price at that output, not at the output where marginal cost equals average total cost. The correct diagram is shown here. (252)

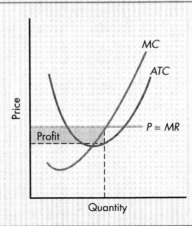

7. The marginal cost for airlines is significantly below average total cost. Since they're recovering their average variable cost, they continue to operate. In the long run, if this continues, some airlines will be forced out of business. (253)

CHAPTER 11 ▪ PERFECT COMPETITION

8. The costs for a firm include the normal costs, which in turn include a return for all factors. Thus it is worthwhile for a competitive firm to stay in business, since it is doing better, or at least as well, as it could in any other activity. *(255)*

9. Suddenly becoming the "in" thing to wear would cause the demand for berets to shift out to the right, pushing the price up in the short run. In the long run it would probably push the price down, as there probably are considerable economies of scale in the production of berets. *(256)*

10. A decline in demand pushed the short-run price of these burkhas down. In the long run, however, once a number of burkha makers go out of business, the price of burkhas should eventually move back to approximately where it was before the decline, assuming constant returns to scale. *(257)*

Frank–Bernanke:
Principles of
Microeconomics, Second
Edition

II. Competition and the
Invisible Hand

7. Efficiency and Exchange

© The McGraw–Hill
Companies, 2004

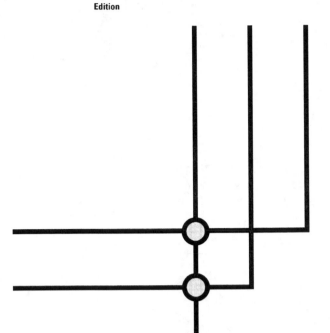

EFFICIENCY AND EXCHANGE

Armando Lopez sat watching one of the national political conventions on television one August night as one orator after another extolled the virtues of the free enterprise system. "The greatest engine of progress mankind has ever witnessed," one of the speakers called it. "A rising tide that will lift all boats," said another.

Lopez, however, was skeptical, for though he had worked hard and played by society's rules, his standard of living had been deteriorating rather than improving. Downsized from his draftsman's position at an aircraft plant the year before, Lopez was working as a janitor for a local office-cleaning company, the best job he had been able to find after months of searching. He could not afford to repair the leaky roof and faulty plumbing at his house in East Los Angeles. Indeed, his two older children had dropped out of college because he could no longer afford their tuition bills. Though his commute to work was only six miles each way, freeway congestion made it a 90-minute trip most mornings. His wife's recurrent asthma attacks, triggered by local air pollution, had recently worsened. Without health insurance, the family's medical bills had been mounting rapidly. And there had been four deaths from drive-by shootings in their neighborhood in the last year.

Given the stark contrast between his own experience and the lofty claims of the orators he was listening to, Lopez's skepticism about the virtues of the free enterprise system was understandable. Yet informed students of the market system understand that it could never have been expected to prevent Lopez's problems in the first place. *In certain domains*—indeed, in very broad domains—markets are every bit as remarkable as their strongest proponents assert. Yet there are many problems they simply cannot be expected to solve. For example, private markets cannot by themselves guarantee an income distribution that most people regard as fair. Nor can they ensure clean air, uncongested highways, or safe neighborhoods for all.

Frank–Bernanke:
Principles of
Microeconomics, Second
Edition

II. Competition and the
Invisible Hand

7. Efficiency and Exchange

© The McGraw–Hill
Companies, 2004

CHAPTER 7 EFFICIENCY AND EXCHANGE

Yet markets do enable society to produce sufficient resources to meet all these goals and more. In virtually all successful societies, however, markets are supplemented by active political coordination in at least some instances. We will almost always achieve our goals more effectively if we know what tasks private markets can do well, and then allow them to perform those tasks. Unfortunately, the discovery that markets cannot solve *every* problem seems to have led some critics to conclude that markets cannot solve *any* problems. This misperception is a dangerous one, because it has prompted attempts to prevent markets from doing even those tasks for which they are ideally suited.

Our task in this chapter will be to explore why many tasks are best left to the market. We will explore the conditions under which unregulated markets generate the largest possible economic surplus. We will also discuss why attempts to interfere with market outcomes often lead to unintended and undesired consequences. We will see why public utilities can more efficiently serve their customers if they set prices in a way that closely mimics the market. And we will also discuss why the economic burden of a tax does not always fall most heavily on the parties from whom it is directly collected.

MARKET EQUILIBRIUM AND EFFICIENCY

As noted in Chapter 3, the mere fact that markets coordinate the production of a large and complex list of goods and services is reason enough to marvel at them. But economists make an even stronger claim—namely, that markets not only produce these goods, but also produce them as efficiently as possible.

efficient (or Pareto efficient) a situation is efficient if no change is possible that will help some people without harming others

The term **efficient**, as economists use it, has a narrow technical meaning. When we say that market equilibrium is efficient, we mean simply this: *If price and quantity take anything other than their equilibrium values, a transaction that will make at least some people better off without harming others can always be found.* This conception of efficiency is also known as **Pareto efficiency**, after Vilfredo Pareto, the nineteenth-century Italian economist who introduced it.

Why is market equilibrium efficient in this sense? The answer is that it is always possible to construct an exchange that helps some without harming others whenever a market is out of equilibrium. Suppose, for example, that the supply and demand curves for milk are as shown in Figure 7.1, and that the current price of milk is $1 per gallon. At that price, sellers offer only 2,000 gallons of milk a day. At that quantity, the marginal buyer values an extra gallon of milk at $2. This is the price that corresponds to 2,000 gallons a day on the demand curve, which represents what the marginal buyer is willing to pay for an additional gallon (another application of the vertical interpretation of the demand curve). We also know that the cost of producing an extra gallon of milk is only $1. This is the price that corresponds to 2,000 gallons a day on the supply curve,

FIGURE 7.1

A Market in Which Price Is Below the Equilibrium Level.

In this market, milk is currently selling for $1 per gallon, $0.50 below the equilibrium price of $1.50 per gallon.

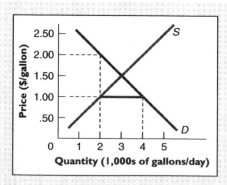

MARKET EQUILIBRIUM AND EFFICIENCY

which equals marginal cost (another application of the vertical interpretation of the supply curve).

Furthermore, a price of $1 per gallon leads to excess demand of 2,000 gallons per day, which means that many frustrated buyers cannot buy as much milk as they want at the going price. Now suppose a supplier sells an extra gallon of milk to the most eager of these buyers for $1.25, as in Figure 7.2. Since the extra gallon cost only $1 to produce, the seller is $0.25 better off than before. And since the most eager buyer values the extra gallon at $2, that buyer is $0.75 better off than before. In sum, the transaction creates an extra $1 of economic surplus out of thin air!

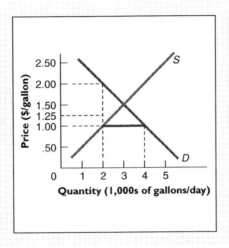

FIGURE 7.2

How Excess Demand Creates an Opportunity for a Surplus-Enhancing Transaction.

At a market price of $1 per gallon, the most intensely dissatisfied buyer is willing to pay $2 for an additional gallon, which a seller can produce at a cost of only $1. If this buyer pays the seller $1.25 for the extra gallon, the buyer gains an economic surplus of $0.75 and the seller gains an economic surplus of $0.25.

Note that none of the other buyers or sellers is harmed by this transaction. Thus milk selling for only $1 per gallon cannot be efficient. As the following exercise illustrates, there was nothing special about the price of $1 per gallon. Indeed, if milk sells for *any* price below $1.50 per gallon (the market equilibrium price), we can design a similar transaction, which means that selling milk for any price less than $1.50 per gallon cannot be efficient.

EXERCISE 7.1

In Figure 7.1, suppose that milk initially sells for 50 cents per gallon. Describe a transaction that will create additional economic surplus for both buyer and seller without causing harm to anyone else.

What is more, it is always possible to describe a transaction that will create additional surplus for both buyer and seller whenever the price lies above the market equilibrium level. Suppose, for example, that the current price is $2 per gallon in the milk market shown in Figure 7.1. At that price, we have excess supply of 2,000 gallons per day (see Figure 7.3). Suppose the most dissatisfied producer sells a gallon of milk for $1.75 to the buyer who values it most highly. This buyer, who would have been willing to pay $2, will be $0.25 better off than before. Likewise the producer, who would have been willing to sell milk for as little as $1 per gallon (the marginal cost of production at 2,000 gallons per day), will be $0.75 better off than before. As when the price was $1 per gallon, the new transaction creates $1 of additional economic surplus without harming any other buyer or seller. Since we could design a similar surplus-enhancing transaction at any price above the equilibrium level, selling milk for more than $1.50 per gallon cannot be efficient.

CHAPTER 7   EFFICIENCY AND EXCHANGE

FIGURE 7.3
How Excess Supply Creates an Opportunity for a Surplus-Enhancing Transaction.
At a market price of $2 per gallon, dissatisfied sellers can produce an additional gallon of milk at a cost of only $1, which is $1 less than a buyer would be willing to pay for it. If the buyer pays the seller $1.75 for an extra gallon, the buyer gains an economic surplus of $0.25 and the seller gains an economic surplus of $0.75.

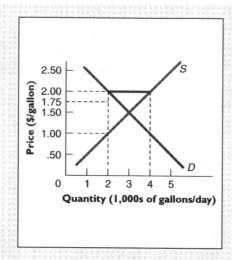

The vertical interpretations of the supply and demand curves thus make it clear why only the equilibrium price in a market can be efficient. When the price is either higher or lower than the equilibrium price, the quantity exchanged in the market will always be lower than the equilibrium quantity. If the price is below equilibrium, the quantity sold will be the amount that sellers offer. If the price is above equilibrium, the quantity sold will be the amount that buyers wish to buy. In either case, the vertical value on the demand curve at the quantity exchanged, which is the value of an extra unit to buyers, must be larger than the vertical value on the supply curve, which is the marginal cost of producing that unit.

So the market equilibrium price is the *only* price at which buyers and sellers cannot design a surplus-enhancing transaction. The market equilibrium price leads, in other words, to the largest possible total economic surplus. In this specific, limited sense, free markets are said to produce and distribute goods and services efficiently.

Actually, to claim that market equilibrium is always efficient even in this limited sense is an overstatement. The claim holds only if buyers and sellers are well informed, if markets are perfectly competitive, and if the demand and supply curves satisfy certain other restrictions. For example, market equilibrium will not be efficient if the individual marginal cost curves that add up to the market supply curve fail to include all relevant costs of producing the product. Thus, as we saw in Chapter 3, the true cost of expanding output will be higher than indicated by the market supply curve if production generates pollution that harms others. The equilibrium output will then be inefficiently large and the equilibrium price inefficiently low.

Likewise, market equilibrium will not be efficient if the individual demand curves that make up the market demand curve do not capture all the relevant benefits of buying additional units of the product. For instance, if a homeowner's willingness to pay for ornamental shrubs is based only on the enjoyment she herself gains from them, and not on any benefits that may accrue to her neighbors, the market demand curve for shrubs will understate their value to the neighborhood. The equilibrium quantity of ornamental shrubs will be inefficiently small, and the market price for shrubs will be inefficiently low.

We will take up such market imperfections in greater detail in later chapters. For now, we will confine our attention to perfectly competitive markets whose demand curves capture all relevant benefits and whose supply curves capture all relevant costs. For such goods, market equilibrium will always be efficient in the limited sense described earlier.

Frank–Bernanke:
Principles of
Microeconomics, Second
Edition

II. Competition and the
Invisible Hand

7. Efficiency and Exchange

© The McGraw–Hill
Companies, 2004

MARKET EQUILIBRIUM AND EFFICIENCY

EFFICIENCY IS NOT THE ONLY GOAL

The fact that market equilibrium maximizes economic surplus is an attractive feature, to be sure. Bear in mind, however, that "efficient" does not mean the same thing as "good." For example, the market for milk may be in equilibrium at a price of $1.50 per gallon, yet many poor families may be unable to afford milk for their children at that price. Still others may not even have a place for their children to sleep.

Efficiency is a concept that that is based on predetermined attributes of buyers and sellers—their incomes, tastes, abilities, knowledge, and so on. Through the combined effects of individual cost-benefit decisions, these attributes give rise to the supply and demand curves for each good produced in an economy. If we are concerned about inequality in the distribution of attributes like income, we should not be surprised to discover that markets do not always yield outcomes we like.

Most of us could agree, for example, that the world would be a better one if all people had enough income to feed their families adequately. The claim that equilibrium in the market for milk is efficient means simply that *taking people's incomes as given,* the resulting allocation of milk cannot be altered so as to help some people without at the same time harming others.

To this a critic of the market system might respond: So what? As such critics rightly point out, imposing costs on others may be justified if doing so will help those with sufficiently important unmet demands. For example, most people would prefer to fund homeless shelters with their tax dollars rather than let the homeless freeze to death. Arguing in these terms, American policymakers responded to rapid increases in the price of oil in the late 1970s by imposing price controls on home heating oil. And many of us might agree that if the alternative had been to take no action at all, price controls might have been justified in the name of social justice.

But the economist's concept of market efficiency makes clear that there *must* be a better alternative policy. Price controls on oil prevent the market from reaching equilibrium, and as we've seen, that means forgoing transactions that would benefit some people without harming others.

WHY EFFICIENCY SHOULD BE THE FIRST GOAL

Efficiency is important not because it is a desirable end in itself, but because it enables us to achieve all our other goals to the fullest possible extent. Whenever a market is out of equilibrium, it is always possible to generate additional economic surplus. To gain additional economic surplus is to gain more of the resources we need to do the things we want to do. Whenever any market is out of equilibrium, there is waste, and waste is always bad thing.

 RECAP   **EQUILIBRIUM AND EFFICIENCY**

When a market is not in equilibrium—because price is either above the equilibrium level or below it—the quantity exchanged is always less than the equilibrium level. At such a quantity, a transaction can always be made in which both buyer and seller benefit from the exchange of an additional unit of output. A market in equilibrium is said to be efficient, or Pareto efficient, meaning that no reallocation is possible that will benefit some people without harming others.

Total economic surplus in a market is maximized when exchange occurs at the equilibrium price. But the fact that equilibrium is "efficient" in this sense does not mean that it is "good." All markets can be in equilibrium, yet many people may lack sufficient income to buy even basic goods and services. Still, permitting markets to reach equilibrium is important, because when economic surplus is maximized, it is possible to pursue every goal more fully.

CHAPTER 7 EFFICIENCY AND EXCHANGE

THE COST OF PREVENTING PRICE ADJUSTMENTS

PRICE CEILINGS

During 1979, an interruption in oil supplies from the Middle East caused the price of home heating oil to rise by more than 100 percent. Concern about the hardship this sudden price increase would impose on poor families in northern states led the government to impose a price ceiling in the market for home heating oil. This price ceiling prohibited sellers from charging more than a specified amount for heating oil.

The following example illustrates why imposing a price ceiling on heating oil, though well intended, was a bad idea.

EXAMPLE 7.1

How much waste does a price ceiling on heating oil cause?

Suppose the demand and supply curves for home heating oil are as shown in Figure 7.4, in which the equilibrium price is $1.40 per gallon. And suppose that at that price, many poor families cannot heat their homes adequately. Out of concern for the poor, legislators pass a law setting the maximum price at $1 per gallon. How much lost economic surplus does this policy cost society?

FIGURE 7.4
Economic Surplus in an Unregulated Market for Home Heating Oil.
For the supply and demand curves shown, the equilibrium price of home heating oil is $1.40 per gallon, and the equilibrium quantity is 3,000 gallons per day. Consumer surplus is the area of the upper shaded triangle ($900 per day). Producer surplus is the area of the lower shaded triangle (also $900 per day).

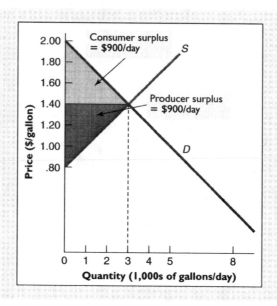

First, let's calculate total economic surplus without price controls. If this market is not regulated, 3,000 gallons per day will be sold at a price of $1.40 per gallon. In Figure 7.4, the economic surplus received by buyers is the area of the upper shaded triangle. Since the height of this triangle is $0.60 per gallon, and its base is 3,000 gallons per day, its area is equal to (1/2)(3,000 gallons/day)($0.60/gallon) = $900 per day. The economic surplus received by producers is the area of the lower shaded triangle. Since this triangle also has an area of $900 per day, total economic surplus in this market will be $1,800 per day.

If the price of heating oil is prevented from rising above $1 per gallon, only 1,000 gallons per day will be sold, and the total economic surplus will be reduced by the area of the lined triangle shown in Figure 7.5. Since the height of this triangle is $0.80 per gallon, and its base is 2,000 gallons per day, its area is (1/2)(2,000 gallons/day)($0.80/gallon) = $800 per day. Producer surplus falls from

THE COST OF PREVENTING PRICE ADJUSTMENTS

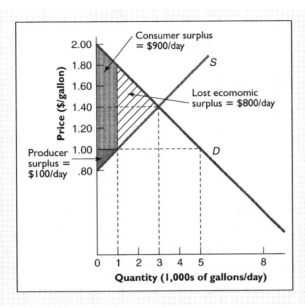

FIGURE 7.5
The Waste Caused by Price Controls.
By limiting output in the home heating oil market to 1,000 gallons per day, price controls cause a loss in economic surplus of $800 per day (area of the lined triangle).

$900 per day in the unregulated market to the area of the lower shaded triangle, or $(1/2)(1,000 \text{ gallons/day})(\$0.20/\text{gallon}) = \$100$ per day, which is a loss of $800 per day. Thus the loss in total economic surplus is equal to the loss in producer surplus, which means that the new consumer surplus must be the same as the original consumer surplus. To verify this, note that consumer surplus with the price ceiling is the area of the upper shaded figure, which is again $900 per day. (Hint: To compute this area, first split the figure into a rectangle and a triangle.) By preventing the home heating oil market from reaching equilibrium, price controls waste $800 of producer surplus per day without creating any additional surplus for consumers!

EXERCISE 7.2

In Example 7.1, by how much would total economic surplus have been reduced if the price ceiling had been set not at $1 but at $1.20 per gallon?

For several reasons the reduction in total economic surplus shown in Figure 7.5 is a conservative estimate of the waste caused by attempts to hold price below its equilibrium level. For one thing, the analysis assumes that each of the 1,000 gallons per day that are sold in this market will end up in the hands of the consumers who value them most—in the diagram, those whose reservation prices are above $1.80 per gallon. But since any buyer whose reservation price is above $1 per gallon will want to buy at the ceiling price, much of the oil actually sold is likely to go to buyers whose reservation prices are below $1.80. Suppose, for example, that a buyer whose reservation price was $1.50 per gallon made it into the line outside a heating oil supplier just ahead of a buyer whose reservation price was $1.90 per gallon. If each buyer had a 20-gallon tank to fill, and if the first buyer got the last of the day's available oil, then total surplus would be smaller by $8 that day than if the oil had gone to the second buyer.

A second reason that the reduction in surplus shown in Figure 7.5 is likely to be an underestimate is that shortages typically prompt buyers to take costly actions to enhance their chances of being served. For example, if the heating oil distributor begins selling its available supplies at 6:00 A.M., many buyers may arrive several hours early to ensure a place near the front of the line. Yet when all buyers incur the cost of arriving earlier, no one gets any more oil than before.

Notwithstanding the fact that price ceilings reduce total economic surplus, their defenders might argue that controls are justified because they enable at least some low-income families to buy heating oil at affordable prices. Yes, but the same objective could have been accomplished in a much less costly way—namely, by giving the poor more income with which to buy heating oil.

It may seem natural to wonder whether the poor, who have limited political power, can really hope to receive income transfers that would enable them to heat their homes. On reflection, the answer to this question would seem to be yes, *if the alternative is to impose price controls that would be even more costly than the income transfers.* After all, the price ceiling as implemented ends up costing heating oil sellers $800 per day in lost economic surplus. So they ought to be willing to pay some amount less than $800 a day in additional taxes in order to escape the burden of controls. The additional tax revenue could finance income transfers that would be far more beneficial to the poor than price controls.

This point is so important, and so often misunderstood by voters and policymakers, that we will emphasize it by putting it another way. Think of the economic surplus from a market as a pie to be divided among the various market participants. Figure 7.6(a) represents the $1,000 per day of total economic surplus available to participants in the home heating oil market when the government limits the price of oil to $1 per gallon. We divided this pie into two slices, labeled *R* and *P*, to denote the surpluses received by rich and poor participants. Figure 7.6(b) represents the $1,800 per day of total economic surplus available when the price of home heating oil is free to reach its equilibrium level. This pie is divided among rich and poor participants in the same proportion as the pie in the left panel.

The important point to notice is this: *Because the pie on the right side is larger, both rich and poor participants in the home heating oil market can get a bigger slice of the pie than they would have had under price controls.* Rather than tinker with the market price of oil, it is in everyone's interest to simply transfer additional income to the poor.

FIGURE 7.6
When the Pie Is Larger, Everyone Can Have a Bigger Slice.
Any policy that reduces total economic surplus is a missed opportunity to make everyone better off.

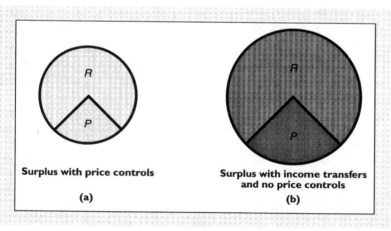

Surplus with price controls

(a)

Surplus with income transfers and no price controls

(b)

Supporters of price controls may object that income transfers to the poor might weaken people's incentive to work, and thus might prove extremely costly in the long run. Difficult issues do indeed arise in the design of programs for transferring income to the poor—issues we will consider in some detail in later chapters. But for now, suffice it to say that ways exist to transfer income without undermining work incentives significantly. One such method is the "earned-income tax credit," a program that supplements the wages of low-income workers. Given such programs, transferring income to the poor will always be more efficient than trying to boost their living standard through price controls.

PRICE SUBSIDIES

Sometimes governments try to assist low-income consumers by subsidizing the prices of "essential" goods and services. France and Russia, for example, have taken this approach at various points by subsidizing the price of bread. But as the following example illustrates, such subsidies are like price ceilings in that they reduce total economic surplus.

By how much do subsidies reduce total economic surplus in the market for bread?

EXAMPLE 7.2

A small island nation imports bread for its population at the world price of $2 per loaf. If the domestic demand curve for bread is as shown in Figure 7.7, by how much will total economic surplus decline in this market if the government provides a $1 per loaf subsidy?

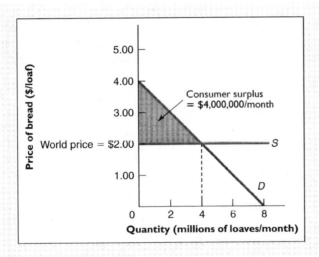

FIGURE 7.7
Economic Surplus in a Bread Market without Subsidy.
For the demand curve shown, consumer surplus (area of the shaded triangle) is $4,000,000. This amount is equal to total economic surplus in the domestic bread market, since no bread is produced domestically.

With no subsidy, the equilibrium price of bread in this market would be the world price of $2 per loaf, and the equilibrium quantity would be 4,000,000 loaves per month. The shaded triangle in Figure 7.7 represents consumer economic surplus for buyers in the domestic bread market. The height of this triangle is $2 per loaf, and its base is 4,000,000 loaves per month, so its area is equal to (1/2)(4,000,000 loaves/month)($2/loaf) = $4,000,000 per month. Because the country can import as much bread as it wishes at the world price of $2 per loaf, supply is perfectly elastic in this market. Because the marginal cost of each loaf of bread to sellers is exactly the same as the price buyers pay, producer surplus in this market is zero. So total economic surplus is exactly equal to consumer surplus, which, again, is $4,000,000 per month.

Now suppose that the government administers its $1 per loaf subsidy program by purchasing bread in the world market at $2 per loaf and reselling it in the domestic market for only $1 per loaf. At the new lower price buyers will now consume not 4,000,000 loaves per month but 6,000,000. Consumer surplus for buyers in the bread market is now the area of the larger shaded triangle in Figure 7.8: (1/2)($3/loaf) (6,000,000 loaves/month) = $9,000,000 per month, or $5,000,000 per month more than before. The catch is that the subsidy wasn't free. Its cost, which must be borne by taxpayers, is ($1/loaf)(6,000,000 loaves/month) = $6,000,000 per month. So even though consumer surplus in the bread market is larger than before, the net effect of the subsidy program is actually to reduce total economic surplus by $1,000,000 per month.

Frank–Bernanke:
Principles of
Microeconomics, Second
Edition

II. Competition and the
Invisible Hand

7. Efficiency and Exchange

© The McGraw–Hill
Companies, 2004

FIGURE 7.8
The Reduction in Economic Surplus from a Subsidy.
Since the marginal cost of bread is $2 per loaf, total economic surplus is maximized at 4,000,000 loaves per month, the quantity for which the marginal buyer's reservation price is equal to marginal cost. The reduction in economic surplus from consuming an additional 2,000,000 loaves per month is $1,000,000 per month, the area of the smaller shaded triangle.

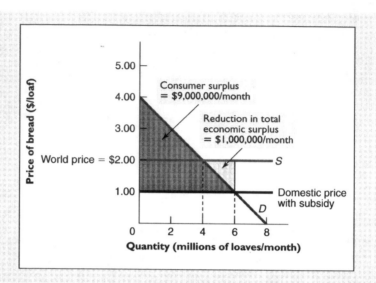

Another way to see why the subsidy reduces total economic surplus by that amount is to note that total economic surplus is maximized at 4,000,000 loaves per month, the quantity for which the marginal buyer's reservation price is equal to marginal cost, and that the subsidy induces additional consumption of 2,000,000 loaves per month. Each additional loaf has a marginal cost of $2 but is worth less than that to the buyer (as indicated by the fact that the vertical coordinate of the demand curve lies below $2 for consumption beyond 4,000,000). As monthly consumption expands from 4,000,000 to 6,000,000 loaves per month, the cumulative difference between the marginal cost of bread and its value to buyers is the area of the smaller shaded triangle in Figure 7.8, which is $1,000,000 per month.

This reduction in economic surplus constitutes pure waste—no different, from the perspective of participants in this market, than if someone had siphoned that much cash out of their bank accounts each month and thrown it into a bonfire.

EXERCISE 7.3

How much total economic surplus would have been lost if the bread subsidy been set at $0.50 per loaf instead of $1.00?

Compared to a bread subsidy, a much better policy would be to give low-income people some additional income and then let them bid for bread on the open market. Subsidy advocates who complain that taxpayers would be unwilling to give low-income people income transfers must be asked to explain why people would be willing to tolerate subsidies, which are so much *more* costly than income transfers. Logically, if voters are willing to support subsidies, they should be even more eager to support income transfers to low-income persons.

This is not to say that the poor reap no benefit at all from bread subsidies. Since they get to buy bread at lower prices and since the subsidy program is financed by taxes collected primarily from middle- and upper-income families, poor families probably come out ahead on balance. *The point is that for the same expense, we could do much more to help the poor.* Their problem is that they have too little income. The simplest and best solution is not to try to peg the prices of the goods they and others buy below equilibrium levels, but rather to give them some additional money.

THE COST OF PREVENTING PRICE ADJUSTMENTS

FIRST-COME, FIRST-SERVED POLICIES

Governments are not the only institutions that attempt to promote social goals by preventing markets from reaching equilibrium. Some universities, for example, attempt to protect access by low-income students to concerts and sporting events by selling a limited number of tickets below the market-clearing price on a first-come, first-served basis.

The commercial airline industry was an early proponent of the use of the first-come, first-served allocation method, which it employed to ration seats on overbooked flights. Throughout the industry's history, most airlines have routinely accepted more reservations for their flights than there are seats on those flights. Most of the time, this practice causes no difficulty, because many reservation holders don't show up to claim their seats. Indeed, if airlines did not overbook their flights, most flights would take off with many more empty seats, forcing airlines to charge higher ticket prices to cover their costs.

The only real difficulty is that every so often, more people actually do show up for a flight than there are seats on the plane. Until the late 1970s, airlines dealt with this problem by boarding passengers on a first-come, first-served basis. For example, if 120 people showed up for a flight with 110 seats, the last 10 to arrive were "bumped," or forced to wait for the next available flight.

The bumped passengers often complained bitterly, and no wonder, since many of them ended up missing important business meetings or family events. As the following example illustrates, there was fortunately a simple solution to this problem.

Why does no one complain any longer about being bumped from an overbooked flight?

In 1978, airlines abandoned their first-come, first-served policy in favor of a new procedure. Since then, their practice has been to solicit volunteers to give up their seats on oversold flights in return for a cash payment or free ticket. Now, the only people who give up their seats are those who volunteer to do so in return for compensation. And hence the complete disappearance of complaints about being bumped from overbooked flights.

Which of the two policies—first-come, first-served or compensation for volunteers—is more efficient? The difficulty with the first-come, first-served policy is that it gives little weight to the interests of passengers with pressing reasons for arriving at their destination on time. Such passengers can sometimes avoid losing their seats by showing up early, but passengers coming in on connecting flights often cannot control when they arrive. And the cost of showing up early is likely to be highest for precisely those people who place the highest value on not missing a flight (such as business executives, whose opportunity cost of waiting in airports is high).

For the sake of illustration, suppose that 37 people show up for a flight with only 33 seats. One way or another, four people will have to wait for another flight. Suppose we ask each of them "What is the most you would be willing to pay to fly now rather than wait?" Typically, different passengers will have different reservation prices for avoiding the wait. Suppose that the person who is most willing to pay would pay up to $60 rather than miss the flight; that the person second-most willing to pay would pay up to $59; that the person third-most willing to pay would pay up to $58; and so on. In that case, the person with the smallest reservation price for avoiding the wait would have a reservation price of $24. For the entire group of 37 passengers, the average reservation price for avoiding the wait would be ($60 + $59 + $58 + · · · + $24)/37 = $42.

Given the difficulty of controlling airport arrival times, the passengers who get bumped under the first-come, first-served policy are not likely to differ systematically from others with respect to their reservation price for not missing the flight. On average, then, the total cost imposed on the four bumped passengers

ECONOMIC NATURALIST 7.1

Why are passenger complaints about overbooked flights a thing of the past?

Frank–Bernanke:
Principles of
Microeconomics, Second
Edition

II. Competition and the
Invisible Hand

7. Efficiency and Exchange

© The McGraw–Hill
Companies, 2004

CHAPTER 7   EFFICIENCY AND EXCHANGE

would be four times the average reservation price of $42, or $168. As far as those four passengers are concerned, that total is a pure loss of consumer surplus.

How does this cost compare with the cost imposed on bumped passengers when the airline compensates volunteers? Suppose the airline solicits volunteers by conducting an informal auction, increasing its cash compensation offer by $1 increments until it has the desired number of volunteers. As the incentive to stay behind rises, more people will volunteer; those whose reservation prices are the lowest will volunteer first. In this example, offers below $24 would generate no volunteers. An offer of $24 would generate one volunteer; an offer of $25 would generate two volunteers; and so on. A compensation payment of $27 would generate the necessary four volunteers.

What is the net cost of the compensation policy? While the airline pays out (4)($27) = $108 in compensation payments, not all that amount represents lost economic surplus. Thus the passenger whose reservation price for missing the flight is $24 receives a net gain in economic surplus of $3—the difference between the $27 compensation payment and her $24 reservation price. Similarly, those whose reservation prices were $25 and $26 receive a net gain of $2 and $1, respectively. The cost of the cash compensation policy net of these gains is thus $108 − $6 = $102, or $66 less than under the first-come, first-served policy.

The compensation policy is more efficient than the first-come, first-served policy because it establishes a market for a scarce resource that would otherwise be allocated by nonmarket means. Figure 7.9 shows the supply and demand curves for seats under the compensation policy. In this market, the equilibrium price of not having to wait is $27. People who choose not to volunteer at that price incur an opportunity cost of $27 in order not to miss the flight. The four people who do volunteer accept $27 as ample compensation—indeed, more than ample for three of them.

FIGURE 7.9

Equilibrium in the Market for Seats on Oversold Flights.

The demand curve for remaining on the flight is generated by plotting the reservation prices in descending order. The equilibrium compensation payment for volunteers who give up their seats is $27— the price at which 4 passengers volunteer to wait and the remaining 33 choose not to wait.

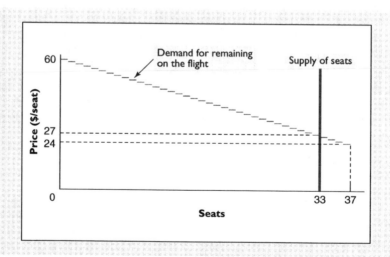

An interesting footnote to this example is that the airlines' policy change evoked a fierce protest from the Aviation Consumer Action Project (ACAP), a group that portrayed itself as a watchdog for the interests of airline passengers. ACAP's concern was that the shift to a system of compensation payments would mean that poor people would most often end up waiting for the next flight. This was a curious objection, for several reasons. Although the people who volunteer to wait in return for a compensation payment probably have lower incomes, on average, than those who don't volunteer, the income distributions of the two groups overlap considerably. Many financially comfortable persons with no pressing appointments will gladly volunteer to wait, while many people with lower

THE COST OF PREVENTING PRICE ADJUSTMENTS

incomes will choose not to. But more important, the previous policy of first-come, first-served was manifestly less attractive to the poor than the new policy. After all, passengers give up their seats under the volunteer policy only when they find the payment offered sufficient to compensate for the inconvenience of waiting. We may suspect that few poor persons would be grateful if ACAP had succeeded in persuading the government to block the switch to compensation payments.

How should a tennis pro handle the overbooking problem?

EXAMPLE 7.3

Anticipating a high proportion of no-shows, a tennis pro routinely books five people for each of his group lesson slots, even though he is able to teach only three people at a time. One day, all five people show up for their lessons at 10 A.M., the first lesson slot of the morning. Their respective arrival times and the maximum amounts each would be willing to pay to avoid postponing his or her lesson are as given in the table.

Player	Arrival time	Reservation price
Ann	9:50 A.M.	$ 4
Bill	9:52 A.M.	3
Carrie	9:55 A.M.	6
Dana	9:56 A.M.	10
Earl	9:59 A.M.	3

If the tennis pro accommodates the players on a first-come, first-served basis, by how much will total economic surplus be smaller than if he had offered cash compensation to induce two volunteers to reschedule? Which system is more efficient?

The result of using a first-come, first-served policy will be that Dana and Earl, the last two to arrive, will have to postpone their lessons. Since the cost of waiting is $10 for Dana and $3 for Earl, the total cost of the first-come, first-served policy is $13.

Suppose that the pro had instead offered cash compensation payments to elicit volunteers. If he offered a payment of $3, both Bill and Earl would be willing to wait. The total cost of the cash compensation policy would therefore be only $6, or $7 less than under the first-come, first-served policy. So the cash compensation policy is more efficient.

You might feel tempted to ask why the tennis pro would bother to offer cash compensation when he has the option of saving the $6 by continuing with his current policy of first-come, first-served. Or you might wonder why an airline would bother to offer cash compensation to elicit volunteers to wait for the next flight. But we know that it is possible for *everyone* to do better under an efficient policy than under an inefficient one. (When the pie is bigger, everyone can have a larger slice.) The following exercise asks you to design such a transaction for the tennis-lesson example.

EXERCISE 7.4

Describe a set of cash transfers in Example 7.3 that would make each of the five students and the tennis pro better off than under the first-come, first-served policy. (Hint: Imagine that the tennis pro tells his students that he will stick with first-come, first served unless they agree to contribute to the compensation pool as he requests.)

In practice, transactions like the one called for in Exercise 7.4 would be cumbersome to administer. Typically, the seller is in a position to solve such problems

| Frank–Bernanke: Principles of Microeconomics, Second Edition | II. Competition and the Invisible Hand | 7. Efficiency and Exchange | | © The McGraw–Hill Companies, 2004 |

more easily by offering cash payments to elicit volunteers, and then financing those cash payments by charging slightly higher prices. Buyers, for their part, are willing to pay the higher prices because they value the seller's promise not to cancel their reservations without compensation.

 RECAP **THE COST OF BLOCKING PRICE ADJUSTMENTS**

In an effort to increase the economic welfare of disadvantaged consumers, governments often implement policies that attempt to prevent markets from reaching equilibrium. Price ceilings and subsidies attempt to make housing and other basic goods more affordable for poor families. Private organizations also implement policies that prevent markets from reaching equilibrium, such as allocation on a first-come, first-served basis. Such policies always reduce total economic surplus relative to the alternative of letting prices seek their equilibrium levels. It is always possible to design alternative policies under which rich and poor alike fare better.

MARGINAL COST PRICING OF PUBLIC SERVICES

The largest possible total economic surplus is achieved in private markets when goods are exchanged at equilibrium prices, where the value of the last unit to the buyer is exactly equal to the seller's marginal cost of producing it. Suppose the government has decided to become the provider of a good or service, such as water or electricity. If the government's goal is to maximize the resulting total economic surplus, how much should it charge its customers? The theory of market exchange, normally applied to perfectly competitive firms that can sell any quantity they choose at a constant market price, helps to answer this question. Consider the following example, in which a local government supplies water to its residents.

EXAMPLE 7.4

What is the marginal cost of water in Gainesville?

The municipal water supply company in Gainesville, Florida, has three potential sources of water: an underground spring, a nearby lake, and the Atlantic Ocean. The spring can supply up to 1 million gallons per day at a cost of 0.2 cents per gallon. The lake can supply an additional 2 million gallons per day at a cost of 0.8 cents per gallon. Additional water must be distilled from the ocean

FIGURE 7.10
The Marginal Cost Curve for Water.
The current marginal cost of water is the cost of producing an extra gallon by means of the most expensive production source currently in use.

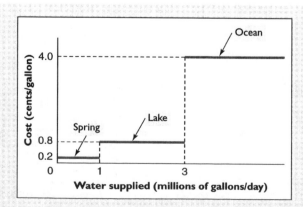

at a cost of 4.0 cents per gallon. Draw the marginal cost curve for water in Gainesville.

The low-hanging-fruit principle tells us that the city will use the cheapest source of water first (the spring). Only when the quantity demanded exceeds the spring's capacity will the city turn to the next least expensive source, the lake; and only when the lake's capacity is exhausted will the city supply water from the ocean. The marginal cost curve will thus be as shown in Figure 7.10.

As the next example illustrates, total economic surplus is maximized when the government charges each customer exactly the marginal cost of the water he or she consumes.

How much should the government charge for water?

EXAMPLE 7.5

In the preceding example, suppose that if the price of water were 4.0 cents per gallon, citizens of Gainesville would consume 4 million gallons per day. Given the marginal cost curve shown in Figure 7.10, how much should the city charge a citizen whose water comes from the underground spring? How much should it charge someone whose water comes from the lake?

The citizens of Gainesville will enjoy the largest possible economic surplus if the price they pay for water exactly equals the marginal cost of providing it. Since the total amount of water demanded at 4.0 cents per gallon exceeds 3 million gallons per day, the city will have to supply at least some households with water distilled from the Atlantic Ocean, at a cost of 4.0 cents per gallon. At 4 million gallons per day, the marginal cost of water is thus 4.0 cents per gallon, and *this is true no matter where the water comes from.* As long as the city must get *some* of its water from the ocean, the marginal cost of water taken from the underground spring is also 4.0 cents per gallon. Water taken from the lake has a marginal cost of 4.0 cents per gallon as well.

This statement might seem to contradict the claim that water drawn from the spring costs only 0.2 cents per gallon, water drawn from the lake, only 0.8 cents per gallon. But there is no contradiction. To see why, ask yourself how much the city would save if a family that currently gets its water from the spring were to reduce its consumption by 1 gallon per day. The cutback would enable the city to divert that gallon of spring water to some other household that currently gets its water from the ocean, which in turn would reduce consumption of ocean water by 1 gallon. So if a family currently served by the spring were to reduce its daily consumption by 1 gallon, the cost savings would be exactly 4.0 cents. And that, by definition, is the marginal cost of water.

To encourage the efficient use of water, the city should charge every household 4.0 cents per gallon for all the water it consumes. Charging any household less than that would encourage households to use water whose marginal benefit is less than its marginal cost. For example, suppose the city charged households who get their water from the spring only 0.2 cents per gallon. Those households would then expand their use of water until the benefit they received from the last gallon used equaled 0.2 cents. Because that gallon could have been used to serve someone who is currently using water distilled from the ocean, for whom the value of the marginal gallon is 4 cents, its use would entail a loss in economic surplus of 3.8 cents.

EXERCISE 7.5

Suppose that at a price of 0.8 cents per gallon of water, the citizens of Gainesville would consume a total of only 2 million gallons per day. If the marginal cost of water is as shown in Figure 7.10, how much should the city charge for water? Should that same charge apply to people who get their water from the spring?

Frank–Bernanke:
Principles of
Microeconomics, Second
Edition

II. Competition and the
Invisible Hand

7. Efficiency and Exchange

© The McGraw–Hill
Companies, 2004

 RECAP   **MARGINAL COST PRICING OF PUBLIC SERVICES**

When a good is provided by a public utility from several sources, the marginal cost of serving a customer is the cost associated with the least efficient source in use. A public utility should set price equal to marginal cost if its goal is to maximizes economic surplus.

TAXES AND EFFICIENCY

WHO PAYS A TAX IMPOSED ON SELLERS OF A GOOD?

Politicians of all stripes seem loath to propose new taxes. But when additional public revenue must be raised, most seem to feel more comfortable proposing taxes paid by sellers than taxes paid by consumers. When pressed to explain why, many respond that businesses can more easily afford to pay extra taxes. Yet the burden of a tax collected from the sellers of a good need not fall exclusively on sellers. Suppose, for example, that a tax of $1 per pound is collected from potato farmers in the market whose demand and supply curves are shown as D and S in Figure 7.11.

FIGURE 7.11

The Effect of a Tax on the Equilibrium Quantity and Price of Potatoes.
With no tax, 3 million pounds of potatoes are sold each month at a price of $3 per pound. With a tax of $1 per pound collected from sellers, consumers end up paying $3.50 per pound (including tax), while sellers receive only $2.50 per pound (net of tax). Equilibrium quantity falls from 3 million pounds per month to 2.5 million.

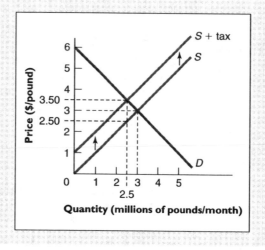

In this market the initial equilibrium price and quantity are $3 per pound and 3 million pounds per month, respectively. From the farmers' perspective, the imposition of a tax of $1 per pound is essentially the same as a $1 increase in the marginal cost of producing each pound of potatoes, and hence the tax results in an upward shift in the supply curve by $1 per pound.

As shown in Figure 7.11, the new equilibrium price (including the tax) will be $3.50, and the new equilibrium quantity will be 2.5 million pounds per month. The net price per pound received by producers is one dollar less than the price paid by the consumer, or $2.50. Even though the tax was collected entirely from potato sellers, the burden of the tax fell on both buyers and sellers—on buyers, because they pay $0.50 per pound more than before the tax; and on sellers, because they receive $0.50 per pound less than before the tax.

The burden of the tax need not fall equally on buyers and sellers, as in the illustration just discussed. Indeed, as the following example illustrates, a tax levied on sellers may end up being paid entirely by buyers.

How will a tax on cars affect their prices in the long run?

ECONOMIC NATURALIST 7.2

Suppose that, given sufficient time, all the inputs required to produce cars can be acquired in unlimited quantities at fixed market prices. If the inputs required to produce each car cost $20,000, how will the long-run equilibrium price of automobiles be affected if a tax of $100 per car is levied on manufacturers?

The fact that all the inputs needed to build cars can be acquired at constant prices suggests that the long-run marginal cost of making cars is constant—or, in other words, that the long-run supply curve of cars is horizontal at $20,000 per car. A tax of $100 per car effectively raises marginal cost by $100 per car, and thus shifts the supply curve upward by exactly $100. If the demand curve for cars is as shown by curve D in Figure 7.12, the effect is to raise the equilibrium price of cars by exactly $100, to $20,100. The equilibrium quantity of cars falls from 2 million per month to 1.9 million.

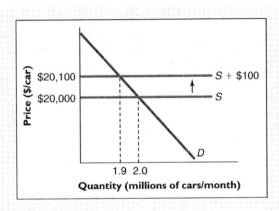

FIGURE 7.12
The Effect of a Tax on Sellers of a Good with Infinite Price Elasticity of Supply.
When the supply curve for a good is perfectly elastic, the burden of a tax collected from sellers falls entirely on buyers.

Although the long-run supply curve shown in Figure 7.12 is in one sense an extreme case (since its price elasticity is infinite), it is by no means an unrepresentative one. For as we discussed in Chapter 4, the long-run supply curve will tend to be horizontal when it is possible to acquire more of all the necessary inputs at constant prices. As a first approximation, this can be accomplished for many—perhaps even most—goods and services in a typical economy.

For goods with perfectly elastic supply curves, the entire burden of any tax is borne by the buyer.[1] That is, the increase in the equilibrium price is exactly equal to the tax. For this empirically relevant case, then, there is special irony in the common political practice of justifying taxes on business by saying that businesses have greater ability to pay than consumers.

HOW A TAX COLLECTED FROM A SELLER AFFECTS ECONOMIC SURPLUS

We saw earlier that perfectly competitive markets distribute goods and services efficiently if demand curves reflect all relevant benefits and supply curves reflect all relevant costs. If a tax is imposed on sellers in such a market, will the new market equilibrium still be efficient? Consider again the potato market discussed earlier, whose supply and demand curves are reproduced in Figure 7.13. In the absence of a tax, 3 million pounds of potatoes a month would be sold in this market at a price of $3 per pound, and the resulting total economic surplus would be $9 million per month (the area of the shaded triangle).

---

[1] In the example given, the tax was collected from sellers. If you go on to take intermediate microeconomics, you will see that the same conclusions apply when a tax is collected from buyers.

CHAPTER 7 EFFICIENCY AND EXCHANGE

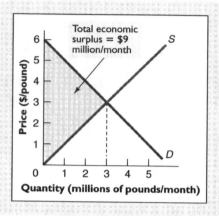

FIGURE 7.13
The Market for Potatoes without Taxes.
Without taxes, total surplus in the potato market equals the area of the shaded triangle, $9 million per month.

With a tax of $1 per pound collected from potato sellers, the new equilibrium price of potatoes would be $3.50 per pound (of which sellers receive $2.50, net of tax), and only 2.5 millions pounds of potatoes would be sold each month (see Figure 7.14). The total economic surplus reaped by buyers and sellers in the potato market would be the area of the shaded triangle shown in Figure 7.14, which is $6.25 million per month—or $2.75 million less than before.

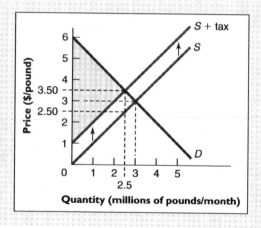

FIGURE 7.14
The Effect of a $1 per Pound Tax on Potatoes.
A $1 per pound tax on potatoes would cause an upward shift in the supply curve by $1. The sum of producer and consumer surplus would shrink to the area of the shaded triangle, $6.25 million per month.

This drop in surplus may sound like an enormous loss. But it is a misleading figure, because it fails to take account of the value of the additional tax revenue collected, which is equal to $2.5 million per month ($1 per pound on 2.5 million pounds of potatoes). If the government needs to collect no more than a given total amount of tax revenue in order to pay for the services it provides, then the potato tax revenue should enable it to reduce other taxes by $2.5 million per month. So although buyers and sellers lose $2.75 million per month in economic surplus from their participation in the potato market, they also enjoy a $2.5 million reduction in the other taxes they pay. On balance, then, the net reduction in total economic surplus is only $0.25 million.

Graphically, the loss in total economic surplus caused by the imposition of the tax can be shown as the small shaded triangle in Figure 7.15. This loss in surplus is often described as the **deadweight loss** from the tax.

Still, a loss in economic surplus, however small, is something people would prefer to avoid, and taxes like the one just described undoubtedly reduce economic surplus in the markets on which they are imposed. As Federal Reserve

deadweight loss the reduction in total economic surplus that results from the adoption of a policy

TAXES AND EFFICIENCY

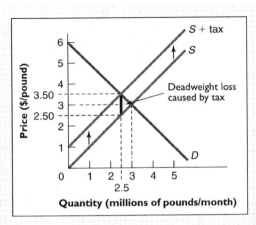

FIGURE 7.15

The Deadweight Loss Caused by a Tax.
For the market shown, the loss in economic surplus caused by a tax of $1 per pound of potatoes equals the area of the small shaded triangle, or $250,000 per month.

Board chairman Alan Greenspan remarked, "All taxes are a drag on economic growth. It's only a question of degree."[1]

A tax reduces economic surplus because it distorts the basic cost-benefit criterion that would ordinarily guide efficient decisions about production and consumption. In the example just considered, the cost-benefit principle tells us that we should expand potato production up to the point at which the benefit of the last pound of potatoes consumed (as measured by what buyers are willing to pay for it) equals the cost of producing it (as measured by the producer's marginal cost). That condition was satisfied in the potato market before the tax, but it is not satisfied once the tax is imposed. In Figure 7.15, for example, note that when potato consumption is 2.5 million pounds per month, the value of an additional pound of potatoes to consumers is $3.50, whereas the cost to producers is only $2.50, not including the tax. (The cost to producers, including the tax, is $3.50 per pound, but again we note that this tax is not a cost to society as a whole because it offsets other taxes that would otherwise have to be collected.)

Is a tax on potatoes necessarily "bad"? (When economists say that a policy, such as a tax, is "bad," they mean that it lowers total economic surplus.) To answer this question, we must first identify the best alternative to taxing potatoes. You may be tempted to say "Don't tax anything at all!" On a moment's reflection, however, you will realize that this is surely not the best option. After all, a country that taxed nothing could not pay for even the most minimal public services, such as road maintenance, fire protection, and national defense. And a country without at least minimal defense capability could not hope to maintain its independence for long. (We will consider why we often empower government to provide public goods in Chapter 15.) On balance, if taxing potatoes were the best way to avoid doing without highly valued public services, then a small deadweight loss in the potato market would be a small price indeed.

So the real question is whether there are other things we could tax that would be better than taxing potatoes. The problem with a tax on any activity is that if market incentives encourage people to pursue the "right" amount of the activity (that is, the surplus-maximizing amount), then a tax will encourage them to pursue too little of it. As economists have long recognized, this observation suggests that taxes will cause smaller deadweight losses if they are imposed on goods for which the equilibrium quantity is not highly sensitive to changes in production costs.

[1]*The Wall Street Journal,* March 26, 1997, p. A1.

Frank–Bernanke:
Principles of
Microeconomics, Second
Edition

II. Competition and the
Invisible Hand

7. Efficiency and Exchange

© The McGraw–Hill
Companies, 2004

CHAPTER 7   EFFICIENCY AND EXCHANGE

TAXES, ELASTICITY, AND EFFICIENCY

Suppose the government put a tax of 50 cents per pound on table salt. How would this affect the amount of salt you and others use? In Chapter 4 we saw that the demand for salt is highly inelastic with respect to price, because salt has few substitutes and occupies only a minuscule share in most family budgets. Because the imposition of a tax on table salt would not result in a significant reduction in the amount of it consumed, the deadweight loss from this tax would be relatively small. More generally, the deadweight loss from a per-unit tax imposed on the seller of a good will be smaller the smaller is the price elasticity of demand for the good.

Figure 7.16 illustrates how the deadweight loss from a tax declines as the demand for a good becomes less elastic with respect to price. In both (a) and (b), the original supply and demand curves yield an equilibrium price of $2 per unit and an equilibrium quantity of 24 units per day. The deadweight loss from a tax of $1 per unit imposed on the good shown in Figure 7.16(a) is the area of the shaded triangle in (a), which is $2.50 per day. The demand curve in Figure 7.16(b), D_2, is less elastic at the equilibrium price of $2 than the demand curve in (a), D_1 [this follows from the fact that P/Q is the same in both cases, whereas 1/slope is smaller in (b)]. The deadweight loss from the same $1 per unit tax imposed on the good in Figure 7.16(b) is the area of the shaded triangle in (b), which is only $1.50 per day.

FIGURE 7.16

Elasticity of Demand and the Deadweight Loss from a Tax.

At the equilibrium price and quantity, price elasticity of demand is smaller for the good shown in (b) than for the good shown in (a). The area of the deadweight loss triangle in (b), $1.50 per day, is smaller than the area of the deadweight loss triangle in (a), $2.50 per day.

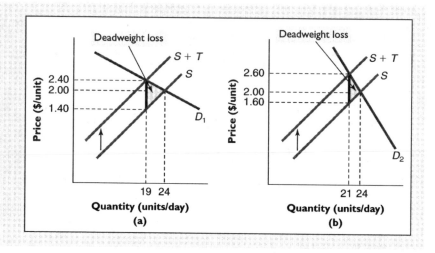

The reduction in equilibrium quantity that results from a tax on a good will also be smaller the smaller is the elasticity of supply of the good. In Figure 7.17, for example, the original supply and demand curves for the markets portrayed in each part yield an equilibrium price of $2 per unit and an equilibrium quantity of 72 units per day. The deadweight loss from a tax of $1 per unit imposed on the good shown in Figure 7.17(a) is the area of the shaded triangle in (a), which is $7.50 per day. The supply curve in Figure 7.17(b), S_2, is less elastic at the equilibrium price than the supply curve in the (a), S_1 [again because P/Q is the same in both cases, whereas 1/slope is smaller in (b)]. The deadweight loss from the same $1 per unit tax imposed on the good in Figure 7.17(b) is the area of the shaded triangle in (b), which is only $4.50 per day.

The deadweight loss from a tax imposed on a good whose supply curve is perfectly inelastic will be zero. This explains why many economists continue to favor the tax advocated by Henry George in the nineteenth century. George proposed that all taxes on labor and goods be abolished and replaced by a single tax on land. Such a tax, he argued, would cause no significant loss in economic surplus because the supply of land is almost perfectly inelastic.

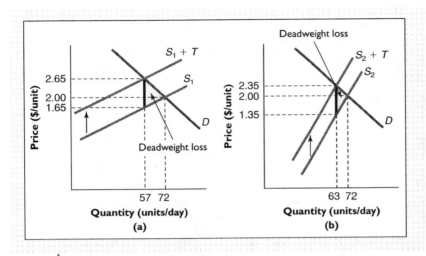

FIGURE 7.17
Elasticity of Supply and the Deadweight Loss from a Tax.
At the equilibrium price and quantity, price elasticity of supply is smaller for the good shown in (b) than for the good shown in (a). The area of the deadweight loss triangle in (b), $4.50 per day, is smaller than the area of the deadweight loss triangle in (a), $7.50 per day.

TAXES, EXTERNAL COSTS, AND EFFICIENCY

Even more attractive than taxing land, from an efficiency standpoint, is taxing activities that people tend to pursue to excess. We have mentioned activities that generate environmental pollution as one example; in later chapters we will discuss others. Whereas a tax on land does not reduce economic surplus, a tax on pollution can actually increase total economic surplus. Taxes on activities that cause harm to others kill two birds with one stone: They generate revenue to pay for useful public services and at the same time discourage people from pursuing the harmful activities. The notion that taxes always and everywhere constitute an obstacle to efficiency simply does not withstand careful scrutiny.

RECAP **TAXES AND EFFICIENCY**

A tax levied on the seller of a product has the same effect on equilibrium quantity and price as a rise in marginal cost equal to the amount of the tax. The burden of a tax imposed on sellers will generally be shared among both buyers and sellers. In the extreme case of a good whose elasticity of supply is infinite, the entire burden of the tax is borne by buyers.

A tax imposed on a product whose supply and demand curves embody all relevant costs and benefits associated with its production and use will result in a deadweight loss—a reduction in total economic surplus in the market for the taxed good. Such taxes may nonetheless be justified if the value of the public services financed by the tax outweighs this deadweight loss. In general, the deadweight loss from a tax on a good will be smaller the smaller are the good's price elasticities of supply and demand. Taxes on activities that generate harm to others may produce a net gain in economic surplus, even apart from the value of public services they finance.

■ SUMMARY ■

- When the supply and demand curves for a product capture all the relevant costs and benefits of producing that product, then market equilibrium for that product will be efficient. In

such a market, if price and quantity do not equal their equilibrium values, a transaction can be found that will make at least some people better off without harming others.

Frank–Bernanke:
Principles of
Microeconomics, Second
Edition

II. Competition and the
Invisible Hand

7. Efficiency and Exchange

© The McGraw–Hill
Companies, 2004

CHAPTER 7   EFFICIENCY AND EXCHANGE

- Total economic surplus is a measure of the amount by which participants in a market benefit by participating in it. It is the sum of total consumer surplus and total producer surplus in the market. One of the attractive properties of market equilibrium is that it maximizes the value of total economic surplus.

- Efficiency should not be equated with social justice. If we believe that the distribution of income among people is unjust, we won't like the results produced by the intersection of the supply and demand curves based on that income distribution, even though those results are efficient.

- Even so, we should always strive for efficiency because it enables us to achieve all our other goals to the fullest possible extent. Whenever a market is out of equilibrium, the economic pie can be made larger. And with a larger pie, everyone can have a larger slice.

- Regulations or policies that prevent markets from reaching equilibrium—such as price ceilings, price subsidies, and first-come, first-served allocation schemes—are often defended on the grounds that they help the poor. But such schemes reduce economic surplus, meaning that we can find alternatives under which both rich and poor would be better off. The main difficulty of the poor is that they have too little income. Rather than trying to control the prices of the goods they buy, we could do better by enacting policies that raise the incomes of the poor and then letting prices seek their equilibrium levels. Those who complain that the poor lack the political power to obtain such income transfers must explain why the poor have the power to impose regulations that are far more costly than income transfers.

- Even when a good is provided by a public utility rather than a private firm, the theory of competitive supply has important implications for how to provide the good most efficiently. The general rule is that a public utility maximizes economic surplus by charging its customers the marginal cost of the goods it provides.

- Critics often complain that taxes make the economy less efficient. A tax will indeed reduce economic surplus if the supply and demand curves in the market for the taxed good reflect all the relevant costs and benefits of its production and consumption. But this decline in surplus may be more than offset by the increase in economic surplus made possible by public goods financed with the proceeds of the tax. The best taxes are imposed on activities that would otherwise be pursued to excess, such as activities that generate environmental pollution. Such taxes not only do not reduce economic surplus; they actually increase it.

■ KEY TERMS ■

deadweight loss (184)

efficiency (or Pareto efficiency) (168)

■ REVIEW QUESTIONS ■

1. Why do economists emphasize efficiency as an important goal of public policy?

2. You are a senator considering how to vote on a policy that would increase the economic surplus of workers by $100 million per year but reduce the economic surplus of retirees by $1 million per year. What additional measure might you combine with the policy to ensure that the overall result is a better outcome for everyone?

3. Why does the loss in total economic surplus directly experienced by participants in the market for a good that is taxed overstate the overall loss in economic surplus that results from the tax?

4. Why is compensating volunteers to relinquish their seats on overbooked flights more efficient than a policy of first-come, first-served?

5. Why do price ceilings reduce economic surplus?

■ PROBLEMS ■

1. Suppose the weekly demand and supply curves for used DVDs in Lincoln, Nebraska, are as shown in the diagram. Calculate
   a. The weekly consumer surplus.
   b. The weekly producer surplus.
   c. The maximum weekly amount that producers and consumers in Lincoln would be willing to pay to be able to buy and sell used DVDs in any given week.

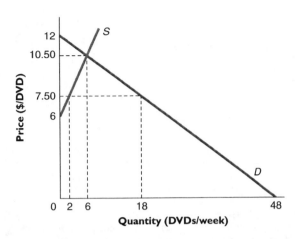

2. Refer to Problem 1. Suppose a coalition of students from Lincoln High School succeeds in persuading the local government to impose a price ceiling of $7.50 on used DVDs, on the grounds that local suppliers are taking advantage of teenagers by charging exorbitant prices.
   a. Calculate the weekly shortage of used DVDs that will result from this policy.
   b. Calculate the total economic surplus lost every week as a result of the price ceiling.

3. The Kubak crystal caves are renowned for their stalactites and stalagmites. The warden of the caves offers a tour each afternoon at 2 P.M. sharp. The caves can be shown to only four people per day without disturbing their fragile ecology. Occasionally, however, more than four people want to see the caves on the same day. The following table lists the people who wanted to see the caves on September 24, 2003, together with their respective times of arrival and reservation prices for taking the tour that day.

	Arrival time	Reservation price ($)
Herman	1:48	20
Jon	1:50	14
Kate	1:53	30
Jack	1:56	15
Penny	1:57	40
Fran	1:59	12
Faith	2:00	17

   a. If the tour is "free" and the warden operates it on a first-come, first-served basis, what will the total consumer surplus be for the four people who get to go on the tour on that day?
   b. Suppose the warden solicits volunteers to postpone their tour by offering increasing amounts of cash compensation until only four people still wish to see the caves that day. If he gives each volunteer the same compensation payment, how much money will he have to offer to generate the required number of volunteers? What is the total economic surplus under this policy?
   c. Why is the compensation policy more efficient than the first-come, first-served policy?
   d. Describe a way of financing the warden's compensation payments that will make everyone, including the warden, either better off or no worse off than under the first-come, first-served approach.

4. Suppose the weekly demand for a certain good, in thousands of units, is given by the equation $P = 8 - Q$, and the weekly supply of the good is given by the equation $P = 2 + Q$, where P is the price in dollars.
   a. Calculate the total weekly economic surplus generated at the market equilibrium.

CHAPTER 7   EFFICIENCY AND EXCHANGE

    b. Suppose a per-unit tax of $2, to be collected from sellers, is imposed in this market. Calculate the direct loss in economic surplus experienced by participants in this market as a result of the tax.

    c. How much government revenue will this tax generate each week? If the revenue is used to offset other taxes paid by participants in this market, what will be their net reduction in total economic surplus?

5. Is a company's producer surplus the same as its profit? (Hint: A company's total cost is equal to the sum of all marginal costs incurred in producing its output, plus any fixed costs.)

6. In Charlotte, North Carolina, citizens can get their electric power from two sources: a hydroelectric generator and a coal-fired steam generator. The hydroelectric generator can supply up to 100 units of power per day at a constant marginal cost of 1 cent per unit. The steam generator can supply any additional power that is needed at a constant marginal cost of 10 cents per unit. When electricity costs 10 cents per unit, residents of Charlotte demand 200 units per day.

    a. Draw the marginal cost curve of electric power production in Charlotte.

    b. How much should the city charge for electric power? Explain. Should it charge the same price for a family whose power comes from the hydroelectric generator as it does for a family whose power comes from the steam generator?

7. The municipal water works of Cortland draws water from two sources, an underground spring and a nearby lake. Water from the spring costs 2 cents per 100 gallons to deliver, and the spring has a capacity of 1 million gallons per day. Water from the lake costs 4 cents per 100 gallons to deliver and is available in unlimited quantities. The demand for water in the summer months in Cortland is $P = 20 - 0.001Q$, where P is the price of water in cents per 100 gallons, and Q is quantity demanded in hundreds of gallons per day. The demand curve for water in the winter months is $P = 10 - 0.001Q$. If the water works wants to encourage efficient water use, how much should it charge for water in the summer months? In the winter months?

8.* Phil's demand curve for visits to the Gannett walk-in medical clinic is given by $P = 48 - 8Q$, where P is the price per visit in dollars and Q is the number of visits per semester. The marginal cost of providing medical services at Gannett is $24 per visit. Phil has a choice between two health policies, A and B. Both policies cover all the costs of any serious illness from which Phil might suffer. Policy A also covers the cost of visits to the walk-in clinic, whereas policy B does not. Thus if Phil chooses policy B, he must pay $24 per visit to the walk-in clinic.

    a. If the premiums the insurance company charges for policies A and B must cover their respective costs, by how much will the two premiums differ, and what will be the difference in Phil's total expenditure for medical care under the two policies?

    b. Which policy will Phil choose?

    c. What is the most Phil would be willing to pay for the right to continue buying that policy?

9.* The government of Islandia, a small island nation, imports heating oil at a price of $2 per gallon and makes it available to citizens at a price of $1 per gallon. If Islandians' demand curve for heating oil is given by $P = 6 - Q$, where P is the price per gallon in dollars and Q is the quantity in millions of gallons per year, how much economic surplus is lost as a result of the government's policy?

10.* Refer to Problem 9. Suppose each of the 1 million Islandian households has the same demand curve for heating oil.

    a. What is the household demand curve?

    b. How much consumer surplus would each household lose if it had to pay $2 per gallon instead of $1 per gallon for heating oil, assuming there were no other changes in the household budget?

    c. With the money saved by not subsidizing oil, by how much could the Islandian government afford to cut each family's annual taxes?

    d. If the government abandoned its oil subsidy and implemented the tax cut, by how much would each family be better off?

    e. How does the resulting total gain for the 1 million families compare with your calculation of the lost surplus in the Problem 9?

*Problems marked with an asterisk (*) are more difficult.

■ ANSWERS TO IN-CHAPTER EXERCISES ■

7.1 At a price of 50 cents per gallon, there is excess demand of 4,000 gallons per day. Suppose a seller produces an extra gallon of milk (marginal cost = 50 cents) and sells it to the buyer who values it most (reservation price = $2.50) for $1.50. Both buyer and seller will gain additional economic surplus of $1, and no other buyers or sellers will be hurt by the transaction.

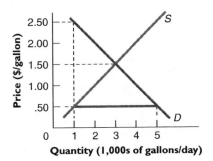

7.2 As shown in the accompanying diagram, the new loss in total economic surplus is $200 per day.

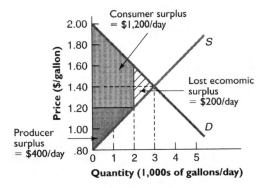

7.3 With a $0.50 per loaf subsidy, the new domestic price becomes $1.50 per loaf. The new lost surplus is the area of the small shaded triangle in the diagram: (1/2)($0.50/ loaf)(1,000,000 loaves/month) = $250,000 per month.

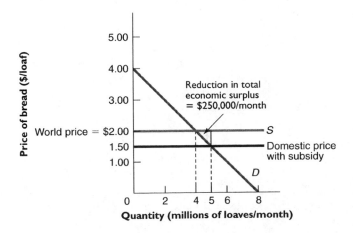

CHAPTER 7   EFFICIENCY AND EXCHANGE

7.4 Under first-come, first-served, Dana will have to postpone his lesson. Since Dana would be willing to pay up to $10 to avoid postponing it, he will be better off if the pro asks for a contribution of, say, $8, and then lets him take Bill's place at the scheduled time. The pro could then give $4 to Bill, which would make him $1 better off than if he had not postponed his lesson. The remaining $4 of Dana's payment could be distributed by giving $1 each to Ann, Carrie, Earl, and the tennis pro.

Player	Arrival time	Reservation price ($)
Ann	9:50 A.M.	4
Bill	9:52 A.M.	3
Carrie	9:55 A.M.	6
Dana	9:56 A.M.	10
Earl	9:59 A.M.	3

7.5 At a consumption level of 2 million gallons per day, the marginal source of water is the lake, which has a marginal cost of 0.8 cents per gallon. The city should charge everyone 0.8 cents per gallon, including those who get their water from the spring.

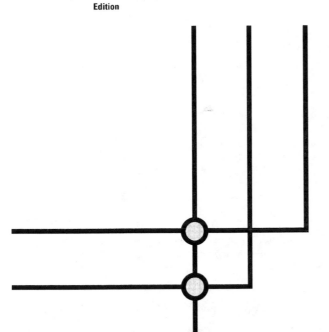

CHAPTER

11

EXTERNALITIES AND PROPERTY RIGHTS

A droll television ad for a British brand of pipe tobacco opens with a distinguished-looking gentleman sitting quietly on a park bench, smoking his pipe and reading a book of poetry. Before him lies a pond, unrippled except for a mother duck swimming peacefully with her ducklings. Suddenly a raucous group of teenage boys bursts onto the scene with a remote-controlled toy warship. Yelling and chortling, they launch their boat and maneuver it in aggressive pursuit of the terrified ducks.

Interrupted from his reverie, the gentleman looks up from his book and draws calmly on his pipe as he surveys the scene before him. He then reaches into his bag, pulls out a remote control of his own, and begins manipulating the joystick. The scene shifts underwater, where a miniature submarine rises from the depths of the pond. Once the boys' boat is in the sub's sights, the gentleman pushes a button on his remote control. Seconds later, the boat is blown to smithereens by a torpedo. The scene fades to a close-up of the tobacco company's label.

EXTERNAL COSTS AND BENEFITS

Many activities generate costs or benefits that accrue to people not directly involved in those activities. These effects are generally unintended. They are called **external costs** and **benefits**—**externalities,** for short. From the pipe smoker's point of view, the noise generated by the marauding boys was an external cost. And had others been disturbed by the boys' rowdiness, they may well have regarded the pipe smoker's retaliatory gesture as an external benefit.

CHAPTER II   EXTERNALITIES AND PROPERTY RIGHTS

external cost (or negative externality) a cost of an activity that falls on people other than those who pursue the activity

external benefit (or positive externality) a benefit of an activity received by people other than those who pursue the activity

externality an external cost or benefit of an activity

This chapter focuses on how externalities affect the allocation of resources. Adam Smith's theory of the invisible hand applies to an ideal marketplace in which externalities do not exist. In such situations, Smith argued, the self-interested actions of individuals would lead to socially efficient outcomes. We will see that when the parties affected by externalities can easily negotiate with one another, the invisible hand will still produce an efficient outcome.

But in many cases, such as the scene depicted in the tobacco ad, negotiation is impractical. In those cases, the self-serving actions of individuals simply will not lead to efficient outcomes. Because externalities are widespread, the attempt to forge solutions to the problems they cause is one of the most important rationales, not only for the existence of government but for a variety of other forms of collective action as well.

HOW EXTERNALITIES AFFECT RESOURCE ALLOCATION

The way in which externalities distort the allocation of resources can be seen clearly in the next several examples.

EXAMPLE 11.1

Does the honeybee keeper face the right incentives? (Part 1)

Phoebe earns her living as a keeper of honeybees. Her neighbors on all sides grow apples. Because bees pollinate apple trees as they forage for nectar, the more hives Phoebe keeps, the larger the harvests will be in the surrounding orchards. If Phoebe takes only her own costs and benefits into account in deciding how many hives to keep, will she keep the socially optimal number of hives?

For the orchard owners, Phoebe's hives constitute an external benefit, or a positive externality. If she takes only her own personal costs and benefits into account, she will add hives only until the added revenue she gets from the last hive just equals the cost of adding it. But since the orchard owners also benefit from additional hives, the total benefit of adding another hive at that point will be greater than its cost. Phoebe, then, will keep too few hives.

As we will discuss later in the chapter, problems like the one just discussed have several possible solutions. One is for orchard owners to pay beekeepers for keeping additional hives. But such solutions often require complex negotiations between the affected parties. For the moment, we assume that such negotiations are not practical.

EXAMPLE 11.2

Does the honeybee keeper face the right incentives? (Part 2)

As in Example 11.1, Phoebe earns her living as a keeper of honeybees. But now her neighbors are not apple growers but an elementary school and a nursing home. The more hives Phoebe keeps, the more students and nursing home residents will be stung by bees. If Phoebe takes only her own costs and benefits into account in deciding how many hives to keep, will she keep the socially optimal number of hives?

For the students and nursing home residents, Phoebe's hives constitute an external cost, or a negative externality. If she considers only her own costs and benefits in deciding how many hives to keep, she will continue to add hives until the added revenue from the last hive is just enough to cover its cost. But since Phoebe's neighbors also incur costs when she adds a hive, the benefit of the last hive at that point will be smaller than its cost. Phoebe, in other words, will keep too many hives.

Every activity involves costs and benefits. When all the relevant costs and benefits of an activity accrue directly to the person who carries it out—that is, when the activity generates no externalities—the level of the activity that is best for the individual will be best for society as a whole. But when an activity generates externalities, be they positive or negative, individual self-interest does not produce the best allocation of resources. Individuals who consider only their own costs and benefits will tend to engage too much in activities that generate negative externalities and too little in activities that generate positive externalities. When an activity generates both positive and negative externalities, private and social interests will coincide only in the unlikely event that the opposing effects offset one another exactly.

THE GRAPHICAL PORTRAYAL OF EXTERNALITIES

The effects of externalities on resource allocation can be portrayed graphically. Consider first the case of negative externalities. Figure 11.1(a) depicts the supply (Private *MC*) and demand curves for a product whose production involves no external costs or benefits. We may imagine, for example, that the energy that powers the factories in this market comes from nonpolluting hydroelectric generators. The resulting equilibrium price and quantity in the market for this product will then be socially optimal, for the reasons discussed in Chapters 3 and 7: The value to buyers of the last unit of the product consumed will be exactly equal to the marginal cost of producing it ($1,300 per ton in each case), leaving no further possible gains from exchange.

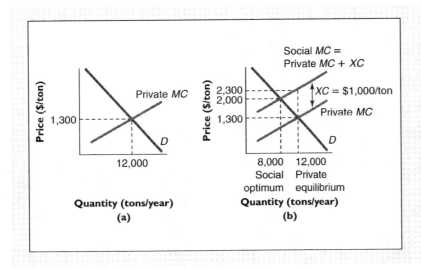

FIGURE 11.1

How External Costs Affect Resource Allocation.

When a market has no external costs or benefits (a), the resulting equilibrium quantity and price are socially optimal. By contrast, when production of a good is accompanied by an external cost (b), the market equilibrium price ($1,300 per ton) is too low, and the market equilibrium quantity (12,000 tons per year) is too high.

But now suppose that a protracted drought has eliminated hydroelectric power generation, forcing factories to rely instead on electric power produced by coal-burning generators. Now each ton of output produced is accompanied by an external pollution cost of *XC* = $1,000, as shown in Figure 11.1(b). Since the external pollution cost falls not on firm owners but on others who live downwind from their factories, Private *MC* is again the supply curve for this product, and its demand curve is again as before, so the equilibrium price and quantity will be exactly the same as in Figure 11.1(a), as determined by the intersection of the demand curve *(D)* and the supply curve (Private *MC*). But this time the private market equilibrium is not socially optimal. To see why, note that at $Q_{pvt} = 12,000$ tons per year, the value to consumers of the last unit of output produced was only $1,300 per ton, while the cost of producing that last unit (including the external cost) was $2,300 per ton. This means that society could gain additional economic surplus by producing fewer units of the product. Indeed, the same conclusion will continue to hold whenever the current output exceeds 8,000 tons per year,

CHAPTER 11 EXTERNALITIES AND PROPERTY RIGHTS

the output level at which the demand curve intersects Social MC. Social MC, the socially optimal supply curve of the product, is the result of adding the external cost, XC, to every value along Private MC. The socially optimal level of output of the good shown in Figure 11.1(b) is 8,000 tons per year, the level that exhausts all possibilities from exchange. For a good whose production generates external costs, the market equilibrium quantity will be higher than the socially optimal quantity.

What about a good whose production generates external benefits? In Figure 11.2, Private Demand is the demand curve for a product whose production generates an external benefit of XB per unit. The market equilibrium quantity of this good, Q_{pvt}, is the output level at which Private Demand intersects the supply curve of the product (MC). This time market equilibrium quantity is smaller than the socially optimal level, denoted Q_{soc}. Q_{soc} is the output level at which MC intersects the socially optimal demand curve (Social Demand), which is obtained by adding the external benefit, XB, to every value along Private Demand. Note in the figure that in the case of positive externalities the private market equilibrium again fails to exhaust all possible gains from exchange. Thus at Q_{pvt} the marginal cost of producing an additional unit of output is only MB_{pvt}, which is smaller than the marginal benefit of an additional unit by the amount XB. For a good whose production generates external benefits, the market equilibrium quantity will be smaller than the socially optimal quantity.

FIGURE 11.2

A Good Whose Production Generates a Positive Externality for Consumers.
The market equilibrium quantity, Q_{pvt}, is smaller than the socially optimal quantity, Q_{soc}, because individual buyers are willing to pay only for the benefits they reap from directly consuming the product.

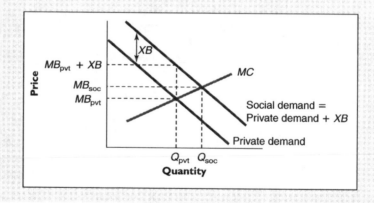

No matter whether externalities are positive or negative, they distort the allocation of resources in otherwise efficient markets. When externalities are present, the individual pursuit of self-interest will not result in the largest possible economic surplus. And when it does not, the outcome is by definition inefficient.

THE COASE THEOREM

To say that a situation is inefficient means that it can be rearranged in a way that would make at least some people better off without harming others. Such situations, we have seen, are a source of creative tension. The existence of inefficiency, after all, means that there is cash on the table, which usually triggers a race to see who can capture it. For example, we saw that because monopoly pricing results in an inefficiently low output level, the potential for gain gave monopolists an incentive to make discounts available to price-sensitive buyers. As the next examples illustrate, the inefficiencies that result from externalities create similar incentives for remedial action.

EXAMPLE 11.3

Will Abercrombie dump toxins in the river? (Part I)

Abercrombie's factory produces a toxic waste by-product. If Abercrombie dumps it in the river, he causes damage to Fitch, a fisherman located downstream. The

Frank–Bernanke:
Principles of
Microeconomics, Second
Edition

III. Market Imperfections

11. Externalities and
Property Rights

© The McGraw–Hill
Companies, 2004

toxins are short-lived and cause no damage to anyone other than Fitch. At a cost, Abercrombie can filter out the toxins, in which case Fitch will suffer no damage at all. The relevant gains and losses for the two individuals are listed in Table 11.1.

TABLE 11.1
Costs and Benefits of Eliminating Toxic Waste (Part 1)

	With filter	Without filter
Gains to Abercrombie	$100/day	$130/day
Gains to Fitch	$100/day	$50/day

If the law does not penalize Abercrombie for dumping toxins in the river, and if Abercrombie and Fitch cannot communicate with one another, will Abercrombie operate with or without a filter? Is that choice socially efficient?

Since Abercrombie earns $30 per day more without a filter than with one, his natural incentive is to operate without one. But the outcome when he does so is socially inefficient. Thus, when Abercrombie operates without a filter, the total daily gain to both parties is only $130 + $50 = $180, compared to $100 + $100 = $200 if Abercrombie had operated with a filter. The daily cost of the filter to Abercrombie is only $130 − $100 = $30, which is smaller than its daily benefit to Fitch of $100 − $50 = $50. The fact that Abercrombie does not install the filter implies a squandered daily surplus of $20.

Will Abercrombie dump toxins in the river? (Part 2)

Suppose the costs and benefits of using the filter are as in Example 11.3 except that Abercrombie and Fitch can now communicate with one another at no cost. Even though the law does not require him to do so, will Abercrombie use a filter?

This time, Abercrombie will use a filter. Recall from Chapter 7 the observation that when the economic pie grows larger, everyone can have a larger slice (the efficiency principle). Because use of a filter would result in the largest possible economic surplus, it would enable both Abercrombie and Fitch to have a larger net gain than before. Fitch thus has an incentive to *pay* Abercrombie to use a filter. For example, suppose Fitch offers Abercrombie $40 per day to compensate him for operating with a filter. Both Abercrombie and Fitch will then be exactly $10 per day better off than before, for a total daily net gain of $20.

EXAMPLE 11.4

EXERCISE 11.1

In Example 11.4, what is the largest whole-dollar amount by which Fitch could compensate Abercrombie for operating with a filter and still be better off than before?

Ronald Coase, a professor at the University of Chicago Law School, was the first to see clearly that if people can negotiate with one another at no cost over the right to perform activities that cause externalities, they will always arrive at an efficient solution. This insight, which is often called the **Coase theorem**, is a profoundly important idea, for which Coase (rhymes with "dose") was awarded the 1991 Nobel Prize in Economics.

Why, you might ask, should Fitch pay Abercrombie to filter out toxins that would not be there in the first place if not for Abercrombie's factory? The rhetorical force of this question is undeniable. Yet Coase points out that externalities are reciprocal in nature. The toxins do harm Fitch, to be sure, but preventing

Coase theorem if at no cost people can negotiate the purchase and sale of the right to perform activities that cause externalities, they can always arrive at efficient solutions to the problems caused by externalities

Frank–Bernanke:
Principles of
Microeconomics, Second
Edition

III. Market Imperfections

11. Externalities and
Property Rights

© The McGraw–Hill
Companies, 2004

Abercrombie from emitting them would penalize Abercrombie, by exactly $30 per day. Why should Fitch necessarily have the right to harm Abercrombie? Indeed, as Example 11.5 illustrates, even if Fitch had that right, he would exercise it only if filtering the toxins proved the most efficient outcome.

EXAMPLE 11.5

Will Abercrombie dump toxins in the river? (Part 3)

Suppose the law says that Abercrombie may *not* dump toxins in the river unless he has Fitch's permission. If the relevant costs and benefits of filtering the toxins are as shown in Table 11.2, and if Abercrombie and Fitch can negotiate with one another at no cost, will Abercrombie filter the toxins?

TABLE 11.2
Costs and Benefits of Eliminating Toxic Waste (Part 3)

	With filter	Without filter
Gains to Abercrombie	$100/day	$150/day
Gains to Fitch	$100/day	$70/day

Note that this time the most efficient outcome is for Abercrombie to operate without a filter, for the total daily surplus in that case will be $220 as compared to only $200 with a filter. Under the law, however, Fitch has the right to insist that Abercrombie use a filter. We might expect him to exercise that right, since his own gain would rise from $70 to $100 per day if he did so. But because this outcome would be socially inefficient, we know that each party can do better.

Suppose, for example, that Abercrombie gives Fitch $40 per day in return for Fitch's permission to operate without a filter. Each would then have a net daily gain of $110, which is $10 better for each of them than if Fitch had insisted that Abercrombie use a filter. Abercrombie's pollution harms Fitch, sure enough. But failure to allow the pollution would have caused even greater harm to Abercrombie.

The Coase theorem tells us that regardless of whether the law holds polluters liable for damages, the affected parties will achieve efficient solutions to externalities if they can negotiate costlessly with one another. But note carefully that this does not imply that affected parties will be indifferent about whether the law holds polluters responsible for damages. If polluters are liable, they will end up with lower incomes and those who are injured by pollutants will end up with higher incomes than if the law does not hold polluters liable—even though the same efficient production methods are adopted in each case. When polluters are held liable, they must remove the pollution at their own expense. When they are not held liable, those who are injured by pollution must pay polluters to cut back.

Externalities are hardly rare and isolated occurrences. On the contrary, finding examples of actions that are altogether free of them is difficult. And because externalities can distort the allocation of resources, it is important to recognize them and deal intelligently with them. Consider the following example of an externality that arises because of shared living arrangements.

EXAMPLE 11.6

Will Ann and Betty share an apartment?

Ann and Betty can live together in a two-bedroom apartment for $600 per month, or separately in 2 one-bedroom apartments, each for $400 per month. If the rent

EXTERNAL COSTS AND BENEFITS

paid were the same for both alternatives, the two women would be indifferent between living together or separately, except for one problem: Ann talks constantly on the telephone. Ann would pay up to $250 per month for this privilege. Betty, for her part, would pay up to $150 per month to have better access to the phone. If the two cannot install a second phone line, should they live together or separately?

Ann and Betty should live together only if the benefit of doing so exceeds the cost. The benefit of living together is the reduction in their rent. Since 2 one-bedroom apartments would cost a total of $800 per month, compared to $600 for a two-bedroom unit, their benefit from living together is $200 per month. Their cost of living together is the least costly accommodation they can make to Ann's objectionable telephone habits. Since Ann would be willing to pay up to $250 per month to avoid changing her behavior, the $200 rent saving is too small to persuade her to change. But Betty is willing to put up with Ann's behavior for a compensation payment of only $150 per month. Since that amount is smaller than the total saving in rent, the least costly solution to the problem is for Betty to live with Ann and simply put up with her behavior.

Table 11.3 summarizes the relevant costs and benefits of this shared living arrangement. The cost-benefit principle tells us that Ann and Betty should live together if and only if the benefit of living together exceeds the cost. The cost of the shared living arrangement is not the sum of all possible costs but the least costly accommodation to the problem (or problems) of shared living. Since the $200 per month saving in rent exceeds the least costly accommodation to the phone problem, Ann and Betty can reap a total gain in economic surplus of $50 per month by sharing their living quarters.

TABLE 11.3
The Gain in Surplus from Shared Living Arrangements

Benefits of Shared Living		
Total cost of separate apartments	Total cost of shared apartment	Rent savings from sharing
(2)($400/month) = $800/month	$600/month	$200/month

Costs of Shared Living			
Problem	Ann's cost of solving problem	Betty's cost of solving problem	Least costly solution to the problem
Ann's phone usage	Curtailed phone usage: $250/month	Tolerate phone usage: $150/month	Betty tolerates Ann's phone usage: $150/month

Gain in Surplus from Shared Living			
Rent savings ($200/month)	−	Least costly accommodation to shared living problems ($150/month) =	Gain in surplus: $50/month

Some people might conclude that Ann and Betty should not live together, because if the two share the rent equally, Betty will end up paying $300 per month—which when added to the $150 cost of putting up with Ann's phone behavior comes to $50 more than the cost of living alone. As persuasive as that argument may sound, however, it is mistaken. The source of the error, as Example 11.7 makes clear, is the assumption that the two must share the rent equally.

CHAPTER 11 EXTERNALITIES AND PROPERTY RIGHTS

EXAMPLE 11.7

What is the highest rent Betty would be willing to pay for the two-bedroom apartment?

In Example 11.6, what is the highest rent Betty would be willing to pay to share an apartment with Ann?

Betty's alternative is to live alone, which would mean paying $400 per month, her reservation price for a living arrangement with no phone problem. Since the most she would be willing to pay to avoid the phone problem is $150 per month, the highest monthly rent she would be willing to pay for the shared apartment is $400 − $150 = $250. If she pays that amount, Ann will have to pay the difference, namely, $350 per month, which is clearly a better alternative for Ann than paying $400 to live alone.

EXAMPLE 11.8

How much should Ann and Betty pay if they agree to split their economic surplus equally?

If Ann and Betty agree to live together and split the resulting gain in economic surplus equally, how much rent will each of them pay?

As we saw in Table 11.3, the total rent saving from the shared apartment is $200, and since the least costly solution to the phone problem is $150, the monthly gain in economic surplus is $50. We know that Ann's reservation price for living together is $400 per month and Betty's is $250 (see Example 11.7). So if the two women want to split the $50 monthly surplus equally, each should pay $25 less than her reservation price. Ann's monthly rent will thus be $375 and Betty's, $225. The result is that each is $25 per month better off than if she had lived alone.

EXERCISE 11.2

As in Example 11.6, Ann and Betty can live together in a two-bedroom apartment for $600 per month or separately in 2 one-bedroom apartments, each for $400 per month. Ann would pay up to $250 per month rather than moderate her telephone habits, and Betty would pay up to $150 per month to achieve reasonable access to the telephone. But Betty would also be willing to pay up to $60 per month to avoid the loss of privacy that comes with shared living space. Should the two women live together?

LEGAL REMEDIES FOR EXTERNALITIES

We have seen that efficient solutions to externalities can be found whenever the affected parties can negotiate with one another at no cost. But negotiation is not always practical. A motorist with a noisy muffler, for example, imposes costs on others, yet they cannot flag him down and offer him a compensation payment to fix his muffler. In recognition of this difficulty, most governments simply require that cars have working mufflers. Indeed, the explicit or implicit purpose of a large share—perhaps the lion's share—of laws is to solve problems caused by externalities. The goal of such laws is to help people achieve the solutions they might have reached had they been able to negotiate with one another.

When negotiation is costless, the task of adjustment generally falls on the party who can accomplish it at the lowest cost. For instance, in Example 11.6, Betty put up with Ann's annoying phone habits because doing so was less costly than asking Ann to change her habits. Many municipal noise ordinances also place the burden of adjustment on those who can accomplish it at lowest cost. Consider, for example, the restrictions on loud party music, which often take effect at a later hour on weekends than on weekdays. This pattern reflects both the fact that the gains from loud music tend to be larger on weekends and the fact that such music is more likely to disturb people on weekdays. By setting the noise curfew at different hours on different days of the week, the law places the burden

Frank–Bernanke:
Principles of
Microeconomics, Second
Edition

III. Market Imperfections

11. Externalities and
Property Rights

© The McGraw–Hill
Companies, 2004

EXTERNAL COSTS AND BENEFITS

on partygoers during the week and on sleepers during the weekend. Similar logic explains why noise ordinances allow motorists to honk their horns in most neighborhoods, but not in the immediate vicinity of a hospital.

As the following examples demonstrate, economic naturalists can hone their craft by focusing on laws whose purpose is to solve the problems caused by externalities.

What is the purpose of speed limits and other traffic laws?

A motorist driving a car at high speed endangers not just her own life and property but also the lives and property of others. Speed limits, no-passing zones, right-of-way rules, and a host of other traffic laws may be seen as reasoned attempts to limit the harm one party inflicts on another. Many jurisdictions even have laws requiring that motorists install snow tires on their cars by November 1. These laws promote not just safety but also the smooth flow of traffic: A single motorist who can't get up a snow-covered hill delays not only herself but also the motorists behind her.

Why do most communities have zoning laws?

Most communities restrict the kinds of activities that take place in various parts of the city. Because many residents place a high value on living in an uncongested neighborhood, some cities have enacted zoning laws specifying minimum lot sizes. In places like Manhattan, where a shortage of land encourages developers to build very large and tall buildings, zoning laws limit both a building's height and the proportion of a lot it may occupy. Such restrictions recognize that the taller a building is, and the greater the proportion of its lot that it occupies, the more it blocks sunlight from reaching surrounding properties. The desire to control external costs also helps to explain why many cities establish separate zones for business and residential activity. Even within business districts, many cities limit certain kinds of commercial activity. For example, in an effort to revitalize the Times Square neighborhood, New York City enacted a zoning law banning adult bookstores and pornographic movie theaters from the area.

Why do many governments enact laws that limit the discharge of environmental pollutants?

Limitations on the discharge of pollutants into the environment are perhaps the clearest examples of laws aimed at solving problems caused by externalities. The details of these laws reflect the cost-benefit principle. The discharge of toxic wastes into rivers, for example, tends to be most strictly regulated on those waterways whose commercial fishing or recreational uses are most highly valued. On other waterways, the burden of adjustment is likely to fall more heavily on fishermen, recreational boaters, and swimmers. Similarly, air quality regulations tend to be strictest in the most heavily populated regions of the country, where the marginal benefit of pollution reduction is the greatest.

What is the purpose of free speech laws?

The First Amendment's protection of free speech and the pattern of exceptions to that protection are another illustration of how legal remedies are used to solve the problems caused by externalities. The First Amendment acknowledges the decisive value of open communication, as well as the practical difficulty of identifying and regulating acts of speech that cause more harm than good. Yet it does allow some important exceptions. For instance, it does not allow someone to yell "fire" in a crowded theater if there is no fire, nor does it allow someone to advocate the violent overthrow of the government. In those instances, the external benefits of free speech are far too small to justify the external costs.

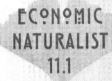

ECONOMIC
NATURALIST
11.1

ECONOMIC
NATURALIST
11.2

ECONOMIC
NATURALIST
11.3

ECONOMIC
NATURALIST
11.4

ECONOMIC NATURALIST 11.5

Why does government subsidize the planting of trees on hillsides?

The laws discussed in the preceding examples are meant to regulate activities that generate negative externalities. But government also uses the law to encourage activities that generate positive externalities. The planting of trees on hillsides, for example, benefits not just the landowner but also his neighbors by limiting the danger of flooding. In recognition of this fact, many jurisdictions subsidize the planting of trees. Similarly, Congress budgets millions of dollars each year in support of basic research, an implicit acknowledgment of the positive externalities associated with the generation of new knowledge.

THE OPTIMAL AMOUNT OF NEGATIVE EXTERNALITIES IS NOT ZERO

Curbing pollution and other negative externalities entails both costs and benefits. As we saw in Chapter 6, the best policy is to curtail pollution until the cost of further abatement just equals the marginal benefit. In general, the marginal cost of abatement rises with the amount of pollution eliminated. (Following the low-hanging-fruit principle, polluters use the cheapest cleanup methods first and then turn to more expensive ones.) And the law of diminishing marginal utility suggests that beyond some point, the marginal benefit of pollution reduction tends to fall as more pollution is removed. As a result, the marginal cost and marginal benefit curves almost always intersect at less than the maximum amount of pollution reduction.

The intersection of the two curves marks instead the socially optimal level of pollution reduction. If pollution is curtailed by any less than that amount, society will gain more than it will lose by pushing the cleanup effort a little further. But if regulators push beyond the point at which the marginal cost and benefit curves intersect, society will incur costs that exceed the benefits. The existence of a socially optimal level of pollution reduction implies the existence of a socially optimal level of pollution, and that level will almost always be greater than zero.

As we saw in Chapter 6, because people have been conditioned to think of pollution as bad, many cringe when they hear the phrase "socially optimal level of pollution." How can any positive level of pollution be socially optimal? *But to speak of a socially optimal level of pollution is not the same as saying that pollution is good.* It is merely to recognize that society has an interest in cleaning up the environment, but only up to a certain point. The underlying idea is no different from the idea of an optimal level of dirt in an apartment. After all, even if you spent the whole day, every day, vacuuming your apartment, there would be *some* dirt left in it. And because you have better things to do than vacuum all day, you probably tolerate substantially more than the minimal amount of dirt. A dirty apartment is not good, nor is pollution in the air you breathe. But in both cases, the cleanup effort should be expanded only until the marginal benefit equals the marginal cost.

 RECAP   EXTERNAL COSTS AND BENEFITS

Externalities occur when the costs or benefits of an activity accrue to people other than those directly involved in the activity. The Coase theorem says that when affected parties can negotiate with one another without cost, activities will be pursued at efficient levels, even in the presence of positive or negative externalities. But when negotiation is prohibitively costly, inefficient behavior generally results. Activities that generate negative externalities are pursued to excess, while those that generate positive externalities are pursued too little. Laws and regulations are often adopted in an effort to alter inefficient behavior that results from externalities.

Frank–Bernanke:
Principles of
Microeconomics, Second
Edition

III. Market Imperfections

11. Externalities and
Property Rights

© The McGraw–Hill
Companies, 2004

PROPERTY RIGHTS AND THE TRAGEDY OF THE COMMONS

People who grow up in the industrialized nations tend to take the institution of private property for granted. Our intuitive sense is that people have the right to own any property they acquire by lawful means and to do with that property much as they see fit. In reality, however, property laws are considerably more complex in terms of the rights they confer and the obligations they impose.

THE PROBLEM OF UNPRICED RESOURCES

To understand the laws that govern the use of property, we must begin by asking why societies created the institution of private property in the first place. The following examples, which show what happens to property that nobody owns, suggest an answer.

How many steers will villagers send onto the commons?

EXAMPLE 11.9

A village has five residents, each of whom has accumulated savings of $100. Each villager can use the money to buy a government bond that pays 13 percent interest per year or to buy a year-old steer, send it onto the commons to graze, and sell it after 1 year. The price the villager will get for the 2-year-old steer depends on the amount of weight it gains while grazing on the commons, which in turn depends on the number of steers sent onto the commons, as shown in Table 11.4.

The price of a 2-year-old steer declines with the number of steers grazing on the commons, because the more steers, the less grass available to each. The villagers make their investment decisions one at a time, and the results are public. If each villager decides how to invest individually, how many steers will be sent onto the commons, and what will be the village's total income?

TABLE 11.4
The Relationship between Herd Size and Steer Price

Number of steers on the commons	Price per 2-year-old steer ($)	Income per steer ($/year)
1	126	26
2	119	19
3	116	16
4	113	13
5	111	11

If a villager buys a $100 government bond, he will earn $13 of interest income at the end of 1 year. Thus he should send a steer onto the commons if and only if that steer will command a price of at least $113 as a 2-year-old. When each villager chooses in this self-interested way, we can expect four villagers to send a steer onto the commons. (Actually, the fourth villager would be indifferent between investing in a steer or buying a bond, since he would earn $13 either way. For the sake of discussion, we'll assume that in the case of a tie, people choose to be cattlemen.) The fifth villager, seeing that he would earn only $11 by sending a fifth steer onto the commons, will choose instead to buy a government bond. As a result of these decisions, the total village income will be $65 per year—$13 for the one bondholder and 4($13) = $52 for the four cattlemen.

Has Adam Smith's invisible hand produced the most efficient allocation of these villagers' resources? We can tell at a glance that it has not, since their total

Frank–Bernanke:
Principles of
Microeconomics, Second
Edition

III. Market Imperfections

11. Externalities and
Property Rights

© The McGraw–Hill
Companies, 2004

village income is only $65—precisely the same as it would have been had the possibility of cattle raising not existed. The source of the difficulty will become evident in Example 11.10.

EXAMPLE 11.10

What is the socially optimal number of steers to send onto the commons?

Suppose the five villagers in Example 11.9 confront the same investment opportunities as before, except that this time they are free to make their decisions as a group rather than individually. How many steers will they send onto the commons, and what will be their total village income?

This time the villagers' goal is to maximize the income received by the group as a whole. When decisions are made from this perspective, the criterion is to send a steer onto the commons only if its marginal contribution to village income is at least $13, the amount that could be earned from a government bond. As the entries in the last column of Table 11.5 indicate, the first steer clearly meets this criterion, since it contributes $26 to total village income. But the second steer does not. Sending that steer onto the commons raises the village's income from cattle raising from $26 to $38, a gain of just $12. The $100 required to buy the second steer would thus have been better invested in a government bond. Worse, the collective return from sending a third steer is only $10; from a fourth, only $4; and from a fifth, only $3.

TABLE 11.5
Marginal Income and the Socially Optimal Herd Size

Number of steers on the commons	Price per 2-year-old steer ($)	Income per steer ($/year)	Total cattle income ($/year)	Marginal income ($/year)
1	126	26	26	26
2	119	19	38	12
3	116	16	48	10
4	113	13	52	4
5	111	11	55	3

In sum, when investment decisions are made with the goal of maximizing total village income, the best choice is to buy four government bonds and send only a single steer onto the commons. The resulting village income will be $78: $26 from sending the single steer and $52 from the four government bonds. That amount is $13 more than the total income that resulted when villagers made their investment decisions individually. Once again, the reward from moving from an inefficient allocation to an efficient one is that the economic pie grows larger. And when the pie grows larger, everyone can get a larger slice. For instance, if the villagers agree to pool their income and share it equally, each will get $15.60, or $2.60 more than before.

EXERCISE 11.3

How would your answers to Examples 11.9 and 11.10 differ if the interest rate were not 13 percent but 11 percent per year?

Why do the villagers in Examples 11.9 and 11.10 do better when they make their investment decisions collectively? The answer is that when individuals decide alone, they ignore the fact that sending another steer onto the commons will cause existing steers to gain less weight. Their failure to consider this effect makes the return from sending another steer seem misleadingly high to them.

PROPERTY RIGHTS AND THE TRAGEDY OF THE COMMONS

The grazing land on the commons is a valuable economic resource. When no one owns it, no one has any incentive to take the opportunity cost of using it into account. And when that happens, people will tend to use it until its marginal benefit is zero. This problem, and others similar to it, are known as the **tragedy of the commons.** The essential cause of the tragedy of the commons is the fact that one person's use of commonly held property imposes an external cost on others by making the property less valuable. The tragedy of the commons also provides a vivid illustration of the equilibrium principle (see Chapter 3). Each individual villager behaves rationally by sending an additional steer onto the commons, yet the overall outcome falls far short of the attainable ideal.

tragedy of the commons the tendency for a resource that has no price to be used until its marginal benefit falls to zero

THE EFFECT OF PRIVATE OWNERSHIP

As Example 11.11 illustrates, one solution to the tragedy of the commons is to place the village grazing land under private ownership.

How much will the right to control the village commons sell for?

Suppose the five villagers face the same investment opportunities as before, except that this time they decide to auction off the right to use the commons to the highest bidder. Assuming that villagers can borrow as well as lend at an annual interest rate of 13 percent, what price will the right to use the commons fetch? How will the owner of that property right use it, and what will be the resulting village income?

To answer these questions, simply ask yourself what you would do if you had complete control over how the grazing land were used. As we saw in Example 11.10, the most profitable way to use this land is to send only a single steer to graze on it. If you do so, you will earn a total of $26 per year. Since the opportunity cost of the $100 you spent on the single yearling steer is the $13 in interest you could have earned from a bond, your economic profit from sending a single steer onto the commons will be $13 per year, provided you can use the land for free. But you cannot; to finance your purchase of the property right, you must borrow money (since you used your $100 savings to buy a year-old steer).

What is the most you would be willing to pay for the right to use the commons? Since its use generates an income of $26 per year, or $13 more than the opportunity cost of your investment in the steer, the most you would pay is $100 (because that amount used to purchase a bond that pays 13 percent interest would also generate income of $13 per year). If the land were sold at auction, $100 is precisely the amount you would have to pay. Your annual earnings from the land would be exactly enough to pay the $13 interest on your loan and cover the opportunity cost of not having put your savings into a bond.

Note that when the right to use the land is auctioned to the highest bidder, the village achieves a more efficient allocation of its resources, because the owner has a strong incentive to take the opportunity cost of more intensive grazing fully into account. Total village income in this case will again be $78. If the annual interest on the $100 proceeds from selling the land rights is shared equally among the five villagers, each will again have an annual investment income of $15.60.

EXAMPLE 11.11

The logic of economic surplus maximization helps to explain why the most economically successful nations have all been ones with well-developed private property laws. Property that belongs to everyone belongs, in effect, to no one. Not only is its potential economic value never fully realized; it usually ends up being of no value at all.

Bear in mind, however, that in most countries the owners of private property are not free to do *precisely* as they wish with it. For example, local zoning laws may give the owner of a residential building lot the right to build a three-story house but not a six-story house. Here, too, the logic of economic surplus maximization applies, for a fully informed and rational legislature would define

CHAPTER 11 EXTERNALITIES AND PROPERTY RIGHTS

property rights so as to create the largest possible total economic surplus. In practice, of course, such ideal legislatures never really exist. Yet the essence of politics is the cutting of deals that make people better off. If a legislator could propose a change in the property laws that would enlarge the total economic surplus, she could also propose a scheme that would give each of her constituents a larger slice, thus enhancing her chances for reelection.

As an economic naturalist, challenge yourself to use this framework when thinking about the various restrictions you encounter in private property laws: zoning laws that constrain what you can build and what types of activities you can conduct on your land; traffic laws that constrain what you can do with your car; employment and environmental laws that constrain how you can operate your business. Your understanding of these and countless other laws will be enhanced by the insight that everyone can gain when the private property laws are defined so as to create the largest total economic surplus.

WHEN PRIVATE OWNERSHIP IS IMPRACTICAL

Do not be misled into thinking that the law provides an *ideal* resolution of all problems associated with externalities and the tragedy of the commons. Defining and enforcing efficient property rights entails costs, after all, and sometimes, as in the following examples, the costs outweigh the gains.

Why do blackberries in public parks get picked too soon?

Wild blackberries grow profusely at the edge of a wooded area in a crowded city park. The blackberries will taste best if left to ripen fully, but they still taste reasonably good if picked and eaten a few days early. Will the blackberries be left to ripen fully?

Obviously, the costs of defining and enforcing the property rights to blackberries growing in a public park are larger than the potential gains, so the blackberries will remain common property. That means that whoever picks them first gets them. Even though everyone would benefit if people waited until the berries were fully ripe, everyone knows that those who wait are likely to end up with no berries at all. And that means that the berries will be eaten too soon.

Why are shared milkshakes consumed too quickly?

Sara and Susan are identical twins who have been given a chocolate milkshake to share. If each has a straw and each knows that the other is self-interested, will the twins consume the milkshake at an optimal rate?

Because drinking a milkshake too quickly chills the taste buds, the twins will enjoy their shake more if they drink it slowly. Yet each knows that the other will drink any part of the milkshake she doesn't finish herself. The result is that each will consume the shake at a faster rate than she would if she had half a shake all to herself.

Here are some further examples of the type of tragedy of the commons that is not easily solved by defining private ownership rights.

Harvesting timber on remote public land On remote public lands, enforcing restrictions against cutting down trees may be impractical. Each tree cutter knows that a tree that is not harvested this year will be bigger, and hence more valuable, next year. But he also knows that if he doesn't cut the tree down this year, someone else will. In contrast, private companies that grow trees on their own land have no incentive to harvest timber prematurely and a strong incentive to prevent outsiders from doing so.

Harvesting whales in international waters Each individual whaler knows that harvesting an extra whale reduces the breeding population, and hence the

Why are shared milkshakes drunk too quickly?

ECONOMIC NATURALIST 11.6

ECONOMIC NATURALIST 11.7

Frank–Bernanke:
Principles of
Microeconomics, Second
Edition

III. Market Imperfections

11. Externalities and
Property Rights

© The McGraw–Hill
Companies, 2004

POSITIONAL EXTERNALITIES

size of the future whale population. But the whaler also knows that any whale that is not harvested today will be taken by some other whaler. The solution would be to define and enforce property rights to whales. But the oceans are vast, and the behavior of whalers is hard to monitor. And even if their behavior could be monitored, the concept of national sovereignty would make the international enforcement of property rights problematic.

More generally, the animal species that are most severely threatened with extinction tend to be those that are economically valuable to humans but that are not privately owned by anyone. This is the situation confronting whales. Contrast it with the situation confronting chickens, which are also economically valuable to humans but which, unlike whales, are governed by traditional laws of private property. This difference explains why no one worries that Colonel Sanders might threaten the extinction of chickens.

Controlling multinational environmental pollution Each individual polluter may know that if he and all others pollute, the damage to the environment will be greater than the cost of not polluting. But if the environment is common property into which all are free to dump, each has a powerful incentive to pollute. If all polluters live under the jurisdiction of a single government, enforcing laws and regulations that limit the discharge of pollution may be practical. But if polluters come from many different countries, solutions are much more difficult to implement. Thus the Mediterranean Sea has long suffered serious pollution, because none of the many nations that border it has an economic incentive to consider the effects of its discharges on other countries.

As the world's population continues to grow, the absence of an effective system of international property rights will become an economic problem of increasing significance.

 RECAP **PROPERTY RIGHTS AND THE TRAGEDY OF THE COMMONS**

When a valuable resource has a price of zero, people will continue to exploit it as long as its marginal benefit remains positive. The tragedy of the commons describes situations in which valuable resources are squandered because users are not charged for them. In many cases, an efficient remedy for such waste is to define and enforce rights to the use of valuable property. But this solution is difficult to implement for resources such as the oceans and the atmosphere, because no single government has the authority to enforce property rights for these resources.

POSITIONAL EXTERNALITIES

Steffi Graf received more than $1.6 million in tournament winnings in 1992; her endorsement and exhibition earnings totaled several times that amount. By any reasonable measure, the quality of her play was outstanding, yet she consistently lost to archrival Monica Seles. But in April of 1993, Seles was stabbed in the back by a deranged fan and forced to withdraw from the tour. In the ensuing months, Graf's tournament winnings accumulated at almost double her 1992 pace, despite little change in the quality of her play.

PAYOFFS THAT DEPEND ON RELATIVE PERFORMANCE

In professional tennis and a host of other competitive situations, the rewards people receive typically depend not only on how they perform in absolute terms but also on how they perform relative to their closest rivals. In these situations,

Frank–Bernanke:
Principles of
Microeconomics, Second
Edition

III. Market Imperfections

11. Externalities and
Property Rights

© The McGraw–Hill
Companies, 2004

competitors have an incentive to take actions that will increase their odds of winning. For example, tennis players can increase their chances of winning by hiring personal fitness trainers and sports psychologists to travel with them on the tour. Yet the simple mathematics of competition tells us that the sum of all individual payoffs from such investments will be larger than the collective payoff. In any tennis match, for example, each contestant will get a sizable payoff from money spent on fitness trainers and sports psychologists, yet each match will have exactly one winner and one loser, no matter how much players spend. The overall gain to tennis spectators is likely to be small, and the overall gain to players as a group must be zero. To the extent that each contestant's payoff depends on his or her relative performance, then, the incentive to undertake such investments will be excessive, from a collective point of view.

Consider the following example.

Why do football players take anabolic steroids?

ECONOMIC NATURALIST 11.8

The offensive linemen of many National Football League teams currently average more than 330 pounds. In the 1970s, by contrast, offensive linemen in the league averaged barely 280 pounds, and the all-decade linemen of the 1940s averaged only 229 pounds. One reason that today's players are so much heavier is that players' salaries have escalated sharply over the last two decades, which has intensified competition for the positions. Size and strength are the two cardinal virtues of an offensive lineman, and other things being equal, the job will go to the larger and stronger of two rivals.

Size and strength, in turn, can be enhanced by the consumption of anabolic steroids. But if all players consume these substances, the rank ordering of players by size and strength—and hence the question of who lands the jobs—will be largely unaffected. And since the consumption of anabolic steroids entails potentially serious long-term health consequences, as a group football players are clearly worse off if they consume these drugs. So why do football players take steroids?

The problem here is that contestants for starting berths on the offensive line confront a prisoner's dilemma, like the ones analyzed in Chapter 10. Consider two closely matched rivals—Smith and Jones—who are competing for a single position. If neither takes steroids, each has a 50 percent chance of winning the job and a starting salary of $1 million per year. If both take steroids, each again has a 50 percent chance of winning the job. But if one takes steroids and the other doesn't, the first is sure to win the job. The loser ends up selling insurance for $30,000 per year. Neither likes the fact that the drugs may have adverse health consequences, but each would be willing to take that risk in return for a shot at the big salary. Given these choices, the two competitors face a payoff matrix like the one shown in Table 11.6.

TABLE 11.6
Payoff Matrix for Steroid Consumption

		Jones	
		Don't take steroids	Take steroids
Smith	Don't take steroids	Second best for each	Best for Jones Worst for Smith
	Take steroids	Best for Smith Worst for Jones	Third best for each

Clearly, the dominant strategy for both Smith and Jones is to take steroids. Yet when they do, each gets only the third-best outcome, whereas they could have gotten the second-best outcome by not taking the drugs. Hence the attraction of rules that forbid the consumption of anabolic steroids.

POSITIONAL ARMS RACES

The steroid problem is an example of a **positional externality**. Whenever the payoffs to one contestant depend at least in part on how he or she performs relative to a rival, any step that improves one side's relative position must necessarily worsen the other's. The standing-at-concerts example discussed in Chapter 10 (Economic Naturalist 10.3) is another instance of a positional externality. Just as the invisible hand of the market is weakened by the presence of standard externalities, it is also weakened by positional externalities.

positional externality occurs when an increase in one person's performance reduces the expected reward of another in situations in which reward depends on relative performance

"I don't know why McGillicuddy is so pleased with himself. We're __all__ wee, darlin' men here."

Here is another example of a positional externality.

Why do many grocery stores stay open all night, even in small towns?

Ithaca, New York, has seven large supermarkets, five of which are open 24 hours a day. The convenience of all-night shopping could be maintained at lower cost if all but one of the stores were to close during late-night hours. Why do many remain open?

Most people do the bulk of their shopping at a single store. If other relevant factors—price, location, merchandise quality, and so on—are essentially the same, people will choose the store with the most convenient hours. Suppose the two leading stores, Tops and Wegmans, currently close at midnight and are considering whether to stay open until 1 A.M. If one does so and the other doesn't, the store that is open longer will capture the lion's share of all business, not just from midnight to 1 A.M. but during other hours as well, because most people will do most of their shopping at the store with the most attractive offering. But suppose the benefit the public receives when each store stays open an extra hour—as measured by the higher prices people are willing to pay—is smaller than the cost to both stores of staying open the extra hour. Each store will then face a payoff matrix like the one shown in Table 11.7.

ECONOMIC NATURALIST 11.9

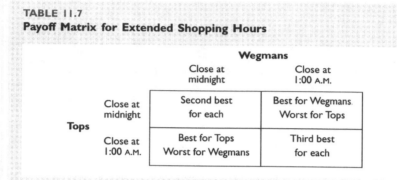

TABLE 11.7
Payoff Matrix for Extended Shopping Hours

		Wegmans	
		Close at midnight	Close at 1:00 A.M.
Tops	Close at midnight	Second best for each	Best for Wegmans Worst for Tops
	Close at 1:00 A.M.	Best for Tops Worst for Wegmans	Third best for each

In this situation, the dominant strategy for each store is to remain open an extra hour, even though each would be better off if both closed at midnight. And of course, the rivalry does not stop there, for if both stay open until 1 A.M., each will see an opportunity to better its rival by staying open until 2. As long as the cost of staying open another hour is small relative to the gains received, all stores will stay open 24 hours a day. But though consumers do gain when stores remain open longer, beyond some point, the benefit to consumers is small relative to the costs borne by merchants. The problem is that for any individual merchant who fails to match a rival's hours, the costs will be even larger.

In such situations, the public might be well served by an amendment to the antitrust laws that permits stores to cooperate to limit their hours, perhaps through an agreement calling for each store to serve in rotation as the only all-night grocery. Local statutes that limit business hours might serve the same purpose. Such statutes, often called *blue laws,* remain on the books in many jurisdictions.

We have seen that positional externalities often lead contestants to engage in an escalating series of mutually offsetting investments in performance enhancement. We call such spending patterns **positional arms races.**

POSITIONAL ARMS CONTROL AGREEMENTS

positional arms race a series of mutually offsetting investments in performance enhancement that is stimulated by a positional externality

positional arms control agreement an agreement in which contestants attempt to limit mutually offsetting investments in performance enhancement

Because positional arms races produce inefficient outcomes, people have an incentive to curtail them. Steps taken to reduce positional arms races, such as blue laws and rules against anabolic steroids, may therefore be thought of as **positional arms control agreements.**

Once you become aware of positional arms races, you will begin to see examples of them almost everywhere. You can hone your skills as an economic naturalist by asking these questions about every competitive situation you observe: What form do the investments in performance enhancement take? What steps have contestants taken to limit these investments? Sometimes positional arms control agreements are achieved by the imposition of formal rules or by the signing of legal contracts. Some examples of this type of agreement follow.

Campaign spending limits In the United States, presidential candidates routinely spend more than $100 million on advertising. Yet if both candidates double their spending on ads, each one's odds of winning will remain essentially the same. Recognition of this pattern led Congress to adopt strict spending limits for presidential candidates. (That those regulations have proved difficult to enforce does not call into question the logic behind the legislation.)

Roster limits Major League Baseball permits franchises to have only 25 players on the roster during the regular season. The National Football League sets its roster limit at 49; the National Basketball Association at 12. Why these limits? In their absence, any team could increase its chance of winning by simply adding players. Inevitably, other teams would follow suit. On the plausible assumption that, beyond some point, larger rosters do not add much to the entertainment value for fans, roster limits are a sensible way to deliver sports entertainment at a more reasonable cost.

Arbitration agreements In the business world, contracting parties often sign a binding agreement that commits them to arbitration in the event of a dispute. By doing so, they sacrifice the option of pursuing their interests as fully as they might wish to later, but they also insulate themselves from costly legal battles. Other parties in the legal system may sometimes take steps to limit spending on litigation. For example, a federal judge in South Dakota recently announced—presumably to the approval of litigants—that he would read only the first 15 pages of any brief submitted to his court.

Mandatory starting dates for kindergarten A child who is a year or so older than most of her kindergarten classmates is likely to perform better, in relative terms, than if she had entered school with children her own age. And since most parents are aware that admission to prestigious universities and eligibility for top jobs upon graduation depend largely on *relative* academic performance, many are tempted to keep their children out of kindergarten a year longer than necessary. Yet there is no social advantage in holding *all* children back an extra year, since their relative performance would essentially be unaffected. In most jurisdictions, therefore, the law requires children who reach their fifth birthday before December 1 of a given year to start kindergarten the same year.

SOCIAL NORMS AS POSITIONAL ARMS CONTROL AGREEMENTS

In some cases, social norms may take the place of formal agreements to curtail positional arms races. Some familiar examples follow.

Nerd norms Some students care more—in the short run, at least—about the grades they get than how much they actually learn. When such students are graded on the curve—that is, on the basis of their performance relative to other students—a positional arms race ensues, because if all students were to double the amount of time they studied, the distribution of grades would remain essentially the same. Students who find themselves in this situation are often quick to embrace "nerd norms," which brand as social misfits those who "study too hard."

Fashion norms Social norms regarding dress and fashion often change quickly because of positional competitions. Consider, for instance, the person who wishes to be on the cutting edge of fashion. In some American social circles during the 1950s, that goal could be accomplished by having pierced ears. But as more and more people adopted the practice, it ceased to communicate avant-garde status. At the same time, those who wanted to make a conservative fashion statement gradually became freer to have their ears pierced.

For a period during the 1960s and 1970s, one could be on fashion's cutting edge by wearing two earrings in one earlobe. But by the 1990s multiple ear piercings had lost much of their social significance, the threshold of cutting-edge status having been raised to upward of a dozen piercings of each ear, or a smaller number of piercings of the nose, eyebrows, or other body parts. A similar escalation has taken place in the number, size, and placement of tattoos.

The increase in the required number of tattoos or body piercings has not changed the value of avant-garde fashion status to those who desire it. Being on the outer limits of fashion has much the same meaning now as it once did. So to the extent that there are costs associated with body piercings, tattoos, and other steps required to achieve avant-garde status, the current fashions are wasteful compared to earlier ones. In this sense, the erosion of social norms against tattoos and body piercings has produced a social loss. Of course, the costs

Is being on fashion's cutting edge more valuable now than in the 1950s?

Frank–Bernanke:
Principles of
Microeconomics, Second
Edition

III. Market Imperfections

11. Externalities and
Property Rights

© The McGraw–Hill
Companies, 2004

associated with this loss are small in most cases. Yet since each body piercing entails a small risk of infection, the costs will continue to rise with the number of piercings. And once those costs reach a certain threshold, support may mobilize on behalf of social norms that discourage body mutilation.

Norms of taste   Similar cycles occur with respect to behaviors considered to be in bad taste. In the 1950s, for example, prevailing norms prevented major national magazines from accepting ads that featured nude photographs. Naturally, advertisers had a powerful incentive to chip away at such norms in an effort to capture the reader's limited attention. And indeed, taboos against nude photographs have eroded in the same way as taboos against body mutilation.

Consider, for instance, the evolution of perfume ads. First came the nude silhouette; then, increasingly well-lighted and detailed nude photographs; and more recently, photographs of what appear to be group sex acts. Each innovation achieved just the desired effect: capturing the reader's instant and rapt attention. Inevitably, however, other advertisers followed suit, causing a shift in our sense of what is considered attention-grabbing. Photographs that once would have shocked readers now often draw little more than a bored glance.

Opinions differ, of course, about whether this change is an improvement. Many believe that the earlier, stricter norms were ill-advised, the legacy of a more prudish and repressive era. Yet even people who take that view are likely to believe that *some* kinds of photographic material ought not to be used in magazine advertisements. Obviously, what is acceptable will differ from person to person, and each person's threshold of discomfort will depend in part on current standards. But as advertisers continue to break new ground in their struggle to capture attention, the point may come when people begin to mobilize in favor of stricter standards of "public decency." Such a campaign would provide yet another example of a positional arms control agreement.

Norms against vanity   Cosmetic and reconstructive surgery has produced dramatic benefits for many people, enabling badly disfigured accident victims to recover

"We're looking for the kind of bad taste that will grab—but not appall."

a normal appearance. It has also eliminated the extreme self-consciousness felt by people born with strikingly unusual features. Such surgery, however, is by no means confined to the conspicuously disfigured. Increasingly, "normal" people are seeking surgical improvements to their appearance. Some 2 million cosmetic "procedures" were done in 1991—six times the number just a decade earlier[1]—and demand has continued to grow steadily in the years since. Once a carefully guarded secret, these procedures are now offered as prizes in southern California charity raffles. And morticians have begun to complain that the noncombustible silicon implants used in breast and buttocks augmentation are clogging their crematoria.

In individual cases, cosmetic surgery may be just as beneficial as reconstructive surgery is for accident victims. Buoyed by the confidence of having a straight nose or a wrinkle-free complexion, patients sometimes go on to achieve much more than they ever thought possible. But the growing use of cosmetic surgery has also had an unintended side effect: It has altered the standards of normal appearance. A nose that once would have seemed only slightly larger than average may now seem jarringly big. The same person who once would have looked like an average 55-year-old may now look nearly 70. And someone who once would have tolerated slightly thinning hair or an average amount of cellulite may now feel compelled to undergo hair transplantation or liposuction. Because such procedures shift people's frame of reference, their payoffs to individuals are misleadingly large. From a social perspective, therefore, reliance on them is likely to be excessive.

Legal sanctions against cosmetic surgery are difficult to imagine. But some communities have embraced powerful social norms against cosmetic, surgery, heaping scorn and ridicule on the consumers of face-lifts and tummy tucks. In individual cases, such norms may seem cruel. Yet without them, many more people might feel compelled to bear the risk and expense of cosmetic surgery.

▪ SUMMARY ▪

- Externalities are the costs and benefits of activities that accrue to people who are not directly involved in those activities. When all parties affected by externalities can negotiate with one another at no cost, the invisible hand of the market will produce an efficient allocation of resources. According to the Coase theorem, the allocation of resources is efficient in such cases because the parties affected by externalities can compensate others for taking remedial action.

- Negotiation over externalities is often impractical, however. In these cases, the self-serving actions of individuals typically will not lead to an efficient outcome. The attempt to forge solutions to the problems caused by externalities is one of the most important rationales for collective action. Sometimes collective action takes the form of laws and government regulations that alter the incentives facing those who generate, or are affected by, externalities. Such remedies work best when they place the burden of accommodation on the parties who can accomplish it at the lowest cost. Traffic laws, zoning laws, environmental protection laws, and free speech laws are examples.

- Curbing pollution and other negative externalities entails costs as well as benefits. The optimal amount of pollution reduction is the amount for which the marginal benefit of further reduction just equals the marginal cost. In general,

this formula implies that the socially optimal level of pollution, or of any other negative externality, is greater than zero.

- When grazing land and other valuable resources are owned in common, no one has an incentive to take the opportunity cost of using those resources into account. This problem is known as the tragedy of the commons. Defining and enforcing private rights governing the use of valuable resources is often an effective solution to the tragedy of the commons. Not surprisingly, most economically successful nations have well-developed institutions of private property. Property that belongs to everyone belongs, in effect, to no one. Not only is its potential economic value never fully realized; it usually ends up having no value at all.

- The difficulty of enforcing property rights in certain situations explains a variety of inefficient outcomes, such as the excessive harvest of whales in international waters and the premature harvest of timber on remote public lands. The excessive pollution of seas that are bordered by many countries also results from a lack of enforceable property rights.

- Situations in which people's rewards depend on how well they perform in relation to their rivals give rise to positional externalities. In these situations, any step that improves one side's relative position necessarily worsens the other's.

[1]*The Economist,* January 11, 1992, p. 25.

CHAPTER 11 EXTERNALITIES AND PROPERTY RIGHTS

Positional externalities tend to spawn positional arms races—escalating patterns of mutually offsetting investments in performance enhancement. Collective measures to curb positional arms races are known as positional arms control agreements. These collective actions may take the form of formal regulations or rules, such as rules against anabolic steroids in sports, campaign spending limits, and binding arbitration agreements. Informal social norms can also curtail positional arms races.

▪ KEY TERMS ▪

Coase theorem (281)
external benefit (278)
external cost (278)
externality (278)

negative externality (278)
positional arms control agreement
  (294)
positional arms race (294)

positional externality (293)
positive externality (278)
tragedy of the commons (289)

▪ REVIEW QUESTIONS ▪

1. What incentive problem explains why the freeways in cities like Los Angeles suffer from excessive congestion?

2. How would you explain to a friend why the optimal amount of freeway congestion is not zero?

3. If Congress could declare any activity that imposes external costs on others illegal, would such legislation be advisable?

4. Why does the Great Salt Lake, which is located wholly within the state of Utah, suffer lower levels of pollution than Lake Erie, which is bordered by several states and Canada?

5. Explain why the wearing of high-heeled shoes might be viewed as the result of a positional externality.

▪ PROBLEMS ▪

1. Determine whether the following statements are true or false, and briefly explain why:
   a. A given total emission reduction in a polluting industry will be achieved at the lowest possible total cost when the cost of the last unit of pollution curbed is equal for each firm in the industry.
   b. In an attempt to lower their costs of production, firms sometimes succeed merely in shifting costs to outsiders.

2. Phoebe keeps a bee farm next door to an apple orchard. She chooses her optimal number of beehives by selecting the honey output level at which her private marginal benefit from beekeeping equals her private marginal cost.
   a. Assume that Phoebe's private marginal benefit and marginal cost curves from beekeeping are normally shaped. Draw a diagram of them.
   b. Phoebe's bees help to pollinate the blossoms in the apple orchard, increasing the fruit yield. Show the social marginal benefit from Phoebe's beekeeping in your diagram.
   c. Phoebe's bees are Africanized killer bees that aggressively sting anyone who steps into their flight path. Phoebe, fortunately, is naturally immune to the bees' venom. Show the social marginal cost curve from Phoebe's beekeeping in your diagram.
   d. Indicate the socially optimal quantity of beehives on your diagram. Is it higher or lower than the privately optimal quantity? Explain.

3. Suppose the supply curve of boom box rentals in Golden Gate Park is given by $P = 5 + 0.1Q$, where P is the daily rent per unit in dollars and Q is the volume of units rented in hundreds per day. The demand curve for boom boxes is $20 - 0.2Q$. If each boom box imposes $3 per day in noise costs on others, by how much will the equilibrium number of boom boxes rented exceed the socially optimal number?

4. Refer to Problem 3. How would the imposition of a tax of $3 per unit on each daily boom box rental affect efficiency in this market?

5. Suppose the law says that Jones may *not* emit smoke from his factory unless he gets permission from Smith, who lives downwind. If the relevant costs and benefits of filtering the smoke from Jones's production process are as shown in the following table, and if Jones and Smith can negotiate with one another at no cost, will Jones emit smoke?

	Jones emits smoke	Jones does not emit smoke
Surplus for Jones	$200	$160
Surplus for Smith	400	420

6. John and Karl can live together in a two-bedroom apartment for $500 per month, or each can rent a single-bedroom apartment for $350 per month. Aside from the rent, the two would be indifferent between living together and living separately, except for one problem: John leaves dirty dishes in the sink every night. Karl would be willing to pay up to $175 per month to avoid John's dirty dishes. John, for his part, would be willing to pay up to $225 to be able to continue his sloppiness. Should John and Karl live together? If they do, will there be dirty dishes in the sink? Explain.

7. How, if at all, would your answer to Problem 6 differ if John would be willing to pay up to $30 per month to avoid giving up his privacy by sharing quarters with Karl?

8. Barton and Statler are neighbors in an apartment complex in downtown Manhattan. Barton is a concert pianist, and Statler is a poet working on an epic poem. Barton rehearses his concert pieces on the baby grand piano in his front room, which is directly above Statler's study. The following matrix shows the monthly payoffs to Barton and Statler when Barton's front room is and is not soundproofed. The soundproofing will be effective only if it is installed in Barton's apartment.

	Soundproofed	Not soundproofed
Gains to Barton	$100/month	$150/month
Gains to Statler	$120/month	$80/month

a. If Barton has the legal right to make any amount of noise he wants and he and Statler can negotiate with one another at no cost, will Barton install and maintain soundproofing? Explain. Is his choice socially efficient?

b. If Statler has the legal right to peace and quiet and can negotiate with Barton at no cost, will Barton install and maintain soundproofing? Explain. Is his choice socially efficient?

c. Does the attainment of an efficient outcome depend on whether Barton has the legal right to make noise, or Statler the legal right to peace and quiet?

9. Refer to Problem 8. Barton decides to buy a full-sized grand piano. The new payoff matrix is as follows:

	Soundproofed	Not soundproofed
Gains to Barton	$100/month	$150/month
Gains to Statler	$120/month	$60/month

a. If Statler has the legal right to peace and quiet and Barton and Statler can negotiate at no cost, will Barton install and maintain soundproofing? Explain. Is this outcome socially efficient?

b. Suppose that Barton has the legal right to make as much noise as he likes and that negotiating an agreement with Barton costs $15 per month. Will Barton install and maintain soundproofing? Explain. Is this outcome socially efficient?

c. Suppose Statler has the legal right to peace and quiet, and it costs $15 per month for Statler and Barton to negotiate any agreement. (Compensation for noise damage can be paid without incurring negotiation cost.) Will Barton install and maintain soundproofing? Is this outcome socially efficient?

d. Why does the attainment of a socially efficient outcome now depend on whether Barton has the legal right to make noise?

Frank–Bernanke:
Principles of
Microeconomics, Second
Edition

III. Market Imperfections

11. Externalities and
Property Rights

© The McGraw–Hill
Companies, 2004

CHAPTER 11   EXTERNALITIES AND PROPERTY RIGHTS

10.* A village has six residents, each of whom has accumulated savings of $100. Each villager can use this money either to buy a government bond that pays 15 percent interest per year or to buy a year-old llama, send it onto the commons to graze, and sell it after 1 year. The price the villager gets for the 2-year-old llama depends on the quality of the fleece it grows while grazing on the commons. That in turn depends on the animal's access to grazing, which depends on the number of llamas sent to the commons, as shown in the following table:

Number of llamas on the commons	Price per 2-year-old llama ($)
1	122
2	118
3	116
4	114
5	112
6	109

The villagers make their investment decisions one after another, and their decisions are public.

a. If each villager decides individually how to invest, how many llamas will be sent onto the commons, and what will be the resulting net village income?

b. What is the socially optimal number of llamas for this village? Why is that different from the actual number? What would net village income be if the socially optimal number of llamas were sent onto the commons?

c. The village committee votes to auction the right to graze llamas on the commons to the highest bidder. Assuming villagers can both borrow and lend at 15 percent annual interest, how much will the right sell for at auction? How will the new owner use the right, and what will be the resulting village income?

■ ANSWERS TO IN-CHAPTER EXERCISES ■

11.1 Since Fitch gains $50 per day when Abercrombie operates with a filter, he could pay Abercrombie as much as $49 per day and still come out ahead.

11.2 If the two were to live together, the most efficient way to resolve the telephone problem would be as before, for Betty to give up reasonable access to the phone. But on top of that cost, which is $150, Betty would also bear a $60 cost from the loss of her privacy. The total cost of their living together would thus be $210 per month. Since that amount is greater than the $200 saving in rent, the two should live separately.

11.3 The income figures from the different levels of investment in cattle would remain as before, as shown in the table. What is different is the opportunity cost of investing in each steer, which is now $11 per year instead of $13. The last column of the table shows that the socially optimal number of steers is now 2 instead of 1. And if individuals still favor holding cattle, all other things being equal, they will now send 5 steers onto the commons instead of 4, as shown in the middle column.

Number of steers on the commons	Price per 2-year-old steer ($)	Income per steer ($/year)	Total village income ($/year)	Marginal income ($/year)
1	126	26	26	26
2	119	19	38	12
3	116	16	48	10
4	113	13	52	4
5	111	11	55	3

*Problems marked with an asterisk (*) are more difficult.

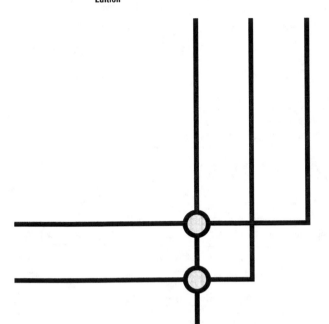

CHAPTER

15

PUBLIC GOODS
AND TAX POLICY

■

Government has the power to tax. Unlike a private business, which can get our money only if we voluntarily buy its product, the government can take our money even if we don't want the particular mix of goods and services provided.

Government also has a monopoly on the legitimate use of force. If people break the law, government has the power to restrain them, using force if necessary. It also has the power to deprive lawbreakers of their liberty for extended periods, and, in some places, even to execute them. Government can draft law-abiding citizens into the armed forces and send them into situations in which they must kill others and risk being killed themselves.

These are awesome powers. And although they are often used in the pursuit of noble ends, the historical record abounds with illustrations of their abuse. Voters and politicians of both parties are keenly aware of these abuses. Indeed, contemporary political rhetoric almost invariably entails criticism of bloated, out-of-control government bureaucracy. Even mainstream Democrats—ostensibly the party of activist government in the United States—have conceded the need to curb government's role. For example, as former president Clinton remarked in his 1996 State of the Union Message, "the era of big government is over."

Others advocate even more radical retrenchment. For instance, Harry Browne, the 1996 Libertarian Party presidential candidate, called for abolition of the Internal Revenue Service, the agency responsible for collecting the federal income tax. This step would be tantamount to abolishing the federal government itself, for without tax revenues, there would be no way to pay for public goods and services.

Browne is right, of course, that a sure way to prevent government abuse of power is simply to have no government. But since virtually no society on earth lacks a government, we may suspect that governments, on balance, do more good than harm.

But how big, exactly, should government be? What goods and services should it provide? How should it raise the revenue to pay for them? What other powers should it have to constrain the behavior of its citizens? And how should the various powers we assign to government be apportioned among local, state, and federal levels? Our goal in this chapter will be to employ the principles of micro-economics in an attempt to answer these pragmatic questions.

GOVERNMENT PROVISION OF PUBLIC GOODS

public good a good or service that, to at least some degree, is both nonrival and nonexcludable

One of the primary tasks of government is to provide what economists call **public goods,** such as national defense and the criminal justice system.

PUBLIC GOODS VERSUS PRIVATE GOODS

nonrival good a good whose consumption by one person does not diminish its availability for others

nonexcludable good a good that is difficult, or costly, to exclude nonpayers from consuming

Public goods are those goods or services that are, in varying degrees, **nonrival** and **nonexcludable.** A nonrival good is one whose consumption by one person does not diminish its availability for others. For example, if the military prevents a hostile nation from invading your city, your enjoyment of that protection does not diminish its value to your neighbors. A good is nonexcludable if it is difficult to exclude nonpayers from consuming it. For instance, even if your neighbors don't pay their share of the cost of maintaining an army, they will still enjoy its protection.

Another example of a nonrival and nonexcludable good is an over-the-air broadcast of the *David Letterman Show.* The fact that you tune in one evening does not make the program any less available to others, and once the broadcast has been beamed out over the airwaves, it is difficult to prevent anyone from tuning in. Similarly, if the City of New York puts on a fireworks display in New York harbor to celebrate a special occasion, it cannot charge admission, because the harbor may be viewed from so many different locations in the city. And the fact that additional persons view the display does not in any way diminish its value to other potential viewers.

In contrast, the typical private good is diminished one-for-one by any individual's consumption of it. For instance, when you eat a cheeseburger, it is no longer available for anyone else. Moreover, people can be easily prevented from consuming cheeseburgers they don't pay for.

> **EXERCISE 15.1**
>
> **Which of the following, if any, is nonrival?**
>
> **a. The web site of the Bureau of Labor Statistics at 3 A.M.**
>
> **b. The World Cup Soccer championship game watched in person.**
>
> **c. The World Cup Soccer championship game watched on television.**

pure public good a good or service that, to a high degree, is both nonrival and nonexcludable

Goods that are both highly nonexcludable and nonrival are often called **pure public goods.** Two reasons favor government provision of such goods. First, for-profit private companies would have obvious difficulty recovering their cost of production. Many people might be willing to pay enough to cover the cost of producing the good, but if it is nonexcludable, the company cannot easily charge for it (an example of the free-rider problem discussed in Chapter 12). And second, if the marginal cost of serving additional users is zero once the good has been produced, then charging for the good would be inefficient, even if there were

GOVERNMENT PROVISION OF PUBLIC GOODS

some practical way to do so. This inefficiency often characterizes the provision of **collective goods**—nonrival goods for which it is possible to exclude nonpayers. Pay-per-view cable television is an example. People who don't pay to get HBO don't get to watch *The Sopranos,* a restriction that excludes many viewers who would have benefited from watching. Since the marginal cost to society of their tuning in is literally zero, excluding these viewers is wasteful.

A **pure private good** is one from which nonpayers can easily be excluded and for which one person's consumption creates a one-for-one reduction in the good's availability for others. The theory of perfectly competitive supply developed in Chapter 6 applies to pure private goods, of which basic agricultural products are perhaps the best examples. A **pure commons good** is a rival good that is also nonexcludable, so-called because goods with this combination of properties almost always result in a tragedy of the commons (see Chapter 11). Fish in ocean waters are an example.

The classification scheme defined by the nonrival and nonexcludable properties is summarized in Table 15.1. The columns of the table indicate the extent to which one person's consumption of a good fails to diminish its availability for others. Goods in the right column are nonrival, and those in the left column are not. The rows of the table indicate the difficulty of excluding nonpayers from consuming the good. Goods in the top row are nonexcludable, those in the bottom row, excludable. Private goods (lower-left cell) are rival and excludable. Public goods (upper-right cell) are nonrival and nonexcludable. The two hybrid categories are commons goods (upper-left cell), which are rival but nonexcludable, and collective goods (lower-right cell), which are excludable but nonrival.

collective good a good or service that, to at least some degree, is nonrival but excludable

pure private good one for which nonpayers can easily be excluded and for which each unit consumed by one person means one less unit available for others

pure commons good one for which nonpayers cannot easily be excluded and for which each unit consumed by one person means one less unit available for others

TABLE 15.1
Private, Public, and Hybrid Goods

		Nonrival	
		Low	High
Nonexcludable	High	Commons good (fish in the ocean)	Public good (national defense)
	Low	Private good (wheat)	Collective good (pay-per-view TV)

Collective goods are provided sometimes by government, sometimes by private companies. Most pure public goods are provided by government, but even private companies can sometimes find profitable ways of producing goods that are both nonrival *and* nonexcludable. An example is broadcast radio and television, which covers its costs by selling airtime to advertisers.

The mere fact that a good is a pure public good does not necessarily mean that government ought to provide it. On the contrary, the only public goods the government should even *consider* providing are those whose benefits exceed their costs. The cost of a public good is simply the sum of all explicit and implicit costs incurred to provide it. The benefit of a public good is measured by asking how much people would be willing to pay for it. Although that sounds similar to the way we measure the benefit of a private good, an important distinction exists. The benefit of an additional unit of a private good, such as a cheeseburger, is the highest sum that any individual buyer would be willing to pay for it. In contrast, the benefit of an additional unit of a public good, such as an additional broadcast episode of *Sesame Street,* is the sum of the reservation prices of all people who will watch that episode.

CHAPTER 15 PUBLIC GOODS AND TAX POLICY

Even if the amount that all beneficiaries of a public good would be willing to pay exceeds its cost, government provision of that good makes sense only if there is no other less costly way of providing it. For example, whereas city governments often pay for fireworks displays, they almost invariably hire private companies to put on these events. Finally, if the benefit of a public good does not exceed its cost, we are better off without it.

PAYING FOR PUBLIC GOODS

Not everyone benefits equally from the provision of a given public good. For example, some people find fireworks displays highly entertaining, but others simply don't care about them, and still others actively dislike them. Ideally, it might seem that the most equitable method of financing a given public good would be to tax people in proportion to their willingness to pay for the good. To illustrate this approach, suppose Jones values a public good at $100, Smith values the same good at $200, and the cost of the good is $240. Jones would then be taxed $80, and Smith would be taxed $160. The good would be provided, and each taxpayer in this example would reap a surplus equal to 25 percent of his tax payment: $20 for Jones, $40 for Smith.

In practice, however, government officials usually lack the information they would need to tax people in proportion to their willingness to pay for specific public goods. (Think about it: If an IRS agent asked you how much you would be willing to pay to have a new freeway and you knew you would be taxed in proportion to the amount you responded, what would you say?) Examples 15.1 to 15.3 illustrate some of the problems that arise in financing public goods and suggests possible solutions to these problems.

EXAMPLE 15.1

Will Prentice and Wilson buy a water filter?

Prentice and Wilson own adjacent summer cottages along an isolated stretch of shoreline on Cayuga Lake. Because of a recent invasion of zebra mussels, each must add chlorine to his water intake valve each week to prevent it from becoming clogged by the tiny mollusks. A manufacturer has introduced a new filtration device that eliminates the nuisance of weekly chlorination. The cost of the device, which has the capacity to serve both houses, is $1,000. Both owners feel equally strongly about having the filter. But because Wilson earns twice as much as Prentice, Wilson is willing to pay up to $800 to have the filter, whereas its value to Prentice, a retired schoolteacher, is only $400. Would either person be willing to purchase the device individually? Is it efficient for them to share its purchase?

Neither will purchase the filter individually because each has a reservation price that is below its selling price. But because the two together value the filter at $1,200, sharing its use would be socially efficient. If they were to do so, total economic surplus would be $200 higher than if they did not buy the filter.

Since sharing the filter is the efficient outcome, we might expect that Prentice and Wilson would quickly reach agreement to purchase it. Unfortunately, however, the joint purchase and sharing of facilities is often easier proposed than accomplished. One hurdle is that people must incur costs merely to get together to discuss joint purchases. With only two people involved, those costs might not be significant. But if hundreds or thousands of people were involved, communication costs could be prohibitive.

With large numbers of people, the free-rider problem also emerges (see Chapter 12). After all, everyone knows that the project will either succeed or fail independently of any one person's contribution to it. Everyone thus has an incentive to withhold contributions—or get a free ride—in the hope that others will give.

GOVERNMENT PROVISION OF PUBLIC GOODS

Finally, even when only a few people are involved, reaching agreement on a fair sharing of the total expense may be difficult. For example, Prentice and Wilson might be reluctant to disclose their true reservation prices to one another for the same reason that you might be reluctant to disclose your reservation price for a public good to an IRS agent.

These practical concerns may lead us to empower government to buy public goods on our behalf. But as Example 15.2 makes clear, this approach does not eliminate the need to reach political agreement on how public purchases are to be financed.

Will government buy the water filter if there is an "equal tax" rule?

Suppose Prentice and Wilson from Example 15.1 could ask the government to help broker the water filter purchase. And suppose that the government's tax policy must follow a "nondiscrimination" rule that prohibits charging any citizen more for a public good than it charges his or her neighbor. Another rule is that public goods can be provided only if a majority of citizens approve of them. Will a government bound by these rules provide the filter that Prentice and Wilson want?

A tax that collects the same amount from every citizen is called a **head tax**. If the government must rely on a head tax, it must raise $500 from Prentice and $500 from Wilson. But since the device is worth only $400 to Prentice, he will vote against the project, thus denying it a majority. So a democratic government cannot provide the water filter if it must rely on a head tax.

A head tax is an example of a **regressive tax**, one for which the proportion of a taxpayer's income that is paid in taxes declines as the taxpayer's income rises.

The point illustrated by Example 15.2 is not confined to the specific public good considered. It applies whenever taxpayers place significantly different valuations on public goods, as will almost always happen whenever people earn significantly different incomes. An equal-tax rule under these circumstances will almost invariably rule out the provision of many worthwhile public goods.

As Example 15.3 suggests, one solution to this problem is to allow taxes to vary by income.

EXAMPLE 15.2

head tax a tax that collects the same amount from every taxpayer

regressive tax a tax under which the proportion of income paid in taxes declines as income rises

CHAPTER 15 PUBLIC GOODS AND TAX POLICY

EXAMPLE 15.3

proportional income tax one under which all taxpayers pay the same proportion of their incomes in taxes

Will the government buy the filter if there is a proportional tax on income?

Suppose that Prentice proposes that the government raise revenue by imposing a proportional tax on income to finance the provision of the water filter described in Example 15.1. Will Wilson, who earns twice as much as Prentice, support this proposal?

A **proportional income tax** is one under which all taxpayers pay the same percentage of their incomes in taxes. Under such a tax, Wilson would support Prentice's proposal, because if he didn't, each would fail to enjoy a public good whose benefit exceeds his share of its cost. Under the proportional tax on income, Prentice would contribute $333 toward the $1,000 purchase price of the filter and Wilson would contribute $667. The government would buy the filter, resulting in additional surpluses of $67 for Prentice and $133 for Wilson.

The following example makes the point that just as equal contributions are often a poor way to pay for public goods, they are also often a poor way to share expenses within the household.

Why don't most married couples contribute equally to joint purchases?

Suppose Hillary earns $2,000,000 per year while her husband Bill earns only $20,000. Given her income, Hillary as an individual would want to spend much more than Bill would on housing, travel, entertainment, education for their children, and the many other items they consume jointly. What will happen if the couple adopts a rule that each must contribute an equal amount toward the purchase of such items?

This rule would constrain the couple to live in a small house, take only inexpensive vacations, and skimp on entertainment, dining out, and their children's education. It is therefore easy to see why Hillary might find it attractive to pay considerably more than 50 percent for jointly consumed goods, because doing so would enable *both* of them to consume in the manner their combined income permits.

Public goods and jointly consumed private goods are different from individually consumed private goods in the following important way: *Different individuals are free to consume whatever quantity and quality of most private goods they choose to buy, but jointly consumed goods must be provided in the same quantity and quality for all persons.*

As in the case of private goods, people's willingness to pay for public goods is generally an increasing function of income. Wealthy individuals tend to assign greater value to public goods than low-income people do, not because the wealthy have different tastes but because they have more money. A head tax would result in high-income persons getting smaller amounts of public goods than they want. By increasing the total economic surplus available for all to share, a tax system that assigns a larger share of the tax burden to people with higher incomes makes possible a better outcome for both rich and poor alike. Indeed, virtually all industrialized nations have tax systems that are at least mildly **progressive**, which means that the proportion of income paid in taxes actually rises with a family's income.

progressive tax one in which the proportion of income paid in taxes rises as income rises

Progressive taxation and even proportional taxation have often been criticized as being unfair to the wealthy, who are forced to pay more than others for public goods that all consume in common. The irony in this charge, however, is that exclusive reliance on head taxes, or even proportional taxes, would curtail the provision of public goods and services that are of greatest value to high-income families. Studies have shown, for example, that the income elasticity of demand for public goods such as parks and recreation facilities, clean air and water, public safety, uncongested roads, and aesthetically pleasing public spaces is substantially greater than 1. Failure to rely on progressive taxation would result in gross underprovision of such public goods and services.

 PUBLIC GOODS

A public good is both nonrival and nonexcludable. Private firms typically cannot recover the costs of producing such goods because they cannot exclude nonpayers from consuming them. Nor would charging for a public good promote efficiency, since one person's consumption of the good does not diminish its availability for others.

Both obstacles can be overcome by creating a government with the power to levy taxes. Even high-income citizens often favor progressive taxes, because proportional or regressive taxes may generate insufficient revenue to pay for the public goods those taxpayers favor.

THE OPTIMAL QUANTITY OF A PUBLIC GOOD

In the examples considered thus far, the question was whether to provide a particular public good and, if so, how to pay for it. In practice, we often confront additional questions about what level and quality of a public good to provide.

Standard cost-benefit logic also applies to these questions. For example, New York City should add another rocket to a fireworks display if and only if the amount that citizens would collectively be willing to pay to see the rocket is at least as great as its cost.

THE DEMAND CURVE FOR A PUBLIC GOOD

To calculate the socially optimal quantity of a public good, we must first construct the demand curve for that public good. The process for doing so differs in an important way from the one we use to generate the market demand curve for a private good.

For a private good, all buyers face the same price and each chooses the quantity he or she wishes to purchase at that price. Recall that to construct the demand curve for a private good from the demand curves for individual consumers, we place the individual demand curves side by side and add them horizontally. That is, for each of a series of fixed prices, we add the resulting quantities demanded on the individual demand curves. In Figure 15.1, for example, we add the individual demand curves for a private good, D_1 and D_2 [parts (a) and (b)], horizontally to obtain the market demand curve for the good D [part (c)].

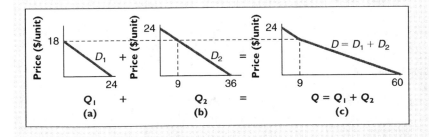

FIGURE 15.1

Generating the Market Demand Curve for a Private Good.

To construct the market demand curve for a private good (c), we add the individual demand curves (a) and (b) horizontally.

For a public good, all buyers necessarily consume the same quantity, although each may differ in terms of willingness to pay for additional units of

Frank–Bernanke:
Principles of
Microeconomics, Second
Edition

IV. Economics of Public
Policy

15. Public Goods and Tax
Policy

© The McGraw–Hill
Companies, 2004

the good. Constructing the demand curve for a public good thus entails not horizontal summation of the individual demand curves but vertical summation. That is, for each of a series of quantity values, we must add the prices that individuals are willing to pay for an additional unit of the good. The curves D_1 and D_2 in Figure 15.2(c) and (b) show individual demand curves for a public good by two different people. At each quantity, these curves tell how much the individual would be willing to pay for an additional unit of the public good. If we add D_1 and D_2 vertically, we obtain the total demand curve D for the public good [part (a)].

FIGURE 15.2

**Generating the Demand
Curve for a Public Good.**
To construct the demand
curve for a public good (a),
we add the individual
demand curves (c) and (b)
vertically.

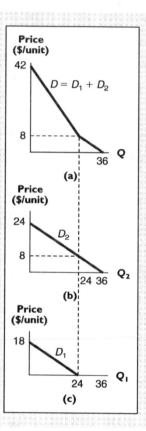

EXERCISE 15.2

**Bill and Tom are the only demanders of a public good. If Bill's demand
curve is $P_B = 6 - 0.5Q$ and Tom's is $P_T = 12 - Q$, construct the demand
curve for this public good.**

In Example 15.4, we see how the demand curve for a public good might be used in conjunction with information about costs to determine the optimal level of parkland in a city.

EXAMPLE 15.4

What is the optimal quantity of urban parkland?

The city government of a new planned community must decide how much parkland to provide. The marginal cost curve and the public demand curve for urban parkland are as shown in Figure 15.3. Why is the marginal cost curve upward-sloping and the demand curve downward-sloping? Given these curves, what is the optimal quantity of parkland?

The marginal cost schedule for urban parkland is upward-sloping because of the low-hanging-fruit principle: The city acquires the cheapest parcels of land first, and only then turns to more expensive parcels. Likewise, the marginal willingness-to-pay curve is downward-sloping because of the law of diminishing marginal utility. Just as people are generally willing to pay less for their fifth hot dog than for their first, they are also willing to pay less for the 101st acre of parkland than for the 100th acre. Given these curves, A^* is the optimal quantity of parkland. For any quantity less than A^*, the benefit of additional parkland exceeds its cost, which means that total economic surplus can be made larger by expanding the amount of parkland. For example, at A_0, the community would be willing to pay $200,000 for an additional acre of urban parkland, but its cost is only $80,000. Similarly, for any quantity of parkland in excess of A^*, the community would gain more than it would lose by selling off some parkland.

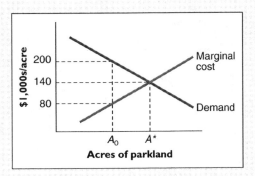

FIGURE 15.3
The Optimal Quantity of Parkland.
The optimal number of acres of urban parkland is A^*, the quantity at which the public's willingness to pay for additional parkland is equal to the marginal cost of parkland.

PRIVATE PROVISION OF PUBLIC GOODS

One advantage of using the government to provide public goods is that once a tax collection agency has been established to finance a single public good, it can be expanded at relatively low cost to generate revenue for additional public goods. Another advantage is that because government has the power to tax, it can summarily assign responsibility for the cost of a public good without endless haggling over who bears what share of the burden. And in the case of goods for which nonpayers cannot be excluded, the government may be the only feasible provider.

But exclusive reliance on government also entails disadvantages. Most fundamentally, the government's one-size-fits-all approach invariably requires many people to pay for public goods they don't want, while others end up having to do without public goods they want desperately. For example, many people vehemently oppose the provision of *any* sex education in the public schools, while others fervently believe that far more such instruction should be provided than is currently offered in most current public school curriculums. In addition, mandatory taxation strikes many people as coercive, even if they approve of the particular public goods being provided.

It is no surprise, then, that governments are not the exclusive providers of public goods in any society. Indeed, many public goods are routinely provided through private channels. The challenge, in each case, is to devise a scheme for raising the required revenues. Here are some methods that seem to work.

Funding by donation In 2001 Americans gave more than $200 billion to private charities, many of which provide public goods to their communities. People also volunteer their time on behalf of organizations that provide public goods. When you paint your house, mow your lawn, or plant a flower garden, you are enhancing the quality of life in your neighborhood, and in that sense you are voluntarily providing a public good to your neighbors.

Development of new means to exclude nonpayers New electronic technology makes it possible to exclude nonpayers from many goods that in the past could not be thus restricted. For instance, broadcast television stations now have the ability to scramble their signals, making them available only to those consumers who purchase descrambling devices.

Private contracting More than 8 million Americans now live in gated private communities—private homeowners' associations that wall off contiguous properties and provide various services to residents. Many of these associations provide security services, schools, and fire protection and in other ways function much like ordinary local governments. Recognizing that individual incentives may not be strong enough to assure socially optimal levels of maintenance and landscaping, these associations often bill homeowners for those services directly. Many of the rules imposed by these associations are even more restrictive than those imposed by local governments, a distinction that is defended on the grounds that people are always free to choose some other neighborhood if they don't like the rules of any particular homeowners' association. Many people would be reluctant to tolerate a municipal ordinance that prevents people from painting their houses purple, yet such restrictions are common in the bylaws of homeowners' associations.

Sale of by-products Many public goods are financed by the sale of rights or services that are generated as by-products of the public goods. For instance, as noted earlier, radio and television programming is a public good that is paid for in many cases by the sale of advertising messages. Internet services are also underwritten in part by commercial messages that pop up or appear in the headers or margins of web pages.

Given the quintessentially voluntary nature of privately provided public goods, it might seem that reliance on private provision might be preferred whenever it proved feasible. But as the following example makes clear, private provision often entails problems of its own.

ECONOMIC NATURALIST 15.2

Why do television networks favor Jerry Springer over Masterpiece Theater?

In a given time slot, a television network faces the alternative of broadcasting either the *Jerry Springer Show* or *Masterpiece Theater*. If it chooses *Springer*, it will win 20 percent of the viewing audience, but only 18 percent if it chooses *Masterpiece Theater*. Suppose those who would choose *Springer* would collectively be willing to pay $10 million for the right to see that program, while those who choose *Masterpiece Theater* would be willing to pay $30 million. And suppose, finally, that the time slot is to be financed by a detergent company. Which program will the network choose? Which program would be socially optimal?

A detergent maker cares primarily about the number of people who will see its advertisements and will thus choose the program that will attract the largest audience—here, the *Springer Show*. The fact that those who prefer *Masterpiece Theater* would be willing to pay a lot more to see it is of little concern to the sponsor. But to identify the optimal result from society's point of view, we must take this difference into account. Because the people who prefer *Masterpiece Theater* could pay the *Springer* viewers more than enough to compensate them for relinquishing the time slot, *Masterpiece Theater* is the efficient outcome. But unless its supporters happen to buy more soap in total than the *Springer* viewers, the latter will prevail. In short, reliance on advertising and other indirect mechanisms for financing public goods provides no assurance that the goods chosen will maximize economic surplus.

THE OPTIMAL QUANTITY OF A PUBLIC GOOD

Of course, the fact that the programs that best suit advertisers' needs may not be socially optimal does not mean that government decisions would necessarily be better. One can imagine, for example, a cultural affairs ministry that would choose television programming that would be "good for us" but that few of us would want to watch.

One way to avoid the inefficiency that arises when advertisers choose programming is to employ pay-per-view methods of paying for television programming. These methods allow viewers to register not just which programs they prefer but also the strength of their preferences, as measured by how much they are willing to pay.

But although pay-per-view TV is more likely to select the programs the public most values, it is also less efficient than broadcast TV in one important respect. As noted earlier, charging each household a fee for viewing discourages some households from tuning in. And since the marginal social cost of serving an additional household is exactly zero, limiting the audience in this way is inefficient. Which of the two inefficiencies is more important—free TV's inefficiency in choosing among programs or pay TV's inefficiency in excluding potential beneficiaries—is an empirical question.

In any event, the mix between private and public provision of public goods and services differs substantially from society to society and from arena to arena within any given society. These differences depend on the nature of available technologies for delivering and paying for public goods, and also on people's preferences.

Why do detergent companies care more about audience size than about how much people would be willing to pay to see the programs they sponsor?

By how much is economic surplus reduced by a pay-per-view charge?

If *Mystery Theater* is shown on pay-per-view television at 10 P.M. on Thursdays, the demand curve for each episode is given by $P = 20 - Q$, where P is the price per household in dollars and Q is the number of households who choose to watch the program (in millions). If the regulated pay-per-view charge is $10 per household, by how much would economic surplus rise if the same episode were shown instead on "free" broadcast public TV?

With a fee of $10 per episode, 10 million households will watch (see Figure 15.4). But if the same episode were shown instead on broadcast public TV, 20 million households would watch. The additional economic surplus reaped by the extra 10 million households is the area of the blue triangle, which is $50 million. The marginal cost of permitting these additional households to watch the episode is zero, so the total gain in surplus is $50 million.

EXAMPLE 15.5

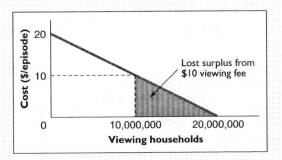

FIGURE 15.4
The Loss in Surplus from a Pay-per-View Fee.
Twice as many households would watch the program if its price were zero instead of $10. The additional economic surplus is the area of the blue triangle, or $50 million.

In general, charging a positive price for a good whose marginal cost is zero will result in a loss in surplus. As we saw in Chapter 7, the size of the loss that results when price is set above marginal cost depends on the price elasticity of

CHAPTER 15 PUBLIC GOODS AND TAX POLICY

demand. When demand is more elastic, the loss in surplus is greater. Exercise 15.3 provides an opportunity to see that principle at work.

EXERCISE 15.3

How would your answer to Example 15.5 have been different if the demand curve had been given instead by $P = 15 - 2Q$?

 RECAP THE OPTIMAL QUANTITY OF A PUBLIC GOOD

Because the quantity of a public good must be the same for every consumer, the total demand curve for a public good is constructed by adding individual demand curves vertically. Optimal production of a public good occurs at the quantity for which the demand curve intersects the marginal cost curve for the public good.

Government need not always be the best way to provide public goods. Such goods can be provided by private organizations that rely on charitable contributions or the sale of by-products. Private for-profit companies can also become providers when new technologies such as pay-per-view television convert public goods into collective goods.

ADDITIONAL FUNCTIONS OF GOVERNMENT

The provision of public goods is not the only rationale for the existence of government. Government also creates and enforces the rules without which the efficient production of private goods would not be possible.

EXTERNALITIES AND PROPERTY RIGHTS

As we saw in Chapter 11, for example, externalities often stand in the way of socially optimal resource allocation in private activities. We saw, too, that optimal allocations are unlikely to result whenever property rights are poorly defined (for example, the tragedy of the commons). These observations suggest the existence of two additional important roles for government: the regulation of activities that generate externalities and the definition and enforcement of property rights.

These rationales for government action explain why most governments regulate activities that generate pollution, subsidize education (on the grounds that an educated public creates positive externalities), control access to fishing waters and public timber lands, and enforce zoning laws. Most laws, in fact, represent attempts to define property rights or to control externalities. The law requiring motorists to drive on the right, for example, is an attempt to prevent the activities of one motorist from causing harm to others.

Proponents of minimalist government often object that the government unjustly curtails our freedom when it uses zoning laws to limit the size of the houses we build or imposes fines on motorists who violate highway speed limits. Yet the justification for such regulations is precisely the same as for the laws that prohibit your fist from occupying the same physical space as your neighbor's nose. You are free to swing your fists as you please, provided you cause no harm to others. But if your fist strikes your neighbor's nose, you become a violator of the law and subject to punishment. If the proponents of minimalist government approve of restricting behavior in this way, why do they disapprove of other attempts to discourage behaviors that cause harm to others?

Perhaps their fear is that because externalities are so pervasive, governments that were empowered to regulate them might quickly get out of control. This is by no means an idle fear, and we emphasize that the mere fact that an externality exists does not necessarily mean that the best outcome is for the government to regulate it. As we will see in the next section, regulation entails costs of its own. The ultimate question is therefore a practical one: Will government regulation of the externality in question do more good than harm? Slogans about being free to live without government interference provide little help in answering such questions.

LOCAL, STATE, OR FEDERAL?

Framers of the American Constitution were deeply skeptical of centralized government power. In drafting the Constitution, therefore, they explicitly tried to limit the powers of the federal government as much as possible, delegating most important powers to the states, who in turn delegated many of their powers to governments at the local level.

That the dangers of remote, centralized government ranked high among founding fathers' concerns is no surprise. After all, fresh in their memories was the autocratic treatment received by the American colonies at the hands of the monarchy in England. The founding fathers recognized that government will be more responsive the shorter the distance between officeholders and the voters who elect them.

Another obvious advantage of giving as much authority to local governments as possible is that different communities often have markedly different preferences about how much to spend on public goods, and even on what kinds of public goods to provide. When such decisions are made at the local level, people can shop for a community whose voters' preferences largely coincide with their own. Those who like high levels of public goods and services can band together and authorize high taxes to pay for them. Others who place less value on public services can choose communities in which both services and taxes are lower.

Why, given the many attractions of decisions made at the local level, did the founding fathers create federal and state governments at all? One reason is economies of scale in defense. For a country to survive politically, it must be able to deter aggression by hostile governments. A country consisting only of, say, Concord, New Hampshire, would be ill-equipped to do that. Large, well-equipped armies and navies cost a lot of money, and countries without sufficient population simply cannot afford them.

Defense, however, is not the only reason to empower governments beyond the local or state level. The problem of pollution, for example, is difficult to solve when the various sources of pollution are not subject to regulatory control by a single government. Much of the acid rain experienced in Canada, for instance, is the result of sulfur dioxide emissions from industrial sources in the upper midwest of the United States. These emissions are beyond the reach of Canadian environmental regulations. In many instances, as with the discharge of greenhouse gases, not even a coalition of all the governments in North, Central, and South America would have power to take effective action. Carbon dioxide emitted anywhere on the planet disperses to uniform concentrations around the globe in a matter of months.

The choice between different levels of government, then, often confronts us with difficult trade-offs. Ceding the power of taxation to a federal government often entails painful compromises for voters in individual states. But the loss of political autonomy is an even less attractive option. Similarly, nations are understandably reluctant to cede any of their sovereign powers to a higher authority, but failure to take such steps may entail unacceptable environmental costs in the long run.

RECAP   **ADDITIONAL FUNCTIONS OF GOVERNMENT**

Government creates economic surplus not only by providing public goods but also by regulating activities that generate externalities and by defining and enforcing property rights. These rationales explain why most governments regulate pollution, subsidize education, control access to fishing waters and public timber lands, and enforce zoning laws.

Although the framers of the Constitution disliked centralized government power, they recognized that some government functions are not best performed at the local or even state level. Economies of scale argue for provision of defense at the national level. Externalities that transcend local boundaries provide an additional rationale for national or even international government.

SOURCES OF INEFFICIENCY IN THE POLITICAL PROCESS

In most countries, expenditures on public goods, tax policy, and laws regulating behavior are determined in large part by the votes of democratically elected representatives. This process is far from perfect. (Winston Churchill called democracy "the worst form of government, except for any other.") Inefficiencies often arise in the public sphere not because of incompetent or ignorant legislators but because of structural incentive problems.

PORK BARREL LEGISLATION

The following example, drawn not from the public sector but from everyday private life, illustrates one of the important incentive gaps.

Why does check-splitting make the total restaurant bill higher?

Sven Torvaldsen and nine friends are having dinner at la Maison de la Casa House, a four-star restaurant in Minneapolis. To simplify the task of paying for their meal, they have agreed in advance to split the cost of their meal equally, with each paying one-tenth of the total check. Having cleared the entree dishes, the waiter arrives with the dessert menu, on which Sven's two favorite items are pumpkin bread pudding ($10) and chocolate mousse ($6). Sven's reservation prices for these items are $4 and $3, respectively. Will he order dessert, and, if so, which one? Would he order dessert if he were dining by himself?

When Sven and his friends split the total check equally, Sven's payment goes up by one-tenth of the menu price of any dessert he orders. Thus the prices—to him—of the bread pudding and chocolate mousse are $1 and 60 cents, respectively. Because he gets $4 − $1 = $3 of consumer surplus from the bread pudding and only $3 − $0.60 = $2.40 from the chocolate mousse, he will order the bread pudding. If Sven were dining alone, however, his bill would increase dollar for dollar with the menu price of any dessert he ordered. And since the menu prices exceed his corresponding reservation prices, he would not order dessert at all.

The irony, of course, is that if Sven's nine friends have the same preferences regarding dessert, each will order bread pudding and each person's share of the total bill will rise not by $1 but by the full $10. Compared to the alternative of no one having dessert, each diner suffers a $6 loss in consumer surplus. Still, it made sense for each to order bread pudding, since failure to do so would have reduced each diner's bill by only $1.

SOURCES OF INEFFICIENCY IN THE POLITICAL PROCESS

EXERCISE 15.4

In the preceding example, would Sven have ordered dessert if there had been only 5 people splitting the check instead of 10?

Alert readers will have noticed the similarity between the problem posed in the preceding example and the one posed in Economic Naturalist 11.7, in which identical twins had a single milkshake to share with two straws. The same incentive problem leads to the inefficient outcome in both cases.

The following example illustrates how the very same incentive problem rears its head in the legislative process.

Why do legislators often support one another's pork barrel spending programs?

Pork barrel programs are government programs that benefit local areas but are of questionable value from a national perspective. Why do voters seem to support legislators who initiate such projects even when the total effect of all such projects on local tax bills far exceeds the local benefits?

Consider a voter in a congressional district that contains one one-hundredth of the country's taxpayers. Suppose that voter's representative is able to deliver a public project that generates benefits of $100 million for the district but that costs the federal government $150 million. Since the district's share of the tax bill for the project will be only $150 million/100 = $1.5 million, residents of the district are $98.5 million better off with the project than without it. And that explains why so many voters favor legislators with a successful record of "bringing home the bacon."

But why would legislator A support such a project in legislator B's home district? After all, B's project will cause A's constituents' taxes to rise—albeit by a small amount—yet they will get no direct benefit from the project. The answer is that if A does not support B's project, then B will not support A's. The practice whereby legislators support one another's pet projects is known as **logrolling**. This practice creates a bias toward excessive spending, much like the bias created when a dinner check is split equally.

ECONOMIC NATURALIST 15.4

pork barrel spending a public expenditure that is larger than the total benefit it creates but that is favored by a legislator because his or her constituents benefit from the expenditure by more than their share of the resulting extra taxes

logrolling the practice whereby legislators support one another's legislative proposals

RENT-SEEKING

A related source of inefficiency in the public sphere occurs because the gains from government projects are often concentrated in the hands of a few beneficiaries, while the costs are spread among many. This means that beneficiaries often have a powerful incentive to organize and lobby in favor of public projects. Individual taxpayers, by contrast, have little at stake in any public project and therefore have little incentive to incur the cost of mobilizing themselves in opposition.

Suppose, for example, that a price support bill for sugar will raise the price of sugar by 10 cents per pound and that the average American family currently consumes 100 pounds of sugar per year. How will this legislation affect the average family's consumption of sugar? Recall from Chapter 5 that a good, such as salt or sugar, whose share in most family budgets is small is likely to have a low price elasticity of demand. Hence each family's sugar consumption will decline only slightly as a result of the 10-cent price hike. The resulting increase in each family's annual expenditures on sugar—slightly less than $10—is scarcely a noticeable burden, and surely not enough to induce many people to complain to their representatives. The same legislation, however, will raise sugar industry revenues by nearly $1 billion annually. With a sum that large at stake, it is certain that the industry will lobby vigorously in its favor.

Why don't citizens vote against those legislators who support such bills? One reason is the problem of rational ignorance, discussed in Chapter 12. Most voters

Frank–Bernanke:
Principles of
Microeconomics, Second
Edition

IV. Economics of Public
Policy

15. Public Goods and Tax
Policy

© The McGraw–Hill
Companies, 2004

have no idea that a price support bill for sugar and other special-interest bills even exist, much less how individual legislators vote on them. If all voters became well-informed about such bills, the resulting increase in the quality of legislation might well be sufficient to compensate each voter for the cost of becoming informed. But because of the free-rider problem, each voter knows that the outcome of votes in Congress will not be much affected by whether he becomes well-informed.

Still other sources of inefficiency arise even in the case of projects whose benefits exceed their costs. Several years ago, for example, the federal government announced its decision to build a $25 billion high-energy physics research facility (the "superconducting supercollider"), which ignited an intense competition among more than 20 states vying to be chosen as the site for this facility. Hundreds of millions of dollars was spent on proposal preparation, consultants' fees, and various other lobbying activities. Such investments are known as **rent-seeking**, and they tend to be inefficient for the same reason that investments by contestants in other positional arms races are inefficient (see Chapter 11).

rent-seeking the socially unproductive efforts of people or firms to win a prize

Efforts devoted to rent-seeking are socially unproductive because of the simple incentive problem illustrated in Example 15.6.

EXAMPLE 15.6

Why would anyone pay $50 for a $20 bill?

Suppose a $20 bill is to be auctioned off to the highest bidder. The rules of this particular auction require an initial bid of at least 50 cents, and succeeding bids must exceed the previous high bid by at least 50 cents. When the bidding ceases, both the highest bidder and the second-highest bidder must give the amounts they bid to the auctioneer. The highest bidder then receives the $20, and the second-highest bidder gets nothing. For example, if the highest bid is $11 and the second-highest bid is $10.50, the winner earns a net payment of $20 − $11 = $9, and the runner-up loses $10.50. How high will the winning bid be, on average?

Auctions like this one have been extensively studied in the laboratory. And although subjects in these experiments have ranged from business executives to college undergraduates, the pattern of bidding is almost always the same. Following the opening bid, offers proceed quickly to $10, or half the amount being auctioned. A pause then occurs as the subjects appear to digest the fact that with the next bid the sum of the two highest bids will exceed $20, thus taking the auctioneer off the hook. At this point, the second-highest bidder, whose bid stands at $9.50, invariably offers $10.50, apparently preferring a shot at winning $9.50 to a sure loss of $9.50.

In most cases, all but the top two bidders drop out at this point, and the top two quickly escalate their bids. As the bidding approaches $20, a second pause occurs, this time as the bidders appear to recognize that even the highest bidder is likely to come out behind. The second-highest bidder, at $19.50, is understandably reluctant to offer $20.50. But consider the alternative. If he drops out, he will lose $19.50 for sure. But if he offers $20.50 and wins, he will lose only 50 cents. So as long as he thinks there is even a small chance that the other bidder will drop out, it makes sense to continue. Once the $20 threshold has been crossed, the pace of the bidding quickens again, and from then on it is a war of nerves between the two remaining bidders. It is common for the bidding to reach $50 before someone finally yields in frustration.

One might be tempted to think that any intelligent, well-informed person would know better than to become involved in an auction whose incentives so strongly favor costly escalation. But many of the subjects in these auctions have been experienced business professionals; many others have had formal training in the theory of games and strategic interaction. For example, the psychologist Max Bazerman reports that during a recent 10-year period he earned more than $17,000 by auctioning $20 bills to his MBA students at Northwestern University's Kellogg Graduate School of Management, which is consistently among the top-rated MBA programs in the world. In the course of almost 200 of his auctions, the top two bids never totaled less than $39, and in one instance they totaled $407.

As Example 15.7 shows, the incentives that confront participants in the $20 bill auction are strikingly similar to those that confront companies that are vying for lucrative government contracts.

How much will cellular phone companies bid for an exclusive license?

EXAMPLE 15.7

The State of Wyoming has announced its intention to grant an exclusive license to provide cellular phone services within its borders. Two firms have met the deadline for applying for this license. The franchise lasts for exactly one year, during which time the franchisee can expect to make an economic profit of $20 million. The state legislature will choose the applicant that spends the most money lobbying legislators. If the applicants cannot collude, how much will each spend on lobbying?

If both spend the same, each will have a 50-50 chance at the $20 million prize, which means an expected profit of $10 million minus the amount spent lobbying. If the lobbyists could collude, each would agree to spend the same small, token amount on lobbying. But in the absence of a binding agreement, each will be strongly tempted to try to outspend the other. Once each firm's spending reaches $10 million, each will have an expected profit of zero (a 50-50 chance to earn $20 million, minus the $10 million spent on lobbying).

Further bidding would guarantee an expected loss. And yet, if one firm spent $10,000,001 while the other stayed at $10 million, the first firm would get the franchise for sure and earn an economic profit of $9,999,999. The other firm would have an economic loss of $10 million. Rather than face a sure loss of $10 million, it may be tempted to bid $10,000,002. But then, of course, its rival would face a similar incentive to respond to that bid. No matter where the escalation stops, it is sure to dissipate much of the gains that could have been had from the project. And perhaps, as in the $20 bill auction, the total amount dissipated will be even more than the value of the franchise itself.

From the individual perspective, it is easy to see why firms might lobby in this fashion for a chance to win government benefits. From society's perspective, however, this activity is almost purely wasteful. Lobbyists are typically intelligent, well-educated, and socially skilled. The opportunity cost of their time is high. If they were not lobbying government officials on behalf of their clients, they could be producing other goods or services of value. Governments can discourage such waste by selecting contractors not according to the amount they spend lobbying but on the basis of the price they promise to charge for their services. Society will be more successful the more its institutions encourage citizens to pursue activities that create wealth rather than activities that merely transfer existing wealth from one person or company to another.

STARVE THE GOVERNMENT?

The Nobel laureate Milton Friedman has said that no bureaucrat spends taxpayers' money as carefully as those taxpayers themselves would have. And indeed, there can be little doubt that many government expenditures are wasteful. Beyond the fact that logrolling often results in pork barrel programs that would not satisfy the cost-benefit test, we must worry that government employees may not always face strong incentives to get the most for what they spend. The Pentagon, for example, once purchased a coffeemaker for $7,600 and on another occasion paid $600 for a toilet seat. Such expenditures may have been aberrations, but there seems little doubt that private contractors often deliver comparable services at substantially lower costs than their public counterparts.

In their understandable outrage over government waste, many critics have urged major cutbacks in the volume of public goods and services. These critics reason that if we let the government spend more money, there will be more waste. This is true, of course, but only in the trivial sense that there would be more of *everything* the government does—good and bad—if public spending were higher.

One of our most extensive experiences with the consequences of major reductions in government spending comes from the Proposition 13 movement in California. This movement began with the passage of State Proposition 13 in 1978, which mandated large reductions in property taxes. As Californians have belatedly recognized, this remedy for government waste is like trying to starve a tapeworm by not eating. Fasting does harm the tapeworm, sure enough, but it harms the host even more. Residents of the Golden State, who once proudly sent their children to the nation's best schools, are now sending them to some of its worst.

The physician treats an infected patient by prescribing drugs that are toxic to the parasite but not to the host. A similar strategy should guide our attack on government waste. For example, we might consider the adoption of campaign-finance reform laws that would prevent legislators from accepting campaign contributions from the tobacco industry and other special interests whose government subsidies they support.

The question, then, isn't whether bureaucrats know best how to spend our money. Rather, it's "How much of our money do *we* want to spend on public services?" Although we must remain vigilant against government waste, we must also remember that many public services deliver good value for our money.

 RECAP

SOURCES OF INEFFICIENCY IN THE POLITICAL PROCESS

Government does much to help the economy function more efficiently, but it can also be a source of waste. For example, legislators may support pork barrel projects, which do not satisfy the cost-benefit criterion but which benefit constituents by more than their share of the extra taxes required to pay for the projects.

Rent-seeking, a second important source of inefficiency, occurs when individuals or firms use real resources in an effort to win favors from the government. Voters often fail to discipline legislators who abet rent-seeking, because the free-rider problem gives rise to rational ignorance on the part of many voters.

Concern about government waste has led many to conclude that the best government is necessarily the smallest one. The solution favored by these critics is to starve government by reducing the amount of money it can collect in taxes. Yet starving the government reduces one kind of waste only to increase another by curtailing public services whose benefit exceeds their cost.

WHAT SHOULD WE TAX?

Although the primary purpose of the tax system is to generate the revenue needed to fund public goods and other government expenditures, taxes also have many other consequences, some intended, others not. For example, taxes alter the relative costs and benefits of engaging in different activities. They also affect the distribution of real purchasing power in the economy. The best tax system is one that raises the needed revenues while at the same time having the most beneficial, or least deleterious, side effects.

On the first criterion, the federal tax system has not performed particularly well. Although the federal budget began to show a modest surplus in the late 1990s, until then it had been in continuous deficit since 1969, during which time the federal government had to borrow trillions of dollars to pay its bills. And now, early in the twenty-first century, the federal budget is again in deficit.

WHAT SHOULD WE TAX?

The fact that governments and private corporations borrow money in the same capital market explains the phenomenon economists call **crowding out**. When government increases its demand in the market for borrowed funds, interest rates rise, causing firms to cancel some of their planned investment projects. When the government fails to raise enough revenue from taxes to cover the amount it spends on public goods and services, it thus diverts funds from investments that would have helped the economy to grow.

crowding out government borrowing leads to higher interest rates, causing private firms to cancel planned investment projects

What about the effect of taxes on incentives? As discussed in Chapter 7, taxes will hold production and consumption below socially optimal levels in markets in which the private costs and benefits coincide exactly with all relevant social costs and benefits. Suppose, for example, that the long-run private marginal cost of producing cars is $20,000 per unit and that the demand curve for cars is as shown in Figure 15.5. The equilibrium quantity and price will be 6 million per year and $20,000, respectively. If no externalities accompany the production or consumption of cars, these will be the socially optimal levels for quantity and price. But if we now add a tax of $2,000 per car, the new equilibrium price and quantity will be $22,000 and 4 million, respectively. The loss in economic surplus will be equal to the area of the blue triangle ($2 billion per year), which is the cumulative sum of the differences between what excluded buyers would have been willing to pay for extra cars and the marginal cost of producing those cars.

Economists who write for the popular press have long focused on the loss in surplus caused by taxes like the one shown in Figure 15.5. These economists argue that the economy would perform better if taxes were lower and total government expenditures were smaller.

But arguments for that claim are far from compelling. As discussed in Chapter 7, for example, even if a tax in a market like the one shown in Figure 15.5 did produce a loss in surplus for participants in that market, it might nonetheless be justified if it led to an even larger gain in surplus from the public expenditures it financed. We also saw in Chapter 7 that the deadweight loss from taxing a good (or activity) will be smaller the smaller is the elasticity of demand or supply for the good. This principle suggests that deadweight losses could be minimized by concentrating taxes on goods with highly inelastic supply or demand curves.

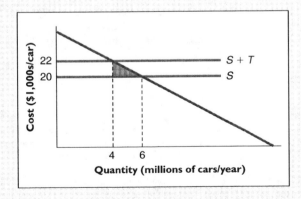

FIGURE 15.5

The Loss in Surplus from a Tax on Cars.
If the supply and demand curves for cars embody all relevant cost benefits of producing and consuming cars, then placing a tax on cars will lead to underproduction of them and a corresponding reduction in economic surplus.

Another difficulty with the argument that taxes harm the economy is more fundamental—namely, that taxes need not cause any loss in surplus at all, even in the markets in which they are directly applied. Suppose, for example, that in the market for cars considered earlier, private marginal cost is again $20,000 but that the production and use of cars now generates air pollution and congestion, negative externalities that sum to $2,000 per car each year. The socially optimal quantity of cars would then be not 6 million per year but only 4 million (see Figure 15.5). Without a tax on cars, the market would reach equilibrium at a price of $20,000 and a quantity of 6 million per year. But with a tax of $2,000 per car,

CHAPTER 15 PUBLIC GOODS AND TAX POLICY

the equilibrium quantity would shrink to 4 million per year, precisely the socially optimal number. Here, the direct effect of the tax is not only not to reduce total economic surplus but actually to augment it by $2 billion per day.

Could we raise enough tax revenue to run the government if we limited ourselves to taxing only those activities that generate negative externalities? No one knows for sure, but it might be possible, for the list of such activities is a long one.

For instance, when someone enters a congested freeway, he creates additional delays for the motorists already there. Existing technology would enable us to levy road-use taxes that reflect these congestion externalities. Each time fossil fuels are burned, they emit greenhouse gases into the atmosphere, which will accelerate the trend toward global warming. A tax on carbon would increase economic surplus by causing decision makers to take this external cost into account. Taxes on other forms of air and water pollution would have similarly benign effects on resource allocation. Recent experience with refundable taxes on food and beverage containers demonstrates that taxes like these can raise needed revenue while at the same time contributing to a cleaner environment.

■ SUMMARY ■

- Our aim in this chapter was to apply principles of microeconomics to the study of the government's role in modern society. One of government's principal tasks is to provide public goods, such as national defense and the criminal justice system. Such goods are, in varying degrees, nonrival and nonexcludable. The first property describes goods for which one person's consumption does not diminish the amount available for others, while the second refers to the difficulty of preventing nonpayers from consuming certain goods.

- Goods that are both highly nonexcludable and nonrival are often called pure public goods. A collective good—such as pay-per-view cable television—is nonrival but excludable. Commons goods are goods that are rival but nonexcludable.

- Because not everyone benefits equally from the provision of any given public good, charging all taxpayers equal amounts for the provision of public goods will generally not be either feasible or desirable. As in the case of private goods, people's willingness to pay for public goods generally increases with income, and most governments therefore levy higher taxes on the rich than on the poor. Tax systems with this property have been criticized on the grounds that they are unfair to the wealthy, but this criticism ignores the fact that alternative tax schemes generally lead to worse outcomes for both rich and poor alike.

- The criterion for providing the optimal quantity or quality of a public good is to keep increasing quantity or quality as long as the marginal benefit of doing so exceeds the marginal cost. One advantage of using the government to provide public goods is that once a tax collection agency has been established to finance a single public good, it can be expanded at relatively low cost to generate revenue to finance additional public goods. A second advantage is that because government has the power to tax, it can easily assign responsibility for the cost of a public good. And in the case of goods for which nonpayers simply cannot be excluded, the government may be the only feasible provider.

- One disadvantage to exclusive reliance on government for public goods provision is the element of coercion inherent in the tax system, which makes some people pay for public goods they don't want, while others do without public goods they do want. Many public goods are provided through private channels, with the necessary funding provided by donations, sale of by-products, by development of new means to exclude nonpayers, and in many cases by private contract. A loss in surplus results, however, whenever monetary charges are levied for the consumption of a nonrival good.

- In addition to providing public goods, government serves two other important roles: the regulation of activities that generate externalities and the definition and enforcement of property rights. Despite a general view that government is more responsive the shorter the distance between citizens and their elected representatives, factors such as economies of scale in the provision of public goods and externalities with broad reach often dictate the assignment of important functions to state or national governments.

- Although history has shown that democracy is the best form of government, it is far from perfect. For example, practices such as logrolling and rent-seeking, common in most democracies, often result in the adoption of laws and public projects whose costs exceed their benefits.

- To finance public goods and services, governments at all levels must tax. But a tax on any activity not only generates revenue, it also creates an incentive to reduce the activity. If the activity would have been pursued at the optimal level in the absence of a tax, taxing it will result in too little of the activity. This observation has led many critics to denounce all taxes as harmful to the economy. Yet the negative effects of taxes on incentives must be weighed against the benefits of the public goods and services financed by tax revenue. Furthermore, taxes on inelastically supplied or demanded activities may generate only small deadweight losses, while taxes on activities that create negative externalities may actually increase economic efficiency.

Frank–Bernanke:
Principles of
Microeconomics, Second
Edition

IV. Economics of Public
Policy

15. Public Goods and Tax
Policy

© The McGraw–Hill
Companies, 2004

■ KEY TERMS ■

collective good (375)
crowding out (391)
head tax (377)
logrolling (387)
nonexcludable good (374)

nonrival good (374)
pork barrel spending (387)
progressive tax (378)
proportional income tax (378)
public good (374)

pure commons good (375)
pure private good (375)
pure public good (374)
regressive tax (377)
rent-seeking (388)

■ REVIEW QUESTIONS ■

1. a. Which of the following goods are nonrival?
   Apples
   Stephen King novels
   Street lighting on campus
   NPR radio broadcasts
   b. Which of these goods are nonexcludable?

2. Give examples of goods that are, for the most part:
   a. Rival but nonexcludable
   b. Nonrival but excludable
   c. Both nonrival and nonexcludable

3. Why might even a wealthy person prefer a proportional income tax to a head tax?

4. True or false: A tax on an activity that generates negative externalities will improve resource allocation in the private sector and also generate revenue that could be used to pay for useful public goods. Explain.

5. Consider a good that would be provided optimally by private market forces. Why is the direct loss in surplus that would result from a tax on this good an overstatement of the loss in surplus caused by the tax?

■ PROBLEMS ■

1. Jack and Jill are the only two residents in a neighborhood, and they would like to hire a security guard. The value of a security guard is $50 per month to Jack and $150 per month to Jill. Irrespective of who pays the guard, the guard will protect the entire neighborhood.
   a. What is the most a guard can charge per month and still be assured of being hired by at least one of them?
   b. Suppose the competitive wage for a security guard is $120 per month. The local government proposes a plan whereby Jack and Jill each pay 50 percent of this monthly fee, and asks them to vote on this plan. Will the plan be voted in? Would economic surplus be higher if the neighborhood had a guard?

2. Refer to Problem 1. Suppose Jack earns $1,000 per month and Jill earns $11,000 per month.
   a. Suggest a proportional tax on income that would be accepted by majority vote and would pay for the security guard.
   b. Suppose instead that Jack proposes a tax scheme under which Jack and Jill would each receive the same net benefit from hiring the guard. How much would Jack and Jill pay now? Would Jill agree to this scheme?
   c. What is the practical problem that prevents ideas like the one in part b from working in real-life situations?

3. The following table shows all the marginal benefits for each voter in a small town whose town council is considering a new swimming pool with capacity for at least three citizens. The cost of the pool would be $18 per week and would not depend on the number of people who actually used it.

Voter	Marginal benefit ($/week)
A	12
B	5
C	2

CHAPTER 15   PUBLIC GOODS AND TAX POLICY

    a. If the pool must be financed by a weekly head tax levied on all voters, will the pool be approved by majority vote? Is this outcome socially efficient? Explain.

    b. The town council instead decides to auction a franchise off to a private monopoly to build and maintain the pool. If it cannot find such a firm willing to operate the pool, then the pool project will be scrapped. If all such monopolies are constrained by law to charge a single price to users, will the franchise be sold, and if so, how much will it sell for? Is this outcome socially efficient? Explain.

4. Refer to Problem 3. Suppose now that all such monopolies can perfectly price-discriminate.

    a. Will the franchise be sold, and if so, how much will it sell for? Is this outcome socially efficient? Explain.

    b. The town council decides that, rather than auction off the franchise, it will give it away to the firm that spends the most money lobbying council members. If there are four identical firms in the bidding and they cannot collude, what will happen?

5. Two consumers, Smith and Jones, have the following demand curves for Podunk Public Radio broadcasts of recorded opera on Saturdays:

$$\text{Smith:} \quad P_S = 12 - Q$$
$$\text{Jones:} \quad P_J = 12 - 2Q,$$

where P_S and P_J represent marginal willingness to pay values for Smith and Jones, respectively, and Q represents the number of hours of opera broadcast each Saturday.

    a. If Smith and Jones are the only public radio listeners in Podunk, construct the demand curve for opera broadcasts.

    b. If the marginal cost of opera broadcasts is $15 per hour, what is the socially optimal number of hours of broadcast opera?

6. Suppose the demand curves for hour-long episodes of the *Jerry Springer Show* and *Masterpiece Theater* are as shown in the following diagram. A television network is considering whether to add one or both programs to its upcoming fall lineup. The only two time slots remaining are sponsored by Colgate, which is under contract to pay the network 10 cents for each viewer who watches the program, out of which the network would have to cover its production costs of $400,000 per episode. (Viewership can be estimated accurately with telephone surveys.) Any time slot the network does not fill with *Springer* or *Masterpiece Theater* will be filled by infomercials for a weight-loss program, for which the network incurs no production costs and for which it receives a fee of $500,000. Viewers will receive $5 million in economic surplus from watching each installment of the infomercial.

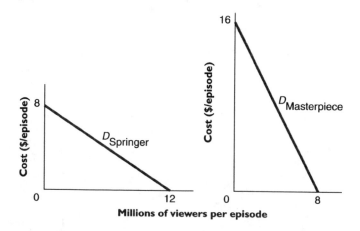

    a. How will the network fill the two remaining slots in its fall lineup?

    b. Is this outcome socially efficient?

7. Refer to Problem 6. By how much would total economic surplus be higher if each episode of *Masterpiece Theater* were shown on PBS free of charge than if it were shown by a profit-maximizing pay-per-view network?

8. When a TV company chooses a pay-per-view scheme to pay for programming, which of the following statements is true? Explain.
   a. The outcome is socially efficient.
   b. The programs selected will maximize advertising revenue.
   c. The marginal cost to an additional viewer of watching the programs is lower than when advertising is used to finance programming.
   d. The outcome is always more socially efficient than when advertising is used to finance programming.
   e. The variety of programs provided is likely to rise.

9. When a group of people must decide whether to buy a shared public good or service, the free-rider problem frequently occurs because:
   a. People have an incentive to understate how much the facility is really worth to them if they have to pay taxes to finance it.
   b. Each individual's needed contribution is an insignificant amount of the total required.
   c. People have an incentive to overstate how much the facility is worth to them if they don't have to pay taxes to finance it.
   d. People hope that others will value the facility enough to pay for it entirely.
   e. Only one of the above statements is not a reason for the existence of the free-rider problem.

10. The town of Smallsville is considering building a museum. The interest on the money Smallsville will have to borrow to build the museum will be $1,000 per year. Each citizen's marginal benefit from the museum is shown in the following table, and this marginal benefit schedule is public information.
    a. Assuming each citizen voted his or her private interests, would a referendum to build the museum and raise each citizen's annual taxes by $200 pass?
    b. A citizen proposes that the city let a private company build the museum and charge the citizens a lump-sum fee each year to view it as much as they like. Only citizens who paid the fee would be allowed to view the museum. If the private company were allowed to set a single fee, would any company offer to build the museum?
    c. A second citizen proposes allowing the private company to charge different prices to different citizens and auctioning the right to build the museum to the highest bidding company. Again, only the citizens who pay the fee may view the museum. What is the highest bid a private company would make to supply the museum to Smallsville?

Citizen	Marginal benefit from museum ($/year)
Anita	340
Brandon	290
Carlena	240
Dallas	190
Eloise	140

■ ANSWERS TO IN-CHAPTER EXERCISES ■

15.1 a. The BLS web site at 3 in the morning has the capacity to serve far more users than it attracts, so an additional user calling up the site does not prevent some other user from doing so. Other web sites, however do not show the nonrival property, at least during certain hours, because they attract more users than their servers can accommodate.
     b. The stadium at the championship game is always full, so anyone who watches the game in person prevents someone else from doing so.
     c. Additional people can watch the game on television without diminishing the availability of the telecast for others.

Frank–Bernanke:
Principles of
Microeconomics, Second
Edition

IV. Economics of Public
Policy

15. Public Goods and Tax
Policy

© The McGraw–Hill
Companies, 2004

CHAPTER 15   PUBLIC GOODS AND TAX POLICY

15.2 To construct the demand curve (a), we first graph Bill's demand curve (c) and Tom's
demand curve (b) and then add the two individual demand curves vertically. The
equation for the demand curve is $P = 18 - 1.5Q$.

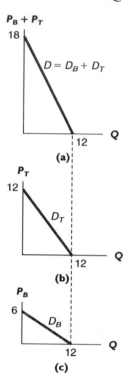

15.3 Whereas elasticity of demand was 1 at a price of $10 on the original demand curve,
it is 1.5 on the new demand curve. As a result, the $10 fee now excludes 20 mil-
lion viewers, and the resulting loss in surplus (again the area of the blue triangle)
is now $100 million.

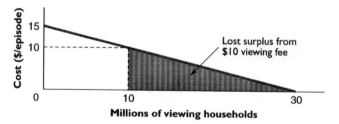

15.4 If Sven orders bread pudding, his share of the bill would now go up by $2 instead
of $1. If he orders chocolate mousse, his share of the bill would go up by $1.20
instead of $0.60. So he would still order the bread pudding (surplus = $4 − $2 =
$2) rather than the chocolate mousse (surplus = $3 − $1.20 = $1.80).

PUBLIC POLICY FOR NATURAL RESOURCES

Public policy refers to the **collective actions** that people undertake through **governmental institutions.** These actions shape the terms under which natural resources are used. Collective action can be pursued at many levels, from the local neighborhood and community level to that of the country or even the world. The public institutions through which policy is pursued differ from level to level, region to region, country to country, and even from time to time.

In this chapter we review some of the major types of **policy alternatives** that are available in a market economy to manage natural resource conservation and utilization. Although the discussion is conceptual to a large extent, we use natural resource examples to illustrate general cases. We are moving closer to the later chapters, which will focus more deeply on issues involving specific natural resources. The objectives are, first, to understand that there are different types of natural resource policies and, second, to assess the applicability of these policies in different circumstances. Policy decisions are not simply technical exercises: They are full of conflict and political controversy. Benefits and costs are involved, but so are political ideologies and strategies. We are not going to deal here with the political dimensions of the public policy process. The goal is, rather, to clarify the economic/incentive aspects of different policy approaches so that we can identify which approaches represent the best course of action for particular circumstances.

SECTION THREE: GENERAL NATURAL RESOURCE ISSUES

THE OBJECTIVES OF PUBLIC POLICY

To say "best course of action" implies that we have a good idea what the **objectives** of public policy should be or, to say it another way, what **criteria** should be used to judge the effectiveness of different resource policies. Controversies over public policy occur for many reasons, one of which is disagreement and/or lack of clarity about policy goals. The most important of these goals are the following.

Economic Efficiency

The attraction of economic efficiency is that it takes into account both the benefits and the costs of taking an action. Efficiency in the use of natural resources implies that the natural assets of society are being utilized in a way that **maximizes their net benefits** to the members of that society. So efficiency would seem to be a reasonable goal for any policy that purports to be in the public interest. A policy that is efficient, or moves toward efficiency, is to be preferred over one that is not, other things equal.

It needs to be said loudly and clearly that efficiency does not presuppose that market values are to be preferred over nonmarket values. Efficiency does not require, in other words, that some strictly monetary aggregate, akin to current gross domestic product (GDP) or gross community product (GCP),[1] be maximized. Many benefits from natural resources, particularly when we are talking preservation rather than commercial harvest, are hard to measure. But the very essence of social efficiency is that all benefits, including nonmarket benefits, are to be counted.

Although efficiency as a goal may be fairly noncontroversial in the abstract, its actual realization in any particular resource-using circumstance is likely to be problematic and contentious for several reasons. One is that people differ in terms of the values they place on different outcomes. If what is involved is a private good, this is not a problem. Some people like cantaloupes and some don't, and it is perfectly plausible for some people to eat lots of cantaloupes and for others to eat few of them. But if what is involved is a public good, production can be only at one level, which by definition is the same for everybody. Thus, conflicts can easily occur as to what that one level should be.

But perhaps the major difficulty leading to conflicts over the achievement of efficiency is the **information problem.** Everyone may agree in the abstract that we want to maximize net social benefits, but how can we be sure that this is being achieved in any particular case? Policies differ in terms of the amount and kinds of information needed in order to achieve outcomes that are reasonably efficient.

---

[1] This is the total monetary output of people living within a given community.

CHAPTER 7:   PUBLIC POLICY FOR NATURAL RESOURCES

Equity

To be **equitable** means to be **fair.** Just because a resource use plan is efficient doesn't mean it is fair. Fairness has to do with how the overall benefits and costs of natural resource use are **distributed** among subgroups of the overall population. Suppose a local community has an important deposit of a nonrenewable resource, such as petroleum. From an economywide perspective, efficiency might call for extraction of the deposit at a rapid rate; depletion of this one deposit may have relatively little national significance, because it is only one of many. From the standpoint of the community, however, it may have great significance. It may represent the primary source of nonhuman wealth in the community. What is an efficient extraction program at the national level may be regarded as unfair at the local level.

One of the major issues in contemporary natural resource economics is that of **preservation vs. extraction.** A local community may have an important resource, such as an expanse of standing timber or a large body of water. Overall national efficiency may call for preservation of these resources or for their utilization at relatively low rates. But this might be regarded as unfair to local communities that rely on these resources for an economic base. For example, a town may rely on fees from timber or mineral sales to finance its schools.

Public resource policies (indeed virtually any type of public policy) very often are characterized by a distributional disconnect regarding their benefits and their costs. It is often the case that either (1) benefits are widely spread among the population while costs are localized or (2) benefits are localized and the costs are widely dispersed. These spreads are illustrated numerically in Table 7-1. The numbers represent benefits and costs from three possible policies as they would accrue to five different individuals. Policy A has benefits and costs that are evenly distributed among the population of five individuals. Policy B has evenly distributed benefits but concentrated costs; costs are

TABLE 7-1
ALTERNATIVE DISTRIBUTION OF BENEFITS AND COSTS

		Individuals				
	Total	1	2	3	4	5
Policy A						
Benefits	100	20	20	20	20	20
Costs	80	16	16	16	16	16
Policy B						
Benefits	100	20	20	20	20	20
Costs	80	40	10	10	10	10
Policy C						
Benefits	100	80	5	5	5	5
Costs	80	16	16	16	16	16

proportionately much higher for Individual 1 than for the other individuals. Policy C has evenly distributed costs but concentrated benefits.

In the case of Policy B total net benefits are positive. However, there are four people for whom individual net benefits are positive, and one for whom they are very negative. An example might be the Endangered Species Act (ESA). Overall, the ESA may have positive net benefits. The benefits of this act are presumably widely diffused, in the sense that all citizens enjoy the benefits (especially the "nonuse" benefits). The costs, on the other hand, are very likely to be concentrated, especially on those individuals owning land where endangered species are found.

In the case of Policy C total net benefits are also positive, but there are four individuals for whom net benefits are negative and only one for whom they are strongly positive. The reason for this is that benefits are so highly concentrated. An example of this might be a beach restoration project, which has substantial benefits locally but few beyond the local area and for which the costs are spread in a very diffuse pattern among general taxpayers.[2]

Another important social dimension of the equity issue is how policies treat people who have different amounts of wealth. Markets are clear in at least one major respect, resources tend to flow toward people who have not only the willingness to pay but also the **ability to pay.** The tastes and preferences of people who lack adequate wealth are relatively unrepresented in normal markets. They may or may not be underrepresented in **political markets.** If they are underrepresented, then charitable or humanitarian causes must take over, and that support may or may not be very strong in particular circumstances.

A major equity issue in current resource controversies is the balance to be struck among the generations, the generation that is here now and the ones that will be around in the future, even the distant future. This is the major focus of the concept of **sustainability,** which refers essentially to the idea that current generations should not undertake actions today that will create conditions making it substantially more difficult for future generations to achieve today's living standards.

Flexibility

The primary national statute governing mineral exploration and extraction on public land in the United States was enacted in 1872. Although it has been significantly amended several times since then, many of the central provisions of that early mining law still apply. The price for purchasing, or "patenting," a mineral claim is still $5 an acre, for example, just as it was when the law was passed. This is an example of a seriously inflexible natural resource management policy. Conditions in mineral industries have obviously changed a lot since the nineteenth century, as have conditions elsewhere in the economy. As

---

[2] Note that if the three programs were voted on by the five individuals, Policies A and B would be approved by a majority, whereas C would not.

CHAPTER 7: PUBLIC POLICY FOR NATURAL RESOURCES

a matter of common sense, if the law was appropriate for the conditions of the nineteenth century, it is unlikely to be appropriate today. Largely for political reasons, however, the law does not change.

This suggests another important criterion for evaluating natural resource policies, namely, how well they adapt to changing circumstances. "Changing circumstances" in economics means essentially two general things: changes on the demand side in terms of social factors and values that affect the willingness to pay for different goods and services and changes on the supply side that affect the availability of resources. As an example on the demand side, major shifts have occurred in recent decades in the concerns that people have about preserving natural resources, as well as in the development of a very substantial natural resource–based outdoor recreation sector. Policies that were appropriate in an era when natural resource development and extraction was a prime objective are not likely to be prudent when values shift strongly toward preservation. As an example on the supply side, urban growth, in terms of number of people and their geographical spread, has led to great reductions in the availability of accessible open land in urban and suburban regions. Policies that guided urban growth in times when open space was ample may not be appropriate when it gets increasingly scarce.

Other things equal, policies that adjust and evolve more or less automatically to changing resource availabilities and human values are to be desired over policies that do not.

Enforceability

Public policies are the outcomes of a political process, in which groups and interests collide and compete, striving for support and influence. The maneuvering and coalition building that go on produce political theater as much as substantive actions. One result of this is that laws are frequently enacted without addressing the enforcement issue. Sometimes they are simply unenforceable at a reasonable cost. Often it is simply assumed that enforcement will be carried out with vigor and with ample resources, but this is never true in the real world. Enforcement resources are always scarce, which is why the **enforceability** of laws and regulations is an important criterion.

TYPES OF PUBLIC POLICIES

In a fundamental sense, the policy problem refers to the question of how to bring about a state of affairs in which people's private behavior is also socially appropriate. There are basically only two general ways of doing this. One is to structure the system so that the **incentives** people face will lead them to make decisions that are simultaneously both in their own best interests and in society's best interest. The other way is to institute **direct controls** that limit the actions of people through fiat, or involve direct public production and/or distribution. These options can be further broken down as follows:

225

SECTION THREE: GENERAL NATURAL RESOURCE ISSUES

I **Incentive-based policies**
  A **Market/property rights policies:** Many natural resource problems can be attributed to inadequate or inappropriate property rights governing access to the resources. The most effective way to solve the problem may be to institute a new system of property rights. Essentially this means establishing and enforcing a new set of rules governing **property rights** and **market transactions,** and then letting the rate of use of natural resources be established by voluntary interaction among suppliers and demanders.
  B **Government-sponsored incentive policies:** Public agencies employ such devices as taxes and subsidies to structure the incentives facing resource users.
II **Direct public action**
  A **Command and control policies:** Public authorities establish direct controls on individual actions, enforcing these controls with standard legal enforcement practices.
  B **Direct public production:** Public agencies themselves own natural resources and themselves pursue programs of production and distribution.

We can best distinguish among these options by considering a specific natural resource. Barnstable Bay on Cape Cod is a large, relatively shallow embayment that contains extensive areas of productive shellfish flats. For many years these resources were open to harvest by any person who was a bona fide resident of the community and had the minimal equipment necessary for the job. For a long time this sufficed, in the sense that the number of fishers and quantities harvested did not substantially reduce the productivity of the clam beds. Around the middle of the twentieth century, however, this began to change, as the number of summer recreators in town began to grow and the commercial shellfish market experienced rapid expansion. This brought added fishers, greater pressure on the fishery, and declining yields in terms of quantity and quality. The problem in this case was one of **open access,** a concept that was introduced in Chapter 6. What are the options for reducing the overfishing and moving toward the efficient utilization of this resource?

Property Rights Policies   In this case the town would divide the bay into a relatively large number of parcels (the water is shallow so markers can be used, or shore points can be used for reference). It would then lease or sell these parcels to individual fishers, who would be free to make their own harvest decisions on their parcels. The leases would be long-term, so leasees would have time to take advantage of long-run management plans, such as seeding the areas with young clam stock and systematically rotating harvest plots within their overall leaseholds. The leaseholds may be bought and sold among fishers. The job of the town shellfish officer now is to keep a record of who holds each parcel, and then make sure that trespassers do not encroach on anyone's holding.

CHAPTER 7: PUBLIC POLICY FOR NATURAL RESOURCES

Government-Sponsored Incentive Policy The town could simply levy a tax per bushel of clams harvested on fishers in the bay. The tax could be different for commercial and recreational diggers, and for different sizes of clams. In effect the tax now becomes a new operating cost for clam diggers. By shifting their cost curves upward, the expectation is that the quantity of clams dug in the bay would decrease, simply as a result of fishers responding to the new financial conditions of harvesting and not because of any direct controls on their operations. The job of the shellfish officer is to get accurate data on the quantity of individual harvests, and then send out and collect the tax bills.

Direct Command and Control The town of Barnstable would establish a set of rules governing the harvesting of shellfish in the bay. It already has a rule limiting access to town residents; different rules could be set for year-round residents and for summer residents. Rules could be established for the maximum allowable individual harvest per day or per year. Rules could be set for the type of fishing gear that would be allowed, for the minimum size of clam that could be kept, and so on. In this case the town shellfish officer would be instructed to take whatever steps were necessary to enforce the rules, such as surveillance, monitoring of landings, examination of financial records, and the like.

Direct Public Production The town of Barnstable, or some other public agency, might go into direct production itself, asserting ownership of the resource, hiring people to do the fishing, selling or giving away the clams, and distributing revenues in whatever way it chooses. A town shellfish officer would patrol the clam beds to make sure there is no unauthorized clamming.

In the real world, of course, mixtures of policy measures are possible. For example, direct controls on harvest quantities can be combined with a tax; private property rights may be combined with rules on clamming operations; and so on. Mixtures are very common. Private ownership of land resources is a dominant system in most western countries. But these ownership institutions are also usually accompanied with rules that limit the uses to which land may be put, as well as taxes on land. Many public parks and forests in the United States (direct government production) make use of entrance fees (financial incentives) and harvest concessions (property rights) to control resource use. The reason for discussing them separately is to make clear the way each works and, especially, the conditions that have to be met for them to achieve efficient and equitable resource use rates.

In the rest of the chapter we consider each one of these alternatives in more detail. To do this, we work with a simple numerical example. Consider the data in Table 7-2, which show the costs and returns of a small clam fishery. The second column is catch per fisher. From 1 to 4 fishers, this is 20 pounds per day. From 5 fishers up, the catch per fisher goes down because of open-access externalities the fishers inflict on one another; more fishers create congestion and greater scarcity, so the catch rates go down. The larger the number

TABLE 7-2
DAILY COSTS AND RETURNS FROM CLAM FISHERY

Number of fishers	Catch per fisher (pounds per day)	Total catch (revenue)*	Cost per fisher	Total costs	Net returns per fisher	Aggregate net returns
1	20	20	$12	$ 12	8	$ 8
2	20	40	12	24	8	16
3	20	60	12	36	8	24
4	20	80	12	48	8	32
5	18	90	12	60	6	30
6	16	96	12	72	4	24
7	14	98	12	84	2	14
8	12	96	12	96	0	0
9	10	90	12	108	-2	-18
10	8	80	12	120	-4	-40

*On the assumption that each unit of shellfish has a market value of $1.

of fishers, the more the decline. The third column shows total catch, which, if we assume the clams sell for $1 per unit, is also equal to total revenue. The last three columns show, respectively, costs per fisher (assumed the same for all fishers), total costs, net returns per fisher, and aggregate net returns (total revenue minus total costs).

You will no doubt recognize these numbers. They are the ones we used to illustrate the concept of an open-access resource back in Chapter 6, except that there they were used to illustrate the problem of visitors to an open-access beach. The rent-maximizing number of fishers is 4, as we can tell by looking at the last column. But the open-access number of fishers will tend toward 8, because the returns per fisher are positive up to this point. The policy question is, how do we achieve a reduction in fishers to efficient levels?

PRIVATE PROPERTY RIGHTS

The overuse of many natural resources can be attributed to the fact that **property rights** to these resources are either ill-defined or not adequately exercised. By this diagnosis, for example, the rent on open-access resources is dissipated, in whole or in part, because the resource does not have an owner, or owners, who will limit its use in order to maximize its value. Consider the following scenario:

A large expanse of remote land contains areas of forests, natural meadows, sizeable streams and several rivers. Over the years substantial amounts of the forests have been logged and some of the meadows have been used for grazing cattle. Many people have also pushed into the area, on the logging roads and trails, to pursue a variety of outdoor recreation activities: hunting, backpacking, canoeing, and camping. In fact in recent years use of the region became so heavy that the natural resources started to be damaged, for example, by erosion from heavily used lands,

CHAPTER 7: PUBLIC POLICY FOR NATURAL RESOURCES

water pollution, fires attributable to humans, littering, and a growing scarcity of certain game animals.

There are calls for intervention by the state department of natural resource management. But the land is currently owned by several dozen large private landowners. The landowners themselves are aware of the resource degradation and the public access that is causing it. They decide that they can act together to reduce this damage and, furthermore, provide themselves with a modest but significant flow of income. What they do is create a number of controlled access points into the area, and then begin charging entry fees to people who want to use the area. The landowners create a small firm whose job is to manage the resources of the region and the outdoor recreators who make use of them. One of the first things they do, for example, is to set some rules for the logging companies who are allowed access, so that logging practices will not substantially impact the outdoor recreation values of the region.

What we have here is an example of resource management pursued through the use of **private property institutions**.[3] The essence of social efficiency is that natural resources be used in ways that maximize their net value to society. The essence of the property rights approach is to define these rights clearly enough so that private owners, in pursuing their own personal interests in maximizing their own wealth, will simultaneously maximize the net benefits flowing from the resource.

The property rights approach to our clam-bed problem is, therefore, to convert the clam beds to private property. It will then be in the interests of the owners to adopt levels of use that maximize the value of the resource. In the numerical example the owner(s) would have the incentive to limit entry to 4 fishers and to defend the boundary of the resource so that the level of extraction does not exceed that level. In fact, however, incentives would go beyond this. In an open-access situation, nobody would invest in efforts to, for example, seed the clam bed or cultivate it so as to increase long-run yields. If somebody were to do this, others could move in to reap the benefits. But privatizing the resource would change this: By allowing owners to exclude others, there would be an incentive to invest in these long-run improvements.

Privatization could be accomplished in various ways. In many instances resources of this type have been privatized informally through self-organization and management by the users without the official sanction of public authorities. Exhibit 7-1 recounts a case of this type, dealing with the harbor gangs of Maine who have sought in effect to privatize portions of the lobster fishery of that state. In some cases, like the example of the forest owners discussed above, boundaries already exist and it is up to the existing owners to agree on joint action to maintain them and manage the resource. In others, new boundaries may be specified and the resource distributed in some way to new owners. In the case of the Barnstable Harbor clam fishery, long-term leaseholds

---

[3] The example is in fact taken from real life. The group of landowners is called North Maine Woods, Inc.

SECTION THREE: GENERAL NATURAL RESOURCE ISSUES

EXHIBIT 7-1

THE MAINE LOBSTER GANGS—INFORMAL PRIVATIZATION

The coast of Maine is heavily indented and studded with small islands. It is also the locale of a very rich lobster fishery. Lobsters are sea creatures, the legal status of which historically has been an open-access resource. But to avoid the excessive harvests and overfishing that open-access resources normally experience, the lobster fishers of Maine have resorted to informal privatization. They have done this through means of harbor gangs, which are informal groups of fishers in each harbor who establish and enforce boundaries around "their" particular harbors or islands. The boundaries do not have legal status but are enforced anyway, essentially through trashing (or threats thereof) the gear of interlopers, that is, people from outside the harbor. Of course, the ability of any harbor gang to do this effectively varies. Where it is small and close-knit (consisting, for example, of family relatives around a smallish island), exclusion can be quite effective. In bigger harbors with more diverse populations and greater demand for lobsters, exclusion is more difficult to pursue and so is less complete. There are other formal, legal constraints in effect also, for example, on minimum sizes for harvested lobsters.

History shows many cases like this, where an open-access resource is privatized to a greater or lesser extent by informal user groups. It demonstrates the potential gains that can be obtained by moving in the direction of private property. When there is open access, there will be rent dissipation. When access is limited, rents will become positive and will accrue to the people doing the excluding (unless they are partially taxed away).

Source: Information on the Maine harbor gangs can be found in James M. Acheson, *The Lobster Gangs of Maine,* University of New Hampshire Press, Hanover, NH, 1988.

---

were identified by boundary markers and these were distributed to some of the people who had been in the clam fishery for many years.

Irrespective of how they are initially distributed, property rights must have several important characteristics if they are to lead to socially efficient resource use. They must be:

1 Complete (or reasonably so)
2 Enforceable at reasonable cost
3 Transferable
4 Combined with a complete set of competitive markets

Complete A fancy way of saying this is that the property rights must not be **attenuated** in any way relevant to the use to which they will be put. In other words, they must not be limited in any way that would reduce the incentives of the owners to search out the way(s) that maximize their value. Suppose the clam-bed leases in the Barnstable case were limited to 1 year, after which they could be rescinded and given to somebody else at the discretion of the local authorities. This would undermine the incentives of leaseholders to make long-run (anything over 1 year) investments to increase the productivity of the leasehold. Or suppose the authorities required that the clams be harvested using a certain type of harvesting technology. This would weaken the incentive for the owners to search out the least-cost method of harvesting clams within the circumstances of this leasehold.

In actual practice, all property rights are attenuated to some extent. For purposes of protecting the public health, owners do not have the right to use their property in a way that would injure others. But the extent of legitimate restrictions is a controversial issue. The people digging clams on private leaseholds in the bay presumably do not have the right to drive large pilings down and construct a hotel on stilts in the middle of the harbor. This would seem to be a restriction that is obviously conducive to the public welfare. But in some circumstances restrictions of this type might foreclose value-increasing courses of action on the part of the owners.

Enforceable, at Reasonable Cost   By enforceable we refer to two things: (1) that would-be trespassers can be excluded at reasonable cost and (2) that owners can be effectively enjoined from using their property in ways that are illegal. **Exclusion** has two dimensions, technical and legal. The **technical** side is the physical means available for stopping trespassers: the ability to mark boundaries, the use of fences in the case of some land boundaries, the costs of surveillance, and so on. The **legal** side relates to whether boundaries are recognized by legal authorities. Both factors are important. In many cases natural resources that are legally open-access resources have been essentially "privatized" by individuals or groups who take it upon themselves to exclude certain outsiders. The Maine lobster gangs are an instance of this. There have also been many cases where property, which legally is owned by defined individuals or groups, is still subject to open access because the costs of excluding encroachers is simply too high relative to the gains the owners would achieve by so doing.

The other part of enforceability is that it must be possible to stop the owners themselves from using their resources in ways that are illegal. We talked in the previous section about the need to have property rights relatively unconstrained. By the same token it is always true that some legal constraints will be found necessary, and constraints of this type have to be enforceable. In most countries there are legal requirements that forestry companies are supposed to follow in harvesting timber—for example, limits on clear cutting. If these limits are not enforceable because of, say, the costs of detection, then they obviously cannot be effective.

Transferable   Suppose I operate a farm on land leased from the community. It is a long-term lease, but it is not transferable. As long as I wish to farm, I can occupy the land. I may even be able to pass it on to my sons and daughters. But I cannot sell it to third parties. Suppose I am thinking of retiring and moving into town. Since I have no heirs, I must relinquish the land at that point in time. This situation effectively reduces to me the **user costs** of mining the fertility of the soil and the productivity of whatever other natural assets exist on the farm (a small groundwater aquifer, for example). It reduces the incentive to maintain the maximum market value of these natural assets, because in effect they are not marketable.

SECTION THREE: GENERAL NATURAL RESOURCE ISSUES

Restrictions on transfers of natural resource assets are a ubiquitous feature throughout history. This is particularly the case with agricultural land. Early farming communities in developed countries, and many existing communities in developing countries, have placed restrictions on selling land to nonresidents. The reasons for this are primarily social and political. If a community's land is the only productive asset it has, it will not wish to see, on either efficiency or equity grounds, that asset falling into the hands of people outside the community. It is only when people have other good alternatives that they will be comfortable with the idea of full and unfettered transferability.

The Presence of Markets   Suppose I own a piece of forest land that I currently use for light timbering and wood pasture for a small herd of cattle. Suppose also that in my region there is some pressure to convert forest land into house lots; some nearby land has already been converted, and the suburban area is expected to continue to spread. Markets for agricultural land and for suburban land are well developed, meaning that there are well-recognized prices for land devoted to these uses; these prices register the social value of these services producible by the land. Suppose my land is also well recognized by biologists as an area of rich biodiversity. In technical terms, the land apparently produces **biodiversity preservation services,** which would be reduced if the farm is either cultivated more intensively or converted to house lots.

If a market exists such that I could obtain a revenue flow equal to the value of these biodiversity services, this flow would be capitalized into the price of the land, which then would function as an opportunity cost of devoting the land to some other use.[4] But if no such market exists, land prices will not reflect these other ecological services that they produce. Market prices for land having unique biological attributes will be too low, relative to land that does not. For private property to lead to efficient resource use patterns, markets must exist so that owners can capture the full value of the services produced by the resource in question. Only then can we be sure that resources will be devoted to the uses that maximize their social value.

Property rights arrangements have efficiency implications; they also have important distributional, or equity, implications. If the clam beds in Barnstable Harbor are allotted to private owners, many people who used to dig clams there may not be able to do so anymore. If an open-access woodland is changed to restricted entry (in the sense of entrants having now to pay for use), local people who used to be able to enter the area may find themselves excluded, especially if their incomes are low. Suppose a resource that was once used widely in an open-access framework is now privatized in the hands of a relatively small number of owners who wish to keep it for their exclusive use. These examples point out that property rights solutions to resource issues will normally have important distributional consequences.

[4] For a discussion of land prices and the capitalization of service flows, see Chapter 14.

CHAPTER 7:   PUBLIC POLICY FOR NATURAL RESOURCES

GOVERNMENT-SPONSORED INCENTIVE POLICIES

A **government-sponsored incentive policy** is one in which regulatory authorities try to shift the incentive aspects of a situation so that resource users will be motivated voluntarily to adjust their behavior in the direction of efficiency. Plans of the sort normally involve taxes or subsidies, or a combination of the two.

Taxes

Consider again the situation depicted in Table 7-2. Suppose authorities now institute a charge of $7 per day per fisher, which acts essentially as an entrance fee that all fishers must pay to gain access to the fishery. This does not change the fundamentals of the fishery, in terms of the harvest rates, harvest costs, and the efficient number of fishers. What it does change is the financial incentives facing each fisher. **From the standpoint of the fishers,** the Cost-per-Fisher column now consists of $19 throughout rather than $12. We know that in an open-access situation entry will increase up to the point where marginal cost (in this case $19) equals average harvest value. This now occurs at a rate of 4 fishers (actually it occurs between 4 and 5 fishers; we are assuming that fishers come only in integer values). The tax, in other words, has shifted the costs of the fishers so that now, even with no direct control over entry, the number of fishers will stop at 4, the socially efficient level. However, from a **distributional standpoint,** the tax approach is quite different from the property rights approach studied earlier. With the $7 tax, the Net Returns column can now be divided as follows:

Number of fishers	Net returns		
	Total	Accruing to fishers	Tax receipts
1	$ 8	$ 1	$ 7
2	16	2	14
3	24	3	21
4	32	4	28
5	30	−5	35
6	24	−18	42
7	14	−35	49
8	0	−56	56
9	−18	−81	63
10	−40	−110	70

Distributionally, then, the tax transfers most of the rent of the fishery from the pockets of the fishers to the coffers of the taxing authorities. In the property rights approach the total rent shared by the 4 fishers would be $32; in the tax approach it would be $4, and the authorities would get the other $28. Of course, such distributional consequences reduce the political attractiveness of using taxes to achieve efficient resource utilization rates.

In order for an efficient tax to be applied, authorities must have accurate knowledge of the cost and revenues of the typical fisher. This is a central weakness of this approach, because the only reasonable place for the authorities to get this knowledge is from the operators themselves. Note that a standard income tax will not have the desired efficiency effects. A normal income tax would take a certain percentage of a fisher's net income. Suppose a 50 percent income tax rate were applied to the fisher example in Table 7-2. The Returns-per-Fisher column would change as if those numbers were all multiplied by 0.5. But the open-access number of fishers would still be 8. To have the desired efficiency effect, in other words, the tax has to be levied per unit of effort (i.e., per fisher) or per unit of harvest. This puts more burden on the taxing authorities, in terms of getting accurate enough information to identify the efficient tax level.

Subsidies

It may not seem obvious, but a cleverly designed system of **subsidies** could have the same efficiency effects as a tax, with entirely different distributional consequences. Suppose the clam fishery is currently operating at open-access levels (i.e., there are 8 fishers on the fishery). The authorities now step in and offer a subsidy of $7 to each fisher **who will refrain from fishing.** Now consider the eighth fisher; this individual is essentially just breaking even: $12 of catch and $12 of cost. He clearly would be better off by taking the subsidy and ceasing operations that year. The same could be said for the seventh fisher (current net gain of $2, as compared to the $7 subsidy), the sixth, and the fifth. But at 4 fishers, no further reduction would occur because the marginal return ($8) is greater than the subsidy.

For this subsidy to have the appropriate efficiency effects, authorities would have to stop people entering the fishery solely for the purpose of obtaining the subsidy by quitting. This means the authorities must have a reasonably accurate knowledge of the open-access level of the fishery, together with the cost and revenue situation of the typical fisher, so that the subsidy could be set at the correct level. It needs to be stressed that this is a very particular type of subsidy. It is essentially a payment to individuals in return for their reduced use of the resource in question; the objective is to affect the rate at which the resource is used. Subsidies in the real world are seldom like this; they usually have a redistribution objective to transfer income, often from the general taxpayer to favored groups or sometimes to individuals. Natural resource industries have often been favored in this respect:

• Many governments around the world have offered financial aid to fishers; in the United States, for example, the federal government has at times taken steps to reduce the costs of purchasing fishing boats.

CHAPTER 7: PUBLIC POLICY FOR NATURAL RESOURCES

- Federally constructed irrigation dams have sold water to farmers and ranchers at below-cost prices.
- Publicly owned land has been leased to ranchers for grazing purposes at extremely low prices.
- Mineral operators have had access to federal land at very low prices.
- In many countries timber companies have won timber harvesting concessions at very low prices.

It is universally the case, of course, that recipients of subsidies never think of them as such, but instead as revenues justified by conditions that are special to their particular circumstances. For the most part, however, they are subsidies gained through the political process, which in most cases have the effect of increasing the rate of use of the affected resource over what it would be without the subsidies. We may regard these as **governmental failures,** where political initiative has been used, not to rectify cases of inefficient use of natural resources, but simply to shift income toward favored groups.

In such cases, a social gain is to be had at no cost, by simply lifting the subsidy. Figure 7-1 depicts the case of an item the production of which is subsidized (through, for example, a subsidy on some important input, such as energy). The real social marginal cost curve (i.e., not counting the subsidy) is MC, while the subsidized marginal cost curve, which determines the effective market supply curve, is MC minus the subsidy, that is, MC – S. The subsidy

FIGURE 7-1
Inefficiency Caused by Subsidized Production

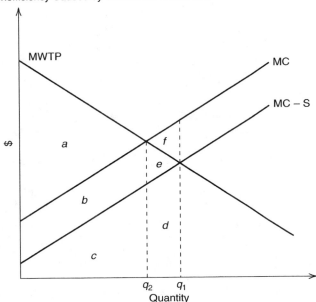

lowers the effective marginal cost curve. Thus, the market output will be q_1, which is somewhat larger than the socially efficient output q_2. At q_2 the net social benefits would be $(a + b + c) - (b + c) = a$; whereas at an output level of q_1, net social benefits are $(a + b + c + d + e) - (b + c + d + e + f) = a - f$. (Remember that although the market output is determined by the subsidized marginal cost curve, net social benefits are still determined by MC, the unsubsidized marginal cost curve.) Thus, a discontinuance of the subsidy would produce a social gain equal to the area f. In effect society would gain simply because it moves to a position that is socially efficient from one that is not.

So why then don't governments end subsidies of this sort? The answer is that although there will be a gain to society, there may not be a gain to each and every group or individual in society. Ending subsidies means ending the flow of redistributed income toward certain groups. Thus, it is in the interests of these groups to use the political process to preserve the subsidies. One should not necessarily conclude that it is individual firms and industries who are always the recipients of subsidies. In many countries consumers in general are the subsidized group. Many developing countries, for example, subsidize the prices of energy and food; in such cases, it is politically very difficult to get rid of the subsidies.

DIRECT CONTROLS

The direct approach to controlling natural resource use, often called the **command-and-control** approach, is simply to enact a regulation specifying, for example, maximum use rates, then using normal means (like monitors and police) to enforce the regulations. In the Barnstable Harbor case the town could establish a regulation saying that only the first 4 fishers to apply would be allowed and after that no further entry would be permitted. Anybody else caught harvesting clams would be arrested and fined. Many different types of controls have been used in different circumstances.

1 An upper limit on the total quantity of fish caught annually from a certain fishery; after the limit is reached the fishery is closed.
2 A limit on the specific uses to which a piece of land may be put, for example, zoning regulations.
3 A limit on the quantity of water that particular users may withdraw each year from a nearby river.
4 A limit on the number of people who are allowed access to a state or national park.
5 A limit on the quantity of timber that may be harvested from a given parcel of land.

The command-and-control approach to regulation appears to be simple and straightforward, deceptively so. Consider Figure 7-2. It shows the market demand (D) and supply (S) of a natural resource; left to itself the market quantity would settle down at q^m. But suppose there are additional costs not being

CHAPTER 7: PUBLIC POLICY FOR NATURAL RESOURCES

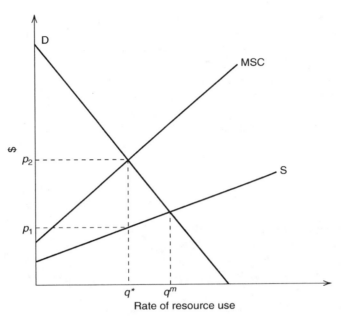

FIGURE 7-2
Direct Controls

taken into account by the market suppliers—ecological costs associated with producing timber, for example. After having studied the situation, the authorities decide that the true social cost function is MSC and that the socially efficient rate of output is q^*, not q^m. A regulation is therefore promulgated stating that the maximum allowable production is q^*.

Rather clearly, if a direct regulation like this is to achieve efficiency, the regulators must have good knowledge of the underlying costs and benefits. In order to identify a policy target level like q^* in the figure, they must know not only the nonmarket ecological costs that the market is currently leaving out, they also must have a good idea about private production costs, as well as the market demand curve. Regulation of this type, therefore, places a very substantial **information burden** on the public agencies responsible for regulations. This burden will be higher than is apparent in Figure 7-2. If q^* is an **aggregate output limit,** this may have to be broken down into individual output limits for the firms making up the aggregate. And to do so effectively requires information about the cost structure of each of these firms. Information on costs of this type usually must come from the regulated community itself, which puts a substantial burden on the agency to get data that is reasonably accurate.

A major issue of the command-and-control approach is the **enforcement** process. Suppose output has been reduced by regulation to q^* in Figure 7-2. At

SECTION THREE: GENERAL NATURAL RESOURCE ISSUES

that point, the market price is going to be p_2, whereas the marginal costs of production are at p_1. Any producing enterprise that can find a way to produce one more unit of this item will profit by an amount equal to $p_2 - p_1$. We might call this the **incentive to be noncomplaint.** The more restrictive the regulation, the larger will be this incentive. This is not to say that regulations of this type are never justified. Historically, direct command-and-control regulations are the primary way that public policy has been pursued. In many cases, however, the enforcement part of the whole process has been overlooked.

DIRECT PUBLIC PRODUCTION

The last policy approach to be discussed in this chapter is **direct government production.** In the case of Barnstable Harbor, the town in this case would claim title to the clam flats. They would appoint a "clam production committee," which would hire clam diggers, police boundaries, sell the harvested clams on the open market, and deposit the proceeds (the rents) in their own bank account. These funds could then be used by the town for whatever purpose it chooses. In fact, this is analogous to privatization, but in this case the owning and acting organization is a public body rather than a private firm.

In fact, direct public production of this general type appears in many places. Public parks at community, state, and national levels operate in this general way, as do national forests, national monuments, and the like. Much of the original public domain in the United States is still in public ownership. In many other countries whole sectors (electricity production, banking) have been nationalized at various times, although at present the trend seems to be going the other way.

In principle there is nothing to stop a natural resource–owning public organization from using that resource in a socially efficient way. To do this, it would have to function much as a private firm would, with the added proviso that it include all external costs and benefits, as well as nonmarket costs and benefits, in its deliberations. In actuality, of course, it is difficult for political firms to function in this way. The incentive for private firms to move toward efficiency is that they are **residual claimants;** that is, they get to keep the net revenues or, in the case of natural resources, the resource rents. But public agencies are seldom in this situation. Revenues collected by public firms usually go into general revenues rather than into the specific bank account of the agency itself. Expenditures of the agencies are not constrained by collected revenues but by budgets that are enacted in the context of a political decision process in which outcomes are a result of the play of interests and influences by affected individuals and groups. The question is whether public agencies involved in direct production can assess and balance these various interests so as to get close to something that qualifies as a socially efficient outcome. In some cases they may, and in other cases they may not.

In the case of natural resources, public production often takes the form of allowing private firms to have access to public domain resources under controlled conditions. That is, the legal title to the in situ resources remains for the most part with the public, but the extraction is actually done by private firms who harvest and sell the resources. The contractual terms of these arrangements, and therefore the prices paid for the resources, varies from one resource to another, as Exhibit 7-2 summarizes.

Contracts of this type have been controversial in recent years and are destined to become more so. Critics often charge that the prices at which public domain resources are sold are often lower than their fair market values. Users of the resources normally argue the opposite. Managers of the public domain are under increasing pressure to shift resource use away from extractive and toward nonextractive uses. And the environmental impacts stemming from the extraction of public domain resources are becoming a growing concern. In subsequent chapters we will revisit this issue as we discuss particular natural resources.

MARKET FAILURE/GOVERNMENT FAILURE

In the previous pages we have focused on the many ways that a society has of managing its natural resource endowment. All approaches to resource management involve collective action of one sort or another. In some cases this consists of the collective establishment of a legal system of property rights and markets, after which natural resource use rates are determined through the decentralized interactions of buyers and sellers. At the other extreme is direct public production. And there are many types of policy intervention involving combinations of public and private actions. The usual justification for overt public action of one type or another is that strictly decentralized property rights and markets don't give results that are socially equitable and efficient. This is called **market failure,** and is linked usually to such problems as the presence of externalities, public goods, and myopia on the part of present generations. When these kinds of problems are present, private markets are incapable of operating efficiently and public policy is called for.

But there is a danger here of evaluating alternative public policy intervention only in terms of what might be called **ideal types,** that is, policy as it would work in theory if it were conducted by totally selfless public servants who always acted in the public interest using good information on possible outcomes. But this is never true. Public policies are normally pursued in a highly politicized environment by public servants who usually mean well but who have their own views of where the public interest lies and who work with information that is usually incomplete and often biased. So public policies in practice are never likely to give the results that they would appear to promise in theory. A way to describe this is **government failure.** Government failure can happen in many ways:

- Regulations are enacted but **inadequately enforced.**
- Regulations are enacted that create **perverse incentives,** making situations worse instead of better.

SECTION THREE: GENERAL NATURAL RESOURCE ISSUES

EXHIBIT 7-2

PROGRAMS THROUGH WHICH THE U.S. GOVERNMENT SELLS PUBLIC DOMAIN RESOURCES

Timber Sales

Responsible agencies: Forest Service (Department of Agriculture); Bureau of Land Management (Interior).

Method: Agencies prepare annual sale programs and individual timber sales; prior to sale the timber is appraised. Sale contracts are offered for sale through competitive bids at oral auctions, with the appraised values acting as minimum acceptable bids.

Grazing Permits

Responsible agencies: Bureau of Land Management (Interior) and Forest Service (Agriculture).

Method: Agencies identify grazing allotments and determine number and timing of grazing; allotments are associated with nearby ranches and usually remain with permitters permanently. Fees are set on a base value (set at $1.23 per animal unit month in 1966) and adjusted by indices of livestock prices and ranch operating costs.

Hard-Rock Minerals

Responsible agency: Bureau of Land Management (Interior).

Method: Claims to areas believed to contain minerals may be made for a fee of $10 and $100 per year thereafter for holding it open. When a valid claim is shown to have recoverable minerals, the minerals may be developed, with or without a patent. A patent application, if approved, gives claimant full title to the surface and mineral rights, at a cost of $2.50 per acre.

Onshore Oil and Gas

Responsible agency: Plans prepared by Bureau of Land Management (BLM); administered by Minerals Management Service (Interior).

Method: BLM determines leasable tracts; these are offered for sale in competitive oral auctions, with the highest bidder awarded the contracts. Leaseholders must pay an annual fee of $1.50 per acre, replaced by a royalty of 12.5 percent of the value of production once production begins.

Offshore Oil and Gas

Responsible agency: Minerals Management Service (Interior).

Method: Agency prepares 5-year leasing plans on leasable tracts, and periodically offers leases for competitive bidding. Sealed bids are normally used, and bidders may make bonus bids, but royalty rates must be at least 12.5 percent and profit shares at least 30 percent.

Mineral Materials

Responsible agency: Minerals Management Service (Interior)

Method: Includes common varieties of minerals such as sand, gravel, cinders, clay, etc. Sales are made at market value, as determined by appraisal, with newspaper advertising preceding sealed or oral bids. However, up to 100,000 cubic yards may be sold non-competitively.

Water

Responsible agency: Bureau of Reclamation (Interior).

Method: Once federal projects are completed, irrigation water is delivered at rates specified in long-term contracts. Factors affecting rates are the reimbursable costs of project, amount of irrigable land in a project area, annual operations and maintenance costs, land class and ownership, and irrigator's ability to pay. Normal rates vary from less than $1 to almost $20 per acre-foot of water.

Source: Compiled from Ross W. Gortz, "Federal Sales of Natural Resources: Allocation and Pricing Systems," Congressional Research Service, Report 97-15, *Engineering News Record,* January 3, 1997.

- Laws and regulations are enacted in the name of efficiency but in reality are **redistributive;** that is, they are attempts by one group to wrest resources away from another group.
- Laws are enacted in the name of correcting **market failures,** whereas the real objective is to protect the privileged position of an existing group with respect to the use of a natural resource.
- Laws and regulations are pursued that essentially require information that public agencies do not have and cannot get.

The implications of this are the following: When considering the possibility of public policy, it is not correct to compare the results we are getting from an imperfectly functioning market system with what we would get from a perfectly designed and implemented public policy. Instead we have to compare imperfect markets with perhaps equally imperfect public policies. In many cases it may be far more effective to determine why markets are not functioning efficiently and solve that problem, than to engage in overt activist public policy. In many cases the opposite will be true.

POLICY CENTRALIZATION/DECENTRALIZATION

The example used earlier in this chapter concerned the management of a local natural resource (a clam bed) by a single community (the town of Barnstable). The resource is local in the sense that it occupies a small part of the territory of the town and in the sense that the question of whether the clam stock is large or small is not a matter of great concern beyond the town's borders. The relevant government body was the town itself, acting through whatever agencies and units were established to deal with the issue. Suppose, however, that the particular species of clam found in the Barnstable clam beds is a unique species found nowhere else, as far as anyone knows at the present time. Now it is reasonable to ask the question: Is the local government still the appropriate place to solve this management question? Might it now be desirable to have this resource case addressed at a higher level of government, either the state or perhaps the federal level?

This is the **centralization/decentralization** problem in natural resource policy.[5] What is the appropriate governmental level at which particular natural resource issues should be addressed? In the United States we can distinguish four main levels: local (the single community), county, state, and federal. The importance of county government varies from region to region. We could perhaps also speak of a regional level, taking in several states. Historically, certain resource issues have been addressed at the federal level (fisheries regulation, managing national parks and forests), whereas others have typically been local (land-use issues).

---

[5] Of course it's a problem that exists in all types of policy areas, not just natural resource policy.

SECTION THREE: GENERAL NATURAL RESOURCE ISSUES

The general principle for assigning a particular natural resource issue to one or another level of government is fairly clear. It should be addressed at the lowest level of government whose geographic scope encompasses all the relevant benefits and costs of the problem.[6] The reason for this rule is that it will make it easier to compare the benefits and costs of the problem and achieve the balance between them that efficiency requires. Most of the benefits and costs of the original Barnstable case are local. Thus the community forum is the one where people can most directly comprehend them and confront the trade-offs that are involved. Political processes at the state and federal levels would not be able to do this as effectively.

Real difficulties come up, however, when the geographical spread of benefits and costs are quite different, as they often are in natural resource issues. Consider again the version of the clam bed case in which the clams are an endangered species. In this case the benefits of preserving them may accrue widely, to all citizens who place a high value on preserving species and encouraging diversity. But the costs of a regulation to limit harvesting below locally efficient levels are concentrated locally. This is a very common pattern in natural resource issues. Widely dispersed benefits argue for a state or federal role; localized costs argue for a local perspective.

The use of markets solves this problem to some extent. When clams are harvested and sold, they presumably go into at least a regional, or perhaps national, market. With established prices for clams, the local clam-managing individuals and groups have an easy way of assessing the benefits produced by digging the clams. But this only works if there are ready markets for the resource. No private market exists for species uniqueness. There is no way for people who value this characteristic of the clams to buy units of it. It might be possible for people to buy the clam bed and preserve the species, if public authorities allowed this sort of thing. The public good aspect of this would still have to be solved, of course.

So, how are the clam beds of Barnstable Harbor managed? The harbor is divided into two areas. In one area long-term leases are granted to commercial fishers who manage and harvest clams on their own leaseholds. The other area is fished as an open-access resource by town residents who must obtain clam digging permits from the town. The leasehold section of the harbor is overseen by the state of Massachusetts, while the permit section is managed by the town of Barnstable.

SUMMARY

Public policy involves collective action to influence the rate and manner in which natural resources are used. There are many types of policy approaches,

---

[6] Wallace E. Oates, "Thinking about Environmental Federalism," in Wallace E. Oates (ed.), *The RFF Reader in Environment and Resource Management*, Resources for the Future, Washington, DC, 1999, p. 119.

each with strengths and weaknesses. To choose among different policies for a particular situation, one must have in mind some criteria with which they will be evaluated. The criteria discussed were **efficiency, equity, enforceability,** and **flexibility.** The four types of policies evaluated for addressing resource issues were the creation of **property rights, government-sponsored incentive programs, command and control regulations,** and **direct governmental production.** No one policy approach is likely to be the best for all situations; which one is best will depend on the characteristics of the problem, the presence of appropriate social institutions and infrastructure, the capabilities and objectives of public officials, and other factors. The chapter also discusses the issues of **market failure** vs. **government failure** and the appropriate governmental level for addressing particular public policy problems.

KEY TERMS

Public policy

Policy criteria (efficiency, equity, enforceability, flexibility)

Incentive-based policies

Property rights

Command-and-control approach

Public production

Residual claimant

Conditions on property rights (complete, enforceable, transferable, presence of competitive markets)

Market failure

Government failure

Policy decentralization/centralization

QUESTIONS FOR FURTHER DISCUSSION

1 Give an example of a policy that is efficient but not equitable, and of one that is the opposite. Do you think that, in general, efficient policies are likely to be equitable, and vice versa?

2 Suppose, in the clam fishing example introduced in Table 7-2, a tax is applied per pound of clams harvested, rather than per fisher day. This tax, in other words, works to lower revenues rather than raise costs. At what level should the tax be set to bring about the socially efficient use level?

3 Besides income (rich vs. poor) and generations (today vs. future), what other demographic and social factors might be important in assessing the fairness of resource policies?

4 From a political perspective, why do subsidies and property rights policies often get more support than taxes and command-and-control policies?

USEFUL WEB SITES

For information about federal policy initiatives and developments:

- U.S. Department of the Interior (http://www.doi.gov)
- Natural Resources Defense Council (http://www.nrdc.org)
- League of Conservation Voters (http://www.lcv.org)

SECTION THREE: GENERAL NATURAL RESOURCE ISSUES

- Findlaw (http://www.findlaw.com/lawecon); search on environmental law
- Environmental Law Institute (http://www.eli.org)

For news and views of using property rights and free markets:

- Public Interest Research Center (http://www.perc.org)
- Center for Private Conservation (http://www.cei.org/cpc)

For information on environmental issues at the community level:

- Local Government Environmental Assistance Network (http://www.lgean.org)

A good source on state level issues is the environmental atlas feature of the:

- Resource Renewal Institute (http://www.rri.org)

SELECTED READINGS

Anderson, Terry L., and Donald R. Leal: *Free Market Environmentalism,* Westview Press, Boulder, CO, 1991.

Conrad, Jon M.: Resource Economics, Cambridge University Press, Cambridge, U.K., 1999.

Hackett, Steven C.: *Environmental and Natural Resource Economics,* M. E. Sharp, Armonk, NY, 1998.

Organization for Economic Cooperation and Development, *Renewable Natural Resources, Economic Incentives for Improved Management,* OECD, Paris, 1989.

Tietenberg, Tom: *Environmental and Natural Resource Economics,* 5th ed., Addison Wesley Longman, New York, 2000.

CHAPTER **8**

PRINCIPLES OF ANALYSIS

Each year federal, state, and local governments pursue all sorts of policies and regulations designed to impact on the ways natural resources are used. Controversies swirl around these actions: whether they are effective, whether the trend should be toward more or toward less public regulation, whether we should have more or less reliance on private markets, and so on. Effective policy, even effective monitoring of markets, requires high-quality information and the presentation of that information in ways that facilitate action. Good analysis does not necessarily produce good decisions. But bad analysis will almost certainly contribute to bad ones.

In this chapter we examine some of the alternative **types of analysis** that are undertaken by policy analysts. Most of the chapter will be devoted to **benefit-cost** analysis, since this is the technique most frequently used. Before examining the basic principles of benefit-cost analysis, however, we look briefly at several other modes of analysis.

IMPACT ANALYSIS

"Impact" is a very general word, meaning the influence that one set of events has on another. In general, impact analysis seeks to measure the impact of a public action, such as a regulation, on a designated sector of the society/economy. Several different types of impact analysis are important in natural resource economics.

CHAPTER 8:   PRINCIPLES OF ANALYSIS

Environmental Impact Analysis

An **environmental impact analysis** is essentially an identification and elaboration of all repercussions of a designated activity on all or part of the **natural and environmental resource base.** Many countries have laws requiring that environmental impact analyses be carried out before a substantial public program or project is undertaken. Analyses are sometimes required also of private actions. In the United States, the relevant law is the **National Environmental Policy Act of 1970** (NEPA). This law requires that agencies of the federal government conduct environmental impact assessments of proposed laws and "of other major federal actions significantly affecting the quality of the human environment." Over the years this has been interpreted to include any actions funded in part or regulated by the federal government, even though the actions may be undertaken by private parties. Many states have analogous laws governing state-funded projects.

The end result of an environmental impact analysis is an **environmental impact assessment** (EIS), sometimes called an Environmental Impact Report (EIR). An EIR is supposed to contain the following information:

- a description of the environmental impact of the proposed action,
- any adverse environmental effects that cannot be avoided should the proposal be implemented,
- alternatives to the proposed action,
- the relationship between short-term uses of man's environment and the maintenance and enhancement of long-term productivity, and
- any irreversible and irretrievable commitments of resources that would be involved in the proposed action should it be implemented.[1]

For the most part EIR's are the work of natural scientists, such as biologists, hydrologists, and ecologists. The main job is to try to clarify the linkages that will spread the impact of a project through the ecosystem and to estimate the qualitative and quantitative repercussions it will have on the various characteristics of that system. These could be impacts on fish and wildlife, the functioning of the water system, or land and plant resources. The objective is to get a clear and comprehensive picture of how these resources are likely to be impacted. The emphasis is not, however, on placing **values** on these resources—on estimating the worth, for example, of losing 20 nesting pairs of spotted owls, or the value associated with moving certain plant species closer to extinction, or the social costs of losing 50 acres of wetlands.

It would appear that valuation could wait until physical impacts are identified, but this may not be possible. Suppose, for example, a certain forest area is

---

[1] Council of Environmental Quality, "Environmental Quality 1984," Washington, DC, 1985, p. 513.

SECTION FOUR: NATURAL RESOURCE ANALYSIS

to be preserved for wildlife protection, and also to be left open to hikers and backpackers. The extent of the human impact on the region will depend in part on the number of people who visit. This includes not only the direct impact of the recreationists on the site in question, but also related impacts such as those stemming from added automobile traffic in the region. To predict these behavioral factors with reasonable accuracy, it is necessary to have good analytical information on consumer (in this case recreationist) demand for this type of natural resource reservation. Economic analysis is the prime source of studies of this type.

Economic Impact Analysis

When interest centers on how particular public or private actions affect certain dimensions of an economic system, we speak of **economic impact analysis.** The perspective might be local, for example, how the opening of a community or regional park will affect local employment rates. It might be national, for example, how a new law on harvesting timber in national forests will affect the price of building materials. It could even be global, for example, how a treaty on protecting biodiversity will impact the economic growth rates of certain developing countries.

The range of economic impacts that may be of interest is very wide, for example,

- Employment numbers (or unemployment rates), total or in certain industries
- Household incomes
- Rates of technical change in certain resource extraction industries
- Rates of inflation
- Trade balances with other countries

Exhibit 8-1 discusses an economic impact analysis recently done by the U.S. Fish and Wildlife Service. The primary concern of the study was to estimate the impact of a wildlife refuge on employment levels and incomes of people living in the vicinity of the refuge. The refuge in this case is located in Wisconsin.

Any impact analysis is only going to be as good as the underlying economic data and model used to do the study. The more one knows about how the affected economies normally function, the better is one able to estimate the impacts that can be expected from whatever public or private program is being evaluated. Economic impact analysis may also be merged into environmental impact studies. It is also important when it comes to evaluating natural resource conservation and preservation initiatives. Many of the target resources have historically been harvested for consumptive uses; forests have been logged, fisheries have been harvested, farmland has been cleared. In most cases these activities have led to the growth of local extractive industries, firms engaged directly in harvesting, transportation, and sometimes a certain amount of processing. Secondary service industries have often appeared to

---

EXHIBIT 8-1

ECONOMIC IMPACTS OF HORICON NATIONAL WILDLIFE REFUGE

Description

Horicon NWR encompasses the northern two-thirds of Horicon Marsh, a 32,000-acre internationally recognized wetland in central Wisconsin. Sometimes called the "Everglades of the North," Horicon Marsh is the largest freshwater cattail marsh in the United States. The refuge includes 16,956 acres of wetlands and 4,309 acres of upland habitat. It is managed to provide habitat for nesting and migrating waterfowl.

The primary recreational activity on the refuge is wildlife watching. . . . Most visitors come in the fall to see the vast flocks of migrating waterfowl and the changing foliage. . . . Fishing, as well as deer and small-game hunting, are permitted in some areas. . . . Waterfowl hunting is not permitted on the refuge, but the southern third of the marsh, which is managed by the Wisconsin Department of Natural Resources, is a premier waterfowl hunting area. . . .

Area Economy

The population of Dodge and Fond du Lac counties has been stable over the last 30 years. The economy of the region is highly diversified. Much of the land is devoted to dairy farming for cheese production, but there is also a strong industrial and government services base. Mayville hosts several metal fabrication plants. Horicon is the home of John Deere's lawn tractor factory. . . . In addition, the area is an hour away from Milwaukee and Madison, so many people commute to work in these cities and their suburbs. . . .

Activity Levels

The Refuge Management Information System (RMIS) recorded 133,810 visitors during FY 1995. Of this number, 80,724 used the nature trails, 2,079 hunted, and 284 fished. . . .

Refuge staff estimate that 90 percent of non-consumptive use visitors live more than 30 miles from the refuge, many of them in the cities of Milwaukee and Madison, which are within a 1-hour drive. Little public hunting land is available in this area of Wisconsin, so hunters travel some distance to reach the refuge. The refuge staff estimate that 60 percent of hunters are local residents. . . .

Regional Economic Analysis

The fall influx of non-resident, non-consumptive visitors generates most of the spending from Horicon visitation. . . . Non-resident refuge visitors spent about $1.8 million in the region [in 1995]. When all of the spending had cycled through the economy, the refuge generated $1.4 million in final demand, $582,000 in employee compensation, and 41 jobs. . . .

In total, refuge visitors spent $1.9 million in the region. The total effect of this spending was $1.53 million in final demand, $616,000 in employee compensation, and 44 jobs, . . .

Fish and Wildlife Service spending for payrolls, operations, and maintenance of Horicon was $333,000 in FY 1995. This spending is an additional stimulus to the local economy that was not included in the impact calculations.

Source: Excerpted from: U.S. Fish and Wildlife Service, "Banking on Nature: The Economic Benefits to Local Communities of National Wildlife Refuge Visitation," Washington, DC, USFWS, July 1997, pp. 40–42.

---

serve the people involved with the direct extractive activities. It is only natural for politicians and policy makers to be concerned with the welfare and status of the people in these firms, and the impacts on them of alternative proposals for utilizing the resources in question.

SECTION FOUR: NATURAL RESOURCE ANALYSIS

COST-EFFECTIVENESS ANALYSIS

Suppose a community has decided that it needs to increase the capacity of its public water supply system. Assume that to accommodate future expected population growth, the community has decided it must find an additional 100,000 gallons of water per day. There are, we suppose, a number of ways it could do this: drill several new wells into an aquifer that is currently not being used, hook up to the system of a neighboring town that has (at least for now) some excess water, build a new reservoir, plug the leaks in the existing system, find a way of getting consumers to reduce their use, and perhaps some others. A **cost-effectiveness analysis** would estimate the costs of these different alternatives to compare them in terms of costs per thousand gallons of water available for use by town residents. A cost-effectiveness analysis, in other words, takes as given the objective of the project, in this case the 100,000 gallons of additional water, and then costs out the different ways of reaching this objective.

Cost effectiveness is particularly useful in cases where there is wide agreement on the objective but not on how to reach it. It does not attempt to measure the objective in the same value terms as costs, but expresses it in terms of some physical target that is to be obtained. Examples, besides the water supply increase mentioned above, include the preservation of an endangered species; the reduction of fish harvest by, say, 50 percent; the reduction of soil erosion by some percentage; and the reduction of aggregate electricity consumption by some amount. But cost-effectiveness analysis cannot tell us what goals are worth, nor compare the value of resources used up in a program with the value of the objective achieved. For this we must broaden the analysis.

BENEFIT-COST ANALYSIS

Suppose an energy company was contemplating the construction and operation of a group of electricity-generating windmills. Since the company is "bottom line"–oriented, it would want to study the **commercial feasibility** of the windmills before it made a commitment to the plan. It would estimate as clearly as possible its costs of production: construction costs, including connecting the windmills to the power grid, operating costs, periodic maintenance, and so on. It would also estimate its expected revenues, based on the electricity prices it expected, wind conditions, etc. It would then compare expected revenues with expected costs and come to a decision on the commercial feasibility of the venture.

Benefit-cost analysis is an analogous exercise for projects and programs undertaken in the public sector. What is being explored in the case of benefit-cost analysis is not commercial feasibility (though commercial aspects may enter in) but **social feasibility,** in the sense of whether the benefits to society exceed the costs to society of undertaking particular courses of action. One very important difference in practice is that, whereas commercial revenue/cost analysis deals only with inputs and outputs that move across markets, benefit-cost analysis typically involves estimating the value of both market and **nonmarket inputs and outputs.**

CHAPTER 8: PRINCIPLES OF ANALYSIS

Benefit-cost analysis was originally developed in the United States in the 1930s as a tool for studying natural resource decisions in the public sector—specifically to study water resource decisions of federal agencies. The primary applications were the dam building programs of the U.S. Army Corps of Engineers (Department of the Army), the Bureau of Reclamation (Department of the Interior), and the Soil Conservation Service (Department of Agriculture). At the time, each agency operated under a somewhat different set of purposes and objectives. In the Flood Control Act of 1936 it was stated that federal dam projects would be justified if "the benefits to whomever they accrue are in excess of the estimated costs." The agencies were instructed to develop a common set of principles for studying the benefits and costs of these projects, which were eventually codified in the *Green Book* published in 1950.[2] In recent years benefit-cost analysis has been applied to a wide range of government programs, such as environmental protection measures, health care programs, and highway construction projects.

Benefit-cost analysis has led two intertwined lives in natural resource policy making. The first has been among its practitioners—economists inside and outside the public sector who have developed the techniques, searched for the needed data, and sought to improve the quality of the results in different types of applications. (The primary goal of the rest of this chapter, in fact, is to consider briefly some of these procedures.) The second has been its political life among the administrators and legislators who have major ideological and political interests in the public programs to which it has been, or might be, applied. In the abstract, few people can be against the idea of having better analysis and more rational decision making in the public sector. But in its concrete application, good analysis can be politically controversial, because it can give results that are contrary to the interests of politicians, agencies, and interest groups.

In 1980 President Reagan issued Executive Order 12291, which required all agencies to conduct benefit-cost analyses of all proposed new regulations issued by federal agencies. His motive was to place a new hurdle in the way of agencies issuing new regulations, since he was committed to a strong antiregulation political agenda. In the 1990s this effort has been revived by Republican Congresses, which have sought to require benefit-cost analyses of all new federal regulations and programs.[3] Proponents argue that this would ensure that no public programs would be approved unless the social costs are adequately considered along with the benefits. Opponents frequently argue that since it is usually harder to measure benefits than it is to measure costs, a requirement like this will make it more difficult to pursue socially beneficial public programs.

---

[2] U.S. Federal Interagency River Basin Committee, Subcommittee on Benefits and Costs, "Proposed Practices for Economic Analysis of River Basin Projects," Washington, DC, 1950.

[3] And the Reagan order was essentially reaffirmed, though in somewhat weaker form, by President Clinton, in his Executive Order 12866 of September 1993.

SECTION FOUR: NATURAL RESOURCE ANALYSIS

Natural resource and environmental groups have often been in this latter category, primarily on the grounds that the benefits of public programs to preserve natural resources are often difficult to estimate with accuracy. This may be changing, however, as new analytical techniques are developed. Exhibit 8-2 describes a case where environmental groups are attempting to use benefit-cost analysis as a weapon in their fight to have timber harvesting operations stopped within national forests. Others may be coming around to the view that it is quite possible to justify current environmental and resource regulations on benefit-cost grounds; in fact, even tighter regulations can be justified in many cases.

In the last chapter we discussed major policy approaches to managing natural resources. One of these was private property and the reliance on private markets to determine how resources will be used. In this case it has been argued that benefit-cost analysis is not needed. If market prices correctly represent all social costs and all social benefits of an activity, then standard commercial feasibility analysis, like the one done by the windmill company, is all that is needed to ensure that resource decisions are in the **public interest.** But this is a fairly extreme position. Although a move in the direction of private markets may be desirable, it can never be a universal policy, good for all circumstances. Such factors as public goods, distributional consequences, intergenerational issues, and externalities will always be with us. Thus, there is always going to be a need for evaluating public programs, as well as private decisions, to assess their social consequences. Benefit-cost analysis is going to be necessary in these cases.

The Basic Framework

As the name implies, benefit-cost analysis involves measuring, adding up, and comparing all the benefits and costs of the public project or program under study. There are essentially five steps in a benefit-cost analysis, each of which has a number of components:

1 Decide the overall perspective from which the analysis is going to be done; which "public" is the relevant one?
2 Specify clearly the project or program under study.
3 Describe quantitatively the inputs and outputs of the program, that is, all the physical consequences that will flow from it.
4 Estimate the social values of all these inputs and outputs; in effect, estimate the benefits and costs.
5 Compare these benefits and costs.

Decide on the Perspective   Benefit-cost analysis is a tool of public analysis, but there are actually many publics. A benefit-cost analysis of a new town park or a wetlands preservation regulation might be done strictly from the perspective of the local community; that is, the objective may be to estimate

CHAPTER 8: PRINCIPLES OF ANALYSIS

EXHIBIT 8-2

CRITICS WHIPSAW THE FOREST SERVICE

Brad Knickerbocker

The United States Forest Service is a bit like comedian Rodney Dangerfield, whose main laugh line is "I don't get no respect."

Environmentalists think it does the bidding of the logging, mining, and ranching industries. Those who make their living from national forests say the agency too often capitulates to "preservationists" more interested in obscure plant and animal species than in hard-working rural folks. Budget hawks say it wastes hundreds of millions of dollars a year, and its policies are continually under pressure by lawmakers.

The latest round came last Thursday when a coalition of environmental groups and businesses filed suit in federal court in Vermont. They want to halt logging on all federal land until the Forest Service compares the economic benefits of a standing forest versus a pile of logs or wood chips.

Perhaps all this political tussle is not surprising, given that the Forest Service, a $3 billion, 30,000-employee organization, controls 192 million acres—with all the wealth and emotional ties to nature that represents. But these days, the agency is under unusual pressure.

Conservative members of Congress charge that the agency is conducting an illegal lobbying campaign to advance its policies, one some lawmakers think is too "green" in its approach to timber cutting and cattle grazing.

From the opposite quarter, meanwhile, conservation groups in Oregon and Washington State recently filed suit to stop the Forest Service from swapping land with corporate owners. Such deals are meant to consolidate "checkerboard" holdings that date back to 19th-century railroad land grants while making commercially valuable timberland available to loggers and mill owners.

The U.S. Department of Agriculture (the Forest Service's parent agency) is investigating the land-exchange program, which critics say does not include enough environmental protection.

Environmentalists and fiscal watchdog groups also criticize the Forest Service for, in effect, subsidizing the timber industry through the below-cost sale of rights to log billions of board-feet of timber. The GAO recently reported that from 1995 to 1997 the federal government lost just over $1 billion.

Industry defenders say managing national forests for timber production as well as wildlife and recreation supplies the nation with wood and paper products while providing thousands of jobs for rural communities. But that argument does not mollify critics, who point to environmental degradation.

"All too often, these logging-based revenues have come at the expense of damaging clearcuts, eroded soils, degraded water quality, and impaired fish and wildlife habitat," says Rep. George Miller of California, senior Democrat on the House Resources Committee.

Forest Service Chief Michael Dombeck concedes that the agency must adjust to an era in which public values demand a different approach—one that emphasizes "watershed health and integrity" over commodity production.

Even though the timber program has decreased by 70 percent in less than 10 years, timber production still drives the priorities and the reward system, and that needs to change, Dr. Dombeck told a meeting of foresters in September.

Field: Natural Resource
Economics — An
Introduction

IV. Natural Resource
Analysis

8. Principles Of Analysis

© The McGraw–Hill
Companies, 2003

the benefits and costs impinging on town residents only. An analysis of a federal regulation would probably be done from the standpoint of all people living in the country, while a global treaty on natural resource use might be undertaken considering the entire population of the earth as the public.

Specify the Project   This involves a complete (as complete as possible) specification of the project or program, including its location, timing, groups involved, and connections with other programs. In any benefit-cost analysis some assumptions have to be made. Will the economy continue to grow? At what rate? Will population growth continue? Will another public agency continue with a related project? Assumptions such as these have to be made as transparently and as realistically as possible right at the beginning.

There are two basic types of public programs for which benefit-cost analysis may be done:

1 Physical projects that involve some type of direct public production such as irrigation water delivery canals, beach restoration, park trails and visitor centers, logging roads, and habitat improvement projects.
2 Regulatory programs aimed at enforcing laws or practices such as restrictions on certain types of activities in national parks or monuments, land-use regulations, regulations to control commercial or recreational fishing, and regulations covering imports of endangered species. This includes also many financial-type programs like fees charged for grazing cattle on public range, subsidies offered for switching to more energy-efficient equipment, and royalty payments made by miners on public lands.

Measure Inputs and Outputs   For some projects this will be relatively easy. The engineering staff will be able to provide a reasonably complete picture of a water supply system, in terms of what it will take to build and operate it over time. The inputs required to lay out a trial system or to carry out a wetland restoration may be fairly easy to estimate. But many types of data outputs will be more difficult to measure. How many visitors can be expected in this wilderness area or at this wildlife viewing area? How might fishers, who are subject to regulations of one type, adjust their operations in an attempt to continue harvesting fish? How fast can we expect industries to grow that would supply essential equipment to backpackers, white-water rafters, or snowmobilers?

A particularly challenging aspect of this analytical element is that virtually all projects and programs extend over time, usually over long periods of time. So the job of specifying inputs and outputs requires making **predictions** about the future, and these are always going to be subject to some uncertainty, perhaps a lot of uncertainty. How does one predict population growth or rates of technological change in the medium-term future? Long-term ecological relationships are also likely to be highly uncertain. What will wolf restoration do in the long run to elk populations? How much will the survival probabilities of the spotted owl increase if we restrict logging in a defined region?

CHAPTER 8:   PRINCIPLES OF ANALYSIS

To answer such questions puts a great premium on being able to draw on diverse sources of expertise and data—like engineers, soil scientists, wildlife biologists, hydrologists, economists, published data, new survey data, and private data collected for other reasons. Benefit-cost analyses are costly in terms of time and expense. To search for existing data or to conduct surveys to get new data takes money and effort. Furthermore, all benefit-cost analyses will be pursued with limited budgets. There is no hard-and-fast rule on how much it takes to do a benefit-cost analysis, other than the principle that the bigger the budget, the better chance one has of getting better information and more accurate results.

Value Inputs and Outputs   This step involves putting values on the items estimated in the last step, in essence to estimate the benefits and costs of the project or program. We could do this in any units we wish, but typically this implies measuring benefits and costs in monetary terms. This does not mean in market-value terms because in many cases we will be dealing with effects, especially on the benefit side, that are not directly registered on markets. Nor does it imply that only monetary values count in some fundamental manner. It means that we need a single metric into which to translate all the impacts of a project or program in order to make them comparable among themselves as well as with other types of public activities. Ultimately, certain impacts of a program may be irreducible to monetary terms because we cannot find a way of measuring how much people value these impacts. In this case we must supplement the monetary results of the benefit-cost analysis with estimates and discussions of these intangible impacts.

Compare Benefits and Costs   Once all benefits and costs have been estimated as well as possible, it's time to take the last step, which is to compare them. There are two ways of doing this:

1 **Net benefits:** Total benefits minus total costs gives net benefits.
2 **Benefit-cost ratio:** Total benefits divided by total costs gives the benefit-cost ratio, the value of benefits produced per dollar of cost.

To understand what is involved in very general terms, consider the numbers in Table 8-1. They are illustrative but realistic numbers for the construction and operation of a new wildlife refuge. The purpose of the refuge is to provide visitors with opportunities both for wildlife watching and, at certain times of the year, hunting and fishing. Another purpose is to provide continued habitat for several species of threatened wildlife.

The refuge involves three types of costs: the costs of acquiring the land, the costs of constructing the refuge, and the annual costs of operating it. The latter costs include the costs of handling the visitors to the refuge and the costs of maintaining both the constructed facilities and the habitat of the refuge. There are also three types of benefits. **Nonconsumptive benefits** include the benefits accruing to those visitors whose primary purpose is wildlife viewing. Benefits

SECTION FOUR: NATURAL RESOURCE ANALYSIS

TABLE 8-1
ILLUSTRATIVE RESULTS: BENEFIT-COST ANALYSIS
OF A NEW WILDLIFE REFUGE

	Estimated annual (dollars)
Costs	
Land purchase	153,000*
Construction	
Visitor center	142,000*
Trail system	64,000*
Operation and maintenance	
Personnel	187,000
Other	63,000
Total	609,000
Benefits	
Wildlife watchers	143,000
Hunters and fishers	627,000
Species preservation	$A^\dagger$
Total	770,000
Net benefits: $\$161,000 + A^\dagger$	
Benefit-cost ratio: $1.26 + a^\dagger$	

   *These are the **annualized costs** of initial one-time outlays. Essentially they are the annual payments necessary to cumulate up, at a given interest rate, to the total initial outlay over the life of the project.

   $\dagger$$A$ and a are used to account for the factors that are non-quantifiable in monetary terms.

to hunters and fishers are the **consumptive benefits** of the refuge. There are also **species preservation benefits** flowing from the refuge, but since we have not been able to develop a realistic measure of these, they are entered as an amount equal to A. Net benefits and the benefit-cost ratio are shown at the bottom, the first with the indeterminate amount "A" included, and the second with an adjustment factor designated "a."

Scope of the Project

Should we devote 1,500 acres to the proposed new public park, or should it be more or less? Should forest clear-cuts be limited to 100 acres, or would 150 acres be better? Should we manage the wolf population at 1,000 individuals, or at some higher or lower level? The example in Table 8-1 relates to a wildlife refuge of some given size, but how do we know that this is in some sense the optimum size? Although benefit-cost analyses are done for programs/projects of a given size, we must also keep in mind that these could be smaller or larger. Even in the case of a regulation, which would seem to be an either/or proposition, there is a question of how many resources to devote to its enforcement, which gets us right back to the problem of scope.

CHAPTER 8:   PRINCIPLES OF ANALYSIS

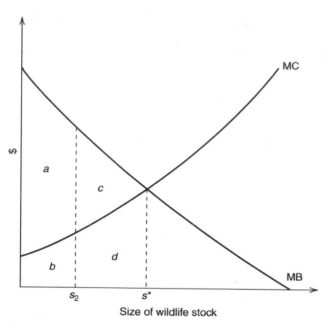

FIGURE 8-1
Scope of a Project

To explore this issue conceptually, consider Figure 8-1. It shows several relationships pertaining to the size of a project, which in this case is assumed to be the maintenance of a wildlife stock. The horizontal axis indexes the stock size, measured in terms of the number of adult individuals in the stock. The curve labeled MB shows **marginal benefits,** that is, it shows how much total benefits will change when there is a small change in stock level. Note that it decreases to the right, which is a reflection of the fact that the total benefits go up less and less rapidly as the stock level increases. The MC curve shows **marginal cost,** which is the amount by which costs change as the stock level changes. This function increases to the right, a reflection of the fact that the total cost curve shown in panel (a) gets increasingly steep at higher stock levels.

The optimal size of wildlife stock is shown as s^*; this is the stock size where marginal benefits and marginal costs are equal. The problem when we do a benefit-cost analysis of a specific project is that we cannot be sure whether we are dealing with a plan such as s^* in the figure or one at some other level, such as s_2? How can we be sure, for example, that the program analyzed in Table 8-1 is close to the **efficient size,** that is, the size that **maximizes net benefits**?

Very often a benefit-cost analyst will be faced with studying a project of predetermined size. That is, the size of the project or program will have been established already, perhaps by engineers (in the case of a structure like a windmill farm), wildlife biologists (in the case of a wildlife refuge or wildlife

SECTION FOUR: NATURAL RESOURCE ANALYSIS

restoration plan), or ecologists (in the case of a new national or state park). In these cases the size, or scope, of the programs has been established on physical grounds, and the benefit-cost analysts must confirm whether this is desirable from a benefit-cost perspective.

The procedure that can be pursued to shed light on this question is **sensitivity analysis.** This refers to the practice of recalculating benefits and costs for several alternative programs, some that are larger than the one shown in the table and some that are smaller. If the program shown in the table is indeed appropriately scaled, each of the alternatives will have lower net benefits. On the other hand, suppose the plan shown in Table 8-1 corresponds to the one shown as s_2 in Figure 8-1. In this case the net benefits shown in the table correspond to an amount equal to $(a + b) - b = a$ in terms of the areas shown in the figure. Sensitivity analysis in this case would allow the analyst to evaluate a larger effort, say, something that would maintain a wildlife stock in the vicinity of s^*. This analysis would show higher net benefits than s_2 (the net benefits would be $(a + c)$.

The With/Without Principle

In doing benefit-cost analyses, we must proceed according to the with/without principle: That is, we must compare the situation that would result if the program or project were pursued with what it **would have been** had the program been rejected. What is sometimes done instead is to compare results with the program with what the situation was **before** the program. But this can lead to false conclusions about the efficacy of the program.

Suppose, for example, we are trying to evaluate the benefits and costs of a wildlife restoration project. The population of the target animal is currently quite low, and the program involves, let us say, captive breeding and release. The benefits come from recreational viewing and are directly related to the size of the population. Estimated benefits are the following:

Before the program	$ 10,000
In the future without the program	$ 5,000
In the future with the program	$ 33,000

It would be a mistake to estimate program benefits at $23,000 ($33,000 − $10,000). This is a before/after comparison. But the base level, if the program is not pursued, is $5,000 rather than $10,000. This is because it has been predicted that there will be some attrition of the stock in the absence of the restoration program. Thus, the basis should be taken as $5,000, meaning that the benefits ascribable to the program are $28,000 ($33,000 − $5,000) rather than $23,000. This is not to imply that a with/without perspective will always give higher benefits than a before/after study. Often the opposite will be the case. If a certain population of wildlife is expected to increase moderately in the absence of a program, the with/without benefits would be larger than the before/after results.

CHAPTER 8: PRINCIPLES OF ANALYSIS

Discounting

In Chapter 3 we discussed the mechanics of **discounting.** Discounting is a way of determining the value today (present value) of benefits and costs that will accrue at some future time. Since virtually any public program or project involving natural resources will extend beyond a single time period (e.g., year), a way has to be found to add benefits that occur in different time periods, and likewise with costs that occur in different time periods. Consider the following illustrative numbers, showing net benefits for two different projects, each of which extends over 4 years (in actuality, of course, most programs will extend much longer than this, but 4 years is enough to illustrate the general principle involved).

| | Net benefits ($) in year[4] | | | | Total (undiscounted) net benefits |
	0	1	2	3	
Program A	20	20	20	20	80
Program B	50	10	10	10	80

If we simply sum the undiscounted net benefits across the 4 years, we get the same total for each, $80. But the **time profile** of benefits is quite different between the two plans: Program A has an equal distribution of net benefits across the 4 years, while Program B has most of its net benefits in the very first year, after which they are substantially lower for the last 3 years. From an intuitive standpoint we might regard Program B as somewhat more valuable because a much greater proportion of its net benefits are concentrated nearer in time. What we need is a way of **weighting** the net benefits accruing in different periods to reflect how near or distant in time they are. This is what discounting does. Thus, to compare the net-benefit streams in a way that allows for differences in their time profiles, we calculate the **present value** of total net benefits for each program. Using a discount rate of 6 percent, we get the following:

$$PV_A = \$20 + \frac{\$20}{1 + 0.06} + \frac{\$20}{(1 + 0.06)^2} + \frac{20}{(1 + 0.06)^3} = \$73.45$$

$$PV_B = \$50 + \frac{\$10}{1 + 0.06} + \frac{\$10}{(1 + 0.06)^2} + \frac{10}{(1 + 0.06)^3} = \$76.73$$

The Effects of Discounting

Note that in both programs the discounting has lowered total net benefits relative to the undiscounted totals. This is because discounting weights a dollar of

---

[4] Remember that we are following the convention that the current period is indexed with zero, and is not discounted.

net benefits accruing in the future at less than a dollar of net benefits accruing today. But the discounting affects Program A more than Program B, because a larger proportion of the net benefits of A occur in later periods, whereas the time profile of the net-benefit stream of B is concentrated more toward the present.

Discounting, then, allows us to compare projects or programs that have very **different time profiles of net benefits.** Consider the following net-benefit profiles for two alternative programs.

	Time period			
	0	1	2	3
Plan A				
Benefits	50	50	50	50
Costs	30	30	30	30
Net benefits	20	20	20	20
Plan B				
Benefits	100	50	25	25
Costs	50	40	15	15
Net benefits	50	10	10	10

The undiscounted sums of the net-benefit streams are the same; there are a total of $80 of net benefits in each of the plans. If we had to make a choice between the two plans, and we chose not to discount, we could essentially flip a coin between them. But suppose we discount net benefits, say, at 5 percent. Then the discounted stream of net benefits for the two projects would be

$$A = \$74.47$$
$$B = \$77.23$$

After the discounting, Program B has higher present value of net benefits than does Program A. The discounting has increased the relative value of the plan that produces its net benefits earlier in time. Or, to say the same thing, discounting penalizes projects in which the net benefits occur farther out into the future.

Discounting and Future Generations

The logic of a discount rate, even a very small one, is inexorable. A thousand dollars, discounted back over a century at 5 percent, has a present value of about $7.60. The logic is even more compelling if we consider a future cost. One of the reasons that environmentalists have looked askance at discounting is that it can have the effect of downgrading future damages that result from today's economic activity. Suppose today's generation is considering a course of action that has certain short-run benefits of $10,000 per year for 50 years, but that, starting 50 years from now, will cost $1 million a year **forever.** This may be somewhat similar to the choice faced by current generations regarding nuclear power or global warming. To people alive today, the present value of that perpetual stream of future cost discounted at 10 percent is only about $85,000. These costs may not weigh particularly heavily on decisions made by the current generation. The present value of the benefits ($10,000 a year for 50 years at 10 percent, or $99,148) exceeds the present value of the future costs. From the standpoint of today, therefore, this might look like a good choice, despite the perpetual cost burden placed on all future generations.

Choice of the Discount Rate

Because discounting is a way of aggregating a series of future net benefits into an estimate of present value, the outcome depends importantly on which particular discount rate is used. A low rate implies that a dollar in 1 year is very similar in value to a dollar in any other year. A high rate implies that a dollar in the near term is much more valuable than one later on. Thus, the higher the discount rate, the more we would be encouraged to put our resources into programs that have relatively high payoffs (i.e., high benefits and/or low costs) in the short run. The lower the discount rate, on the contrary, the more we would be led to select programs that have high net benefits in the more distant future.

The choice of a discount rate has been a controversial topic through the years, and we can only summarize some of the arguments here. First, it is important to keep in mind the difference between **real** and **nominal** interest rates. Nominal rates are those one actually sees on the market. If you take a nominal rate and adjust it for inflation, you get a real interest rate. Suppose you deposit $100 in a bank at an interest rate of 8 percent. In 10 years your deposit would have grown to $216, but this is in monetary terms. Suppose over that 10-year period prices increase 3 percent per year on average. Then the real value of your accumulated deposit would be less; in fact, the real interest rate at which your deposit would accumulate would be only 5 percent (8 percent – 3 percent), so in real terms your deposit would be worth only $161 after the 10 years.[5] If the cost estimates are expected real costs, that is, adjusted for expected inflation, a real interest rate is used for discounting purposes. If our cost estimates are nominal figures, a nominal interest rate is used in the discounting analysis.

The discount rate reflects the current generation's views about the relative weight to be given to benefits and costs occurring in different years. Even a

---

[5] These are slight approximations. The deposit would actually be worth $160.64, and the real rate of accumulation would be 4.89 percent.

brief look, though, will show that there are dozens of different interest rates in use at any one time—rates on normal savings accounts, certificates of deposit, bank loans, government bonds, and so forth. Which rate should be used? There are essentially two schools of thought on this question: the **time preference approach** and the **marginal productivity approach.**

According to the time preference approach, the discount rate should reflect the way people themselves think about time. Any person normally would prefer a dollar today to a dollar in 10 years; in the language of economics, they have a **positive time preference.** We see people making savings decisions by putting money in bank accounts that pay certain rates of interest. These savings account rates show what interest the banks have to offer in order to get people to forgo current consumption. We might, therefore, take the average bank savings account rate as reflecting the average person's rate of time preference.

The problem with this is that there are other ways of determining peoples' rates of time preference, and they don't necessarily give the same answer. Economists at Resources for the Future[6] completed a large survey in which they asked individuals to choose between receiving $10,000 today and larger amounts in 5 or 10 years. The responses yielded implied rates of discount of 20 percent for a 5-year time horizon and 10 percent for a 10-year horizon. These were substantially higher than bank savings rates at the time of the survey, which simply indicates that the actual discount rates people use may not be reflected well in standard market interest rates.

The second approach to determining the "correct" rate of discount is based on the notion of the **marginal productivity of investment.** When investments are made in productive enterprises, people anticipate that the value of future returns will offset today's investment costs; otherwise, these investments would not be made. The thinking here is that when resources are used in the public sector for natural resource and environmental programs, they ought to yield, on average, rates of return to society equivalent to what they could have earned in the private sector. Private sector productivity is reflected in the rates of interest banks charge their business borrowers. Thus, by this reasoning, we should use as our discount rate a rate reflecting the interest rates that private firms pay when they borrow money for investment purposes. These are typically higher than savings account interest rates.

Distributional Issues

From an efficiency standpoint the only thing that is relevant is total benefits and total costs; efficiency requires maximizing the difference between the two. But in many cases we will be interested also in how these benefits and costs are

---

[6] Resources for the Future (RFF) is a well-known Washington organization that specializes in natural resource and environmental economics research. It publishes a quarterly newsletter discussing its work. This information comes from RFF, *Resources,* No, 108, Summer 1992, p. 3.

CHAPTER 8:   PRINCIPLES OF ANALYSIS

distributed among the people and groups affected by the project or program. We talked about the importance of distributional issues earlier, particularly from a political economic perspective.[7] The political conflicts in which many natural resource issues get embroiled are often related to the fact that the groups who enjoy the benefits are not the same as those who bear the costs.

These are matters of equity, or fairness, which is why they can become so controversial. Another important aspect of distributional fairness in resource programs (or in any program, for that matter) is how they impact people with different income levels. This is a major issue in the **environmental justice** movement, and the same problems exist in natural resource projects. There are essentially two main dimensions of equity: horizontal and vertical. **Horizontal equity** means treating people in similar situations alike. From the standpoint of the income dimension, if all people in the same income class are treated alike, in the sense that they experience the same gain (or loss) in net benefits, then horizontal equity has been achieved. Suppose we have a wildlife restoration program that has the following benefit-and-cost profile for a typical urban resident and a typical rural resident:

	Urban resident	Rural resident
Benefits	80	120
Costs	40	80
Net benefits	40	40

Note that both benefits and costs of the rural resident are higher than for the urban citizen, but net benefits are the same for each. Thus, if these people have similar incomes, we would regard this situation as equitable in the horizontal sense.

On the other hand, suppose they do not have the same income. Suppose the rural dweller has an income half that of the urban person. Then there would be a question of equity in the vertical sense, because **vertical equity** refers to how programs impinge on people who are in different circumstances, in particular on people who are at different income levels. Consider the illustrative numbers of Table 8-2. They show monetary benefits and costs of three natural resource projects as they accrue to three different people with, respectively, a low (Person A), medium (Person B) and high (Person C) income. In the adjoining parentheses each number is shown as a percentage of the person's income. Take Project 1, for example. Although the net benefits accruing to each person are different, the percentage of income is the same for all three (1 percent). The project in this case has a **proportional impact;** it affects each consumer in the same proportion.

[7] See Chapter 7.

SECTION FOUR: NATURAL RESOURCE ANALYSIS

TABLE 8-2
VERTICAL EQUITY*

	Person A		Person B		Person C	
Income	$5,000		$20,000		$50,000	
Project 1						
Benefits	$150	(3.0)	$ 300	(1.5)	$ 600	(1.2)
Costs	100	(2.0)	100	(0.5)	100	(0.2)
Net benefits	$ 50	(1.0)	$ 200	(1.0)	$ 500	(1.0)
Project 2						
Benefits	$150	(3.0)	$1,400	(7.0)	$5,500	(11.0)
Costs	100	(2.0)	800	(4.0)	3,000	(6.0)
Net benefits	$ 50	(1.0)	$ 600	(3.0)	$2,500	(5.0)
Project 3						
Benefits	$700	(14.0)	$2,200	(11.0)	$3,000	(6.0)
Costs	200	(4.0)	1,000	(5.0)	1,500	(3.0)
Net benefits	$500	(10.0)	$1,200	(6.0)	$1,500	(3.0)

*Figures in the table show annual monetary values. Numbers in parentheses show the percentage of income these numbers represent.

Project 2, on the other hand, is **regressive;** it provides higher proportional net benefits to high-income people than to low-income people. Project 3 has a **progressive** impact because net benefits represent a higher proportion of the low-income person's income than they do of the rich person's income. Thus a natural resource project (or any project for that matter) is proportional, regressive, or progressive, according to whether the net effect of that project has proportionally the same, a lower, or a higher impact on low-income people as it does on high-income people.

Note that although the net effects of a project may be distributed in one way, the individual components need not be distributed in the same way. For example, although the overall effects of Project 2 are regressive, the costs of that program are in fact distributed progressively (i.e., the cost burden, measured as a percent of income, is greater for high-income people). In this case benefits are distributed so regressively that the overall project is regressive. This is the same in Project 3; although the overall program is progressive, costs are distributed regressively.

These definitions of distributional impacts can be misleading. A project that is technically regressive could actually distribute the bulk of its net benefits to poor people. Suppose a policy raised the net income of one rich person by 10 percent, but raised each of the net incomes of 1,000 poor people by 5 percent. This policy is technically regressive, although more than likely the majority of its aggregate net benefits go to poor people.

Although the terminology of horizontal and vertical equity are reasonably clear, it is usually very hard to figure out whether any specific real-world

CHAPTER 8:   PRINCIPLES OF ANALYSIS

natural resource project or policy has a progressive or regressive impact. To know this, we must know both who the people are that are impacted and what their income levels are. This may be feasible if the analysis is dealing with a reasonably small group of people (e.g., water rights being transferred from a relatively small group of ranchers to a local community), but it is much less so if benefits and/or costs are widely dispersed (e.g., the benefits accruing to society at large from biodiversity preservation).

Dealing with Uncertainty

In each example used so far in this chapter we have assumed that benefits and costs are known **with certainty.** But reality is not like this, especially since the estimation of benefits and costs actually involves predicting the **future values** of variables going into the analysis, values that will often be quite distant in time. We have to recognize and deal with the fact that we can never know these future values with absolute certainty. How can we do this?

We need to recognize, first, that results like those shown earlier are in reality **point estimates** of uncertain situations. We may regard them as the **most likely outcome** to expect, even though we should not be surprised if actual events turn out otherwise. One possible way to acknowledge uncertainty is to estimate a **range** for net benefits (with sensitivity analysis). If one has only informal information about the likelihood of future events, it may be possible to make qualitative statements such as "we are highly confident that net benefits will fall somewhere within a range between $a and $b." If one can get better data on probabilities, it may be possible to derive statistical conclusions: "We are 90 percent confident that the net benefits will fall within a range between $c and $d."

Many natural resource issues involve **biological uncertainty.** In a study by Richard Bishop and his associates,[8] the objective was to measure the benefits and costs of a fish rehabilitation program in a part of the Great Lakes. The Wisconsin Department of Natural Resources was planning to put restrictions on current fishing activities so that the stock of fish (in this case yellow perch) would recover. But there was much uncertainty about biological relationships and how the stocks would respond to the lower levels of fishing activity. Bishop et al. analyzed the case by looking at six different **scenarios,** each one involving a different assumption about how fast and far the fish stock would recover. For each scenario they then estimated the potential benefits. The overall expected benefits were then found by averaging the benefits of the scenarios, with each scenario **weighted by its assumed probability of occurrence,** as in the following example:

---

[8] Richard C. Bishop, "Benefit-Cost Analysis of Fishery Rehabilitation Projects: A Great Lakes Case Study," *Ocean and Shoreline Management,* Vol. 13, 1990, pp. 253–274.

SECTION FOUR: NATURAL RESOURCE ANALYSIS

Scenario	Benefits ($ million)	Probability of occurrence	Benefits × probabilities ($ million)
I	40	.40	16.0
II	30	.20	6.0
III	20	.10	2.0
IV	10	.20	2.0
V	50	.05	2.5
VI	60	.05	3.0
Total		1.00	31.5

The summed benefits of $31.5 million in this case represent what are called **expected benefits.** Expected benefits (or expected costs, if the technique were used for estimating uncertain costs) may be thought of as **the most likely** outcome, given the uncertainty in the biological processes involved. The uncertainty is represented by the scenario probabilities, which in the case of the Bishop study were established by asking fishery biologists to evaluate the likelihood of each scenario. Note that the sum of the probabilities is unity: The six scenarios represent all possible outcomes.

Another source of uncertainty in benefit-cost analyses is **economic uncertainty.** Benefits and costs are based on assumed prices of inputs and outputs, and we know that relative prices can change through time. Very often the analysis will hinge on a strategic piece of economic information, the future course of which can only be assumed. For example, the benefits of wilderness areas are linked to the rapid rise in demand for outdoor recreation, such as backpacking, that has occurred in the United States over the last several decades. Will this activity continue to grow at the same rate in the future? Some assumption will have to be made about this growth rate if we wish to estimate the benefits of designating new wilderness areas.

Another source of uncertainty is the discount rate that should be used. Interest rates vary over time according to economic conditions, and there is no way of knowing with certainty what the rate will be 10 or 20 years from now. We may choose to overlook this and simply use today's rate, or perhaps calculate an average over the last, say, 10 years, to use in discounting future benefits and costs.

SUMMARY

In this chapter we looked at several ways through which economic analysts assess outcomes of natural resource decisions, especially those within the public sector. We looked at **cost-effectiveness analysis** and **economic impact analysis,** but reserved the bulk of our attention for **benefit-cost analysis.** Benefit-cost analysis is simply a technique of accounting for, and valuing, all outputs and inputs of public projects or programs. We considered the economic factors involved in finding the correct size or **scope** of the project: **discounting, distributional** issues, and the question of **uncertainty.**

CHAPTER 8:   PRINCIPLES OF ANALYSIS

KEY TERMS

Environmental impact analysis
Economic impact analysis
Cost-effectiveness analysis
Benefit-cost analysis
Net benefits
Benefit-cost ratio
With/without principle
Discounting

Political economy of benefit and cost
  distribution
Horizontal equity
Vertical equity
Uncertainty
Expected value
Biological uncertainty
Economic uncertainty

QUESTIONS FOR FURTHER DISCUSSION

1 Describe the difference between cost-effectiveness analysis and benefit-cost analysis as these would apply to the question of preserving biological diversity.

2 To restore a depleted fish population, it is often necessary to reduce or stop entirely the harvesting of the stock for a certain period of time. If we are evaluating the question of how long the period of reduced harvest should be, what impact would raising the discount rate have on our conclusion?

3 Suppose we are evaluating the benefits and costs of starting an ecotourism project where visitors will be given guided tours of a particularly rich habitat area. What are the main benefits and costs that should be enumerated?

4 Suppose we were doing an economic impact analysis of the project mentioned in question 3. How would this differ from the cost-benefit analysis?

5 Assume you have been asked to do a benefit-cost analysis of a habitat protection program to help preserve a certain endangered species of wildlife. What distributional issues might be important to examine in the course of your analysis?

6 In question 5, what are the sources of uncertainty that this analysis would have to deal with, and how might this be approached?

USEFUL WEB SITES

For material on resource valuation, discounting, and principles of benefit-cost analysis:

- Resources for the Future (http://www.rff.org).

For general information on benefit-cost analysis:

- United States Environmental Protection Agency (http://www.epa.gov) (search for benefit-cost analysis under projects and programs).

For information on project analysis and impact analysis:

- Bureau of Reclamation in the U.S. Department of Interior (http://www.usbr.gov) has an economics group handling project analysis and impact analysis.

SECTION FOUR: NATURAL RESOURCE ANALYSIS

SELECTED READINGS

Arnold, Frank S: *Economic Analysis of Environmental Policy and Regulation,* John Wiley, New York, 1995.

Dasgupta, Ajit K., and D. W. Pearce: *Cost-Benefit Analysis: Theory and Practice,* Barnes and Noble, New York, 1972.

Hanley, Nick, and Clive L. Spash: *Cost-Benefit Analysis and the Environment,* Edward Elgar, Aldershot, England, 1993.

Nas, Tevfik: *Cost-Benefit Analysis, Theory and Application,* Sage, Thousand Oaks, CA, 1996.

Sassone, Peter G., and William A. Schaffer: *Cost-Benefit Analysis, A Handbook,* Academic Press, New York, 1978.

Sugden, Robert, and Alan Williams: *The Principles of Practical Cost-Benefit Analysis,* Oxford University Press, Oxford, England, 1978.

Helfert: Techniques of
Financial Analysis: A
Guide to Value Creation

Appendixes

IV. Basic Inflation
Concepts

© The McGraw–Hill
Companies, 2003

APPENDIX IV

Basic Inflation Concepts

Throughout this book we've referred to inflation's distorting effects on financial decisions and analysis. In this appendix, we'll offer a brief commentary on the basic nature of the often misunderstood phenomenon of inflation. Financial transactions are carried out and recorded with the help of a common medium of exchange, such as U.S. dollars. Variations in this medium will affect the numerical meaning of these transactions. But we know that underlying the transactions are economic trade-offs; that is, values are given and received. We must be careful not to confuse changes in economic values with changes in the medium used to effect and account for these transactions. We'll examine the ramifications of this important distinction in several contexts below.

Price Level Changes

The economic values of goods and services invariably change over time. The reason for this is as basic as human nature: The law of supply and demand operates, in an uncontrolled market environment, to increase the value of goods and services that are in short supply, and to decrease the value of those available in abundance. This shift in relative values takes place even in a primitive barter economy that doesn't utilize any currency at all. The ratio of exchange of coconuts for beans, for example, will move in favor of coconuts when they're scarce, and in favor of beans when these are out of season.

Many seasonal agricultural products go through a familiar price cycle, beginning with their temporary unavailability, on to the first arrivals in the marketplace, and eventually to an abundance before they become unavailable again. This phenomenon is not limited to seasonal goods, however. Natural resources go through cycles of availability, be it from the need to set up the expensive infrastructure to exploit new sources as old ones expire, or from extreme concerted actions such as OPEC's moves to limit production in the 1970s and 80s that caused world oil prices to surge because of the cartel's control of over half the world's production. As alternative sources of oil and other energy were stimulated by the high prices, the cartel's power began to wane, hastened by inevitable squabbles among the member countries trying to look out for their own interests—and oil prices settled on a much lower, more sustainable level.

We know that the economic value of manufactured goods is similarly subject to the law of supply and demand. For example, as new technology emerges in the market, such as the first digital watches or compact disk players, or successive waves of innovation in electronic chips and other components, the price commanded by the early units will be well above the prices charged later on, after

Helfert: Techniques of
Financial Analysis: A
Guide to Value Creation

Appendixes

IV. Basic Inflation
Concepts

© The McGraw–Hill
Companies, 2003

Techniques of Financial Analysis: A Guide to Value Creation

many suppliers have entered the market and competed for a share of industrial or consumer demand. The same is true of all goods and services for which there are present or potential alternative suppliers, domestic or international.

Our point here is that the economic value underlying personal, commercial, and financial transactions is determined by forces that are largely independent of the monetary expression in which they're recorded. As we'll see, an analysis of price level changes ideally should separate the change in price levels caused by shifts in economic value from those caused by changes in the currency itself. Accurate separation of the two is difficult in practice, but necessary for understanding the meaning of financial projections.

Monetary Inflation

Another phenomenon affecting transaction values is any basic change in the purchasing power of the currency. There are many reasons underlying the decline or strengthening of a currency's value as a medium of exchange. One of the most important factors causing inflationary declines in purchasing power is the amount of currency in circulation relative to economic activity. If the government raises the money supply faster than required to accommodate the growth in economic activity, there will literally be more dollars chasing relatively fewer goods and services, and thus the stated dollar prices for all goods and services will rise—even though the basic demand for any specific item may be unchanged.

This description is oversimplified, of course. A great many more factors affect currency values. One of these is the impact of government deficits and the way they are financed. Another is the value of the dollar relative to other currencies and the impact of exchange rates on international trade. In addition, international money flows and investment in response to more attractive investment opportunities cause shifts in the values of national currencies over and above the effects of the individual countries' fiscal and economic conditions. Union negotiations, wage settlements, and cost of living adjustments in wages, pensions, and Social Security are also related to changing currency values. Every nation's central bank—the Federal Reserve Bank in the case of the United States—is vital in the process because its policies affect both the size of the money supply and the level of interest rates. These in turn affect government fiscal policies, business activity, international trade and money flows, and so forth. And ultimately, serious declines in the value of a currency can also affect the basic supply and demand of goods and services, as, for example, when customers and businesses buy ahead to beat anticipated price increases.

The point here isn't to systematically analyze inflation and its causes, but rather to make the basic distinction between economic and monetary changes influencing price levels. Suffice it to say that price level changes due to monetary effects are largely the ones that distort economic values of personal and commercial transactions. If monetary conditions remained stable (that is, if the amount of currency in circulation always matched the level of economic activity), price level

Helfert: Techniques of
Financial Analysis: A
Guide to Value Creation

Appendixes

IV. Basic Inflation
Concepts

© The McGraw–Hill
Companies, 2003

APPENDIX IV   Basic Inflation Concepts

changes would reflect only changes in economic values—something we've
agreed is at the core of management's efforts to improve the shareholders' economic condition. Because monetary stability is an unrealistic expectation; however, the challenge remains to make the analysis of the actual conditions affecting
prices and economic values truly meaningful.

Nominal and Real Dollars

Business and personal transactions are expressed in terms of *nominal* dollars, also
called current dollars, that reflect today's prices, unadjusted or altered in any way.
For accounting purposes, nominal dollars are used every day to record transactions. However, when dollar prices change over time, the amounts recorded in the
past no longer reflect current prices, either in terms of the underlying economic
values or in terms of the value of the currency at the moment.

To deal with changes in the value of the currency, economists have devised
price indexes intended to separate, at least in part, monetary distortions from fluctuations in economic value. Such an index is constructed by measuring the aggregate change in the prices of a representative group of products and services as a
surrogate for the change in the value of the currency. Yet we already know that
any goods and services chosen for this purpose are themselves also subject to
changes in supply and demand, apart from mere currency fluctuations. But there's
no direct way to measure changes in currency values as such. Inevitably, therefore, the price index approach involves mixing demand/supply conditions and
currency values, and the only hope is that the selection of goods and services employed in a given index is broad enough to compensate somewhat for the underlying demand/supply conditions.

The *consumer price index*, a popular index of inflation, is calculated in this
fashion. It's based on frequent sampling of the prices of a "market basket" of goods
and services purchased by U.S. consumers, including food, housing, clothing, and
transportation. The composition and weighting of this basket is changed gradually to
reflect changing habits and tastes, although there is much room for argument about
how representative and up-to-date the selection is. Another popular index applicable
to business is the *producer price index*, based on a representative weighted sampling
of the wholesale prices of goods produced. Other indexes deal with wholesale commodity prices and a variety of specialized groupings of products and services.

The broadest index in common use is applied to the gross national product
as a whole, the *GNP deflator*, which expresses the price changes experienced in
the total range of goods and services produced in the U.S. economy. Based on
broad statistical sampling, the current level of the GNP deflator is announced frequently throughout the year in connection with other economic statistics about
business and government activity. All of these indexes are prepared by calculating
the changes in prices from those of a selected base year, which is changed only in-
frequently to avoid having to adjust comparative statistical series whenever the
base year is changed.

Helfert: Techniques of
Financial Analysis: A
Guide to Value Creation

Appendixes

IV. Basic Inflation
Concepts

© The McGraw–Hill
Companies, 2003

Techniques of Financial Analysis: A Guide to Value Creation

The price indexes are used to translate nominal dollar values in government statistics and business reports into *real dollar values*. This involves converting nominal dollar values to a chosen standard so that past and present dollar transactions can be compared in equivalent terms. For example, to compare this year's performance of the economy to that of last year, we may choose to express current economic statistics using last year's dollars as the standard. Last year's dollars are then called real, and today's data are expressed in these real terms. To do this, we simply adjust today's dollars by the amount of inflation experienced since last year. If inflation this year was 3 percent over last year as expressed in the GNP deflator, every nominal dollar figure for this year would be adjusted downward by 3 percent. The result would be an expression of this year's results in terms of real dollars, which are based on the prior year.

A real dollar is thus simply a nominal dollar that has been adjusted to the price level of a particular stated base year, using one of the applicable price indexes. The base chosen can be any year, as long as past or future years are consistently stated in terms of the currency value for the base year. In fact, real dollars are often called *constant dollars*, a name that simply recognizes that they're derived from a constant base. The process of adjustment has the following effect: During inflationary periods, the real dollars for the years preceding the base year will be adjusted upward, whereas the real dollars of future years will be adjusted downward. The reverse is true, of course, if the period involves deflation instead.

To illustrate, let's assume that the following price developments took place during a five-year period. We're using the producer price index (PPI). This index was constructed on the basis of Year 0. In the following table, we've set Year 3 as the base year for our analysis.

	Year 1	Year 2	Year 3	Year 4	Year 5
Producer price index (Year 0)	1.09	1.15	1.21	1.25	1.33
Producer price index (Year 3)	0.90	0.95	1.00	1.03	1.10
Real value of $100 (base Year 3)	$111	$105	$100	$97	$91

Note that two steps were involved. First, the producer price index had to be adjusted for our chosen base, Year 3. That is, the index had to be set at 1.00 for Year 3 and then all index numbers were divided by the value of the index for the base year, which is 1.21. (However, the index could have been constructed on any other year because an index measures price changes year by year from whatever starting point is chosen.) The next step was to divide the adjusted index values on the second line into the nominal dollars of each year. We chose to use the amount of $100 for all years, but the process applies, of course, to any amount of nominal dollars in any one of the years. Using a single round figure permitted us to illustrate the shifts in value with a same dollar amount.

The example clearly shows that a dollar's purchasing power in Year 4 versus Year 3 declined by 3 percent. The implication from a business point of view is that a company must increase its nominal earnings power by 3 percent in order to keep up with inflation in the prices it must pay for goods and services. Anything less than that will leave the owners worse off.

Helfert: Techniques of
Financial Analysis: A
Guide to Value Creation

Appendixes

IV. Basic Inflation
Concepts

© The McGraw–Hill
Companies, 2003

APPENDIX IV   Basic Inflation Concepts

This simple process allows us to convert nominal dollars into inflation-adjusted real dollars. Problems arise in choosing the proper index for a business situation, and also from the fact that the index embodies changes in economic value as well as in currency value, as we discussed earlier. Much thought has been expended on refining the process of inflation adjustment, but in the end, the judgment about its usefulness depends on the purpose of the analysis and the degree of accuracy desired.

Applications of Inflation Adjustment in Financial Analysis

Restatement of company data or projections in real dollar terms is at times useful to assess whether the company's performance has kept up with shifts in currency values. Such restatement may be used to value a company's assets and liabilities, or to show the real growth or decline in sales and earnings. As we observed, publicly traded companies are obligated to include an annual inflation-adjusted restatement of key data in their published shareholder reports.

Much effort can be spent on adjusting financial projections for inflation, particularly in the area of capital investment analysis. There are no truly satisfactory general rules for this process, however. When an analyst must project cash flows from a major capital investment, the easiest approach continues to be projection in nominal dollars, taking into account expected cost and price increases of the key variables involved, tailored specifically to the conditions of the business. The discount standard applied against the projection must also be based on nominal return expectations that, of course, embody the inflationary outlook.

To refine the analysis, many companies prepare projections in real dollars, attempting to forecast the true economic increases or decreases in costs and prices. Then an appropriate inflation index is applied to the figures to convert them into nominal dollars. The problem is, however, that the margin between revenues and costs may widen unduly, simply because the same inflation index is applied to the larger revenue numbers and to the smaller cost numbers. Often arbitrary adjustments have to be made to keep the margin spread manageable.

Another approach involves developing projections expressed in real dollars and discounting these with a return standard that has also been converted into real returns. The result will be internally consistent as far as the project is concerned. However, the result is not readily comparable with the current overall performance of the business—recorded and expressed in nominal dollar terms—unless the company has also found a way to convert and measure ongoing performance in real dollar terms. Some companies are beginning to experiment with such restated reports and measures, but the approach involves a massive effort, both in terms of data preparation and education of personnel generating and using the projections and performance data. It's instinctively easier to think about business in nominal dollars than real dollars, and progress in this area is being made only gradually. The complexities are such that the financial and planning staffs of companies wishing to use this approach face a lengthy conceptual and practical conversion problem.

Techniques of Financial Analysis: A Guide to Value Creation

Impact of Inflation

To restate quickly, the basic impact of inflation—and the much less common opposite situation, deflation—is a growing distortion of recorded values on a company's financial statements, and an ongoing partial distortion of operating results. Accounting methods discussed in Chapters 1 and 2 are designed to make the effect of the inflationary distortion at least consistent. In terms of cash flows, inflation distorts a company's tax payments if the taxes due are based on low historical cost apportionment, and it results in a cash drain if dividends are higher than they would be if real dollar earnings were considered, to name two examples. Inflation also affects financing conditions, particularly the repayment of principal on long-term debt obligations. As we observed before, however, the mediating influence of interest rates—which respond to inflation expectations—tends to prevent windfalls for the borrower looking to repay debt with "cheap" dollars. Normally, over the long run, distortions from inflation affect lenders and borrowers alike. Relative advantages gained by one over the other are only temporary.

Overall, the subject of inflation adjustments continues to evolve in financial analysis. It's unlikely that totally consistent methods that are generally applicable will be found.

CHAPTER 3

The Time Value of Money

Knowledge of the time value of money is essential to an understanding of most topics in finance. For example, financial structure decisions, project selection, lease-versus-borrow decisions, bond refunding, security valuation, and the whole question of the cost of capital are subjects that cannot be understood without a knowledge of compound interest. Almost all problems involving compound interest can be handled with only a few basic concepts.

THE NATURE OF FINANCIAL DECISIONS

This chapter on the time value of money is key to the main theme of this book. Growth is a major source of value, and the analysis of expected future cash flows is the basis of the calculation of value. This theme is implemented throughout the chapters that follow. In this chapter we present the foundations for the analysis of growth and value.

Most decisions we face in our everyday lives, as well as the decisions that confront business firms, involve a comparison of the present with the future. This involves comparing cash flows at different times—present outlays versus future benefits, or present consumption versus future payments or forgone future benefits. For example, consider an investment of $1000 today that pays $1100 at the end of 1 year. This returns 10 percent on the investment. If the cost of funds is 12 percent, it is not a good investment because we are not earning the cost of funds. If the funds cost 8 percent, we have made a net gain.

Most financial decisions require comparisons of these kinds. Because funds have earning power, $1000 today is not the same as $1000 received 1 year later. If we have $1000 today, we can invest it to have more than $1000 in the future. Financial decisions, therefore, involve the time value of money—decisions across time. Values are determined by the timing of the future cash flows to be received. Funds received next year are worth more than the same amount of funds received in the fifth or tenth year. What is involved is discounted cash

CHAPTER 3 The Time Value of Money

flow analysis, representing the fundamental technique for measuring the time value of money. Most financial decisions at both the personal and business levels must take into account the time value of money. The materials in this chapter are, therefore, key to the important topics of managerial finance.

FUTURE VALUE

A person invests $1000 in a security that pays 10 percent compounded annually. How much will this person have at the end of 1 year? To treat the matter systematically, let us define the following terms:

P_0 = principal, or beginning amount, at time 0 (that is, $1000)

r = rate of return or interest rate (that is, 10%)[1]

$P_0 r$ = total dollar amount of interest earned at r

$FV_{r,n}$ = future value at end of n periods at r

When n equals 1, then $FV_{r,n}$ can be calculated as follows:

$$FV_{r,1} = P_0 + P_0 r = P_0(1 + r) \qquad (3.1)$$

Equation (3.1) shows that the ending amount $FV_{r,1}$ is equal to the beginning amount P_0 times the factor $1 + r$. In the example, where P_0 is $1000, r is 10 percent, and n is 1 year, $FV_{r,n}$ is determined as follows:

$$FV_{10\%,\,1\,yr} = \$1000(1.0 + 0.10) = \$1000(1.10) = \$1100$$

Multiple Periods

If the person leaves $1000 on deposit for 5 years, to what amount will it have grown at the end of that period if interest is earned on interest? Equation (3.1) can be used to construct Table 3.1, which shows the answer. Note that $FV_{r,2}$, the balance at the end of the second year, is found as follows:

$$FV_{r,2} = FV_{r,1}(1 + r) = P_0(1 + r)(1 + r) = P_0(1 + r)^2$$
$$= \$1000(1.10)^2 = \$1210.00$$

---

1 In this chapter we use r as the rate of return, or interest rate. In later chapters involving topics such as the cost of capital and valuation, the literature uses k instead of r. In one sense, k is a particular kind of rate of return or discount factor. In another sense, r and k could be used interchangeably.

PART ONE   Accounting and Finance Fundamentals

Similarly, $FV_{r,3}$, the balance after 3 years, is found as

$$FV_{r,3} = FV_{r,2}(1 + r) = P_0(1 + r)^3$$
$$= \$1000(1.1)^3 = \$1331.00$$

In general, $FV_{r,n}$, the compound amount at the end of any future year n, is found as

$$FV_{r,n} = P_0(1 + r)^n \qquad (3.2)$$

Equation (3.2) is the fundamental equation of compound interest. Equation (3.1) is simply a special case of Eq. (3.2), where $n = 1$.

The above is straightforward, but some important subtleties need to be drawn out. First, consider simple interest. Under a simple interest contract, the investor would have received interest of $100 for each of the years. While contracts are sometimes written to provide for simple interest, the powerful logic behind the idea of compound interest is demonstrated by Table 3.1. If the money is invested for 5 years and the interest earned each year is left with the financial institution, interest is earned on the interest. Thus, as shown by column 2 in Table 3.1, the amount of interest earned under compound interest rises each year. Therefore, the value of the amount at the start of the year on which interest is earned during the year includes the interest earned in previous time periods.

Second, the rate of interest applied to the interest earned is *assumed* to be the 10 percent provided for in the 5-year contract. However, it is possible that interest rates would be higher or lower during the 5-year period. If so, the contract could provide for adjusting the interest rate upward or downward over the life of the agreement. But conventional practice in compound interest calculations is to assume

TABLE 3.1

Compound Interest Calculations

Year	(1) Amount at Start of Year PV	(2) Interest Earned (1) × 0.10	(3) Amount at End of Year (1) × (1 + 0.10) $FV_{r,n}$
1	$1000.00	$100.00	$1100.00
2	1100.00	110.00	1210.00
3	1210.00	121.00	1331.00
4	1331.00	133.10	1464.10
5	1464.10	146.41	1610.51

CHAPTER 3   The Time Value of Money

reinvestment at the specified interest rate. Thus, the fundamental equation of compound interest set forth in Eq. (3.2) has important assumptions that should be kept in mind when compound interest rate relationships are utilized in the many individual topics of financial management.

Table 3.1 illustrates how compound interest rate relationships can be developed on a year-by-year basis. We could also use Eq. (3.2) to calculate the future value of $1000 at the end of 5 years. Any calculator with a y^x function would enable us to quickly calculate the results shown in Table 3.1. It is recommended that at these early stages the relationships between equations, tables, regular calculators, and financial calculators will all be explored.

To round out this discussion therefore, we illustrate how the same result of $1610.51 as the future value of $1000 at 10 percent interest can also be obtained from a table. Tables have been constructed for values of $(1 + r)^n$ for wide ranges of r and n. (See Table A.1 in App. A at the end of the book.)

Letting the *future value interest factor* (FVIF) equal $(1 + r)^n$, we can write Eq. (3.2) as $\mathrm{FV}_{r,n} = P_0 \, \mathrm{FVIF}(r, n)$. It is necessary only to go to an appropriate interest table to find the proper interest factor. For example, the correct interest factor for the illustration given in Table 3.1 can be found in Table A.1. Look down the period column to 5, then across this row to the appropriate number in the 10 percent column, to find the interest factor, 1.6105. Then with this interest factor, the future value of $1000 after 5 years is

$$\mathrm{FV}_{10\%,\,5\,\mathrm{yr}} = P_0 \, \mathrm{F\,VIF}(10\%,\,5\,\mathrm{yr}) = \$1000(1.6105) = \$1610.50$$

This is the same figure that was obtained by the other methods.

The equation for the future value interest factor is

$$\mathrm{FVIF}_{r,n} = (1 + r)^n \qquad (3.3)$$

This equation can be used to calculate how the interest factor is related to the interest rate and time, as shown numerically in Table 3.2 and graphically in Fig. 3.1.

Table 3.2 and Fig. 3.1 demonstrate the power of compound interest. At a 10 percent interest rate our investment doubles in slightly more than 7 years. At 15 percent, our investment doubles in less than 5 years, and our investment has more than quadrupled in less than 10 years. The nature of the compound interest relationships is the basis for the *rule of 72*. If we divide 72 by the interest rate, we obtain the number of years required for an investment to double. At 6 percent, an investment doubles in 12 years; at 9 percent, in 8 years; at 24 percent, in 3 years. Or if we have the number of years required for an investment to double, we can use the rule of 72 to calculate the compound interest

PART ONE   Accounting and Finance Fundamentals

TABLE 3.2

Interest Factors as a Function of Interest Rates

	$FVIF_{r,n} = (1 + r)^n$			
Period n	0%	5%	10%	15%
1	1.0000	1.0500	1.1000	1.1500
2	1.0000	1.1025	1.2100	1.3225
3	1.0000	1.1576	1.3310	1.5209
4	1.0000	1.2155	1.4641	1.7490
5	1.0000	1.2763	1.6105	2.0114
6	1.0000	1.3401	1.7716	2.3131
7	1.0000	1.4071	1.9487	2.6600
8	1.0000	1.4775	2.1436	3.0590
9	1.0000	1.5513	2.3579	3.5179
10	1.0000	1.6289	2.5937	4.0456

rate. If an investment doubles in 6 years, the interest rate is 12 percent; in 12 years, 6 percent; in 3 years, 24 percent. So if we are told that a stock price will double in 12 years, that represents only a 6 percent return—relatively modest. If a stock price doubles in 3 years, that represents a 24 percent rate of return, which is very good.

PRESENT VALUE

We have observed the power of compound interest to calculate future values. The next concept is the present-value concept, which has numerous applications in finance. The present-value concept leads directly to the *basic principle of investment decisions*, which is this: An investment is acceptable only if it earns at least its opportunity cost. The opportunity cost is what the funds could earn on an investment of equal risk. The *basic principle of investment decisions* may then be stated as follows: An investment is acceptable only if it earns at least the risk-adjusted market interest rate or opportunity cost of funds.

An example will illustrate the relationship between future value, present value, and the basic principle of investment decisions under certainty. We have the opportunity to invest $1000 today for an asset which can be sold 1 year later for $1210; the applicable market rate of interest is 10 percent. We can analyze the decision, using the concepts of future value, present value, and rate of return.

Under future-value analysis, we could invest the $1000 at the market interest rate of 10 percent. At the end of the year, we would have

$$\$1000(1 + 0.10) = \$1100$$

CHAPTER 3   The Time Value of Money

But the asset investment would have a value of $1210, which is higher than the market investment. Alternatively, we can use the concept of present value to compare the two investments.

Finding present values (*discounting*, as it is commonly called) is simply the reverse of compounding, and Eq. (3.2) can readily be transformed into a present value formula by dividing both sides by the discount factor $(1 + r)^n$ and expressing P_0 as $\mathrm{PV}_{r,\,n}$.

$$\mathrm{FV}_{r,n} = P_0(1 + r)^n \qquad\qquad (3.2)$$

$$\text{Present value} = \frac{\mathrm{FV}_{r,\,n}}{(1+r)^n} = \mathrm{FV}_{r,\,n}\left[\frac{1}{(1+r)^n}\right]$$

$$\mathrm{PV}_{r,n} = \mathrm{FV}_{r,n}\left[(1+r)^{-n}\right] = \mathrm{FV}_{r,n}\,\mathrm{PVIF}(r,\,n) \qquad (3.4)$$

The subscript zero in the term P_0 indicates the present. Hence, present-value quantities can be identified by either P_0 or $\mathrm{PV}_{r,n}$ or more generally as PV (Present Value).

FIGURE 3.1

Interest Factors as a Function of Interest Rates

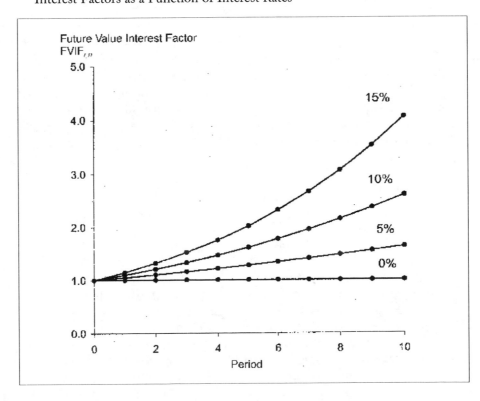

Weaver–Weston: Finance and Accounting for Nonfinancial Managers: The McGraw–Hill Executive MBA Series | I. Accounting and Finance Fundamentals | 3. The Time Value of Money | © The McGraw–Hill Companies, 2001

PART ONE   Accounting and Finance Fundamentals

For our simple examples the present values of the two investments are

Market investment $P_0 = \$1100/1.10 = \$1000 = \$1100(0.9091)$

Asset investment $P_0 = \$1210/1.10 = \$1100 = \$1210(0.9091)$

We can calculate the present value by dividing by 1 plus the interest rate expressed as a decimal or by multiplying the future value by $1/(1 + r) = (1 + r)^{-1}$. Finally, we note that the market investment has a rate of return of 10 percent, while the asset investment has a return of 21 percent. To summarize the three comparisons, we have

	Asset Investment	Market Investment
Future value	$1210	$1100
Present value at market rate	$1100	$1000
Rate of return	21%	10%

By all three methods or criteria, the asset investment is superior to an investment at the market rate. In these comparisons we have explained the concept of present value and illustrated its use. More generally, to obtain the present value we divide by $(1 + r)^n$ or multiply by $(1 + r)^{-n}$.

Tables have been constructed for the present-value interest rate factors—$(1 + r)^{-n}$—for various rates r and time intervals n. (See Table A.2.) For example, to determine the present value of $1610.51 to be received 5 years hence when the discount factor is 10 percent, look down the 10 percent column in Table A.2 to the fifth row. The figure shown there, 0.6209, is the present-value interest factor (PVIF) used to determine the present value of $1610.51 payable in 5 years, discounted at 10 percent.

$$PV_{r,n} = P_0 = FV_{10\%,5\,yr}[PVIF(10\%, 5\,yr)]$$
$$= \$1610.51(0.6209)$$
$$= \$1000$$

The present value tells us what a future sum or sums would be worth to us if we had those funds today. It is obtained by discounting the future sum or sums back to the starting point, which is the present. Present-value analysis clearly involves discounting future cash flows back to the present. It should be understood, however, that the standard practice in finance is to call all compound interest calculations involving present values *discounted cash flow (DCF) analysis*.

CHAPTER 3   The Time Value of Money

ANNUITIES

Thus far we have discussed the concepts of future value and present value for a single outflow or inflow. We next consider multiple outflows and/or inflows. These are called annuities.

Future Value of an Annuity

An annuity is defined as a series of payments or receipts for a specified number of periods. The payment or receipt may occur at the end of the year or at the beginning of the year. If it occurs at the end of the year, it is called an *ordinary annuity* (or annuity paid in arrears); if it occurs at the beginning of the year, it is called an *annuity due* (or an annuity paid in advance). Mortgage payments are typically made at the end of the period; lease payments are usually made at the beginning of the period. For most problems payments are received at the end of the period, so our emphasis will be on ordinary annuities.

The sum of a geometric series can be expressed as

$$S_n = a\left(\frac{r^n - 1}{r - 1}\right) \tag{3.5}$$

For calculating the future value of an annuity at an interest rate of r and the number of periods reflected in t, denoted by $FVA_{r,t}$, the rate of geometric growth is $1 + r$. Hence we can write

$$FVA_{r,t} = a\left[\frac{(1+r)^n - 1}{1 + r - 1}\right]$$

Solving for $FVA_{r,t}$ results in Eq. (3.6), which is the formula for calculating the future value of an annuity.

$$FVA_{r,t} = a\left[\frac{(1+r)^n - 1}{r}\right] \tag{3.6}$$

The interest factor in Eq. (3.6) can also be written with an abbreviation in letters, as shown in Eq. (3.6a).

$$FVA_{r,t} = a\, FVIFA(r,\ t) \tag{3.6a}$$

FVIFA has been given values for various combinations of r and t. To find these, see Table A.3. To find the answer to the 3-year, $1000 annuity problem, simply refer to Table A.3. Look down the 10 percent column to the row for the third year, and multiply the factor 3.3100 by $1000, as shown below:

$$FVA_{r,t} = a\, FVIFA(r,\ t)$$
$$FVA_{10\%,3\ yr} = \$1000(3.3100) = \$3310$$

PART ONE   Accounting and Finance Fundamentals

Notice that the FVIFA for the sum of an annuity is always larger than the number of years that the annuity runs. The reader should verify that the same result can be obtained with a hand calculator, using the formula in Eq. (3.6).

Present Value of an Annuity

Many decisions in finance use the concept of the present value of an annuity. Its basic formulation is used in analyzing investment decisions, in valuation calculations, and in many other applications. We start with a simple investment decision. Abacus Company is considering the purchase of a power saw; the saw will cost $2000 and will generate additional cash flows of $1000 per year for 3 years. The cash flows are considered available at the end of each year (ordinary annuity); the applicable discount rate is 10 percent. Will Abacus gain from the investment?

The present value of an annuity ($PVA_{r,t}$) is expressed in Eq. (3.7).

$$PVA_{r,t} = a\left[\frac{1-(1+r)^{-n}}{r}\right] \tag{3.7}$$

Equation (3.7) can also be written as shown below:

$$PVA_{r,t} = a\,PVIFA_{r,t} \tag{3.7a}$$

We can derive Eq. (3.7) from the future-value formula:

$$PVA_{r,t} = FVA_{r,t}(1+r)^{-n}$$

$$= a\left[\frac{(1+r)^{n}-1}{r}\right](1+r)^{-n} = a\left[\frac{1-(1+r)^{-n}}{r}\right]$$

Using PVIFA, the present value of an annuity interest factor, we can write $PVA_{r,t} = a\,PVIFA_{r,t}$. For our simple numerical example, we have

$$\$1000\left[\frac{1-(1.10)^{-3}}{0.10}\right] = \$1000\left(\frac{1-0.7513}{0.10}\right) = \$2486.85$$

Notice that the PVIFA for the present value of an annuity is always less than the number of years the annuity runs, whereas the FVIFA for the sum of an annuity is larger than the number of years for which it runs.

The analysis is a comparison between the present value of the future cash inflows and the initial investment cash outflow. The present value of the future cash inflows is $2486.85. The net present value NPV of the investment is the present value of benefits less the present value of costs. In our example, the NPV is $2486.85 – $2000 = $486.85. The

CHAPTER 3   The Time Value of Money

investment adds value to the firm, so it should be made. (We use the NPV concept, which is the basis for value creation, throughout the book.)

Unequal Payments

Thus far we have used constant annual inflows to develop the basic relationships. The concepts can easily be applied to uneven payments by using the simple present-value formula. The assumed cash inflows and their present value are shown in Table 3.3.

PERPETUITIES

Some securities carry no maturity date. They are a perpetuity—an annuity that continues forever. The future value of a perpetuity is infinite since the number of periodic payments is infinite. The present value of an annuity can be calculated by starting with Eq. (3.8).

$$PVA_{r,t} = a\left[\frac{1 - (1 + r)^{-n}}{r}\right] \tag{3.8}$$

Notice that the term $(1 + r)^{-n} = 1/(1 + r)^n$ is always less than 1 for positive interest rates. For example, suppose $r = 10$ percent; then

$$(1 + r)^{-1} = 0.909, (1 + r)^{-2} = 0.826, (1 + r)^{-3} = 0.751, \dots, (1 + r)^{-100} = 0.000073$$

As the number of years becomes very large (i.e., infinite), the term $(1 + r)^{-n}$ goes to zero. Thus, if the annuity of constant payments is perpetual, we have as our final result

TABLE 3.3

PVA for Unequal Inflows

Period	Cash Inflows	$\times$	$PVIF_{10\%,n}$	$=$	PV of Each Cash Inflow
1	100		0.9091		$ 90.91
2	200		0.8264		165.29
3	300		0.7513		225.39
4	500		0.6830		341.51
5	400		0.6209		248.37
6	600		0.5645		338.68
7	200		0.5132		102.63
		Present value of unequal inflows		$=$	$ 1512.78

PART ONE   Accounting and Finance Fundamentals

$$PVA_{r,\,\infty} = \frac{a}{r} \tag{3.9}$$

So the present value of a perpetuity is the periodic flow a, divided by the discount factor. Equation (3.9) is a simple expression rich in implications.

Impact of Changing the Discount Rate

Assume that initially $a = \$120$ and $r = 10$ percent; the PV is

$$PV = \frac{\$120}{0.10} = \$1200$$

If r rises to 12 percent, PV falls to $1000. If r falls to 8 percent, PV rises to $1500. Thus PV is very sensitive to the size of the discount factor. This is also generally true for investments, even if they do not have infinite lives; however, the impact is largest for a perpetuity.

Interrelationships among the Terms

The formula for a perpetuity also facilitates an understanding of another set of relationships. For all the interest formulas we have three basic terms, as shown by Eq. (3.10).

$$\text{Value} = (\text{Periodic Flow}) \times (\text{Interest Factor}) \tag{3.10}$$

For our basic example above, we have

$$\text{Value} = \$120\left(\frac{1}{0.10}\right) = \$120(10)$$

If we know any two of the three terms, we can calculate the third. If we have a value of $1000 and a flow of $120, the discount factor can be solved for and is found to be 12 percent. If we have a value of $1500 and a discount factor of 10 percent, the flow must be $150.

GENERALIZATION OF INTERRELATIONSHIPS

We present some practical illustrations of how we may solve for a third term when we have two of the three factors: present or future value, the periodic flow, and the interest factor.

Determining Interest Rates

In many instances, the present values and cash flows associated with a payment stream are known, but the interest rate is not known. Suppose a bank offers to lend you $1000 today if you sign a note agreeing to pay the bank $1762.30 at the end of 5 years. What rate of interest would you be paying on the loans? To answer the question, we use Eq. (3.2):

CHAPTER 3   The Time Value of Money

$$FV_{r,n} = P_0(1 + r)^n = P_0 FVIF(r, n) \qquad (3.2)$$

We simply solve for the FVIF and then look up this value in Table A.1 along the row for the fifth year:

$$FVIF(r, n) = \frac{FV_{r,\,5\,yr}}{P_0} = \frac{\$1762.30}{\$1000} = 1.7623$$

Looking across the row for the fifth year, we find the value 1.7623 in the 12 percent column; therefore, the interest rate on the loan is 12 percent.

Precisely the same approach is taken to determine the interest rate implicit in an annuity. For example, suppose a bank will lend you $2401.80 if you sign a note in which you agree to pay the bank $1000 at the end of each of the next 3 years. What interest rate is the bank charging you? To answer the question, we solve Eq. (3.7a) for PVIFA and then look up the PVIFA in Table A.4:

$$PVA_{r,t} = a\,PVIFA_{r,t} \qquad (3.7a)$$

$$PVIFA_{r,t} = \frac{PV_{r,\,3\,yr}}{a} = \frac{\$2401.80}{\$1000} = 2.4018$$

Looking across the third-year row, we find the factor 2.4018 under the 12 percent column; therefore, the bank is lending you money at a 12 percent interest rate.

A third illustration of finding interest rates involves determining the growth rates. One method is the endpoints method. Data for ABC's revenue are presented in Table 3.4. We can calculate (geometric average) growth rates using the future-value formula, Eq. (3.2):

$$FV_{r,n} = P_0(1 + r)^n$$

For the revenue stream, the future amount after 5 years of growth to 1996 is $64.7 billion, and the present amount in 1991 is $50.7 million. Substituting these into the formula, we have

$$\$64.7 = \$50.7(1 + r)^5$$

TABLE 3.4

ABC Financial Data

	2001	2000	1996	1991
Revenue ($ billions)	75.9	62.7	64.7	50.7

PART ONE   Accounting and Finance Fundamentals

$$\left(\frac{\$64.7}{\$50.7}\right)^{1/5} - 1 = r$$

$$r = 5.00\%$$

Similarly, for 1996–2000, we have:

$$FV_{r,n} = PV_0 (1 + r)^n$$

$$62.7 = 64.7(1 + r)^4$$

$$\left(\frac{62.7}{64.7}\right)^{1/4} - 1 = r = -0.78\%$$

For 2000–2001, ABC's revenues grew at a compound annual rate of 21.05 percent. For the entire 10-year period 1991–2001, ABC's revenues grew at a compound annual rate of 4.12 percent.

More generally,

$$g = \left(\frac{X_n}{X_0}\right)^{1/n} - 1 \tag{3.11}$$

where g = compound (geometric average) growth rate over the period

X_n = endpoint value

X_0 = beginning value

n = number of periods of growth

This example illustrates the strength and weakness of the endpoints method. A plus is that it is easy to calculate. A negative is that it may not reflect the data patterns for the periods between the endpoints. For the 10 years between 1991 and 2001, ABC's revenues grew at a compound annual rate of 4.12 percent. But in the intervening subperiods, higher and lower (even negative) growth rates were experienced.

NONINTEGER VALUES OF INTEREST RATES

In the interest tables at the end of the book, we have given interest factor values for integer values such as 8 or 9 percent. Sometimes practical problems involve fractional interest rates, such as $8\frac{1}{4}$ percent. Or the interest rate calculation problem you encounter may involve time periods outside the range of the years provided in the tables. (Compounding for periods other than the annual basis given in the tables will be discussed in the following section.) For fractional interest rates, the use of the formulas and a hand calculator enables us to determine

CHAPTER 3   The Time Value of Money

the interest factors required. Recall that in the interest rate formulas presented, there was a component (FVIF, PVIF, FVIFA, or PVIFA) for the interest factor. Assuming that our problem involved alternatively using each of the four types of interest factors for an interest rate of $8\frac{1}{4}$ percent and a 10-year period, the formulas and the resulting values are as shown below:

$$FVIF = (1 + r)^n = 1.0825^{10} = 2.2094$$

$$PVIF = 1/(1 + r)^n = 1/1.0825^{10} = 0.4526$$

$$FVIFA = [(1 + r)^n - 1]/r = [1.0825^{10} - 1]/0.0825 = 14.6597$$

$$PVIFA = [1 - (1 + r)^{-n}]/r = [1 - 1.0825^{-10}]/0.0825 = 6.6351$$

Notice that in performing the calculations, we take $(1.0825)^{10}$ and then simply use this result in a slightly different way for each of the four interest factors that we calculate. Many handheld calculators are pre-programmed to carry out these kinds of calculations. However, all these internal programs are based on the logic involved in using each of the four basic compound interest formulas.

Sometimes the problem involves obtaining interest rates when only the interest factors are provided. For example, suppose we make an investment of $663,510, which will yield $100,000 per year for 10 years. We want to know the rate of return on that investment. We use Eq. (3.7a) to find the PVIFA:

$$PVIFA = \$663,510/\$100,000 = 6.6351$$

From our calculations above, we recognize that this result is the PVIFA in which the interest rate is $8\frac{1}{4}$ percent. If we are using a prepro-grammed hand calculator, we can solve for the required interest rate. With a less sophisticated hand calculator, we would have to obtain the result by trial and error. But with hand calculators of any degree of sophistication, if we keep in mind the expressions for the four basic compound interest relations, we can obtain what we need to solve any real-world problem that might come up. This is even true when compounding is on a basis other than annual, as we shall demonstrate in the following section.

PART ONE   Accounting and Finance Fundamentals

SEMIANNUAL AND OTHER COMPOUNDING PERIODS

In all the examples used thus far, it has been assumed that returns were received annually. For example, in the section dealing with future values, it was assumed that the funds earned 10 percent a year. However, suppose the earnings rate had been 10 percent compounded semiannually (i.e., every 6 months). What would this have meant? Consider the following example.

You invest $1000 in a security to receive a return of 10 percent compounded semiannually. How much will you have at the end of 1 year? Since semiannual compounding means that interest is actually paid each 6 months, this fact is taken into account in the tabular calculations in Table 3.5. Here the annual interest rate is divided by 2, but twice as many compounding periods are used because interest is paid twice a year. Comparing the amount on hand at the end of the second 6-month period, $1102.50, with what would have been on hand under annual compounding, $1100.00, shows that semiannual compounding is better for the investor. This result occurs because the saver earns interest on interest more frequently. Thus semiannual compounding results in higher effective annual rates. If we required that the annual rates stay at 12 percent, then the semiannual rate would be not $12/2 = 6$ percent but rather $(1.12)^{1/2} - 1 = 0.0583 = 5.83$ percent. By market convention, however, the yield to maturity based on compounding at intervals of 6 months is doubled to obtain the annual yield, which understates the effective annual yield.

We can extend this simple example for more frequent compounding within the year. We shall calculate the future sum for 1 year for multiple compounding within the year for an interest rate of 12 percent and an initial principal of $1, as shown in Table 3.6. We see that daily compounding increases the effective annual interest rate by 0.75 percent.

TABLE 3.5

Compound Interest Calculations with Semiannual Compounding

Period	Period Beginning Amount	$\times$	$1 + r$	$=$	Ending Amount $(FV_{r,n})$
1	$ 1000.00		1.05		$ 1050.00
2	1050.00		1.05		1102.50

CHAPTER 3   The Time Value of Money

TABLE 3.6

Effective Annual Yields with Multiple Compounding within the Year

Annual	$FV_{r,1} = P_0(1 + r)$	=	1.1200	$(q = 1)$
Semiannual	$= P_0\left(1 + \dfrac{r}{2}\right)^2$	=	1.1236	$(q = 2)$
Quarterly	$= P_0\left(1 + \dfrac{r}{4}\right)^4$	=	1.1255	$(q = 4)$
Monthly	$= P_0\left(1 + \dfrac{r}{12}\right)^{12}$	=	1.1268	$(q = 12)$
Daily	$= P_0\left(1 + \dfrac{r}{365}\right)^{365}$	=	1.1275	$(q = 365)$

Equation (3.12) is a generalization of the procedure for within-the-year compounding, where q is frequency and n is years:

$$FV_{r,n} = P_0\left(1 + \frac{r}{q}\right)^{nq} \qquad (3.12)$$

The four interest tables presented can be used when compounding occurs more than once a year. Simply divide the nominal (stated) interest rate by the number of times compounding occurs, and multiply the years by the number of compounding periods per year. For example, to find the amount to which $1000 will grow after 5 years if semiannual compounding is applied to a stated 10 percent interest rate, divide 10 percent by 2 and multiply the 5 years by 2. Then look in Table A.1 at the end of the book under the 5 percent column and in the row for the tenth period, where you will find an interest factor of 1.6289. Multiplying this by the initial $1000 gives a value of $1628.90, the amount to which $1000 will grow in 5 years at 10 percent compounded semiannually. This compares with $1610.50 for annual compounding.

The same procedure is applied in all cases covered—compounding, discounting, single payments, and annuities. To illustrate semiannual compounding in calculating the present value of an annuity, e.g., consider the case described in the section on the present value of an annuity—$1000 a year for 3 years, discounted at 10 percent. With annual discounting or compounding, the interest factor is 2.4869, and the present value of the annuity is $2486.90. For semiannual compounding, look under the 5 percent column and in the year 6 row of Table A.4 to find an interest factor of 5.0757. Then multiply by one-half of $1000, or the $500 received each 6 months, to get the present value of the annuity, or $2537.85. The payments come a little more rapidly (the first

$500 is paid after only 6 months), so the annuity is a little more valuable if payments are received semiannually rather than annually.

CONTINUOUS COMPOUNDING AND DISCOUNTING

By letting the frequency of compounding q approach infinity, Eq. (3.12) can be modified to the special case of *continuous compounding*. Continuous compounding is extremely useful in theoretical finance as well as in practical applications. Also as shown in later chapters, computations are often simplified when continuously compounded interest rates are used.

When we compound continuously, the result is the equation for continuous compounding

$$FV_{r,t} = P_0\, e^{rt} \tag{3.13}$$

where e is the constant 2.718. Letting $P_0 = 1$, we can rewrite Eq. (3.13) as

$$FV_{r,t} = e^{rt} \tag{3.13a}$$

Expressing Eq. (3.13a) in logarithmic form and noting that ln denotes the log to the base e, we obtain

$$\ln FV_{r,t} = rt \ln e \tag{3.13b}$$

Since e is defined as the base of the system of natural logarithms, ln e must equal 1.0. Therefore,

$$\ln FV_{r,t} = rt \tag{3.13c}$$

For example, if $t = 5$ years and $r = 10$ percent, the product is 0.50. To use Eq. (3.13a) requires a hand calculator with an e^x key. If your hand calculator has an e^x function, use Eq. (3.13a); enter the 0.5 and push the e^x key to obtain 1.648721. If your hand calculator has a ln x key (but not an e^x key) use Eq. (3.13c); enter the 0.5 and push INV and then the ln x key to obtain the same result. Most calculators have some provision for performing logarithmic functions. For annual compounding, the calculation is $(1.1)^5 = 1.610510$.

Continuous Discounting

Equation (3.13) can be solved for P_0 ($= PV_{r,t}$) and used to determine present values under continuous compounding.

$$P_0 = PV_{r,t} = \frac{FV_{r,t}}{e^{r,t}} = FV_{r,t}\, e^{-rt} \tag{3.14}$$

CHAPTER 3   The Time Value of Money

Thus, if $1649 is due in 5 years and if the appropriate *continuous* discount rate r is 10 percent, the present value of this future payment is

$$PV = \frac{\$1649}{1.649} = \$1000$$

The present value of an infinite stream of payments growing at a constant rate g with continuous discounting at rate r can be calculated by using Eq. (3.15).

$$PV_{r, \infty} = \frac{a_0}{r - g} \tag{3.15}$$

Equation (3.15) is the formula for the present value of a continuous stream of payments growing to infinity at the constant rate g and discounted at rate r. For example, when $a_0 = \$12$, $r = 12$ percent, and $g = 4$ percent, the (present) value of the stream of inflows is $12/0.08 = \$150$.

THE ANNUAL PERCENTAGE RATE (APR)

Different types of financial contracts use different compounding periods. Most bonds pay interest semiannually. Some savings accounts pay interest quarterly, but the new money market accounts at most financial institutions pay interest daily. Department stores, oil companies, and credit cards also specify a daily rate of interest. In addition, to obtain a home mortgage loan, the lender charges points up front. To compare the costs of different credit sources, it is necessary to calculate the effective rate of interest, or the annual percentage rate (APR), as it is generally called. The APR is always compounded once per year.

To calculate APR, we should recognize that we are simply making another application of Eq. (3.12), where $n = 1$. Equation (3.12) then becomes Eq. (3.16).

$$PV_{r, 1} = P_0 \left(1 + \frac{r}{q} \right)^q \tag{3.16}$$

The annual effective rate of interest (APR) can be determined as follows:

$$\frac{PV_{r, 1}}{P_0} = \left(1 + \frac{r}{q} \right)^q = 1 + APR$$

Solving for the APR, we have

$$APR = \left(1 + \frac{r}{q} \right)^q - 1 \tag{3.16a}$$

Since we have already calculated 1 + APR in Table 3.6, the APR in each of the examples is obtained by subtracting 1. For example, the

APR rises from 12.36 percent for semiannual compounding to 12.68 percent for monthly compounding.

We can generalize further. At an interest rate of 12 percent, we want to know the future sum of $100 with quarterly compounding for 5 years. First we use Eq. (3.12):

$$FV_{r,n} = P_0\left(1 + \frac{r}{q}\right)^{nq} = \$100\left(1 + \frac{0.12}{4}\right)^{5(4)} = \$100(1.03)^{20} = \$180.611$$

Alternatively, we can use the APR in Table 3.6 for quarterly compounding. This is 12.55 percent, which we can use in Eq. (3.2):

$$FV_{r,n} = P_0(1 + APR)^n = \$100(1.1255)^5 = \$180.604$$

Since the results are the same (except for rounding), we can use either method in making calculations. In many transactions, government regulations require that the lender provide the borrower with a written statement of the APR in the transaction. We have described how it can be calculated.

THE RELATIONSHIP BETWEEN DISCRETE AND CONTINUOUS INTEREST RATES

Discrete growth or compounding can always be transformed to an equivalent continuous version. Let d represent a discrete rate of compounding, while c is a continuous compounding rate. In general,

$$\ln(1 + d) = c \tag{3.17}$$

The continuous rate will, in general, be lower than the discrete rate. For example, if the discrete rate of interest is 12 percent, the continuous rate would be ln 1.12 = 11.33 percent. This is quite logical, since the interest is working harder, e.g., when it is compounding every second than when it is compounding only once a year.

Conversely, if a given interest rate is being compounded continuously, the equivalent discrete rate is larger. Thus, if we are using a nominal 12 percent rate but applying it continuously, the equivalent discrete rate will be higher. The appropriate formula to apply requires solving Eq. (3.18) for d.

$$d = e^c - 1 \tag{3.18a}$$

Compounding a 12 percent nominal rate continuously, we see the equivalent discrete rate is 12.7497 percent. Note that Eq. (3.18a) is the continuous compounding equivalent of Eq. (3.16), which was the expression for calculating the annual percentage rate under discrete

CHAPTER 3   The Time Value of Money

compounding. Thus, we see that the equivalent discrete rate when a nominal interest rate is compounded continuously represents the annual percentage rate.

SUMMARY

A knowledge of compound interest and present-value techniques is essential to an understanding of important aspects of finance covered in subsequent chapters: capital budgeting, financial structure, security valuation, and other topics.

The four basic equations with the notation that will be used throughout the book are

$$FV_{r,n} = P_0\,FVIF(r,n) \equiv P(1+r)^n \tag{3.2}$$
$$PV_{r,n} = FV_{r,n}\,PVIF(r,n) \equiv FV_{r,n}\,(1+r)^{-n} \tag{3.4}$$
$$FVA_{r,t} = a\,FVIFA(r,t) \equiv a[(1+r)^n - 1]/r \tag{3.6}$$
$$PVA_{r,t} = a\,PVIFA(r,t) \equiv a[1-(1+r)^{-n}]/r \tag{3.7}$$

With continuous compounding, the first two formulas become

$$FV_{r,t} = P_0\,e^{rt} \tag{3.13}$$
$$PV_{r,t} = FV_{r,t}\,e^{-rt} \tag{3.14}$$

These interest formulas can be used for either an even or uneven series of receipts or payments. The basic formulas can be used to find (1) the annual payments necessary to accumulate a future sum, (2) the annual receipts from a specified annuity, (3) the periodic payments necessary to amortize a loan, and (4) the interest rate implicit in a loan contract. They are the basis for all valuation formulas. The formulas can also be used with more frequent periods than annual compounding, including semiannual, monthly, daily, and continuous compounding.

The general formula for within-the-year compounding is

$$FV_{r,n} = P_0\left(1+\frac{r}{q}\right)^{n,\,q} \qquad q \text{ frequency, } n \text{ years} \tag{3.12}$$

This expression is used in determining the APR (annual percentage rate) implicit in a contract where the *effective interest rate* is not the same as the stated rate because of the frequency of compounding. The formula for the annual percentage rate is

$$APR = \left(1+\frac{r}{q}\right)^q - 1 \tag{3.16a}$$

Finally, the relationship between discrete and continuously compounded discount rate is

$$d = e^c - 1 \tag{3.18}$$

where d is also the (higher) APR for a continuously compounded discount rate c.

QUESTIONS AND PROBLEMS

3.1   The current production target for the 5-year plan of Logo Company is to increase output by 8 percent per year. If the 2000 production is 3.81 million tons, what is the target production for 2005?

3.2   At a growth rate of 9 percent, how long does it take a sum to double?

3.3   If, at age 25, you open an IRA account paying 10 percent annual interest and you put $2000 in at the end of each year, what will be your balance at age 65?

3.4   You are offered two alternatives: a $2000 annuity for 7 years or a lump sum today. If current interest rates are 9 percent, how large will the lump sum have to be to make you indifferent between the alternatives?

3.5   You have just purchased a newly issued $1000 five-year Malley Company bond at par. The bond (bond A) pays $60 in interest semiannually ($120 per year). You are also negotiating the purchase of a $1000 six-year Malley Company bond (bond B) that returns $30 in semiannual interest payments and has 6 years remaining before it matures.

    A.   What is the going rate of return on bonds of risk and maturity of Malley Company's bond A?

    B.   What should you be willing to pay for bond B?

3.6   On December 31, George Smith buys a building for $175,000, paying 20 percent down and agreeing to pay the balance in 20 equal annual installments that are to include principal plus 15 percent compound interest on the declining balance. How much are the equal installments?

3.7   You wish to borrow $50,000 for a home mortgage. The quoted interest rate is 11 percent compounded monthly for a 25-year mortgage.

    A.   What annual percentage rate is equal to 11 percent compounded monthly?

    B.   What will your monthly mortgage payments be (assuming that they are paid at the end of each month)?

3.8   If you have an account that compounds interest continuously and has an effective annual interest yield of 6.18 percent, what is the stated annual interest rate?

CHAPTER 3   The Time Value of Money

3.9   What rate of interest compounded monthly is equivalent to 18 percent compounded continuously?

SOLUTIONS TO QUESTIONS AND PROBLEMS

3.1 $3.81 \times$ FVIF(8%, 5 years) = production during year 2005
$3.81(1.4693) = 5.60$ million tons

3.2   Eight years. Referring to Table A.1 and reading down the 9 percent column, FVIF = 1.9926 (approximately 2) in the eighth year, so at the beginning of the ninth year, the amount will have grown to twice its size.

3.3   Forty total payments are made. Their value is found as the compound value of an annuity. From Table A.3, FVIFA(10%, 40 years) = 442.59.

Compound value = 442.59($2000) = $885,180

Note that the compound value is more than 10 times the total of $80,000 of actual payments.

3.4   From Table A.4, PVIFA(9%, 7 years) = 5.033
Present value = 5.033($2000) = $10,066
At a 9 percent interest rate, you will be indifferent between receiving a lump sum of $10,066 today versus a $2000 annuity for 7 years.

3.5   A.   You are receiving $120 interest annually, or $60 semiannually, on a $1000 investment. Thus, the going rate of return is 12 percent compounded semiannually, an effective rate of 12.36 percent.

B.   The other bond should provide a similar yield; the price that forces this bond to yield 12 percent, with semiannual compounding, is found as follows:

$$\text{Price} = PV = \sum_{t=1}^{12} \frac{\$30}{(1.06)^t} + \frac{\$1000}{(1.06)^{12}}$$
$$= \$30(8.3838) + \$1000(0.4970)$$
$$= \$251.51 + \$497$$
$$= \$748.51$$

3.6

Price of building	$175,000
Down payment	35,000
Amount due	$140,000

PART ONE   Accounting and Finance Fundamentals

The present value of a 20-year annuity at 15 percent equals $140,000. The present value of a $1 annuity for 20 years at 15 percent equals $6.2593.

$$\frac{\$140,000}{6.2593} = \$22,366.72 = \text{amount of each installment}$$

Note: Total payments will be $22,366.72 $\times$ 20 = $447,334.40, or more than 3 times $140,000.

3.7   A. $APR = \left(1 + \dfrac{r}{q}\right)^{q} - 1$

$$= \left(1 + \frac{0.11}{12}\right)^{12} - 1 = 11.57\%$$

B.

$$PV = a\left[\frac{1 - (1+r)^{-n}}{r}\right]$$

$$\$50,000 = a\left[\frac{1 - (1 + 0.11/12)^{-(12)(25)}}{0.11/12}\right]$$

$$\$50,000 = a(102.03)$$

$$a = \frac{\$50,000}{102.03} = \$490 \text{ monthly payment}$$

3.8 $(1 + d)^n$ $= e^{cn}$

       $1 + d$ $= e^{c}$

       1.0618 $= e^{c}$

       $\ln 1.0618$ $= c$

       0.059966 $= c$

c equal approximately 0.06, or 6 percent.

CHAPTER 3   The Time Value of Money

3.9 $\left(1 + \dfrac{d}{m}\right)^{mn} = e^{cn}$ **Take the nth root.**

$\left(1 + \dfrac{d}{12}\right)^{12} = e^{0.18}$

$\left(1 + \dfrac{d}{12}\right) = (e^{0.18})^{1/12}$

$\left(1 + \dfrac{d}{12}\right) = (1.197217)^{1/12}$

$1 + \dfrac{d}{12} = 1.015113$

$\dfrac{d}{12} = 0.015113$

$d = 0.181357$ $= 18.14$ percent

CAPITAL BUDGETING IN FORESTRY

An enormous number of forestry decisions involve capital management. This capital might be landowners' or stockholders' cash, loans, or public agencies' tax revenues to be invested in buying new forests or improving existing tracts. Other capital assets could be thousands or millions of dollars worth of existing timber, land, equipment, and other resources. In fact the biggest inputs in forestry are time and capital. Labor is a relatively small factor. And since capital is limited, we have an economic problem: how best to manage assets—forest and nonforest—to maximize satisfaction of the owners or, more broadly, of society. I'll consider natural resources, including land, as capital in the sense that funds are spent to obtain them, and they represent a store of value. These assets yield benefits and could be put to other uses yielding larger or smaller benefits. Even resources like fish and wildlife, which aren't easy to value, have a capital value that you can see in the marketplace. For example, forestlands yielding hunting lease income will tend to sell for more than those without such income, other things being equal. The wildlife income is **capitalized** into the value of the property, becoming part of the capital asset.

THE CAPITAL BUDGETING PROBLEM

The **capital budgeting** problem is to decide how to invest money—the "capital budget"—so that its value is maximized. The kinds of spending considered here will be on fairly durable assets or projects that require an initial cost followed by incomes, and usually further costs, over several years. Examples are expenditures on bare land, reforestation, fertilization, timber for future harvest, equipment, entire forested properties, and processing facilities. First let's assume that all outputs can be measured in dollars. Nondollar values will be considered later.

In the broadest sense, investors try to spend money in a way that maximizes satisfaction. In financial terms, this means maximizing the value of assets for the owners. Managers, for example, may wish to maximize the value of a firm for stockholders. To do this, they need criteria for ranking investments and deciding which is best. Chapters 4 and 5 explained **net present value (NPV)** as a maximum willingness to pay for assets, given expected costs and revenues and a desired earning rate. That's one capital budgeting criterion: choose first the projects with the highest net present value. Let's now look at the pros and cons of NPV and several other criteria for ranking investments. *Throughout the chapter, let interest rates and cash flows be real (in constant dollars).* Assume that all taxes have been paid, so that cash flows and rates of return are after taxes (or before taxes for government agencies not paying taxes). Let the amount added to the discount rate for risk—the **risk premium**—be equal for costs and revenues and for any group of investments being compared, unless stated otherwise. Notation for this is in Table 6-1.

CRITERIA FOR ACCEPTING OR REJECTING INVESTMENTS

I'll first describe four criteria for accepting or rejecting investment projects: net present value, internal rate of return, benefit/cost ratio, and payback period. Then let's consider problems in ranking investments from best to worst.

Table 6-2 shows two investments: project D has more *D*istant income than project N with *N*earer income. These are simple examples; in reality, many more costs and revenues would usually occur. You could think of both projects as afforestation investments, with D yielding timber harvests at ages 15 and 30, and N yielding Christmas trees at age 8 and a residual timber stand at age 30. First let's look only at project D; the ranking discussion considers both.

TABLE 6-1
NOTATION FOR CHAPTER 6

ARR = alternative rate of return	n = project life, years
B = annual nonmarket value, dollars	NPV = net present value
B/C ratio = benefit/cost ratio	PV = present value
C_y = cost in year y	r = real interest rate, percent/100
EAA = equivalent annual annuity	R_y = revenue in year y
IRR = internal rate of return	y = an index for years
MAR = minimum acceptable rate of return	

TABLE 6-2
CASH FLOWS FOR PROJECTS WITH DISTANT INCOME
(D) AND NEARER INCOME (N)

Year	Cash flows, project D $	Cash flows, project N $
0	−400	−400
5	−100	−100
8		+1,200
15	+200	
30	+6,600	+2,500

Net Present Value

Net present value of a project is the present value of its revenues minus the present value of its costs:

$$NPV = \sum_{y=0}^{n} \frac{R_y}{(1+r)^y} - \sum_{y=0}^{n} \frac{C_y}{(1+r)^y} \qquad (6\text{-}1)$$

where R_y and C_y are revenues and costs in any year y. Or, more specifically, from equation (4-5):

$$NPV = R_0 + \frac{R_1}{(1+r)^1} + \frac{R_2}{(1+r)^2} + \frac{R_3}{(1+r)^3} + \ldots + \frac{R_n}{(1+r)^n}$$

$$- C_0 - \frac{C_1}{(1+r)^1} - \frac{C_2}{(1+r)^2} - \frac{C_3}{(1+r)^3} - \ldots - \frac{C_n}{(1+r)^n}$$

Note that R_0 and C_0 are not discounted, since they are already at the present. Applying equation (6-1) to project D of Table 6-2, and assuming the decision maker wishes to earn a 6 percent real rate of return (the **minimum acceptable rate,** MAR), net present value is:

$$\frac{6,600}{(1.06)^{30}} + \frac{200}{(1.06)^{15}} - \frac{100}{(1.06)^5} - 400 = \$758 \qquad (6\text{-}2)$$

Given an initial project cost of $400, this means that the investor could pay up to $758 *more* and still earn a 6 percent rate of return.

For project D, Figure 6-1 graphs the **present value** (PV) of revenues and PV of costs, computed with different interest rates shown on the x axis. The PV of revenues is the first term of equation (6-1), and PV of costs is the second term without the negative sign. Why does the PV revenues curve fall faster than PV costs as the interest rate is increased? [It's because revenues are further in the

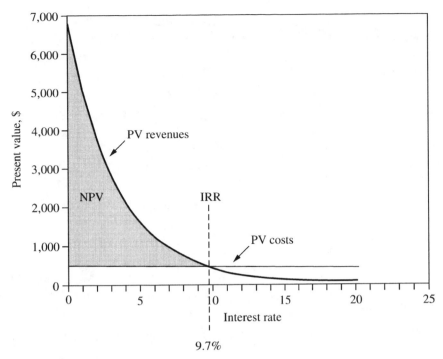

FIGURE 6-1
Present values, project D.

future than costs, which is typical of most investments, especially forestry.[1] Thus, the larger exponents (years) in the revenue denominators of equation (6-2) cause the present value of revenues to fall faster than PV costs as the interest rate is increased.] The shaded area, NPV in Figure 6-1, is PV revenues minus PV costs. You can see that for interest rates up to about 9.7 percent, NPV is greater than zero. If the investor computes NPV of project D with an interest rate greater than 9.7 percent, NPV will be negative (PV costs > PV revenues).

According to the NPV guideline, a project is acceptable if NPV is zero or greater. Projects with a negative NPV are unacceptable. In other words, the present value of revenues must be greater than or equal to the present value of costs, both computed with the investor's minimum acceptable rate of return (MAR).

Interpreting NPVs   Net present values can easily cause confusion. For example, suppose you compute the net present value of project D for an investor with an MAR of 9.68 percent. Substituting 0.0968 in place of $i = 0.06$ in equation (6-2) will yield an NPV of about zero. According to the NPV criterion, the project is just barely acceptable. Incredulous, the investor exclaims, "You're asking me to spend $400 on my property, and it increases the value by *zero?*" "Well,

---

[1]Revenues aren't always more distant than costs. For example, borrowing money is a project where revenue (the loan amount) occurs first, and costs (loan payments) occur later. In that case the PV cost curve would be steeper than the PV revenue.

not exactly," you respond. "The value will increase by the initial expenditure of $400, but by no more than that." It's like putting $400 in a certificate of deposit earning 9.68 percent interest. Using 9.68 percent, the present value of the future receipts will be exactly $400, and subtracting the $400 deposit gives an NPV of $0. But immediately after deposit, the CD is worth $400.

If you didn't subtract the original cost when computing NPV, you couldn't tell from NPV alone whether a project was acceptable. For example, without subtracting the $400 initial cost, the present value of project D at 10 percent interest is $364. That figure alone, although positive, doesn't tell you much until you compare it with the $400 cost. That's why, by convention, for capital budgeting purposes, NPVs are net of original cost. But such values are easily misinterpreted. What adds to the confusion is that some types of present values do *not* have the initial cost subtracted; for example, when you compute a maximum bid price for an asset based on present value of future income, you should not subtract the seller's asking price. *When interpreting net present values, make sure you know whether original expenditure has been subtracted. Otherwise, serious misunderstanding can result.* In this chapter, original cost will always be subtracted in computing NPV. You'll see more on this issue in the chapter on valuation.

Internal Rate of Return

Another common criterion for evaluating investments is the **internal rate of return (IRR).** As given in equation (6-3), the IRR of a project is the discount rate at which the present value of revenues minus the present value of costs equals 0, or where NPV = 0:

$$\sum_{y=0}^{n} \frac{R_y}{(1 + IRR)^y} - \sum_{y=0}^{n} \frac{C_y}{(1 + IRR)^y} = 0 \qquad (6\text{-}3)$$

The IRR is the rate of return earned on funds invested in a project. The above equation also says that the *IRR is the interest rate at which the present value of revenues equals the present value of costs.* For project D of Table 6-2, Figure 6-1 shows that the IRR is about 9.7 percent, since at that interest rate the cost and revenue present value curves cross, and NPV = 0. Note that the IRR is unique (or "internal") to a project. The MAR is the minimum rate an investor wishes to earn; it is based on individual desires or the best earning rate widely available elsewhere and is external to a project being evaluated. With complex cash flow patterns, IRR usually must be found by trial and error. Many modern business calculators and spreadsheet programs can quickly find IRRs when you enter a project's positive and negative cash flows and the years when they occur. Without such tools, finding an IRR for a complex project can be tedious.

Table 6-3 shows a trial and error approach for finding the IRR of project D to the nearest hundredth of a percentage point, using equation (6-3). For the interest

TABLE 6-3
PROJECT D NET PRESENT VALUES AT DIFFERENT INTEREST RATES

(a) Interest rate %	(b) Present value, revenues, $	(c) Present value, costs, $	(d) Net present value $ (b − c)
0.00	6,800.00	500.00	6,300.00
4.00	2,145.96	482.19	1,663.76
9.00	552.36	464.99	87.36
9.66	465.20	463.06	2.14
9.67	464.00	463.03	0.97
9.68*	462.80	463.00	−0.20
9.69	461.60	462.97	−1.37
10.00	426.11	462.09	−35.98

*Internal rate of return to the nearest 1/100 percentage point. Trials first show that the IRR (or zero NPV) is between 9 and 10 percent. Then more detailed trials between these two rates reveal that 9.68 percent brings NPV closest to 0.

rates shown, columns (b) and (c) are the values plotted in Figure 6-1, and the last column gives NPVs. Since the net present value is $0.97 at 9.67 percent interest and −$0.20 at 9.68 percent, the IRR (where NPV = 0) must be between these two rates, and closer to 9.68 percent. Given the uncertainty in projecting most cash flows, such hairsplitting usually isn't too meaningful. In general, you can think of the IRR as an average rate of return on all capital invested in a project.

The IRR investment guideline says that a project is acceptable if its IRR is equal to or greater than the minimum acceptable rate of return. Projects with IRR < MAR are unacceptable. Looking at Figure 6-1, you can see that's just another way of expressing the net present value guideline: If the MAR is less than or equal to the IRR (here ~ 9.7 percent), the NPV will be ≥ 0, and the project will be acceptable. Otherwise it is rejected. An advantage of the IRR is that many investors with different MARs can look at one IRR and decide whether it's acceptable. But an NPV is meaningful only for an investor whose MAR equals the one discount rate used to compute that NPV.

Many firms use internal rate of return rather than net present value to decide whether to accept or reject projects. But it's important to note that for the accept/reject decision, the two guidelines are fundamentally the same (as long as there's a unique IRR solution). You can't compute an IRR without calculating net present values, and both guidelines essentially say, "Accept projects if NPV is ≥ 0, using the MAR" (see Figure 6-1). We'll see shortly, however, that for ranking several projects from best to worst, NPV and IRR don't always give the same ordering.

Benefit/Cost Ratio

A project's **benefit/cost ratio** (*B/C*) is the present value of benefits (revenues) divided by the present value of costs, using the investor's MAR. The *B/C* ratio, also called the **profitability index,** is:

$$B/C \text{ ratio} = \frac{\text{PV revenues}}{\text{PV costs}} = \frac{\sum\limits_{y=0}^{n} \dfrac{R_y}{(1+r)^y}}{\sum\limits_{y=0}^{n} \dfrac{C_y}{(1+r)^y}} \qquad (6\text{-}4)$$

From this equation you can see that when PV revenues equals PV costs, the *B/C* ratio is 1, and NPV is 0. Also, if PV revenues exceeds PV costs, *B/C* must be greater than 1. And if PV costs exceeds PV revenues, $(B/C) < 1$. *Thus, according to the B/C ratio criterion, projects are acceptable when the B/C ratio is 1 or greater, and unacceptable if $(B/C) < 1$.* This gives the same accept/reject decisions as the NPV approach, because a negative NPV makes $(B/C) < 1$.

Using 6 percent interest, the benefit/cost ratio for project D in Table 6-2 is:

$$B/C = \frac{\dfrac{6,600}{(1.06)^{30}} + \dfrac{200}{(1.06)^{15}}}{\dfrac{100}{(1.06)^5} + 400} = \frac{1232.58}{474.73} = 2.60 \qquad (6\text{-}5)$$

Since $(B/C) > 1$, the project is acceptable, as it was when a positive NPV was computed at 6 percent interest.

For project D, Figure 6-2 ties together the NPV, IRR, and *B/C* ratio criteria. Study this carefully, because it shows how the three criteria are very closely related. The vertical dashed line marks the IRR—where PV costs = PV revenues—and thus where $B/C = 1$. To the right of the dashed line, the interest rate exceeds the IRR: there NPV is negative, and therefore B/C must be < 1. So when the MAR exceeds a project's IRR, the project is unacceptable by any of the three foregoing criteria. To the left of the dashed line, where the IRR exceeds the MAR, NPV is positive, and $(B/C) > 1$. In that range, the project is acceptable by all three criteria. *If you can understand Figure 6-2 and sketch it from memory, with all its labels but without numerical values, you'll have a firm grasp of the three investment evaluation criteria discussed so far.*

Payback Period

Another criterion is to choose the project with the shortest **payback period,** which is the number of years it takes to recover the invested capital. For example, looking at Table 6-2, it takes 30 years for the net income from project D to offset the $500 total investment; so the payback period is 30 years. (Some analysts will count only the initial investment, here $400.) For project N, the payback period is 8 years. Based on payback period alone, project N would be preferred. Or a firm requiring payback periods of 8 years or less would accept project N and reject project D.

The major problem with payback period is that it says nothing about a project's present value or rate of return. For example, suppose project N yielded only $500

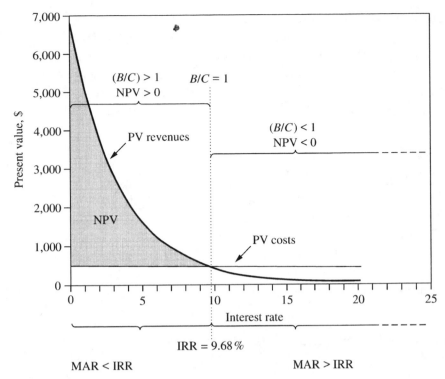

FIGURE 6-2
Capital budgeting criteria, project D.

in year 8 and nothing thereafter. Its payback period would still be 8 years, but the rate of return would be 0 percent (only a 0 percent discount rate would make the present value of costs and revenues be equal—at $500). Despite its shortcomings, payback period is often useful *if considered together with measures such as NPV and IRR.* For instance, investors with short time horizons or those projecting cash flow problems may reject ventures with long payback periods. Also, other things being equal, more distant income tends to be more uncertain; hence, long payback periods suggest greater risk. Banks can be wary of lending funds for projects with long payback periods.

THE REINVESTMENT RATE, ARR, AND MAR CONUNDRUM

A source of confusion in capital budgeting is the assumed rate of return that a project's capital and intermediate income could earn elsewhere. Theoretically, at a competitive equilibrium, we could expect the best rates of return on added capital to be the same in all areas, given equal risk. The real world isn't this neat. Investors often perceive several different available earning rates, even if risk premiums are equal, as assumed in this chapter. Suppose an investor's best alternatives yield 15 percent, 13 percent, 10 percent, and 8 percent, but projects earning the top rates aren't large enough to absorb all available capital. There's obviously no single **alternative rate of return** (ARR), which is why I avoid that term for the investor's discount rate.

Unless noted otherwise, this book will use the investor's minimum acceptable rate of return (MAR) to calculate present values or to judge IRRs. In the above example, that could be, say, 10 percent. Note that some people's MARs *exceed* available rates of return, in which case they don't invest at all. Also, some intermediate income from a project can often earn a rate of return—the **reinvestment rate**—which exceeds the MAR. Thus you need to clarify reinvestment rates and discount rates.

RANKING PROJECTS

The accept/reject decision is easier than ranking several projects from best to worst. The above criteria don't necessarily give the same rankings. As before, we'll assume that investors wish to maximize the value of their assets. Consider ranking the two projects in Table 6-2: project D with distant income and project N with nearer income. For comparability, both projects have the same capital requirements and the same 30-year life.

Mutually Exclusive, Independent, Divisible, and Indivisible

Certain features of projects are important in the ranking process. If several projects are **mutually exclusive,** only one can be chosen. An example is the choice between investments in planting pure loblolly pine timber, pure scotch pine Christmas trees, or only forage on a given acre. If projects are not mutually exclusive, they are **independent** and could all be adopted—for example, investments in fertilization, precommercial thinning, brush control, and purchase of a timber tract. If the two investments in Table 6-2 were reforestation choices for the same acre, they would be mutually exclusive; if for different acres, they'd be independent.

If you can invest in part of a project, it is **divisible**—as in the case of adding money to a savings account or acres to a fertilization project. If a project is all-or-nothing, as in buying a truck or a pulp mill, it is **indivisible.**

Possible Inconsistency between NPV and IRR Rankings

You can rank projects in order of decreasing net present value or internal rate of return. But one problem is that internal rate of return rankings aren't always consistent with NPV rankings. By plotting NPVs of projects D and N (from Table 6-2) over the interest rate, Figure 6-3 shows such a case. Notice that the curves for each project are the difference between PV revenues and PV costs: in the case of project D, that's the shaded area in Figure 6-1. Thus, in Figure 6-3, IRR is where the NPV curve meets the *x* axis (where NPV = 0). In the figure, the IRR for D is 9.7 percent compared with 14.5 percent for N.

Which project is better? To decide, we need more information. If the investor's hurdle rate is 9.7 percent or less, if the projects are independent, and if enough capital is available, both D and N should be accepted. But if they are mutually

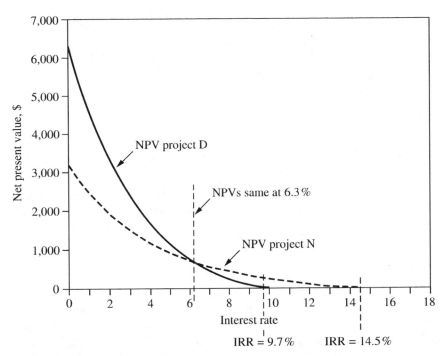

FIGURE 6-3
Net present values, projects D and N.

exclusive or if initially available capital is less than $800, we need to know which project to choose. Based on IRR, N wins at 14.5 percent. For minimum accept-able rates above 6.3 percent, project N also has the highest NPV, as shown in Figure 6-3. But at interest rates < 6.3 percent, project D has the highest NPV and is preferred according to the NPV criterion. With a 6.3 percent interest rate, you're indifferent between the two. If your MAR is less than 6.3 percent, say 5 percent, and the goal is to maximize NPV, project D is the correct choice in spite of its lower IRR. At 5 percent interest, D's NPV = $1,144.94, and N's NPV = $912.30.

This is confusing, because N's 14.5 percent rate of return sounds so much better than D's 9.7 percent. The above choice of D is based on the assumption that the *reinvestment rate* for intermediate income from either project is the 5 percent MAR. To see that D is best under this constraint, compare your future wealth in 30 years from investing in D or N, as shown below:

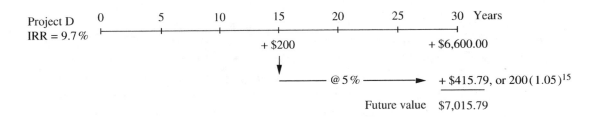

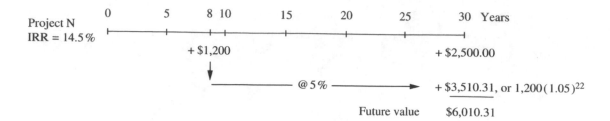

Since both projects have the same capital investment, we need only compare the future values of income accumulated at the 5 percent reinvestment rate. In each case, compound the first income at 5 percent interest for the number of years *remaining* in the period (15 years for D and 22 years for N), and add the final incomes. By investing in D, you'd have a higher future value ($7,015.79) than you would from N ($6,010.31), despite N's higher internal rate of return. Given the same investment lives, if the future value of D's income is greater, present value must also be greater. In part for this reason, net present value enjoys greater theoretical support than internal rate of return as a capital budgeting criterion. Note that projects with the same capital requirements and durations, as in Figure 6-3, will be ranked the same by benefit/cost ratio or NPV. If NPV > 0, $(B/C) > 1$. But if capital requirements differ, rankings by B/C ratio and NPV will *not* always be consistent.

Before rushing to condemn the IRR, note that in many cases, projects' NPV curves over interest never cross, in which case NPV and IRR will rank projects consistently. Also, even when NPV curves do cross, inconsistency is a problem only for a range of interest rates (e.g., under 6.3 percent in Figure 6-3).

Multiple IRRs Major costs during or at the end of a venture can sometimes cause more than one IRR to occur. In such cases the IRR criterion is ambiguous. For example, applying equation (6-3) to the hypothetical project below gives IRRs of 4.0 percent and 9.9 percent (both rates give NPVs of 0):

Between 4.0 percent and 9.9 percent interest, NPV is positive, and at all other rates NPV is negative. This inconsistency in the NPV trend with increasing discount rate is just as ambiguous as multiple IRRs, since we normally expect NPV to steadily decrease as we increase the discount rate from zero. Thus, as Mills and Dixon (1982) point out, multiple IRRs occur when the investment itself is ambiguous. They note that the IRR criterion can display such ambiguity, while a single NPV calculation hides it. Thus, it is not at all clear that the potential for multiple IRRs is a disadvantage of the IRR criterion. In the above investment, you might wonder why one wouldn't stop the project after 10 years and avoid the $1,100 cost. But the cost might be a legal requirement such as restoring land after mining. Multiple IRRs can also occur when a venture starts with a positive cash

flow from a loan, or no negative cash flow, followed by sufficiently large negative and positive flows. If a project has more than one IRR, you can compute a single NPV to evaluate the venture. But you must realize that the project will still have the above-mentioned ambiguity.[2]

NPV and Project Size

For consistency, capital requirements for projects D and N were kept equal. This is important, because looking at IRR or NPV alone, you can't tell how much capital a project requires. Below, you'll see how NPV can hide the amount of capital needed. Both investments I and II have one initial cost and one revenue a year later and are *indivisible* (all-or-nothing). Let the MAR be 6 percent.

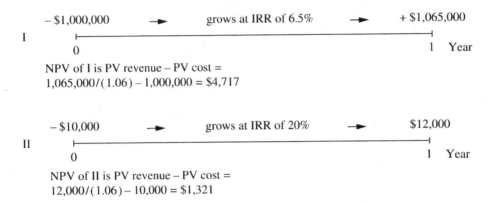

Which is best, I or II? Considering NPV alone, I is best, but II's IRR is an excellent 20 percent, compared with I's 6.5 percent. You really need more information. Are there more opportunities like II? Is there $1,000,000 available to invest in I? The key point of the example is that NPV alone doesn't really give enough information; nor does IRR. You cannot make valid comparisons or rankings of different-sized projects based on NPV or IRR alone.

Suppose no other projects beyond I and II can yield more than the 6 percent MAR, and projects I and II are *independent* (one doesn't preclude the other, say, fertilization and herbicide spraying). In that case, if capital is unlimited, both should be selected because they both earn more than the MAR.

Now suppose capital is limited to $1 million, or the projects are *mutually exclusive* (like homesite development versus reforestation on the same area). You can invest only in one. If 6 percent is the best you can do anywhere else, then project I

---

[2]Both the problems of NPV and IRR ranking-inconsistency and multiple IRRs can be solved by ranking projects with the *modified internal rate of return* (MIRR) (Brigham and Gapenski, 1991, p. 335), also called the *realizable rate of return* (Schallau and Wirth, 1980). To do this for a project, you first accumulate at the MAR each year's net revenues to a future value and discount each net cost at the MAR to year zero. The MIRR is the interest rate that discounts the future value of revenues to exactly equal the present value of costs. In comparing projects with the MIRR, you need to correct for unequal lives and to be aware that, for projects with intermediate incomes, the MIRR tends to get lower as project life lengthens (Klemperer, 1981).

alone will maximize present value at the $4,717 shown above. Suppose $10,000 of the $1 million is spent on project II and the remaining $990,000 must be invested at the 6 percent MAR, yielding $990,000(1.06) = \$1,049,400$ after one year. This would give no increase in net present value beyond the $1,321 shown above for II. The $990,000 compounded at 6 percent interest and discounted at 6 percent for the same time gives $990,000—just enough to offset the added $990,000 cost— and net present value is still $1,321:

NPV of $10,000 spent on II and $990,000 invested at the 6% MAR =
$$12,000/(1.06) - 10,000 + 1,049,400/(1.06) - 990,000 = \$1,321$$

The above procedure of adding other projects to a smaller project so that, in total, they equal the size of a larger one is called **normalizing** for size. But as just shown, if the rate of return on added capital equals the MAR, then net present value is unchanged. So in that case, normalizing for size isn't necessary with NPV calculations.[3] But in calculating IRRs and *B/C* ratios, you should always normalize for size, regardless of the MAR.

I first said that projects I and II were indivisible. If they were *divisible,* and you had $1,000,000 to invest, you'd maximize NPV by investing first in project II, which has the highest NPV per dollar of cost, and putting the remaining $990,000 in I.

Unequal project lives also can cause problems in comparing investments.

Correcting for Unequal Investment Lives

When two equal-sized projects have different durations, it may or may not be valid to compare their NPVs. If the shorter project could be repeated and earns more than the MAR, we need to *normalize for unequal lives* by repeating the project. If repetition isn't possible, and the reinvestment rate is the MAR, no correction is needed for NPVs. Consider the following two *mutually exclusive* reforestation projects S (short duration) and L (long duration) for the same area. Assume an 8 percent MAR.

Project S
(short rotation
fiber crop)

$-\$1,000 \quad\longrightarrow\quad$ grows at 12%/yr $\quad\longrightarrow\quad +\$1,405$

| 0 | 1 | 2 | 3 Years |

$$\text{NPV} = 1,405/(1.08)^3 - 1,000 = \$115$$

Project L
(longer rotation
timber crop)

$-\$1,000 \quad\longrightarrow\quad$ grows at 9%/yr $\quad\longrightarrow\quad +\$13,268$

| 1 | 10 | 20 | 30 Years |

$$\text{NPV} = 13,268/(1.08)^{30} - 1,000 = \$319$$

---

[3]If the rate of return on added capital *exceeds* the MAR, normalizing for size is necessary because it increases present value. Although an available rate of return greater than the minimum acceptable rate suggests that the MAR is too low, limited amounts of capital can sometimes earn more than the MAR.

Without capital limits, if the projects were independent, you'd accept them both, since the IRRs exceed the 8 percent MAR. But they're mutually exclusive, so which one should be accepted?

Let's evaluate the projects under two scenarios:

1 Repeating the shorter project is not possible, and the only opportunities for reinvestment of proceeds are at the 8 percent MAR.

In this case it is valid to compare the above NPVs, and L is preferred. In year 3, reinvesting the $1,405 return from S for 27 more years at the 8 percent MAR would give both projects a 30-year life. But this would have no effect on S's NPV because compounding the reinvestment out for 27 years at 8 percent [multiplying by $(1.08)^{27}$] and discounting it back for 27 years at 8 percent [dividing by $(1.08)^{27}$] gives no added net present value. This also means that the *B/C* ratio would be unchanged. But the above normalizing for length will reduce the IRR on the shorter project, so unnormalized IRRs should not be compared when the reinvestment rate equals the MAR.

This and the previous section show further advantages of the NPV criterion: it requires no normalizing for size or length of mutually exclusive projects when the reinvestment rate equals the MAR.

Now consider the second scenario:

2 The shorter project could be repeated 10 times until its duration equaled that of the 30-year project (or both could be repeated in perpetuity). This means that the reinvestment rate exceeds the MAR for at least some capital.

By repeating project S, $1,000 of the $1,405 harvest could be reinvested in planting at 12 percent, and the rest invested at the MAR of 8 percent. This may or may not offer a present value advantage over project L. A way to find out is to compute for each project an **equivalent annual annuity** (EAA): an equal annual real income with the same present value, over the project life, as the project's NPV, all computed at the same *real* MAR. (An **annuity** is a series of equal payments at regular intervals; here a one-year interval is specified.) The project with the highest EAA would be preferred. The equation for EAA is the same as the capital recovery formula:[4]

$$\text{EAA} = \text{NPV} \frac{r}{1 - (1 + r)^{-n}} \tag{6-6}$$

Since you could conceive of these annuities continuing forever, the EAA implicitly gives both projects a common life of infinity, thus correcting for unequal

---

[4]Here an EAA is assumed to be an equal annual amount in real terms, or rising at the inflation rate. Thus, in computing an EAA, it's important to use a real interest rate r. Otherwise, the EAA increases as more inflation is added to the interest rate, making a project appear better. This result is inconsistent with the fact that inflation should not affect before-tax present values. As more inflation is added to the discount rate, the EAA rankings could incorrectly change. Using a real interest rate avoids this problem.

lives. Below are the EAAs for both projects, computed at the 8 percent discount rate:

$$\text{EAA, project S} = 115\,\frac{0.08}{1 - (1.08)^{-3}} = \$44.62 \qquad (6\text{-}7)$$

$$\text{EAA, project L} = 319\,\frac{0.08}{1 - (1.08)^{-30}} = \$28.34 \qquad (6\text{-}8)$$

Despite the fact that project S's NPV is lower than L's, the EAAs show that project S is preferred to L, *if you assume that the shorter project could be repeated at its IRR (here, 12 percent) for the life of the longer project.* If the shorter investment cannot be repeated, EAA is not a valid ranking criterion. In general, if the shorter project can be repeated, a correction for unequal lives should be made. The correction may not always change NPV rankings, but it could.[5]

Capital Rationing

If capital were unlimited, project scale or precise rankings wouldn't be relevant; managers could maximize asset values by investing in all projects with $\text{NPV} \geq 0$, $\text{IRR} \geq \text{MAR}$, or $(B/C) \geq 1$. But there's almost never enough capital to invest in all acceptable projects (unless the MAR is very high). Thus, the problem is to find the combination of independent projects that maximizes NPV without exceeding a limited investment budget.

Borrowing more money doesn't solve the problem. Even when lenders have abundant funds, they resist lending to firms with too much debt. There's a limit to borrowing, especially at reasonable interest rates. As a debt-ridden firm tries to borrow more, the risk of loan default increases, and lenders will charge higher interest rates (if they're willing to lend at all). Governments have similar problems: as they borrow more—by selling bonds—beyond a point, they must pay higher interest rates to get people to buy more bonds.

Let's consider only cases where *projects are nonrepeating,* and the reinvestment rate on all incomes equals the MAR (here, 10 percent). Assume that the major cost is in the first year and that there's enough income to cover later costs. As before, *the objective is to maximize wealth (NPV).* The optimum allocation of limited capital will depend on whether projects are divisible or indivisible.

Divisible Projects   Suppose you're an analyst for a forest products firm that wants you to recommend which of the eight nonrepeating projects in Table 6-4 to invest in, given a $100,000 budget. For most of the projects, initial costs C_0, lives, and IRRs differ. For simplicity, all projects yield equal annual income, and all costs are in year 0. Assume that output values rise at the inflation rate and are fixed in real terms. Thus, the interest rate and the IRRs are real. A forestry

---

[5]Given the assumed reinvestment of only $1,000 of project S's payoff every 3 years, repeating S will reduce its 12 percent IRR. Thus, to compare IRRs, you should compute S's IRR based on its repetition for 30 years. But that still wouldn't assure consistency of IRR and NPV rankings, because income timing varies (see Figure 6-3).

TABLE 6-4

EIGHT HYPOTHETICAL, INDEPENDENT, NONREPEATING PROJECTS

(Reinvestment Rate = MAR = 10%)

(a) Project	(b) Initial cost, C_0 (dollars)	(c) Life (years)	(d) Annual revenue (dollars)	(e) NPV at 10% MAR (dollars)	(f) IRR (%)	(g) NPV per $1 cost (dollars) (e) : (b)[†]	(h) Accumulated initial cost, all projects (dollars)
1	20,000	14	3,396.50	5,020.95*	14.4	0.251	20,000
2	20,000	6	5,615.92	4,458.80	17.3	0.223	40,000
3	20,000	14	3,236.54	3,842.58	13.4	0.192	60,000
4	100,000	10	18,947.41	16,423.63	13.7	0.164	160,000
5	50,000	20	6,319.89	3,804.79	11.1	0.076	210,000
6	40,000	12	6,015.07	984.83	10.5	0.025	250,000
7	30,000	6	6,293.87	−2,588.55	7.0	−0.086	280,000
8	35,000	10	4,755.38	−5,780.25	6.0	−0.165	315,000

*For project 1, NPV $= 3,396.50 \left[\dfrac{1 - (1.10)^{-14}}{0.10} \right] - 20,000 = \$5,020.95.$

This is the present value (PV) of revenues minus PV costs. Discounting with the 14.4 percent IRR would give a zero NPV.

[†]Because this example has no intermediate costs, the B/C ratio would also give the correct ranking. But in general, when intermediate costs occur, the B/C ratio would *not* always give the correct ranking. For example, a project with a highly ranked NPV/C_0 could have a lower ranked B/C ratio if intermediate costs were high enough.

example would be the purchase of timber cutting rights for a price of C_0 on tracts where future harvests are in equal annual amounts for a contract period. Assume tract owners are willing to sell cutting rights on portions of the tracts. That makes the projects "divisible." Column (e) shows NPVs calculated at the 10 percent MAR.[6] You could immediately rule out all projects with NPV < 0 (projects 7 and 8). Total cost of the remaining projects is $250,000 in column (h), but your budget for the year is only $100,000. Which projects should be selected? We've already noted problems with ranking projects by IRR. So why not just take those with the largest NPVs, since we want to maximize NPV anyway? One problem lies in the capital constraint: the project with maximum NPV may be too large for your budget. That's not the case here; project 4 has the largest NPV and just exhausts the budget. But project 4 has a lower NPV than a combination of the smaller projects.

A solution is to rank projects by decreasing *NPV per dollar of initial cost* (NPV/C_0):

$$\frac{\text{Net present value}}{\text{Initial cost}} = \text{NPV}/C_0 = \frac{\displaystyle\sum_{y=0}^{n} \frac{R_y}{(1+r)^y} - \sum_{y=0}^{n} \frac{C_y}{(1+r)^y}}{C_0} \qquad (6\text{-}9)$$

---

[6]Column (f) shows the problem with calling the investor's minimum acceptable rate the "alternative rate of return." For example, consider project 2, which earns 17.3 percent. Your next best alternative (project 1) earns 14.4 percent. In addition to project 2, five projects earn alternative rates of return higher than the MAR.

Since the numerator is NPV, this is a modified NPV criterion: projects with $(NPV/C_0) < 0$ are unacceptable. By choosing first those projects with the greatest NPV per dollar cost, you'll automatically maximize the net present value of your limited budget. Projects in Table 6-4 have already been ranked by decreasing NPV/C_0 [see column (g)]. Thus, simply take the first three projects and 40 percent of project 4. Table 6-5 shows that this combination exhausts the $100,000 budget and yields a total NPV of $19,892. This is the optimum selection, since no other combination of projects within the budget could yield a higher NPV. From the sections on project size and life, recall that no NPV correction is needed for unequal sizes or lives, given the above assumption that the reinvestment rate equals the MAR.

Figure 6-4 shows the selection process graphically. The y axis is NPV/C_0. Since the x axis is dollars of original cost, the width of each project's bar is its year-0 cost. The hatched area shows each project's positive NPV (original cost times NPV per dollar of cost). Because of the budget constraint, not all projects with positive NPV were accepted. But the graph shows why this ranking process assures NPV maximization. Therefore, the project combination must be optimal. Things are not so simple with indivisible projects.

Notice in Table 6-4 that ranking the projects by decreasing IRR is not optimal: following the IRR, you'd choose first project 2, then project 1, and 60 percent of project 4, yielding a total NPV of $19,334. Percentagewise, that's not much below the optimum, but in some cases, the difference could be substantial. Note also that ranking by NPV per $1 of initial cost addresses only the first year's budget constraint (usually the most important) but ignores the impact of budget constraints in later years.

Indivisible Projects   If projects in Table 6-4 were not divisible, you could no longer use the above ranking by NPV per $1 cost and just skip projects pushing you over the budget. Such a procedure could sometimes lead to rejecting a project that would have fit in the budget under another ordering and that could have yielded a higher total NPV. For example, suppose projects in Table 6-4 were *indivisible,* and you ranked them by decreasing NPV/C_0. With a $100,000 budget, you'd pick numbers 1, 2, and 3; and with $40,000 left, you'd skip 4 and 5 and

TABLE 6-5

OPTIMAL SET OF PROJECTS FROM
TABLE 6-3 GIVEN A $100,000 BUDGET

Project	Initial cost	Net present value
1	$20,000	$5,020.92
2	20,000	4,458.80
3	20,000	3,842.60
40% of 4	40,000	6,569.46
Totals	$100,000	$19,891.78 (maximum)

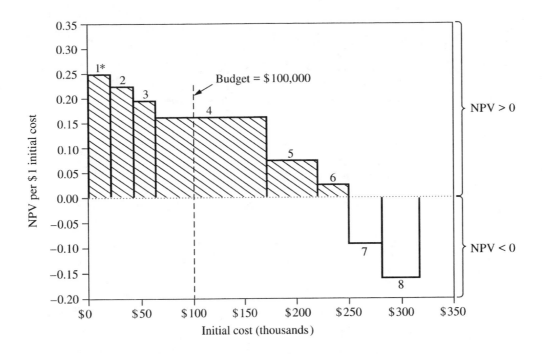

*Project numbers from Table 6-4.

FIGURE 6-4
Ranking divisible projects, given $100,000 budget.

would accept 6. Total NPV from column (e) would be $5,021 + $4,459 + $3,843 + $985 = $14,308. But that's suboptimal, because spending the full budget on project 4 gives an even higher NPV: $16,424.

When capital is limited and projects are indivisible, there is no simple decision rule that always guarantees a project ranking that will maximize net present value. By trial and error you could find the optimal combination of indivisible projects that maximized the present value of a limited budget. But that's very time-consuming when the number of possible projects is large. Although beyond the scope of this book, another approach is to use linear programming to find the optimum project combination. Such "activity scheduling" models with capital constraints are usually covered in forest management courses.

A SUMMARY OF CAPITAL BUDGETING

Given a wealth maximizing goal, the flowchart in Figure 6-5 summarizes the capital budgeting guidelines discussed so far, under limiting assumptions. Although it helps sort out the options, it's still very simplified. For example, the chart assumes that the reinvestment rate is always the MAR and the MAR is fixed over time, that projects are either mutually exclusive or independent, that projects are non-repeating, and that projects are either divisible or indivisible. Imagine the worst possible decision morass: The reinvestment rate for limited amounts of capital each year exceeds the MAR, the MAR changes over time, the group of possible

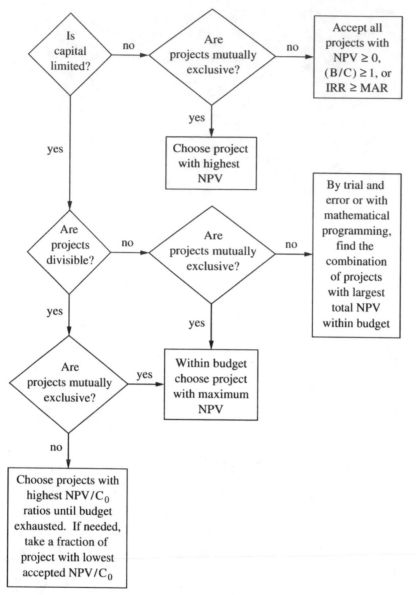

FIGURE 6-5
Capital budgeting flowchart—reinvestment rate equals minimum
acceptable rate of return.

projects includes *both* mutually exclusive and independent projects, *both* repeating and nonrepeating, as well as *both* divisible and indivisible projects,[7] budget limitations change from year to year so that you must consider the level of net negative cash flows in future years as well as today, debt is incurred to extend

_____

[7]When ranking projects by NPV/C_0 under capital rationing, by first selecting from mutually exclusive projects alone and then from independent ones, you might reject a project that would have been in a larger optimal set of indivisible, independent projects. One solution is to first consider all mutually exclusive and independent projects together. Then, as soon as you select a mutually exclusive project, discard all other mutually exclusive projects from that bundle.

budget limits (but how far?), and the degree of risk (expected variation in cash flows) differs among projects. When simplifying assumptions are relaxed and the number of options is large, the capital budgeting decision is tremendously complex.

Large simulation models and mathematical programming approaches are helpful but not always available for solving the above problems. In practice, options are usually limited, so the worst possible decision nightmares aren't common. Even so, choices aren't usually as fine-tuned as theoreticians might like. Several surveys have found that United States businesses, including the forest products industry, use internal rate of return most often to rank investments (Brigham and Gapenski, 1991; Redmond and Cubbage, 1985). While the IRR has theoretical shortcomings, it's easily understood, and for a wide range of forestry investments, Mills and Dixon (1982) and Haley (1969) find that NPV, IRR, and B/C ratio tend to yield similar forestry investment rankings under constrained budgets.

Ideal would be some foolproof guideline like "Choose projects in order of decreasing NPV or IRR," but no single approach applies to all situations. Even when conditions make the NPV guideline or NPV/C_0 seem appropriate, analysts should always give the investor other project measures such as IRR, payback period, and capital requirements over time. These are all relevant. To some extent, capital budgeting is an art that can't always be boiled down to a simple decision rule.

Several computer programs are available for conducting forestry investment analyses and applying many of the capital budgeting guidelines covered here. For lists of these, see Nodine et al. (1994) and Bullard and Straka (1993). When using such software, be sure you understand proper ways to include inflation, taxes, and risk. And to make sure you know what's going on inside a program, always try to have it match some simple hand-calculated examples with a range of inputs. Sometimes these programs don't calculate results in the way that you expect, or they may have errors.

APPLICATIONS INCLUDING NONMONETARY VALUES

Although later we'll look at techniques for valuing nonmonetary outputs, capital budgeting tools allow us to consider such outputs without actually assigning dollar values to them. For example, suppose a public project is unacceptable by one of the financial criteria, but it will yield unmarketed recreation benefits. Below are examples of determining the minimum annual value of these benefits needed in order for the project to become acceptable. This doesn't actually place a value on the benefit, but the procedure often lets us see whether the minimum required value could reasonably be expected.

Perpetual Benefits

Suppose a State Parks Department considers spending $5,500 on a campsite with annual maintenance at $125. Given no camping fees, if the department needs a 7 percent real rate of return (MAR), what must be the minimum value of annual benefits B? *Assuming a perpetual life,* the present value of costs, and hence the present value of required benefits, is:

$$\text{PV costs} = 5{,}500 + 125/0.07 = \$7{,}286$$

where the second term is the present value of perpetual annual costs (equation 4-8). In order to be barely acceptable, NPV (or PV benefits of $\$B$/year minus PV costs) must be 0:

$$\text{PV benefits} - \text{PV costs} = B/0.07 - 7{,}286 = 0$$

Solving for the required perpetual annual benefit B,

$$B = 0.07(7{,}286) = \$510$$

Or, in general,

$$\text{Required perpetual real annual benefits} = r|\text{negative NPV}| \qquad (6\text{-}10)$$
$$= \text{``annualized cost''}$$

You can think of the NPV in equation (6-10) as the difference in NPVs of a project with and without investment for a nonmonetary good. For this example, to provide free camping, a park's financial NPV dropped by $\$7,286$. *For perpetual projects, the above equation shows that the required annual nondollar benefit is the interest rate times the loss in NPV incurred to provide the benefit.* While this doesn't place a value on the recreation, it helps analysts to determine whether the benefits are high enough in this example for the State Parks Department to earn its required 7 percent return. For instance, if projected use of the above campsite is 200 visits per year, benefits need to be $\$510/200 = \$2.55$ per visit. If people readily pay that much, or more, at fee areas (which they do), you could assume the site was worth at least that much, and the project would be justified. If you had simply asked, "Are the benefits worth at least as much as the $\$7,286$ present value of costs?" the answer wouldn't be as obvious.

The above $\$510$ is an example of **annualized costs** (equal annual costs) with the same present value as costs that are not annual. The time horizon above was perpetual; the finite case follows. In both equations (6-10) and (6-11) below, *make sure you use a real interest rate, since the equations assume that the annualized cost is fixed in real terms.* You'd use a nominal discount rate only if you thought the annual value would be fixed in current dollars, regardless of the inflation rate, and declining in real terms.

Terminating Benefits

Suppose investment project 8 in Table 6-4 was a proposed boat launching and picnic site with an expected 10-year life. Annual income would come from projected launching fees charged by the Park Agency. Nonboaters are expected to use the picnic area at no charge. The agency requires a 10 percent rate of return, but the project's internal rate of return is only 6 percent. What must the minimum value of picnicking be in order to raise the rate of return to 10 percent? Recall that the project's NPV of $-\$5,780$ was calculated with a 10 percent discount rate. Thus, still using 10 percent interest, if the present value of picnicking benefits would exactly offset that amount, making NPV $= 0$, the project would earn a 10 percent rate of return. (Remember that IRR is the discount rate at which NPV $= 0$.)

So all we have to do is find the annual picnicking benefit B with a present value of $5,780 over a period of 10 years. The procedure is like finding the equivalent annual annuity (EAA) in equation (6-6):

$$\text{Required terminating real annual benefit} = B = |\text{negative NPV}|\frac{r}{1 - (1 + r)^{-n}}$$

$$= \text{"annualized cost"}$$

$$(6\text{-}11)$$

As in equation (6-10), the negative NPV is in absolute value terms. Substituting the appropriate values for the example:

$$B = 5,780\frac{0.10}{1 - (1.10)^{-10}} = \$941 \text{ per year}$$

Thus, if the annual picnicking benefits were worth at least $941, the project would be acceptable: it would earn at least a 10 percent rate of return and have an NPV of 0 or greater. As above, the Park Agency could estimate projected use and judge whether the benefits were reasonable to expect. Suppose anticipated use was an average of 10 picnic groups per week, or 520 annually. Then required benefits would be 941/520 = $1.81 per group. As above, you'd normally use a real discount rate in equation (6-11), assuming the offsetting benefits would be fixed in real terms and rise at the inflation rate in current dollars.

Although the above examples deal with costs, you can use equations (6-10) and (6-11) to annualize either costs or revenues for perpetual or terminating cases: For revenues, just enter a positive rather than a negative NPV.

Nonmonetary Summary

Remember that the above two sections don't find a value for nonmonetary benefits. The approaches simply organize information in a way that makes it easier to see whether benefits are worth the costs—just another example of economic thinking and asking the right questions.

You can generalize the procedure for finding the needed nonmonetary benefits to make any financial measure become acceptable: Calculate the measure, for example, NPV, B/C ratio, IRR, or NPV/C_0. *If unacceptable, calculate the needed addition to the present value of revenues in order to make the criterion become acceptable* (the above examples aimed for NPV $= 0$, but one could seek an NPV > 0, a B/C ratio > 1, or an IRR $>$ MAR). Then, use equation (6-10) or

(6-11) if you want to calculate the required annual benefit equivalent to the needed increase in present value. Questions at the chapter's end give more examples of such analyses.

The above types of calculations are relevant for public agencies (but that's not to say that they all necessarily make them). Individuals may also find cases where projects, say forestland purchases, may not yield an acceptable NPV strictly on cash flow projections. The above procedures could help them decide whether or not the annual nonmonetary benefits they expected from the property would be worth the annualized costs. Businesses primarily interested in financial rates of return and in income reports to stockholders aren't likely to consider nonmonetary outputs in the above manner. But these procedures are still useful in calculating annualized costs of "goodwill" practices like free forest recreation sites and scenic landscape management zones.

APPLICATIONS IN FOREST DAMAGE CONTROL

Another area for applying capital budgeting is in deciding how much to spend on controlling fire, insects, and diseases. You spend money on forest damage prevention and control (the cost) to prevent losing trees (the benefit). So you can rank damage control expenditures with measures like net present value, internal rate of return, or benefit/cost ratio to see where opportunities are best for improving net benefits. Cost estimates are often the easiest; for example, with bark beetle control, costs might be for spraying, doing precommercial thinning to maintain stand vigor, and removing beetle-damaged trees and other material providing breeding grounds. But benefits are often harder to estimate.

Let's start with a case of all-or-nothing damage control, considering only timber harvest revenues. On a given area, the damage control benefit is the net present value (NPV) of expected timber harvests without damage minus NPV with uncontrolled damage. If you've not subtracted control costs, this NPV difference is the maximum amount you can afford to spend on fully controlling damage, in present value terms. You wouldn't want to spend more preventing damage than its prevention was worth. Things get more complex when you consider damage such as reduced quality of scenery or water, where dollar values are hard to estimate, but the principle is the same.

In present value terms, the maximum you can spend on fully controlling damage and still earn the interest rate used in the present value calculations is:

$$\begin{aligned} \text{Benefits of damage control} &= \text{NPV of the forest with no damage} \\ &\quad - \text{NPV of the forest with uncontrolled damage} \\ &= \text{damage (loss)} \end{aligned}$$

(6-12)

Dealing only with the extremes of no damage versus uncontrolled damage, the equation tells you two things: (1) the benefit of completely controlling the damage and (2) the loss if you let damage occur. Note that *control costs have not been subtracted.* Figure 6-6 graphs the scenarios. The point *N* is NPV with no damage,

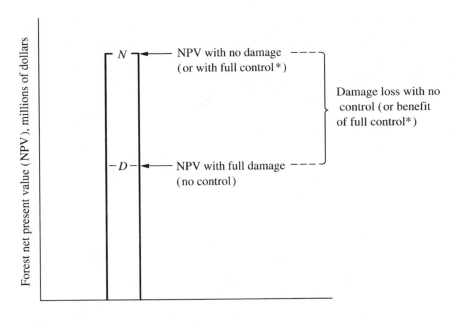

*Control costs have not been subtracted.

FIGURE 6-6
Damage loss and benefits of complete damage control.

and *D* is NPV with damage. Appendix 6A covers cases with various levels of damage control.

Using a simple example of all-or-nothing damage control in one timber stand, and assuming that all costs and benefits can be measured in dollars, let

PV_{Bn} = present value of all *b*enefits expected to occur with *n*o damage—e.g., harvest revenues and values of recreation, water, wildlife, etc.

PV_{Cn} = present value of all *c*osts with *n*o damage—e.g., costs of management and future reforestation, *excluding* damage control and prevention.

PV_{Bd} = present value of all *b*enefits with uncontrolled *d*amage—this would include any salvage cut after damage, plus future cuts and all other future benefits (some of which might be reduced) like recreation, wildlife, and water quality.

PV_{Cd} = present value of *c*osts with uncontrolled *d*amage—e.g., immediate and all later reforestation, erosion control, and management costs.

Remembering that net present value is the present value of benefits minus the present value of costs, equation (6-12) is:

$$\text{Benefits of damage control} = (\text{PV}_{Bn} - \text{PV}_{Cn}) - (\text{PV}_{Bd} - \text{PV}_{Cd}) \qquad (6\text{-}13)$$

Thus, the present value of damage control costs shouldn't exceed the benefits from equation (6-13). In measuring damage control costs, you should consider not only the first year's cost but the present value of all current and future damage control costs for the planning period. You can use this general framework for gauging the loss from any kind of forest damage and thus for finding your maximum willingness to pay, in present value terms, for preventing the loss.

A key point is that a timber loss isn't necessarily how much a logger would have paid for the damaged trees. Damaged trees might be too small to interest a logger, yet they still have value to the owner for future cutting purposes. That's why damage analyses look at present values of future benefits. Also, nontimber values need to be considered.

A Hypothetical Insect Problem—All-or-Nothing Control

Suppose you have a 19-year-old, even-aged forest scheduled for harvest in 11 years at age 30. Given progression of a bark beetle infestation, entomologists predict that, without an insecticide spray schedule, the timber would be so damaged by beetles next year that the wisest choice would be to do a salvage clear-cut yielding $500 after attack and to replant at $100 per acre. With a spray schedule starting next year, no damage would occur, and a harvest 10 years later would yield $1,800/acre minus $100 for reforestation. With or without spraying, after the first cut, later rotations would yield the same $1,800/acre minus $100 every 30 years. To correct for unequal lives, analyses continue in perpetuity for both cases. The present value of nontimber benefits would be $50/acre with damage and $65/acre without.[8] Using equation (6-13), next year's NPV of benefits from insect control, calculated with 6 percent interest, would be:

Benefits of damage control

$$= \left[\frac{1,800 - 100}{(1.06)^{10}} + \frac{(1,800 - 100)/[(1.06)^{30} - 1]}{(1.06)^{10}} + 65 \right]$$

$$- \left[500 - 100 + \frac{1,800 - 100}{(1.06)^{30} - 1} + 50 \right] \tag{6-14}$$

$$= 1,214 - 808$$

$$= \$406 \text{ per acre}$$

In the first set of brackets is NPV with no damage: the first term is the present value of the undamaged clear-cut in 10 years minus reforestation cost; the second term is the present value of subsequent harvests minus reforestation occurring every 30 years and discounted 10 years, since the series starts in 10 years. And the last term is the present value of nontimber benefits. In the second set of brackets is NPV with damage: the first two terms are the value of the salvage cut minus reforestation cost, and the third term is the present value of subsequent cuts minus

---

[8]See Chapter 14 for ways to value nonmarket outputs. Leuschner and Young (1978) have applied one of these methods to estimate losses in recreation values due to southern pine beetle (SPB) damage. See Leuschner et al. (1978) for an actual and more detailed estimate of (SPB) damages excluding nontimber damages.

reforestation every 30 years thereafter. The fourth term is the present value of non-timber benefits. In present value terms, $406/acre is the maximum you can spend on insect control programs and still earn a 6 percent return on your investment, *if* you can attain the complete control assumed in equation (6-14). You needn't include costs or benefits that are the same with or without damage, since they'll cancel out of the equation. Examples could be annual overhead costs or hunting lease income.

If entomologists recommended spraying for 5 years, you could figure an equivalent annual annuity of the above $406, using equation (6-6) at 6 percent interest:

$$406\left[\frac{0.06}{1-(1.06)^{-5}}\right] = \$96 \qquad (6\text{-}15)$$

Thus, you could spend up to $96/acre/year for 5 years on insect control.

This is a highly simplified example. In reality, possible damage levels as well as control results are highly variable, so you'd need to deal with average values or **expected values**. Also, the above example covers only one maximum damage level and its complete control. Rather than the *single* level of complete damage control assumed above, with most kinds of damage there exists a range of control intensities (see Appendix 6A). Let's look at the theory of finding the optimum control expenditure.

Least Cost Plus Loss

The example will be fire control. Many activities can lessen the annual acreage burned on a forest. Total fire control costs include (1) *prevention,* e.g., public education, enforcing fire laws and closures, patrolling; (2) *presuppression,* e.g., maintaining equipment and supply inventories, training and maintaining crews, detection programs, building fire breaks; and (3) *suppression,* i.e., actual fire fighting costs. For simplicity, I'll combine these costs into one total, assuming a least-cost combination for any level of fire control achieved (realizing there are trade-offs—for example, if you spend more on prevention, suppression costs are lower).

For a hypothetical forest, Figure 6-7 plots total fire control costs per year as a 45-degree line from the origin, since the horizontal axis is dollars of control cost per year and the vertical axis is also dollars per year. The dashed line is total annual damage at different levels of control expenditure, starting at the indicated maximum annual damage with no control. The more you spend on control per year, the less the annual loss. The dashed damage curve convex to the origin shows typical diminishing returns to control efforts: eventually you reach a point where adding more to annual fire control cost doesn't decrease the loss much more. The dashed damage curve is average annual forest net revenue with no damage minus average annual net revenue with partially controlled damage—the amount by which net income is reduced below the no damage case. This differs from equation (6-12), which deals only with complete damage control. The solid curve of cost plus loss is the vertical sum of the control cost and loss curves, and

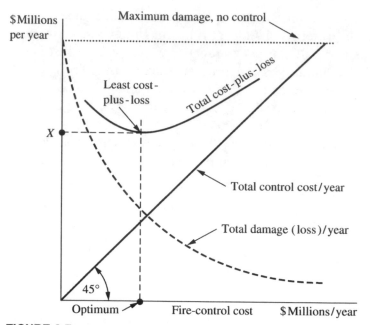

FIGURE 6-7
Model for optimizing annual fire-control expenditures on a hypothetical forest.
    Gorte and Gorte (1979) review the history of such models. Marty and Barney (1981) discuss applications.

cost plus loss is minimized at $ X million per year. Thus, the optimum annual fire control expenditure is as shown on the horizontal axis in Figure 6-7.

The cost-plus-loss curve is a form of "total damage" with different control levels. Thus, the vertical distance between the dotted maximum damage line and the cost-plus-loss curve is the net benefit of control expenditures. So if you want to bend your mind a bit, the cost-plus-loss curve viewed *upside down* is a net benefit curve that is maximized at the optimum fire control cost. This is simple marginal analysis again: Keep adding to control cost until the added cost just equals the added benefit of loss reduction. At that point you've maximized the net benefit (or minimized the cost plus loss—see Appendix 6A for more detail).

Ideally, such analyses should be in present value terms, but in the case of fire, with a large forest area, we can expect that, on average, a given portion would be damaged annually with a certain equal annual control expenditure. Thus, the ratios of costs to benefits would be about the same in terms of average annual cash flows or present values. If you think of Figure 6-7 in present value terms, the model shows the optimum size of a project, where size is expressed as the present value of costs. Appendix 6A looks in more detail at the present value analysis of optimal damage control levels.

KEY POINTS

◆ For a given amount of capital, the capital budgeting problem is to find the pattern of investment spending that maximizes the resulting asset values.

• For the decision to accept or reject investment projects, four major criteria are net present value (NPV), internal rate of return (IRR), benefit/cost ratio (B/C ratio), and payback period.

• NPV is present value of revenues minus present value of costs, calculating with the investor's minimum acceptable rate of return (MAR).

• As calculated here, NPV is net of initial project cost, so that an NPV of zero does not mean the project is worthless. Some discounted cash flows have the initial costs subtracted; some do not. In order to correctly interpret NPVs, it's vital to know how initial costs have been treated.

• The IRR is the discount rate that equates the present value of revenues with the present value of costs.

• The B/C ratio is the present value of revenues divided by the present value of costs, calculated with the MAR.

• Payback period is the number of years it takes for project revenues to off-set costs. This criterion gives no information about IRR or NPV. Thus, astute investors will rarely accept a project just because the payback period meets their approval.

• To compare and rank projects, determine first whether they are mutually exclusive, independent, divisible, or indivisible.

• If capital is unlimited, accept all projects with NPV $\geq$ 0, IRR $\geq$ MAR, or $(B/C) \geq 1$.

• If two projects are of unequal size, adding other projects to the smaller one until it equals the capital requirement of the larger one is called "normalizing for size." When comparing NPVs, such normalizing is not necessary if IRRs on the added projects equal the MAR but *is* necessary if IRRs exceed the MAR. Such normalizing is always necessary when comparing IRRs and B/C ratios.

• If two projects have unequal lives, NPV comparisons are valid if the shorter project cannot be repeated. If repetition is possible, equivalent annual annuities rather than NPVs should be compared.

• With a limited investment budget and divisible, independent projects, opportunities for any year should be ranked by decreasing NPV per dollar of initial cost. To maximize total NPV, invest in the best projects until the year's budget is exhausted.

• Under the above capital rationing, if projects are not divisible, ranking by NPV/C_0 will not necessarily maximize NPV. In that case trial and error or mathematical programming should be used to find the optimal set of projects.

• If dollar values aren't available for nonmonetary outputs from a project, pose the question, "What would the annual dollar value of nonmonetary benefits need to be to increase some financial criterion to a required level?" After computing these needed benefits, decision makers would be in a better position to gauge users' willingness to pay for them.

• The value of preventing a certain forest damage is the NPV of the forest without the damage minus the NPV of the forest with damage. In order for a damage control investment to earn at least the interest rate used in the calculations, the present value of control costs shouldn't exceed the value of damage prevented.

QUESTIONS AND PROBLEMS

6-1 A precommercial thinning investment of $190 now (year 0) is expected to increase timber harvest yields by $300, 15 years from now. On the same timber stand, a $100 fertilization investment in year 5 is expected to increase timber harvest value by an added $195 in year 15.

    a Viewing these practices as a total package, what is the internal rate of return on this investment, to the nearest one percentage point?

    b Why not figure rates of return for fertilization and thinning separately and average them to get IRR on the combination?

6-2 The benefit/cost ratio for an irrigation development project was computed at 1.7, using 6 percent interest. How will this *B/C* ratio change if 10 percent interest is used? (Costs occur earlier than revenues.)

6-3 Using 7 percent interest, the benefit/cost ratio for a federal reforestation project was 1. What was the internal rate of return? Explain your answer.

6-4 Using 10 percent interest, the U.S. Army Corps of Engineers calculated the benefit/cost ratio of a water impoundment project at 0.8, considering only dollar costs and revenues. They also expect nonmonetary recreation benefits from use of the reservoir. What must the present value of these recreation benefits be to obtain a *B/C* ratio of 1, given that the present value of project costs is $5 million?

6-5 The present value of costs was $10,000 for a new public campsite with an expected 17-year life. No camping fees are charged. What is the minimum fixed annual dollar value we must assume the recreation will yield in order for society to receive an 8 percent rate of return on the investment?

6-6 Suppose you're considering the following two mutually exclusive investments of different durations. Let your minimum acceptable rate of return be 7 percent. Note the different lives.

    a Which has the greatest net present value?

    b Which project would you choose, assuming the Christmas tree investment could be repeated?

    c Which would you choose if Christmas trees could not be repeated?

Investment	Cost	Return
Christmas trees	$500 in year 0	1,080 in year *10*
Timber	$500 in year 0	4,400 in year *30*

6-7 Suppose you must choose between the two projects below, which are *independent* and *indivisible.* The only other available alternatives will earn a 7 percent rate of return, and your investment budget is limited to $5,000. Assume your MAR is 7 percent.

    a Cost =   Revenue =

       $200   IRR is 15% $809

       0   10 Years

    b $5,000   IRR is 7.5% $10,305

       0   10 Years

How should you invest your money?

6-8 Suppose, in the previous question, the projects are *divisible,* and all other factors are the same. How should you invest?

6-9 A logging firm is evaluating logging equipment that costs $70,000 and is projected to yield a net after-tax income of $13,000 per year in constant dollars (of year 0) over a 7-year period. Assume that incomes occur at the end of each year and that the equipment will be sold for $5,000 (in constant dollars) at the end of year 7. At an 8 percent real minimum acceptable rate of return, what would be the net present value of such an equipment investment to the firm? Interpret this value: what does it mean?

This is a simplified example. What other types of factors might be considered in a "real-world" situation?

6-10 A park agency estimates the following campground development costs per unit:

Property purchase and construction	$3,500
Maintenance, in perpetuity	$300/year
Reconstruction, in perpetuity	$2,000 every 20 years

a Assuming the agency wants to earn a 5 percent real rate of return, what is the minimum real annual recreation value this campground must yield in perpetuity to justify the above costs?

b Given 5 percent interest and assuming that the campground will be used 125 nights each year, what will be the average cost per group night?

6-11 A park agency estimates the following costs for a new campground unit. Estimated life is 25 years, after which land use is expected to change.

Purchase and construction	$5,000
Annual maintenance	$250

a Assuming a 9 percent real MAR, what is the real minimum annual recreation value this campground unit must yield to justify the above costs?

b Based on a recreation user survey, the park agency feels that the cost per group night should not exceed $4. What is the minimum number of nights per year the campground must be used to justify the costs? Use 9 percent interest.

6-12 Assume $1,000 income today from salvaging a 20-year old timber stand damaged by fire this year. After a $500 reforestation cost, the area is expected to yield harvest income of $6,300 in 34 years. If the fire had not occurred, expected harvest income would have been $6,300 in 14 years. In either case, the $6,300 harvests minus $500 reforestation costs would continue in perpetuity every 34 years. Annual costs would be $20 and annual nontimber benefits would be $15 in both cases. Let the owner's discount rate be 6 percent, and assume no other costs or revenues. What is the dollar value of the fire damage (or the maximum amount the owner would have been willing to pay to prevent the fire)?

APPENDIX 6A: Marginal Analysis in Maximizing Benefits of Damage Control

Figure 6-6 and equation (6-12) equated loss from uncontrolled forest damage with the benefit of damage control because only full damage control was considered. In Figure 6-8, *excluding damage control costs,* the distance *DP* shows the benefit of partial damage control in present value terms: the NPV with partial control minus the NPV with

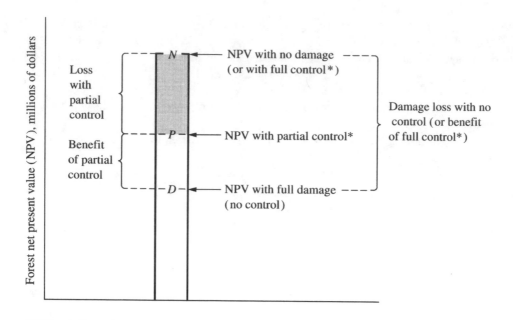

*Control costs have not been subtracted.

FIGURE 6-8
Damage loss and benefits under different levels of control.

full damage. You can imagine P in Figure 6-8 moving up or down depending on the amount spent on control. The shaded area in the figure is the loss with partial control:

$$\text{Damage loss with partial control} =$$
$$\text{forest NPV with no damage} - \text{NPV with partial control} \qquad \text{(6A-1)}$$

Figure 6-9a generalizes the Figure 6-7 fire control model to deal with any type of forest damage. The curves in the upper panel show the same relationships, but now in present value terms. The figure's dashed total damage loss curve is from equation (6A-1), which is the shaded portion of Figure 6-8 with varying damage control expenditure. The NPV of control cost is a 45-degree line from the origin in Figure 6-9 because the x axis is control cost and the y axis is also dollars.

In panel (b) of Figure 6-9, the dashed total benefit curve plots the difference between the dotted maximum damage line in panel (a) and the total damage curve (this difference is also the distance DP in Figure 6-8). The effect is to invert the dashed curve from the upper panel so that it comes from the origin in the lower panel. In Figure 6-9b you can see that net benefit is maximized where the slopes of the two curves are equal: where added benefit per dollar of control cost equals the added cost ($1).

The key point of Figure 6-9 is that you can generalize the marginal analysis to optimize expenditures on controlling any type of damage like insects, fire, and diseases. The major problem is in estimating costs and benefits of different control levels. Abstracting from the forest damage problem, Figure 6-9b also shows the optimum scale of any divisible

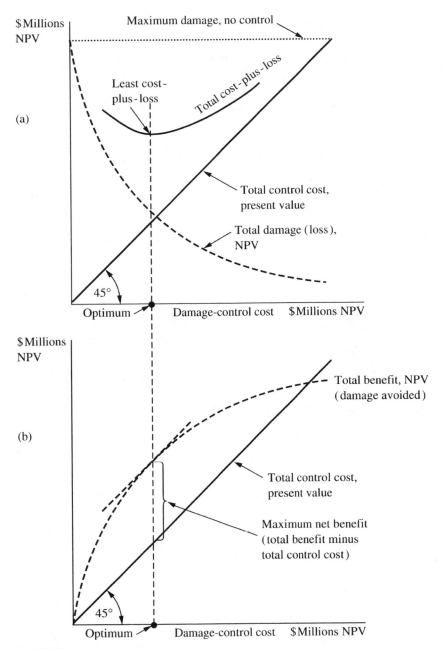

FIGURE 6-9
Model for optimizing present value of damage-control expenditures on a hypothetical forest.

project. Just let the *x* axis read "Present value of costs," and the solid and dashed curves read "Present value of costs" and "Present value of benefits." The optimal scale is where net present value is maximized.

REFERENCES

Baumol, W. J. 1977. *Economic Theory and Operations Analysis.* Prentice Hall, Englewood Cliffs, NJ. 695 pp.

Bierman, H., Jr., and S. Smidt. 1988. *The Capital Budgeting Decision.* Macmillan, New York.

Blank, L. T., and A. J. Tarquin. 1989. *Engineering Economy* (3rd edition). McGraw-Hill, New York. 531 pp.

Brigham, E. F., and L. C. Gapenski. 1991. *Financial Management—Theory and Practice* (6th edition). The Dryden Press, Chicago. 995 pp. plus app.

Bullard, S. H., and T. J. Straka. 1993. *Forest Valuation and Investment Analysis.* GTR Printing, Starkville, MS. 70 pp.

Collier, C. A., and W. B. Ledbetter. 1988. *Engineering Economic and Cost Analysis.* Harper and Row, New York. 635 pp.

Davis, L. S., and K. N. Johnson. 1987. *Forest Management* (3rd edition). McGraw-Hill, New York. 790 pp.

de Steiguer, J. E. 1991. *Comparison of Economic Criteria for Optimal Forest Damage Control.* U.S. Forest Service Southeastern Forest Exp. Sta. Research Note SE-362. Asheville, NC. 3 pp.

Gorte, J. K., and R. W. Gorte. 1979. *Application of Economic Techniques to Fire Management—A Status Review and Evaluation.* Intermountain Forest and Range Exp. Sta. Gen. Tech. Rept. INT-53. U.S. Forest Service, Ogden, UT. 26 pp.

Haley, D. 1969. A Comparison of Alternative Criteria for the Evaluation of Investment Projects in Forestry. Faculty of Forestry, University of British Columbia, Vancouver. 93 pp.

Holmes, T. P. 1991. Price and welfare effects of catastrophic forest damage from southern pine beetle epidemics. *Forest Science.* 37(2):500–516.

Klemperer, W. D. 1981. Interpreting the realizable rate of return. *Journal of Forestry.* 79(9):616–617.

Leuschner, W. A., T. A. Max, G. D. Spittle, and H. W. Wisdom. 1978. Estimating southern pine beetle timber damages. *Bulletin of the Entomological Society of America.* 24(1):29–34.

Leuschner, W. A., and R. L. Young. 1978. Estimating the southern pine beetle's impact on reservoir campsites. *Forest Science.* 24(4):527–537.

Marty, R. J., and R. J. Barney. 1981. *Fire Costs, Losses, and Benefits: An Economic Valuation Procedure.* U.S. Forest Service Intermountain Forest and Range Experiment Station Gen. Tech. Rept. INT-108, Ogden, UT. 11 pp.

Mills, T. J., and G. E. Dixon. 1982. *Ranking Independent Timber Investments by Alternative Investment Criteria.* U.S.D.A. Forest Service Pacific Southwest Forest and Range Experiment Station Research Paper PSW-166, Berkeley, CA. 8 pp.

Nodine, S. K., S. H. Bullard, T. J. Straka, and D. Gilluly. 1994. FORS complete guide to utilizing computer technology for forestry investment analysis. *The Compiler.* 12(3): 3–30.

Redmond, C. H., and F. W. Cubbage. 1985. *Capital Budgeting in the Forest Products Industry: A Survey and Analysis.* University of Georgia College of Agriculture Research Bulletin 333, Athens. 39 pp.

Rideout, D. B., and P. N. Omi. 1990. Alternate expressions for the economic theory of forest fire management. *Forest Science.* 36(3):614–624.

Schallau, C. H., and M. E. Wirth. 1980. Reinvestment rate and the analysis of forestry enterprises. *Journal of Forestry.* 78(12):740–742.

Van Horne, J. C. 1986. *Financial Management and Policy* (7th edition). Prentice Hall, Englewood Cliffs, NJ. 858 pp.

CHAPTER **9**

THE VALUATION OF NATURAL RESOURCES

Having looked at the general framework of benefit-cost analysis, we now consider the question of how one measures the actual **values of input and output flows** in any given situation involving natural resource use. It is easy to say "put each resource to the use that maximizes net social value," but how do we measure what these values actually are in concrete situations? Consider the following scenarios:

- An oceanside community is contemplating the purchase of an expanse of shoreline to use as a town beach. It must buy the land from its current owners. What benefits will town residents receive from this public beach, and are the benefits substantial enough to warrant the purchase?
- The fish and wildlife agency of a midwestern state proposes to devote substantial resources to restoring bald eagles in portions of the state. What benefits and costs will accrue to residents of the state, and what benefits will accrue to nonresidents?
- Authorities managing a river in the West are under pressure to regulate its flow so as to provide better habitat for several species of fish downstream from a large impoundment. What social benefits will flow from such a policy?
- A private logging company is being asked to avoid large clear-cuts so that the effectiveness of a forest to control water runoff is not impaired. What are the net social benefits of this practice?

SECTION FOUR: NATURAL RESOURCE ANALYSIS

- A ranch owner in the West charges hunters a fee for hunting elk on his property. His annual revenues from this activity are about $200,000. Is this an accurate measure of the wildlife preservation benefits on this parcel of land?
- Congress is considering the establishment of a new national park in a western state. What benefits will accrue to people who visit the park, and what benefits will accrue to people who never visit the park?
- An area of wetlands is being altered to allow housing development to take place without any long-run decrease in the total amount of wetlands. But the change will result in the temporary loss of about 5,000 migratory waterfowl. It's expected that after 5 years the waterfowl stock will recover to its original level. What are the social costs of this temporary loss of waterfowl?
- An agency is considering the designation of a remote part of a forest as a wilderness area. It's expected that few people will actually visit the area because of its location. Are there significant social benefits from establishing this area despite the low visitation?

These diverse questions all call for valuation of resources or the service flows stemming from resource use. We do not have sufficient time and space to take up each one in detail. Thus in this chapter we try to deal with certain **principles of valuation** that can be adapted to specific circumstances.

MEASURING BENEFITS

Types of Benefits

We first make some distinctions among types of benefits. Perhaps the most important step is to distinguish between **active** and **passive** sources of value. **Active resource values,** sometimes called **use values,** are those stemming from situations where people come into direct contact with the resource in question. This can be divided into **consumptive** and **nonconsumptive** values. Consumptive values arise from what we have termed extractive resources: timber, minerals, recreational and commercial hunting and fishing,[1] and agriculture are examples. Nonconsumptive values (nonextractive resources) are resources that are utilized but not removed or diminished in quantity or quality, such as ecotourism, animal watching, boating, hiking, camping, and rock climbing.

Passive natural resource values, sometimes called **nonuse values,** are involved when people place value on a resource independent of their actual use of the resource. Various motives have been suggested as the source of these values. Some of these are:

- **Option value:** People may be willing to pay to preserve a resource, or increase the likelihood of continued existence, because they may wish to utilize the resource at some undetermined future time. Example: Value

---

[1] But catch-and-release fishing may be regarded as a nonconsumptive activity.

expressed for maintaining or expanding national parks, with the possibility of later visits.

- **Existence value:** Willingness to pay to maintain the existence of resources even though no future utilization is likely. Example: Preservation of remote wilderness; steps taken to increase the survival probabilities of endangered species.
- **Bequest and gift value:** Willingness to pay to ensure that others, in both current and future generations, will enjoy a world in which the particular resources are present. Example: Willingness to protect open space so one's grandchildren will live in a world with ample amounts of this resource.

In the rest of this chapter we look at techniques that natural resource economists use to measure resource values of these different types.

ACTIVE (USE) BENEFITS

Benefits obtained when people actually use the resource in question, consumptively or nonconsumptively, are called active, or use, benefits. Use values can be further subdivided into those which are expressed through markets of one type or another, and nonmarket values. When markets are involved, interactions among buyers and sellers establish prices and quantities of transactions, which can often be analyzed to determine the willingness to pay of demanders and the marginal costs of suppliers. Market prices and quantities can be used to reveal these values in two ways. They can be used **directly** when the resource being evaluated is actually traded in its own right, and they may be used **indirectly** when what is being traded is not the resource itself but another good or service that is closely associated with it.

Direct Market Price Analysis

Suppose it is proposed that a dam constructed on a stream many years ago be removed. One impact of that removal is that it would restore a trout fishery on portions of the stream below the dam site. In making the decision, we would like to know, among other things, the net benefits this trout fishery would generate. It clearly has to be an estimate, because the trout fishery does not yet exist. But suppose there does currently exist elsewhere a private market in trout fishing. The suppliers in this case are certain people who control access to several trout streams, perhaps the riparian (or adjoining) property owners. "Production" in this case takes the form of maintaining good water quality and other conditions for a productive fish habitat, fishing access points, and the means of regulating entry. Demanders are the people who are willing to pay for access to this type of fishery. Suppose we look at existing operations and determine that the average price for a privately provided day of trout fishing is $25. May we use this value to estimate the benefits of our new trout fishery?

SECTION FOUR: NATURAL RESOURCE ANALYSIS

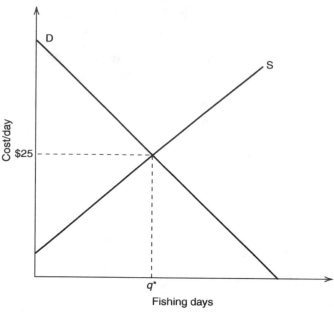

FIGURE 9-1
Market for Fishing Opportunities

Figure 9-1 shows the standard supply and demand functions of a market, which in the present case we suppose is the market for privately provided trout fishing. The price of $25 is the one that brings the quantity supplied into balance with the quantity demanded. On the assumption that there are no externalities on either side of the market and that the market is competitive, this price is an accurate indicator of both **marginal willingness to pay** and **marginal cost** at the number of fisher days represented by the quantity q^*. Therefore, if the new fishing area represents only a marginal addition to supply (i.e., if the market price of fishing days is not expected to change as a result of this new area coming on line) the $25 tells us what the marginal benefits are, and we can multiply this figure by the expected number of visits to get an estimate of total benefits. This must be done under the assumption that the new fishery will be reasonably similar to those now operating, in terms of the expected quality of the fishing.

When markets are present, they provide a good avenue for estimating resource values, because market participants are essentially revealing these values through their interactions. Thus, valuation of timber and minerals is often straightforward because they are traded on markets, both in situ (e.g., markets for trees on the stump) and as commodities after they have been harvested.

Market data may also exist to facilitate some nonextractive resource uses. Valuation of benefits from a public beach might be estimated from data on

CHAPTER 9:   THE VALUATION OF NATURAL RESOURCES

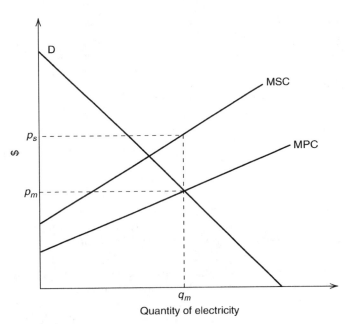

FIGURE 9-2
Market for Electricity with External Costs

visitations to private beaches, if enough of the latter exist in the study region. Or suppose there was a public policy conflict over taking steps to protect whales. The benefits produced by having abundant whales (at least some of the benefits) might be estimated by analyzing the whale watching market. The market suppliers in this case are the whales, together with the private boating firms that conduct whale watching excursions. The demanders are people who are willing to pay to be taken out to the parts of the ocean where they may eavesdrop on the whales. The prices, quantities, and costs in this market are the data we would analyze to get estimates of net benefits.

There may be many situations, however, where market prices do not give an accurate measure of social benefits. This would be true, for example, when environmental externalities are involved. Figure 9-2 presents the standard externality model introduced earlier,[2] in this case applied to the electricity market. D is the electricity demand curve, assumed to be an accurate representation of social marginal willingness to pay for electricity. MPC is the marginal private cost of producing electricity, and MSC is the marginal social cost of production. The difference is accounted for by the external costs of electricity generation, primarily air pollution. In the absence of anything (e.g., property rights changes or government policy) that causes these external effects to be

[2] See Chapter 6.

priced, the private market supply curve for electricity will be MPC, and the market price and quantity of electricity will be, respectively, p_m and q_m.

Suppose, now, that we are interested in building an array of windmills to generate power. It will be a relatively small addition to total electricity generation, but it will replace a part of the present polluting generating technology. Suppose the private cost of the windmill operation is the same as the conventional capacity. How do we value the power that the windmill project will provide? If we use simply the present market price for electricity p_m, we will be undervaluing the new power. This is because this new technology is valuable for two reasons: It produces power and it allows a reduction in the external costs coming from the electric power industry. The correct value to use in estimating the benefits of a small increase in windmill power is p_s, which is equal to the present price of power plus the current marginal value of external costs.

In many other cases market prices may not adequately represent the true social value of a natural resource–related good or service. This would be true, for example, where government subsidies or taxes lead to market prices that do not reflect true social opportunity costs. The search for correct prices to use in cases like this is a search for what economists call **accounting,** or **shadow** prices, which are simply prices that more correctly represent true economic scarcities than do the current or expected market prices. The use of shadow prices is especially important in cases where governmental policies of one type or another have produced these market distortions. We will see later that this is particularly important in developing countries.[3]

Indirect Market Price Analysis

Market prices, even when they have to be adjusted somewhat, are very useful for establishing the value of certain natural resources. But in many cases direct markets simply do not exist, or they exist in such rudimentary form that they do not provide good price data. In some cases the nature of the resource is such that direct markets are difficult to organize (e.g., air quality, which is a strong public good). In other cases government regulations have made it difficult or impossible for a market to form (e.g., wild game harvested within the country, which is illegal to sell on markets in the United States).

There are many such resources. An important natural resource in the United States is suburban wildlife, wildlife that exists in close proximity to areas of intensive human habitation. Issues related to the efficient management of these animals and plants will proliferate as urban sprawl continues at the same time that many people are changing their views about the value of wildlife. But there are no markets where people buy and sell the services of these wildlife. There may be some related markets, such as for hunting or bird watching, but these are likely to give only a very partial answer to the question of the true social value of these biological stocks. Or consider the

[3] See Chapter 20.

CHAPTER 9: THE VALUATION OF NATURAL RESOURCES

benefits associated with wilderness backpacking. Much of this activity takes place in remote publicly owned regions. Relatively little of the activity is arranged through private markets, though there may be related markets; for example, backpacking equipment is bought and sold in private markets, as are the services of wilderness guides.

In some cases activity in related markets can be studied to determine resource values. In such cases the value of the resource may be estimated **indirectly** by examining price, quantity, and quality data of the associated good or service in the related market.[4] As an example, consider the issue of open-space preservation in the suburbs. As suburban development in the United States has continued, more thought is being given to preserving some parcels in open space, like parks, visual buffers, and areas of ecological value. The costs of preservation are the value of development that they foreclose. These costs are fairly easily measured. But how can we assess benefits?

Although there is no market where people buy and sell units of open space directly, there is a closely related market in which open space can be expected to have an impact: the **suburban housing market.** The market for new and used houses is very active throughout the country. The price of a house is affected by many factors: the characteristics of the house itself and those of the neighborhood in which it is located. We assume that buyers purchase houses having the most desirable set of characteristics, given their incomes. One important neighborhood characteristic is the proximity of a house to open space or conservation land. These characteristics, if they indeed are valued (positively or negatively) by the average buyer, will be **capitalized** into the market prices of houses.

Since house prices in the suburbs are affected by many factors, what we need here is a large data set containing, for each house that was sold in a given time period, its transaction price and a description of all the characteristics that could be expected to have a noticeable impact on price. Among these would be, for example, the distance to the nearest significant parcel of open space. Statistical means can then be used to find out how this distance variable affects house prices and eventually to figure out the marginal willingness to pay that homeowners express for living close to preserved open space.

Another type of indirect market-price analysis is the **travel-cost approach.** This method takes advantage of the fact that people have to incur travel costs to visit the natural resource sites. Many resources, for example, are used by people for outdoor recreational purposes. Shoreline areas are used for picnicking, swimming, and fishing; coastal and interior wetlands are used for hunting and bird watching; forest and mountain areas are used for backpacking, camping, hunting; streams, rivers, and lakes are used for boating and fishing activities; and so on. The benefits people get from these experiences depend in large part on the qualitative characteristics of the resources: how broad the beach is, how good the fishing is, or how scenic the mountain trail is. However, most (though not all) of this activity takes place outside the market, in

---

[4] The name given to some of these studies is the **hedonic price approach.**

the sense that it does not involve direct transactions between recreators and private resource suppliers. So there are few direct market prices that could be used to estimate recreational demands for the resources.

Although recreators do not often pay direct admission charges to these resources, as they would going into a movie theater for example, they do normally have to spend money to make the visits. The costs of visiting a national forest, or a coastal wetland, or a distant lake, are the costs of traveling to these areas and engaging in the specific recreational activities chosen. Resource economists have developed techniques for deducing demand and benefit estimates by using these **travel costs as proxies** for the normal market prices that are used in market demand studies.

There are essentially two major components of travel costs: direct monetary costs such as fuel and en route lodging, and the value of the time that travelers require to get from home, or other point of origin, to the recreational site. Both types of cost would be expected to be higher for people living farther from the site in question. The procedure therefore is to survey visitors to recreation sites (and perhaps also nonvisitors in some cases), by asking questions in face-to-face interviews or via mail questionnaires. The surveys provide data on the number of visits (which could be zero), various components of travel costs, and relevant economic and demographic information (such as income levels, age, and educational attainment). These data can be analyzed to yield a demand curve for recreational visits.

Nonmarket Techniques

Resource economists have developed a special technique for estimating willingness to pay when direct or indirect market techniques are not available. It is called **contingent valuation,** and is a survey technique based on the straightforward idea that people's willingness to pay can be determined by asking them directly. The technique is called "contingent valuation" because it attempts to elicit peoples' valuations of contingent, or hypothetical, situations. In the absence of markets, people are essentially asked to choose as if there were a market for the resource in question.

Contingent valuation (CV) studies have been done for a long list of natural and environmental resources: endangered species, wilderness congestion, fishing experiences, clean air, view-related natural amenities, the recreational quality of beaches, and others. In fact, CV methods have spread into nonenvironmental areas, for example, the value of programs for reducing the risks of heart attacks, the value of supermarket price information, and the value of a seniors' companion program. Over time the method has been developed and refined to give what many regard as reasonably reliable measures of the benefits of a variety of public goods, especially environmental quality.

The steps in a CV analysis are the following:

CHAPTER 9: THE VALUATION OF NATURAL RESOURCES

1 Identification and description of the environmental quality characteristic to be evaluated
2 Identification of respondents to be approached, including sampling procedures used to select respondents
3 Design and application of a survey questionnaire through personal, phone, or mail interviews (in recent years, focus groups have sometimes been used)
4 Analysis of results and aggregation of individual responses to estimate values for the group affected by the environmental change

The central purpose of the questionnaire is to elicit from respondents their estimate of what the natural resource is worth to them. In economic terms this means getting them to reveal the maximum amount they would be willing to pay rather than go without the resource in question. A number of techniques have been used to get this response. The most obvious is to ask people outright to provide the amount with no prompting or probing on the part of the interviewer. Other approaches include using a bidding game, where the interviewer starts with a bid at a low level and progressively increases the value until the user indicates that their limit has been reached. Alternatively, the interviewer could start with a high figure and lower it to find where the respondent's threshold value is located. Another method is to give the respondents printed response cards with a range of values, and then ask the respondents to check off their maximum willingness to pay. Exhibit 9-1 shows some examples of questions used in several contingent valuation studies.

NONUSE (PASSIVE) BENEFITS

People may gain benefits from the preservation of the Grand Canyon, or a species of wildlife, or even a regionally significant wetland, even though they never expect to visit the Canyon or the wetland, or to directly observe the wildlife. These are called **nonuse benefits.** The evidence that benefits of this type exist is easy to see. A number of environmental organizations, the most widely known probably being the **Nature Conservancy,** raise money from donations to purchase and preserve important resource areas; it is highly unlikely that the average contributor expects to visit all the preserved sites. Thus a substantial proportion of the benefits obtained must be nonuse benefits.

We mentioned earlier some of the motives that could lie behind the existence of nonuse values and benefits.[5] Here we address the issue of how they might be measured. This is currently a topic of great controversy. There are those who feel that significant benefits will be missed if no attempt is made to measure nonuse values and include them in the overall evaluation of natural

[5] See p. 152.

SECTION FOUR: NATURAL RESOURCE ANALYSIS

EXHIBIT 9-1

EXAMPLES OF QUESTIONS IN CONTINGENT VALUATION STUDIES

Study to Estimate Certain Benefits of Better Water Quality in the Connecticut River

1 Have you heard about the Connecticut River salmon restoration program?
2 Did you make any donations for wildlife management or preservation last year?
3 Suppose that a private foundation is formed to take private donations and use them to support salmon restoration. What is the maximum donation you would make to this foundation?
4 What is your age?
5 How much money do you spend on entertainment each month?

Study to Estimate the Benefits of Outdoor Recreation in Northern New England

1 What is your favorite outdoor activity?
2 Please imagine that you have some time to enjoy the outdoor activity you gave in Question 1. Assume that the following options are the ONLY ones available. Please rate EACH option by using 5 for the option that you would DEFINITELY CHOOSE and a 1 for any option(s) that you would DEFINITELY NOT CHOOSE. If you are not sure, use 2, 3, or 4 to indicate the likelihood that you would choose each option.

OPTION 1:	OPTION 2:	OPTION 3:	OPTION 4:
Stay Home	Go to state park in Vermont	Go to Green Mt. National Forest	Go to White Mt. National Forest
	No garbage pickup Pit toilets 0 increase in wildlife population $1 access fee/visit	Full garbage pickup Pit toilets 25% increase in wildlife population $5 access fee/visit	Full garbage pickup Flush toilets 0 increase in wildlife population $2 access fee/visit
1 2 3 4 5 would would not do definitely do	1 2 3 4 5 would would not do definitely do	1 2 3 4 5 would would not do definitely do	1 2 3 4 5 would would not do definitely do

3 What is your age? _____ (number of years)

4 Are you: _____Female? or _____Male?

5 Excluding yourself, how many family members live with you? _____ (number of people)

---

resource benefits. There are others who think that nonuse values are largely insignificant compared to use values and that attempts to include them will normally lead to the inflation of total benefit estimates.

One possibility is to interpret the contributions that people make to groups such as the Nature Conservancy as estimates of the social benefits flowing from preservation of important natural resources. Nature Conservancy is a na-

CHAPTER 9: THE VALUATION OF NATURAL RESOURCES

EXHIBIT 9-2

THE OREGON WATER TRUST

In Oregon, as in most western states, water rights are something to fight over. One general source of conflict is between people who benefit from traditional water uses like irrigation and those who place greater value on instream uses. In 1987 Oregon passed a law that defined instream water rights. These are water rights that enhance fish, wildlife, habitat, recreation, water quality and navigation; the rights are defined for specific points or sections of streams, and are held in the same legal regard as other beneficial uses. What this does is create the incentives for people to acquire and hold these rights, thus assuring higher instream flows than would otherwise be the case.

In response to this new law the Oregon Water Trust (OWT) was formed in 1993, by a small group of individuals representing agricultural, environmental, legal and tribal interests. OWT's mission is to acquire water rights "through gift, lease, or purchase, and commit these water rights under the Oregon law to instream flows. . . ." Between 1994 and 1998 OWT spent $284,000 to purchase water rights and acquired an ad-

ditional $370,000 worth of water rights through donations. The OWT also leases water rights for shorter periods of time. They focus their efforts on small-scale transactions and negotiate primarily with individual farmers, ranchers, and landowners. At present they are also limiting their activity to a relatively small number of river basins in Oregon.

The OWT was helped in its original formation by a grant from the Northwest Area Foundation, a private group that helps nonprofit groups pursue innovative solutions to public problems. "Private foundations provide 90 percent of its operational budget, and corporations and individuals the remaining 10 percent. Roughly two-thirds of its acquisition budget comes from the private sector, and public funds provide the rest." These public funds come from agencies at the local, state, and federal levels.

Source: This information was taken from: Erin Schiller, "The Oregon Water Trust," Center for Private Conservation, Washington, DC, November 1998.

---

tional (in fact international) group; there are others of this scope, and there are many other regional and local groups that pursue essentially the same agenda and activities. Exhibit 9-2 discusses one such group, the Oregon Water Trust (OWT), whose basic purpose is the acquisition of water rights. OWT obtains funds from a variety of sources: individuals, private firms, private foundations, and public agencies. Clearly, these funds are an indication of the existence of social benefits coming from instream water flows relative to traditional water uses. And the fact that this is a somewhat local group helps pinpoint these benefits to a particular set of rivers and streams in Oregon. On the other hand, a large portion of the benefits from preserving instream flows may be direct use values accruing primarily to recreators; it is unclear how much of the total contributions made to OWT can be attributable to nonuse benefits produced by these particular streams and rivers.

Another potential problem with using contributions as a measure of willingness to pay for nonuse benefits is that the preserved resources that generate

SECTION FOUR: NATURAL RESOURCE ANALYSIS

them are essentially public goods. There is no feasible means of excluding would-be beneficiaries when what is at issue is nonuse benefits, based on the simple knowledge that a resource has been preserved. When public goods are involved, private, market-related economic exchanges will undersupply the goods in question. Thus, there are conceptual reasons for thinking that private contributions to conservancy-type organizations will understate the nonuse values flowing from the resources they seek to preserve.

Since nonuse benefits are, almost by definition, independent of such factors as location or the consumption of other specific goods or services, hedonic and travel cost techniques are of no use in trying to measure them. This means that the only practicable means of assessing their magnitude is with **contingent valuation.** Contingent valuation studies have been controversial when measuring use values; they have been even more controversial when applied to nonuse values. This is because some of the problems inherent in the CV method become more acute in the case of nonuse benefits. Some of these are the following:

1 In the case of use values, beneficiaries may be presumed to be familiar with the resource whose valuation is being sought, through present or past contact with that resource. In the case of nonuse benefits, direct contact is not necessary, though it may have occurred in the past. Thus, there may be more ambiguity about the natural resource being evaluated, and the CV may be obtaining evidence of a general attitude rather than the valuation of a specific resource.

2 In many cases a person may experience both use and nonuse benefits from a natural resource. The difficulty then becomes how to distinguish between the two sources of value. A person living in proximity to a national park, for example, may get nonuse benefits from the knowledge that the park area is preserved and may also get direct use benefits from hiking or hunting in the area.

3 Where use values are concerned, it may be relatively easy to find out who the prime beneficiaries are. For visitors to a national park, for example, a survey will reveal the demographic characteristic of users. But this is not possible when nonuse benefits are involved. Thus, there is a real question about how wide the survey net should be cast to identify nonuse beneficiaries. If we are dealing with a certain species of wildlife in the Rocky Mountains, for example, should we survey people in the local community, the state, the region, or the country?

These, and other problems, make CV studies of nonuse values difficult, but not impossible. Researchers have investigated the magnitude of many nonuse values, such as the preservation of individual species of wildlife; the preservation of sites that have ecological or historical importance; and the characteristics of specific sites, such as water quality in a particular river or lake. Table 9-1 lists some of these studies.

Field: Natural Resource
Economics — An
Introduction

IV. Natural Resource
Analysis

9. The Valuation Of Natural
Resources

© The McGraw–Hill
Companies, 2003

CHAPTER 9: THE VALUATION OF NATURAL RESOURCES

TABLE 9-1
SEVERAL STUDY RESULTS DEALING WITH WILLINGNESS
TO PAY BY NONUSERS OF RESOURCES

Resource:	Protection of land through wilderness designation
Authors:	Walsh, Loomis, and Gillman
Results:	Respondents (expected nonusers) were willing to pay between $14 and $19 just to preserve areas in wilderness states.
Resource:	Humpback whales
Authors:	Samples, Dixon, and Gowen
Results:	Respondents' (nonusers') mean willingness to pay to preserve whales was between $35 and $60.
Resource:	Bald eagles and stripped shiners
Authors:	Boyle and Bishop
Results:	Respondents (expected nonusers) were willing to pay between $4 and $6 for shiner preservation and between $10 and $75 for eagle preservation programs.
Resource:	Whooping cranes
Authors:	Bowker and Stoll
Results:	Nonusers expressed willingness to pay between $21 and $70 for preservation programs.
Resource:	Salmon fishery in Fraser River Basin of British Columbia and fishing resources in southeastern United States.
Authors:	Described by Fisher and Raucher
Results:	Nonuse values approximately half of user values.
Resource:	Bald eagles, wild turkeys, Atlantic salmon, coyote
Authors:	Stevens et al.
Results:	Ninety-three percent of total willingness to pay was identified as nonuse value, only seven percent was use value.

Sources: Bowker, J. M., and John R. Stoll, "Use of Dichotomous Choice, Non-Market Methods to Value the Whooping Crane Resource," *American Journal of Agricultural Economics,* 70(2), 1988, pp. 372–381; Boyle, Kevin J., and Richard C. Bishop, "Valuing Wildlife in Benefit-Cost Analyses: A Case Study Involving Endangered Species," *Water Resources Research,* 23(5), 1987, pp. 943–950; Fisher, Ann, and Robert Raucher, "Intrinsic Benefits of Improved Water Quality: Conceptual and Empirical Perspectives," in *Advances in Applied Microeconomics,* V. Kerry Smith and Ann Dryden Witte (eds.), Greenwich, CT, JAI Press, 1984; Samples, Karl C., John A. Dixon, and Marsha M. Gowen, "Information Disclosure, and Endangered Species Valuation," *Land Economics,* 62(3), 1986, pp. 306–312; Stevens, Thomas H., Jaime Echeverria, Ronald J. Glass, Tim Hager, and Thomas A. More, "Measuring the Existence Value of Wildlife: What Do CVM Estimates Really Show?" *Land Economics,* 67(4), November 1991, pp. 390–400; Walsh, Richard G., John B. Loomis, and Richard A. Gillman, "Valuing Option, Existence, and Bequest Demands for Wilderness," *Land Economics,* 60(1), 1984, pp. 14–29.

MEASURING COSTS

We switch now to the cost side of benefit-cost analysis. All actions have cost consequences, whether this be costs of the obvious sort in classical natural resource extraction or costs of a more subtle kind when we consider resource preservation alternatives. It is easy to overlook the cost side, sometimes under the mistaken belief that "costs don't matter," or under the equally mistaken belief that they are easy to estimate. But costs often are difficult to determine accurately, and they do matter. The results of a benefit-cost analysis can be affected equally by over- or underestimating costs, as by over- or underestimating benefits. Furthermore, in the political realm it is almost axiomatic that options will be selected in the heat of political controversy and enthusiasm, without sufficient regard to the true social costs (or benefits) of the alternatives. All the more reason why the cost side of the analysis should be treated with as much importance as the benefit side.

General Issues

Cost analysis can be done on many levels. At its simplest it focuses on the cost to a single community or firm of a natural resource project or regulation, such as a new state park or a new community wetlands preservation plan. Although these cost estimates may still be hard to produce, the task is made relatively easy by the fact that the geographical extent or the physical nature of the programs is limited and well defined. At a higher level there are regulations or programs that affect relatively large groups: all timbering companies in the Northwest, all farmers in California, all consumers in the Northeast, for example. Here the job of collecting cost data is multiplied: Some sampling is usually necessary, and this will be complicated by a substantial amount of heterogeneity among the groups that must be studied. At the highest level are national cost estimates, for example, of the effects on the American economy of an international oil embargo.

There are two avenues through which social costs are incurred: the **opportunity costs** of using resources[6] in certain ways, and the **costs of price changes.** As discussed earlier,[7] the opportunity cost of using resources in a particular way is the highest-valued alternative use to which they might otherwise have been put. This alternative value is what society forgoes in using the resources in the specified fashion. Note the word "society." Costs are incurred by all sorts of individuals, firms, agencies, industries, and groups. Each will have its own perspective, and each will focus on those costs that directly impinge upon them. As we stressed earlier, social costs include **private costs** plus all other costs that are incurred as a result of resource use, that is, all **external** costs. Most people have an instinctive feel for the concept of opportunity cost;[8] the problem arises when we try to determine what that cost is in concrete circumstances. When an input has a market price, and the market is reasonably competitive, this price will normally be a good measure of its opportunity cost.

Price changes can create costs to producers and consumers that are somewhat different in concept than costs in the form of real resource expenditures.

[6] Remember that "resources" is a word that can have two meanings; it can be a short way of saying "natural resources," or it can be used as a general reference analogous to the word "inputs." Here it is being used in the second sense.

[7] See Chapter 4.

[8] For example, the opportunity cost of time is the relevant concept when allocating a fixed amount of time among several tasks.

CHAPTER 9: THE VALUATION OF NATURAL RESOURCES

In order to measure these costs, we need good data on the supply and demand functions for the markets on which prices change. Regulations on clear-cutting, for example, will change the costs of timbering and perhaps the price of lumber. Knowledge of the supply and demand factors on the timber market is necessary to predict these effects. It is conceivable that the appropriate statistical studies have been done to analyze these factors. If this is not the case, another approach is to carry out an engineering study to predict the effects of the regulation. We deal with these issues at greater length below.

Costs of Physical Facilities

Perhaps the easiest case to deal with is estimating the costs of a project that involves constructing and operating some type of physical facility like dams (and, in recent years, dam removal), irrigation works, parks with trail systems and visitor centers, animal refuges and restoration activities, or beach restoration activities. Most of the relevant costs here relate to the opportunity costs of the inputs used in the project, the **capital costs** of initial construction, and the annual **operating and maintenance** costs that will extend over the life of the project. The source of data on costs of this type is normally **engineering** or **scientific** authorities who can specify in detail the inputs needed for various phases of the projects.

Costs of Public Regulation

A great deal of public activity on natural resource issues is not related to physical projects, but to **public regulation** of private actions. Cost estimation in this case is usually more difficult because it requires knowing something about the costs of the private operations that will be affected by the regulations. As examples, consider the various regulations that public agencies pursue with private timber companies including specifications for clear-cutting, the use of chemicals in forest cultivation, and leaving intact certain wildlife habitat areas. The impacts of these regulations will work through shifting the costs of these private companies. This adds a major complication, however, since the cost shifts, by changing supply functions, may lead to output changes. This complicates the task of determining the costs of the regulation.

As an example, consider Figure 9-3. This diagram might depict the situation, for example, of a small regional forestry operation where local timbering companies are faced with a new regulation designed to protect the habitat of an endangered animal. Since this is a local impact only, it is not expected to have any influence on the national price of wood. In other words, the demand curve for timber harvested by the collection of local companies is flat, as depicted by the line marked D. Before the regulation their marginal cost curve, equal to their supply curve, was $MC_1 = S_1$. Thus, total output was q_1, total costs were $c + f$.

SECTION FOUR: NATURAL RESOURCE ANALYSIS

FIGURE 9-3
Costs of a Regulation on Timber Harvesters

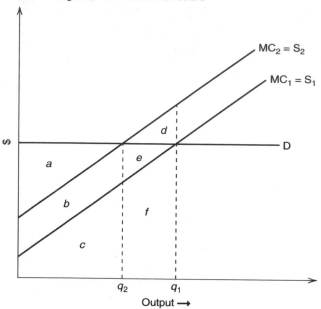

The effect of the regulation is to increase the costs of harvesting timber, depicted by an upward shift in the marginal cost curve to $MC_2 = S_2$. If output were unchanged, the total increase in costs would be measured by the area $b + e + d$. But the added costs, in the face of a constant price, will normally lead to output adjustments. In the depicted case, output would fall to q_2. One way of getting at the significance of the change is to look at net benefits before and after the change. Before the regulation they were $a + b + e$, whereas afterward, they are a; thus, there was a reduction in net benefits of $b + e$. Note that this is a number smaller than the cost increase for a constant output $b + e + d$. By the lowering of output, a part of the cost increase that would have been incurred in the absence of output change is avoided.

The information needed to measure the cost implications of the regulation includes (1) the extent to which the marginal cost/supply function will be shifted up by the regulation and (2) the extent of any output adjustments that firms will make as a result of the cost changes. Where does one get the cost data necessary to analyze the cost structure of an industry? Normally from the industry itself. Much of the data can be generated by **cost surveys,** in which questionnaires are sent to all, or a sample of, the firms in the industry in question. In effect, questionnaires are sent out to these firms asking them to supply information on the number of employees, processes used, costs of energy and materials, and so on. With a sufficiently detailed questionnaire and a reasonably high response rate by firms, researchers hope to get a good idea of basic

FIGURE 9-4
Effects of a Regulation on Consumers

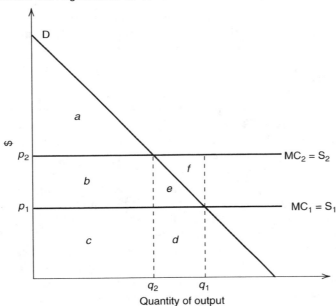

cost conditions in the industry and how they might be affected by regulations on natural resource use. Because the regulated firms themselves are the source of much of the cost data used to develop the regulations, there is clearly a question whether these firms will supply accurate data. By overstating the potential costs of adjusting to regulations, firms may hope to convince agencies to promulgate weaker regulations than they would if the agencies had an accurate idea of costs.

Another problem with cost surveys is that they are usually better at getting information on past data than on future costs under new regulations. Firms can probably report past cost data with more reliability than they can estimate future costs. But historical data may not be a good guide to the future, especially because environmental regulations, almost by definition, confront firms with novel situations and because future technological change can impact costs in major ways. In these cases it is common to supplement survey data with technical engineering data that can be better adapted to costing out the new techniques and procedures that firms may adopt.

Note that in Figure 9-4 the regulation led to an output reduction from q_1 to q_2. What this shows is the extent to which resources currently used in this industry will no longer be needed there. Certain inputs, for example energy and various types of material inputs, will be easily reduced. But inputs like labor are much more complicated. In a reasonably full employment economy, one could expect labor that is withdrawn from one industry to switch to another

SECTION FOUR: NATURAL RESOURCE ANALYSIS

industry; the bigger the economy we are dealing with, the easier this will be. But adjustment problems, some temporary and others longer-run, can be quite challenging in cases like this. Not only is direct income from the affected industries reduced, but the secondary effects on support and service industries can be impacted. It is adjustment costs of this type that have made natural resource management politically sensitive in many cases, such as the reduction of parts of the timbering industry in response to forest regulation and the reduction in a fishing fleet in response to attempts to reduce overfishing.

Regulatory programs often produce other types of costs in the form of **increased prices** paid by consumers. The model of Figure 9-3 did not have this, because it was assumed that only a segment of a much larger industry was involved, and so the regulation would not be expected to affect output price. But with regulations affecting all, or a substantial portion, of an industry, consumers may experience **price effects.** These are costs in a sense different from the notion of opportunity costs. When prices paid by consumers change, there is a gain or loss in welfare: a gain to consumers if prices drop and a loss to consumers if they go up. Figure 9-4 gives the relevant analysis. Here there is a downward-sloping demand function and horizontal marginal cost/supply relationship. The initial price-quantity situation is p_1, q_1. A regulation is now enacted that has the effect of lifting the marginal cost curve to $MC_2 = S_2$. Price now rises to p_2, which makes consumers worse off. By how much? If we took the original quantity q_1 and multiplied it by the price increase, we would get an amount equal to $b + e + f$. But here again, we would expect consumers to respond to the price increase. In the figure, quantity drops to q_2. Looking at the change in net benefits brought on by the cost increase, we see that this comes out to be $b + e$.[9] The adjustment in quantity reduces the cost to consumers relative to what would have been the case with no quantity change.

To estimate this cost, especially to predict it ex ante, we must know not only what the change in cost will be, but also the **conditions of demand** in the industry. This is an important lesson. To measure the costs of the regulation, we must know both costs and the demand function facing the industry that we are studying.

SUMMARY

This chapter is devoted to a discussion of how analysts actually measure the benefits and costs flowing from specific natural resource utilization situations. Benefits can be classified as **consumptive** vs. **nonconsumptive** and as **use** vs. **nonuse.** Nonuse benefits of natural resources consist of **option, existence,** and **bequest** values. In many cases, **direct market prices** can be used to measure benefits of different types of natural resource use; sometimes these prices must

---

[9] Net benefits before the change are $(a + b + c + d + e) - (c + d) = a + b + e$. After the change they are $(a + b + c) - (b + c) = a$. Thus, the change is $b + e$.

CHAPTER 9: THE VALUATION OF NATURAL RESOURCES

be adjusted to take into account external costs and benefits. Market prices may also be used **indirectly,** in cases where natural resource use is closely connected to the consumption of a marketed commodity (e.g., the value of open space in the vicinity of houses). Travel cost analysis has frequently been used to estimate the benefits of outdoor recreation. For nonmarket benefits the most commonly used method is **contingent valuation,** which is essentially a survey technique in which respondents are asked directly about their willingness to pay for using natural resources in certain ways.

Cost measurement often seems easier than benefit measurement, but accurate cost estimates can often be difficult to estimate. In cases where physical-type projects are involved (e.g., dams, wildlife refuges, irrigation works) the relevant concept is **opportunity costs,** being the value the inputs could have produced in their next best alternative use. For regulatory-type programs (e.g., regulations on clear-cutting, regulations on access to fisheries), there may be both opportunity cost changes, as firms respond to the regulations, and costs to consumers stemming from **price changes** in markets for goods and services.

KEY TERMS

Active (use) values
Passive (nonuse) values
Consumptive values
Nonconsumptive values
Option values
Existence values
Bequest values

Market prices as measure of value
Shadow (accounting) prices
Hedonic analysis
Travel cost analysis
Contingent valuation
Opportunity costs
Costs of price changes

QUESTIONS FOR FURTHER DISCUSSION

1 Distinguish between use values and nonuse values in the specific case of preserving the quality of water in an underground aquifer. How might you measure the different types of benefits in this case?

2 A proposal is being made to ban the use of a particular type of gear used by vessels engaged in a certain saltwater fishery. Indicate conceptually how costs would be measured in this case. How might the necessary data be obtained?

3 What is the conceptual relationship between use values, consumptive values, and market values?

4 A proposal has been put forward to remove a dam on a river, which currently produces hydroelectric power. You have been hired to estimate the costs (not the benefits) of this action. What are the main types of costs in this case, and how might you go about measuring each type?

5 What types of questions might you put in a contingent valuation study being done to estimate the benefits of limiting timber harvesting in certain areas so as to preserve habitat for the spotted owl?

SECTION FOUR: NATURAL RESOURCE ANALYSIS

6 Select one of the scenarios given at the beginning of the chapter. Propose a way of answering the question posed in the scenario using one (or more) of the techniques discussed in the chapter.

USEFUL WEB SITES

See the material under nonmarket valuation at

- Resources for the Future (http://www.rff.org)

The USEPA's program in economy and environment has many links to work on benefits measurement:

- (http://www.epa.gov/docs/oppe/eaed/eedhmpg.htm)

Many countries have developed programs in benefits measurement, for example,

- Australian Bureau of Agricultural and Resource Economics (http://www.abare.gov.au).

For a private firm in the valuation business, see

- Damage Valuation Associates, Environmental Damage Valuation and Cost Benefit Web Site (http://www.damagevaluation.com)

SELECTED READINGS

Bateman, Ian, and Ken Willis (eds.): *Valuing Environmental Preferences: Theory and Practice of the Contingent Valuation Method in the U.S., EC, and Developing Countries,* Oxford University Press, Oxford, England.

Batie, Sandra, and Leonard Shabman, "Estimating the Economic Value of Wetlands," *Coastal Zone Management Journal,* Vol. 10, 1982, pp. 255–278.

Brookshire, David S., et al., "Valuing Public Goods: A Comparison of Survey and Hedonic Approaches," *American Economic Review,* 72 (1), March 1982, pp. 165–177.

Constanza, Robert, et al., "The Value of the World's Ecosystem Services and Natural Capital," *Nature,* Vol. 387, May 15, 1997, pp. 253–260.

Cummings, R. G., D. S. Brookshire, and W. D. Schulze, *Valuing Environmental Goods: An Assessment of the Contingent Valuation Method,* Rowman and Littlefield Publishers, Savage, MD, 1986.

Diamond, P., and J. Hansman: "Contingent Valuation: Is Some Number Better than No Number?" *Journal of Economic Perspectives,* Vol. 8, 1994, pp. 45–64.

Freeman, A. Myrick, III: "Nonuse Values in Natural Resource Damage Assessment," in Raymond J. Kopp and V. Kerry Smith (eds.), *Valuing Natural Resource Assets: The Economics of Natural Resource Damage Assessment,* Resources for the Future, Washington, DC, 1993, pp. 264–303.

Freeman, A. Myrick, III: *The Measurement of Environmental and Resource Values, Theory and Methods,* Resources for the Future, Washington, DC, 1993.

Hannemann, W. Michael: "Valuing the Environment through Contingent Valuation," *Journal of Economic Perspectives,* 8 (4), Fall 1994, pp. 19–44.

CHAPTER 9: THE VALUATION OF NATURAL RESOURCES

Hannemann, W. Michael, "Preface: Notes on the History of Environmental Valuation in the U.S.," in Stale Narud (ed.), *Pricing the Environment, The European Experience,* Oxford University Press, London, 1992, pp. 9–35.

Mitchell, R. C., and R. T. Carson: *Using Surveys to Value Public Goods: The Contingent Valuation Method,* Resources for the Future, Washington, DC, 1989.

Portney, Paul: "The Contingent Valuation Debate: Why Economists Should Care," *Journal of Economic Perspectives,* 8 (4), Fall 1994, pp. 3–18.

Smith, V. Kerry: "Lightning Rods, Dart Boards and Contingent Valuation," *Natural Resources Journal,* 1994.

Smith, V. Kerry: *Estimating Economic Values for Nature: Methods for Non-Market Valuation,* Edward Elgar, Cheltenham, England, 1996.

CHAPTER 14

LAND ECONOMICS

Land is the ubiquitous natural resource. Human beings are land-dwelling creatures; for them land is both a **spatial resource,** providing space to live, work, travel, and play, and a **productive resource** from which they draw their sustenance of food, fiber, and other materials. This chapter focuses on some basic **land economics,** which draws on economic principles to examine and understand human decisions about land use.

Table 14-1 shows some of the major land-use categories and how the amounts of land devoted to these uses in the contiguous United States have changed over the last five decades. As one would expect, urban land has increased by almost 300 percent during this period, and land devoted to transportation has increased by about 10 percent. As a percent of total land, these two uses (urban and transportation) represented about 2 percent of the total in 1945 and 4.4 percent of the total in 1992. This is a national (in the contiguous United States sense) average, and does not reflect regional variation. The percentage would be much lower in the mountain states and much higher in the northeastern states, for example. The total amount of agricultural cropland in 1992 was quite close to the figure for 1945. Grazing land (excluding grazing land in forests) declined by about 11 percent during the period. Total forest use land declined during the period, but trends were very different for forest grazing land (a 57 percent decrease from 1947 to 1992) and forest land not grazed (a 61 percent increase during this period). Land devoted to recreation

TABLE 14-1
MAJOR USES OF LAND IN THE CONTIGUOUS 48 STATES, 1945–1992 (MILLION ACRES)

Land use*	1945 m.a.	1945 %	1954 m.a.	1954 %	1964 m.a.	1964 %	1974 m.a.	1974 %	1982 m.a.	1982 %	1992 m.a.	1992 %
Urban land	15.0	0.8	18.6	1.0	29.2	1.5	34.6	1.8	49.6	2.6	58.0	3.0
Transportation	22.6	1.2	24.5	1.3	25.8	1.4	26.0	1.4	26.4	1.4	24.8	1.3
Recreation and wildlife areas	22.6	1.2	27.5	1.4	49.7	2.6	56.9	3.0	71.1	3.8	86.9	4.5
National defense areas	24.8	1.3	27.4	1.4	29.3	1.5	22.4	1.2	21.8	1.4	18.6	1.0
Farmland												
Cropland†	450.7	23.7	465.3	24.4	443.8	23.3	464.7	24.5	468.9	24.7	459.7	24.3
Pasture and range	659.5	34.6	632.4	33.2	636.5	33.5	595.2	31.4	594.3	31.3	589.0	31.1
Miscellaneous farmland	15.1	0.8	12.2	0.1	10.5	0.5	8.0	0.4	8.0	0.4	6.2	0.3
Forest-use land‡												
Forest land grazed	345.0	18.1	301.3	15.8	223.8	11.8	178.9	9.4	157.5	8.3	145.0	7.6
Forest land not grazed	256.7	13.5	314.1	16.5	388.0	20.4	419.6	22.1	409.7	21.6	413.7	21.8
Miscellaneous other land§	93.4	4.9	80.5	4.2	53.0	3.3	90.6	4.8	88.5	4.6	92.4	4.8
Total	1,905.4	100.0	1,903.8	100.0	1,899.6	100.0	1,897.0	100.0	1,895.7	100.0	1,894.1	100.0

*Distributions may not add to totals because of rounding.
†Includes cropland harvested, crop failure land, cultivated summer fallow, cropland used for pasture, and idle cropland.
‡Land that is normally used for forestry purposes.
§Includes cemeteries, golf courses, deserts, wetlands, and miscellaneous uses not included elsewhere.
Source: U.S. Department of Agriculture, Economic Research Service, *Agricultural Resources and Environmental Indicators, 1996–1997*, Washington, DC, ERS Handbook No. 712, July 1997, p. 3.

and wildlife areas increased by 285 percent during this time and is today roughly the same in total (87 million acres) as urban and transportation land (83 million acres).

Within some of these broad categories and trends there have been some very substantial changes. In forest lands, for example, especially publicly owned forest land, there has been a very substantial dropoff recently in timbering and grazing activity and a rapid rise in recreational use. The growth in land area devoted to urban uses testifies to the trend in **urban decentralization** (sprawl), but in recent decades the nature of this trend has also changed. Decentralized **employment subcenters** and **edge cities** have appeared, which will impact on the nature of sprawl and its implications for land-use changes in the future.

The rest of the chapter takes two directions. First, we introduce some conceptual ideas about land values, efficient land use, and the workings of the land market. Then we discuss a number of specific problems in land use applying, insofar as we can, the principles of land-use economics to these issues. A list of important contemporary land-use problems would include the following:

1 **Urban sprawl** There is widespread concern in the United States, and much commentary, about the spread of suburban areas out into areas that were once farmland and forest. Is this loose, decentralized, spread-out pattern of urban/suburban growth the best? Should it be discouraged, encouraged?

2 **Resource preservation** Some of the land subject to strong development pressure has unique ecological values. Wetlands, for example, are tied into basic hydrological systems; scenic lands are well suited to public parks. How are the values of these lands to be recognized, and what steps are appropriate for their protection?

3 **Implications of land-use regulations** Public regulations to affect land use are common throughout the country, and pressure is strong to tighten these regulations to ensure certain land-use patterns. But the benefits and costs of these regulations often (usually) fall on different people. What is the efficient and fair action for society to take in cases like this?

4 **New types of regulations** Traditional land-use control regulations have been based on the police power that the Constitution gives communities to make decisions. Might other types of land-use policies give better results?

SOCIAL EFFICIENCY IN LAND USE

The first question to consider is what do we mean by a pattern of land use that is **socially efficient**? In a given region, such as a community or river basin, there is a large number of "parcels" of land. For example, if we define a parcel as equal to an acre, then the number of parcels is equal to total acreage. Any acre can be put to many purposes: such as agriculture, residential, industrial, commercial, and parks. And within each broad category there are many subcategories, single-family vs. multiple-family homes, small office buildings, light vs. heavy industry, and so on. Any particular use, located on any given acre of land, will produce a stream of net benefits extending into the future. The net social benefits produced by an acre of land is usually called rent or, more appropriately, **land rent.** The rent on a piece of land devoted to any use represents the benefits produced by that use, minus all the other nonland costs of producing these benefits. Suppose an acre of land, if used to grow potatoes, could produce $1,000 of potatoes annually at a cost (fertilizer, seed, labor, etc.) of $600. Then the annual rent this acre would produce in potato production would be $400. Suppose that if a single-family dwelling were built on the acre, it would produce annual housing services of $4,800, at a cost (operating plus annualized capital costs) of $3,900. Then the rent the acre would produce if devoted to houses would be $900 per year.

A socially efficient land-use pattern in a region is one in which each acre of land in the region is devoted to the one use that yields the maximum land rent on that acre. Since each acre is producing its maximum rent, social efficiency obviously implies that **aggregate land rent** in the whole region is at a maximum.

If all parcels of land were exactly the same, it would not matter what uses were made of each one. The interesting thing about the land resource, however, is that every land parcel is by definition unique. In any real-world setting, land will differ according to geological and hydrological characteristics. Certain acreage may be capable of producing greater agricultural rents, some acres may have a scenic view, some acreage may have topographical features that make any sort of structures very costly to build, and so on. **Productivity** differences such as these will produce differences in land rents according to the different types of uses to which the land is put. All land parcels must also be unique in terms of **location,** since no two acres can occupy the same spot. This is important because the benefits produced by a piece of land will normally depend on its location with respect to land that has complementary, or competitive, uses. The rents produced by land devoted to housing will depend on how close the land is to employment opportunities; the value of land devoted to commercial purposes will depend on the geographical location of the land in relation to other enterprises that provide essential inputs; and so on.

Compounding the problem of identifying the distribution of land uses that maximizes overall land rents is the abundant network of environmental and natural resource interrelationships that affect net benefits of nearby parcels of land. A factory built next to a group of houses may produce effects (smoke, scenic disruption) that reduce the value of the housing services, and therefore of the land rents, of these neighboring lots. Land devoted to a highway will often have impacts (noise, dust) that affect the rents of nearby land. Agricultural practices can affect neighboring land both negatively (dust, smells, contamination of groundwater) and positively (scenic values). These impacts are often what we think of as external costs and benefits, though whether they are really external or not depends on ownership factors—how property rights are distributed.

How much rent a piece of land in a particular use produces and how this rent is **distributed** among different parties are two different issues. Suppose I own a small factory and my net profits, after deducting all **nonland costs** (including the opportunity cost of my own skills and time) are $5,000. Suppose the town in which I am located charges me $1,000 per year to lease the land on which the factory sits. Then the land rent of $5,000 ends up partly ($4,000 of it) in my pocket, and partly ($1,000 of it) in the coffers of the community. Besides taxes, the distribution of land rent depends also on the state of **competition** in the various markets in which parcels of land are traded.

LAND MARKETS AND PRICES

Even in a relatively small region, the number and heterogeneity of parcels and the number of different uses to which each parcel could be put mean that the number of different ways of distributing these uses among the parcels will be extraordinarily high. How should we (i.e., society) seek to find the one land-use pattern that maximizes land rents? In the United States, as in most other countries, we rely on a **private land market** to do most of the work of determining what uses of land are located on which parcels of land. The private land market works the way all markets do: Buyers and sellers agree on the terms by which land, or sometimes just the services of land, will be transferred between them. The most important aspect of the transaction is what the price will be, because it is the price that reflects all the thousands of factors that go into determining the usefulness and desirability of using a particular piece of land for a particular purpose.

Consider a parcel of land devoted in perpetuity (or at least for a very long time) to a particular use, say, a house, or a small office building, or a public park. The use in question will generate a stream of **annual net benefits,** or annual land rents. The present value of this stream of annual rents can be written explicitly as

$$PV_R = R_0 + \frac{R_1}{1+r} + \frac{R_2}{(1+r)^2} + \frac{R_3}{(1+r)^3} + \dots$$

where R stands for annual rent and r is the discount rate. If the R's in the numerator are all the same, this sum equals R/r. Each different use of the land would generate a different PV_R. In a completely free, competitive land market, the **market price** of a parcel of land will be equal to the highest of all the different possible PV_R's associated with the different ways that the land could be used.

The reason for this is that in the bids and offers of buyers and sellers in the land market, all the potential net benefits associated with owning a piece of land will be **capitalized** into its price. Suppose, for example, a piece of land is currently used for farming, and in this use it has a value of $5,000 per acre (i.e., the present value of rents when the land is used for agriculture is $5,000). Now suppose that, because of the growth of a nearby town, the land could potentially produce a stream of rents (as house lots) with a present value of $12,000.

SECTION FIVE: APPLIED NATURAL RESOURCE PROBLEMS

If there is a competitive land market, the market price for this (and similarly situated) land will increase to $12,000, even though it is still used for farming. This is because the price will be bid upward to reflect the potential rents the land could produce, not what they happen to be producing in the short run.

Thus, all changes in the net benefits producible by a parcel of land, as long as these will accrue to the owner of that land, will get capitalized into its price. For example, suppose in an urban area steps are taken by pollution control authorities to reduce the level of air pollution. There is no direct market for clean air; people do not literally buy and sell quantities of clean air. But if cleaning up the air in the community adds $85 per year to the net benefits of living in a house there, the prices of land on which to build houses, or of land on which houses already exist, will increase to reflect the capitalized value of these new net benefits. The land prices, in other words, will increase by an amount[1] equal to

$$85 + \frac{85}{1+r} + \frac{85}{(1+r)^2} + \frac{85}{(1+r)^3} + \ldots = \frac{85}{r}$$

There are several provisos to the idea that land prices will reflect land rents. One has to do with **land taxes.** Virtually every community in the country raises a portion of its revenues through land taxes; in many cases this is by far the largest source of funds. The part of land rents that is paid in taxes will not be capitalized into its price, since these rents are not ending up in the pockets of the buyers and sellers in the private land market. Thus, communities have sometimes attempted to use differential tax rates to affect land rents and the uses to which land is put within their borders.

The other proviso is that land prices will not necessarily reflect all the net benefits associated with the use of the land. Land prices will adjust to reflect (i.e., "capitalize") all net benefits that accrue to the user of the land. But if some net benefits accrue to others, they will not be so capitalized. The best example of this is certain environmental impacts that particular land uses may have. Suppose, for example, that a certain large parcel of land is expected to be used for building a number of single-family dwellings. The price of land in this parcel will reflect all the benefits and costs that will accrue to those who end up living in the houses: amenity values (perhaps the land is close to a public park), value of time in commuting (perhaps it is near a rail commuting line), value of time to the nearest grocery store, and so on. But suppose the land is also a strategic piece of watershed and building houses on it will impact negatively (i.e., inflict costs) on others who live downstream from the

---

[1] This is based on the standard relationship for equal annual payoffs over an indefinitely long period of time:

$$\sum_{t=0}^{\infty} \frac{M_t}{(1+r)^t} = \frac{M}{r}$$

new development. These are external costs. Were they to be capitalized into the prices of the land in question, these prices would be lower (because net benefits are lowered). But because they are external costs, they will not be so capitalized. In cases like this, normal market prices of land will not accurately reflect all the social benefits and costs arising from the uses creating the externalities. By the same token, the prices of land in the proposed development may be affected by external costs and/or benefits flowing in from elsewhere. If a factory is built next to this land, for example, land prices will be pushed down because of the external costs stemming from this source.

PUBLIC POLICIES AND LAND USE

Land markets work through the private interactions of individual buyers and sellers. Groups of people, especially groups working through their governmental institutions, can affect the way land is used. We provide first a brief catalog of these means, and then set up a simple example to illustrate each one:

1 **Working through land markets:** Both public and private groups (as well as individuals, for that matter) can simply work through the **private land market;** buying, selling, exchanging, or otherwise engaging in voluntary transactions that affect the way land is used.

2 **Eminent domain:** The power of **eminent domain** essentially means the power that recognized political authorities have to condemn property for a public purpose. Condemnation involves the forced appropriation of property, and must be accompanied by **fair compensation.** This is a power possessed by federal and state governments, and usually delegated by them to local governments and to some quasi-governmental organizations, such as electric companies.

3 **Police power:** The **police power** means the power that governmental authorities have to regulate the behavior of citizens so as to ensure the health, welfare, safety, and morals of the public. This is a power of local governments, not the federal government. Police power regulations include **zoning regulations, subdivision controls** (e.g., minimum lot-size requirements), **building codes,** and **environmental regulations** (e.g., wetlands protection regulations). Whenever these police power tools are applied, the ongoing question in particular circumstances is whether they represent valid exercises of a community's right to govern itself, or "takings" of private property that are forbidden by the U.S. Constitution unless compensation is paid.

4 **Taxes:** Governments have the power to tax, and **property taxes** are an important source of tax revenues. But beyond their revenue-raising capacity, they may also be applied in such a way as to encourage or discourage certain types of land use.

The easiest way to illustrate the strengths and weaknesses of these policy approaches is to apply them to a simple example. Suppose there is a parcel of

SECTION FIVE: APPLIED NATURAL RESOURCE PROBLEMS

TABLE 14-2
LAND RENTS AND PRICES
FOR ALTERNATIVE LAND USES

Land use	Farmer	Society
	Annual land rents per acre ($)	
Agricultural	200	600
House lots	400	400
	Land price per acre ($)*	
Agricultural	4,000	12,000
House lots	8,000	8,000

*The present value of a perpetual stream of rents is equal to $PV = R/r$, where R is the rent and r is the discount rate. The numbers in the table were discounted at 5 percent.

land that is currently owned by a farmer and used to raise crops. Suppose, however, that suburban growth is encroaching into the region and that the land is also valuable as a site for a housing development. Suppose, further, that if the land is used for farming purposes, it produces substantial net benefits from two other sources besides the crop production: scenic values and wildlife protection values. These last two types of net benefits accrue to members of the broader community, however, not simply to the farmer herself.

The numbers are illustrated in Table 14-2. It shows annual flows of net benefits per acre, together with the price per acre of land if these net benefits are fully capitalized, in this case at 5 percent. Actual land prices, however, will represent only those parts of land rents that accrue to the user of the land in question. The scenic and wildlife benefits are **external** to the land user.[2] These two types of resource services are also **public goods.** Thus, land prices will not reflect these sources of value produced by the land when it is used for agricultural purposes. The farmer can maximize her wealth by converting the land from agriculture to house lots. Since land prices reflect private rent flow in these two uses, the farmer can do this simply by selling the land to a developer. Assuming competition in this market, the selling price would be $8,000 per acre, which is twice what the land would sell for if it were to be used as a farm.[3]

---

[2] In actual situations, of course, the farmer would also likely accrue a small portion of these benefits. In Florida, for example, some ranchers receive satisfaction knowing that the Florida panther inhabits their ranches. The vast bulk of the benefits, however, are external.

[3] Of course, the market may not be competitive. There may be relatively few developers to compete with one another; for example, the farmer may not have a good idea of what house lots are being sold for. This simply means that the price agreed upon by farmer and developer will lie somewhere between $4,000 and $8,000. Some of the stream of discounted rents, in other words, will end up in the bank accounts of the developer. The $8,000 is assumed to reflect the costs it would take to convert the land and build the houses; in other words, it is based on the net returns from houses.

Field: Natural Resource
Economics — An
Introduction

V. Applied Natural
Resource Problems

14. Land Economics

© The McGraw–Hill
Companies, 2003

CHAPTER 14:   LAND ECONOMICS

From the community's standpoint the maximum net benefits, or land rent, are achieved if the land is kept in agricultural uses. We are assuming, of course, that these scenic and wildlife values are known. Net benefits accruing as incomes to land users are relatively easy to measure, because they will be capitalized into land prices. But the external values will not, so other means would have to be found for estimating them. Suppose, now, that the community wishes to take steps to make sure that the land remains in agricultural use. We now consider the different ways it has of trying to achieve this.

Working through the Market

The first apparent option is for the community simply to purchase land. Of course, this might forestall the housing development, but may not preserve agriculture. Some additional steps might be needed for this, say, a lease back to the farmer so that she could continue farming the land. The advantage of this approach is that the price the community is willing to pay probably would bear some relation to the net benefits accruing to the community members from the scenic and wildlife preservation functions. On the other hand, there are the public good, free-rider problems, as mentioned above.

If the community does not purchase the land, it perhaps could be purchased by a private group. In the United States and many other countries, there are many private **conservancy groups,** whose objective is to operate in the land market to preserve ecologically sensitive land. Deriving the bulk of their funds from members' contributions, these groups then seek to purchase land areas that, in our terminology, produce substantial values in the form of ecological services; see the discussion of Exhibit 14-1.

Land preservation through purchase can often be achieved if communities or other groups purchase only partial rights from the landowner. They might purchase from the farmer only the right to develop the land, not the entire **fee simple** ownership of the land.[4] In our example, the **development right** alone is worth $4,000 per acre to the farmer. The land without this right attached to it is still worth $4,000 for agricultural purposes. So the community could forestall development by purchasing the development right for $4,000 an acre rather than the entire fee simple right for $8,000 per acre.[5]

There is another way that the private market might provide a solution to this land-use problem. If a market existed, or could be brought into being, that would allow the farmer to receive some or all of the scenic/wildlife values as revenue, then their own private wealth-maximizing decisions could

---

[4] Fee simple is a legal term meaning the entire set of use rights of a piece of land.

[5] There is a substantial caveat here. The community's ultimate objective is to preserve agriculture. Buying the development right will forestall development, but this is not the same as preserving agriculture. If at some future time the net income from farming becomes too low, the land may be abandoned rather than farmed. Of course it may still produce some benefits as abandoned land.

SECTION FIVE: APPLIED NATURAL RESOURCE PROBLEMS

EXHIBIT 14-1

USING THE MARKET TO PROTECT ECOLOGICALLY SENSITIVE LAND

One way to protect ecologically sensitive land is to make use of the land market. The most straightforward way of doing this is to purchase land that has high ecological values and hold it in preservation status. This is what conservancy organizations do.

On the national level in the United States, the **Nature Conservancy,** the **American Land Conservancy,** and the **American Farmland Trust** have active programs through which land is acquired. There are many state-level conservancy organizations (often called **land trusts**) and a great abundance of local groups who work in this way. Altogether there are probably thousands of organizations in the United States that attempt to work through the land market to protect ecologically sensitive land. They may buy land outright, purchase development rights or easements, engage in land swaps, or use other means.

Some federal agencies have also used the market to protect land. The U.S. Forest Service, for example, has an active **land swap program.** The agency and other federal natural resource agencies do not have ample funds to buy land outright, but they have been able to acquire environmentally important acreage, paying for it by swapping other land currently in their ownership inventory. The accompanying tabulation shows the number of acres involved.

Source: U.S. Department of Agriculture, Washington, DC, various years.

---

lead them voluntarily to maintain the land in agriculture. Perhaps the wildlife situation is such that hunters, fishers, or wildlife watchers would be willing to pay to have access to the wildlife resources of the farm.[6] Perhaps tourists would be willing to pay to be close to, or to participate in, actual farm operations. In some cases there may be substantial potential for market revenues of this type.

Eminent Domain

The right of **eminent domain** means the right to condemn property and acquire it for a public purpose. The legal rules of eminent domain require that the landowner be paid **just compensation** for the land. Eminent domain is used primarily to obtain land that is to be devoted to a specific and concrete public purpose, such as a highway, a powerline right of way, or a reservoir. These are essentially public facilities required for the production of what most people would regard as essential services in the modern world. Eminent domain might also be used to acquire land for a public park; in this case it is amenity services that are being produced. In our example, questions would come up as to whether amenity and wildlife values represent public purposes that would justify land condemnation.

---

[6] In the western United States, and in some European countries, private landowners in some cases can generate revenues by selling rights to fish in streams and rivers passing through their lands, or hunting rights for game animals on these lands.

CHAPTER 14: LAND ECONOMICS

Although condemnation might not be legal in our case, we can use the example to illustrate a major problem in eminent domain cases: the problem of what is **just compensation.** Courts usually define this to mean **fair market value.** This sounds quite specific, but problems can easily appear in trying to apply the idea. Which market is appropriate? The market governing the land's current use? In our example the price of agricultural land is $4,000 an acre. Or should the price be the market for a different use? In our case the market price of the land as a housing development is $8,000 an acre. Or should it be a market price adjusted for amenity values that may exist even though they don't show up in standard market prices? In this case the fair price might be something approaching $12,000 an acre.

Another issue in determining just compensation is that current owners may attach personal values to a property that exceed its current market price. Suppose the farmer in our case is one of a long line of mothers and daughters who have been born, have lived, and have died on this farm, and who have an attachment to it in excess of its current market price. The market price is, after all, a number applying to average sale prices of similar properties over some recent time period. The current owner may value it more highly than this, for any number of personal reasons. Is the market price fair in this case?[7]

Police Power

Communities have the constitutional right to exercise the **police power** to ensure conditions that promote public health, welfare, and morals. For example, they can establish speed limits, or require homeowners to fence swimming pools and keep their property picked up, or mandate local factories to avoid conditions that damage public health, and so on. They also have certain powers to regulate the way land is used. The most basic right that communities have under the police power is the power to designate the types of uses to which specific parcels of land may be put. The way this is done is through **zoning ordinances.** A typical zoning ordinance divides a community into zones or districts, and designates the types of uses that are permitted in each zone. A typical zoning plan, for example, would designate zones for single-family dwellings, multiple-family dwellings, light commercial, industrial, and so on.

The basic principle behind zoning is to regulate externalities. Certain uses, if located next to other types of uses, are likely to create external costs that would devalue the affected properties. Thus, a factory constructed in a residential area would be expected to inflict external costs in the form of noise, unsightliness, and congestion.

---

[7] Of course, if the farmer attached such a high value to the farm they might not be tempted to sell it to a developer. But the community may not have a very good idea about the strength of these values. Many farms that have been in families for generations have ended up in houses.

The biggest problem with zoning plans is that they do not address the underlying economic incentives of the situation. Suppose that the farm in our example is placed in an agricultural zone. This does nothing to change the fact that the farmer could realize a substantial increase in wealth if she could get permission to sell the farm to a developer. She could perhaps take the town to court over the zoning plan. More likely she would appeal the zoning designation, asking the local **zoning board of appeals** for a **variance** that would allow the sale to proceed despite the zoning plan. Even though the potential gain from getting a variance might be modest today, in a number of years it could be much greater if the demand for houses continues to grow.

Communities may also use the police power to make specific regulations governing the use of land within their boundaries. Many communities in the United States, for example, have laws that allow a local **conservation commission** to deny a building permit for any structure that would adversely affect wetlands or other ecologically sensitive lands. Most communities also have **planning boards,** which can legally enforce subdivision regulations, such as requirements for streets, sidewalks, and sewers. The regulatory approach to land-use control involves an ongoing struggle between two ideas: the **rights and responsibilities of communities** to encourage conditions that are conducive to the public welfare, and the **rights and freedoms of private individuals** to use and enjoy their property in ways they see fit, without hindrance from political authorities. The struggle has seen a long series of court battles and legal pronouncements that have evolved over time as people have changed and as the problems faced by communities have changed. The conflict centers on the **takings clause** of the U.S. Constitution, and it is of sufficient importance that we devote a section to it later in this chapter.

For now, however, we return to our simple land-use example and consider the last type of policy approach that a community might take to affect land use.

Land Taxation

Communities typically levy **property taxes** to raise government revenues. Taxes affect the flows of the net benefits landowners receive from land in particular uses, so taxes can also affect the incentive landowners have for choosing one use over another. Property taxes are usually set at some proportion of the **appraised value** of a property. The appraised value, in turn, is usually based on the supposed market value of the properties. It is "supposed" because for properties not on the market, which includes most of them, a market value will have to be estimated by comparing them with properties that have recently been traded.

Property taxation strategies are often used on the rural/urban fringe, where the problem is the conversion of land, usually from agricultural uses to domestic uses. One technique that has been employed by many communities is "use-value taxation." Suppose the community in our example is seeking to keep the farm in agriculture. If the farmland is taxed at its market value, this

Field: Natural Resource
Economics — An
Introduction

V. Applied Natural
Resource Problems

14. Land Economics

© The McGraw–Hill
Companies, 2003

would presumably mean basing the tax on what it would expect to sell for if it were devoted to a housing development. In the example this is $8,000 per acre. A way of reducing the tax burden of the farmer, and thus supposedly making it easier for her to continue the farm is to base the tax on its value in current use, or use value. This would be $4,000 per acre, which would imply a tax bill only half as large as if the tax were based on market value.

If land prices are rising rapidly on the rural/urban frontier, the modest effect on farm net income implied by use-value taxation may not be sufficient to outweigh the potential wealth gain that land sale and conversion to houses would produce. Another drawback of some use-value taxation programs has been that by reducing the costs of holding land prior to actually developing it, it can increase the incentive for developers to purchase agricultural land and target it for eventual development. The tax program essentially reduces the developer's cost of holding the land. To reduce this incentive many use-value tax programs require land developers to repay back taxes that were saved by holding the land in agriculture. But the financial penalty of this type of procedure, especially in the face of briskly rising land prices, may not be strong enough to reduce the overall incentives of the practice.

LAND-USE ECONOMICS AND THE "TAKINGS" ISSUE

The fifth amendment to the U.S. Constitution contains the following language: "No person shall be . . . deprived of life, liberty, or property, without due process of law; nor shall private property be taken for a public use, without just compensation." It is clear that this language authorizes governments to take title to private property, provided that it be for the **public purpose** and that it be accompanied by **just compensation.** Eminent domain cases of this type usually involve physical takings, where land, in other words, is taken for the construction of a school, or road, or reservoir. We discussed above the issue of defining **just compensation.** In a number of recent instances of the community exercise of their police powers, however, landowners have argued that the **regulations** have the effect of taking their property, even though there may be no physical invasion of the property. If they are takings, then the Constitution requires that there be a clear public purpose and that the landowners be compensated. In the absence of the compensation, the regulations would be regarded as an unconstitutional taking of private property.

The "takings" issue raises the following question: Under what conditions will a local land-use regulation amount, in effect, to an unconstitutional taking of private property and require, as a result, either just compensation for the effects of the regulation or a rescinding of the regulation by the authority that issued it. Property rights proponents, who wish the language to be interpreted strictly, take the position that any regulation that reduces the value of a property right ought to be considered a taking. Advocates of more active public regulation take the position that communities ought to have leeway to enforce

SECTION FIVE: APPLIED NATURAL RESOURCE PROBLEMS

a wide range of regulations for the public good without having to face the financial burden of paying compensation to affected landowners.

Thoughts and opinions on the interpretation of the takings clause have gone back and forth over the decades and centuries. The final arbiter has been the U.S. Supreme Court, which over the years has rendered many decisions on takings cases. The content of these decisions has reflected both the nature of the cases and the jurisprudential views of changing members of the Court. The most recent case on the takings issue was the **Lucas decision** relative to a conflict in a coastal region of South Carolina.[8] Going into the case, there was reasonably widespread agreement with the view that public regulation via the police power is warranted as long as it does not go "too far," but if a regulation does go beyond some point, it constitutes a taking. The question is, where is that point.

Mr. Lucas had purchased two beachfront lots in 1986, for $975,000. Nearby lots had already been developed with condominiums, and he fully expected to be able to build similar structures on his lots. The lots were not in any publicly recognized critical area, and therefore a permit to develop was not required. Two years later, however, the South Carolina legislature passed the Beachfront Management Act, which effectively prohibited the construction of any occupiable improvements on the lots in question. Lucas sued, on grounds that the regulations effectively denied him all economically valuable use of the lots. The trial court in South Carolina agreed, but the South Carolina Supreme Court reversed, on the grounds that no compensation was required for regulations meant to prevent serious harm to the public.

The U.S. Supreme Court, however, reversed the South Carolina decision, taking the position that the regulation did in fact constitute a taking. The Court based this decision on several grounds:

1 That the regulation essentially deprived Lucas of the entire economic value of the property, that is, that it rendered the land essentially valueless to Lucas

2 That when Lucas purchased the property, there was no prohibition in place, and that, while normal land transactions must be concluded in the light of some possible future regulatory constraints on the land, Lucas had no good reason in this case to expect that the subsequent regulation would render the land totally valueless to him

3 That the Beach-front Management Act was overly vague in terms of the specific social harms it was attempting to avoid and the general types of land-use prohibitions that were necessary to accomplish this

The takings issue will continue to be politically and jurisprudentially controversial in the future. It is a major line of collision between the rights of individuals to be free of outside political interference and the rights of communities to constrain individual behavior in the name of the public good.

---

[8] *Lucas v. South Carolina Coastal Council*, 505 U.S. 1003, 1992.

LAND RENT AND PRICE GRADIENTS

We have discussed how the prices of land ultimately are determined by the maximum potential land rents flowing from parcels of land devoted to particular uses. This also implies that the uses to which land will be put in practice will be related to the prices of land. So by looking at spatial patterns of land rents and land prices, we can (usually) understand land-use patterns as they actually have developed or as they are likely to develop in the future. One common application of this idea is understanding the typical ways that cities develop spatially. Suppose we identify three potential uses of land in a region: commercial (office buildings, small factories), residential (single-family homes) and agricultural. And suppose we consider the capitalized land rents that a parcel of land would produce in each of these uses, as a function of the **distance** of the parcel from the center of the city.

Take commercial uses first. We would normally expect that the net return to land used for commercial purposes would be much higher in the center of town than farther out. If we assumed, for illustrative purposes, that we had a city surrounded by land of more or less equal geographical characteristics, we might expect a commercial **rent gradient** like that labeled as CRG in Figure 14-1. Commercial land rents are highest in the downtown area, where costs of business are reduced by the closeness among buyers and sellers, where communications are the quickest, and where distance to shipping nodes is the least. As the distance from downtown increases, potential commercial land rents fall because of the weakening of these factors, sometimes called **agglomeration economies.** So CRG is downward-sloping and rather steep.

FIGURE 14-1
Commercial, Domestic, and Agricultural Rent Gradients, and the Spatial Pattern of Economic Activity

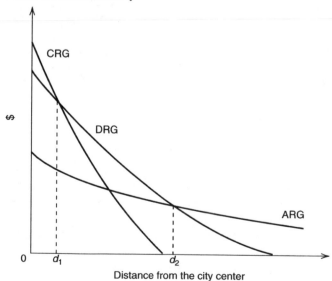

The DRG function shows potential land rents from land devoted to housing. These are also highest in town and decline with distance, primarily because of transportation costs and their impact on commuting costs. But the domestic rent gradient starts at a lower level and declines less rapidly than CRG with distance. Similarly, ARG (the agricultural rent gradient) is highest close in and declines with distance, again for reasons of higher transportation costs. But this is the flattest of these rent gradients; it starts rather low and declines only slowly with distance.

The critical distances are the points where the rent gradients cross. At a distance of d_1, the rents from commercial and domestic parcels are the same. On land closer to downtown than this, commercial rents exceed domestic rents. Similarly, at d_2, ARG = DRG and parcels closer to town are characterized by the fact that rents from land devoted to housing exceed rents of land devoted to agriculture.

If these are accurate depictions of the three rent gradients, we can now predict that the land-use pattern around the city will be the following: From the center to a distance of d_1, land will be devoted primarily to commercial uses. At d_1, the dominant land use will change to houses. The housing zone will extend from d_1 to d_2. At d_2 we will have the **urban/rural fringe,** the point where housing developments stop and agricultural uses begin.

This is a typical urban/rural land-use pattern in and around many cities. These rent gradients create a **land price** gradient, that is, a spatial profile of market prices of land that consists essentially of the maximal portions of each of the underlying rent gradients. From the center to distance d_1, prices would reflect CRG; between d_1 and d_2, land prices would reflect DRG; and from d_2 outward, prices would reflect ARG.

Rent gradients and land price gradients in the real world, however, are never as smooth as those depicted in the figure. Nor are the boundaries between land-use types as sharp and clear as those depicted at d_1 and d_2. Geographical factors such as hills and bodies of water intervene, highway patterns can create irregular patterns of travel cost, and so on. But the basic pattern is accurate. By considering how changes in the underlying factors give rent gradients their basic shapes, we can get an understanding of how they will affect overall land-use patterns in and around urban areas.

THE ECONOMICS OF URBAN SPRAWL

We can use some of these insights to investigate the phenomenon of **urban sprawl.** Sprawl is usually used in a negative sense, as something that is not desirable. From the previous discussion we have seen that there is a natural tendency in any urban area to progress from high-price, high-density commercial use in the city center to low-density, lower-priced lands in the suburbs, with a transition to agriculture on the urban/rural fringe. Sprawl refers essentially to a situation in which the housing rental/land-price gradient has an overly shallow slope such that the entire urban area spreads over a very large region and the rural fringe is pushed out a long way into agricultural areas.

This leads to the conversion of large amounts of increasingly remote agricultural and forest land, with the natural resource consequences this implies.

The visual manifestation of urban sprawl is the construction of low-density suburban housing developments on the fringe. Sometimes there is **leapfrogging,** as developers go out somewhat past the current fringe to build houses, with the land areas over which they have vaulted being left to fill in later with additional developments. Very often, also, open land outside the current fringe will be purchased and held for future development well in advance of planned construction times. This can induce pronounced changes in the ways these close-in rural lands are used. Land in the "holding mode" may not be devoted to particularly productive land uses, so that when the time comes to convert the land to houses, there is no especially strong sense of losing any important natural resource values.

In many places, sprawl has been accentuated in recent years in the development of edge centers, that is, secondary centers of high-density commercial development that have materialized some distance out from the center of the large, parent urban district. These edge developments can cast out new higher land-price gradients into the underdeveloped lands lying beyond the old urban/rural fringe, thus increasing the development pressure on these lands.

What is the efficient level of sprawl? Clearly, sprawl can be managed with vigorous-enough public policies. In Great Britain, for example, sprawl has been more closely controlled with public regulation, so many towns have relatively high density development right up to the rural fringe, which tends to be much more sharply defined as compared to the typical case in the United States.

Sprawl, however, represents a trade-off. On the one hand are the lost natural resource values of the land that comes under urban pressure, as well as the added costs (e.g., transportation costs) of living and working in a geographically dispersed urban/suburban pattern. On the other hand are the benefits accruing to people who are able to live in a way that the majority of them apparently want, which is in a single-family house with a reasonably sized lot around it. Of course, if people did not wish to live in this fashion, but preferred living at high density near city centers, sprawl might not be a problem. The qualifier "might" is necessary because land-use patterns are a direct reflection of housing preferences only if the prices they face are competitively determined, are not affected by unpriced external costs or benefits, and are not subsidized. In urban and suburban regions of the United States, and in many other parts of the world, externalities and subsidies are rampant. The net effect of these may be to encourage urban growth that spreads too rapidly.

A major factor behind sprawl is transportation costs, especially the costs of automobile commuting. Road access is typically unpriced in the United States. While there are some toll roads, most are not, so the cost of driving an extra mile includes only car operating costs and the cost of the time of the people in the car. Because of this, the marginal cost of commuting, that is, the cost of commuting the marginal mile, are below social marginal costs. The effect is to encourage people to commute longer distances than are socially efficient. It is possible that subsidies to home buyers have the same effect. Because of the way that federal and state tax laws are written, tax liabilities may be lowered for those people who have home mortgages. The effect of this may be to lower the **effective price** of homes in the suburbs, thereby increasing the quantity demanded of them and encouraging suburban sprawl.

LAND MANAGEMENT ISSUES ON THE URBAN/RURAL FRINGE

Nowhere is there a more complex and vigorous struggle about the way a natural resource is to be used than on the expanding fringe areas that mark the advance of urban/suburban settlement into surrounding rural/agricultural areas. Colliding interests are the norm: developers, homeowners, farmers and other landowners, environmental interests, economic development interests, transportation groups, community groups, and diverse public agencies are some of the people and organizations normally involved, each with their own views about how land in general, and certain parcels in particular, should be used.

Over the years communities and groups have developed a substantial arsenal of means that can be used to affect land conversion. The main ones are listed in Exhibit 14-2. They vary from classic zoning ordinances to individual contracts between towns and developers to third-party actions (e.g., action by nonprofit environmental groups). The political/demographic/economic complexity of these cases makes it hard to see clearly the major cause-and-effect relationships that are involved. From our standpoint perhaps our biggest interest is in understanding how these various development practices and regulations affect the natural resource and environmental endowments of the urban/rural fringe.

One way in which zoning regulations are used in **edge communities** is to establish **density limits** for development. This can be done through **large-lot zoning,** requiring that all house lots must have a minimum total acreage. Or it might be through establishing explicit limits on development in terms of the number of housing units allowed on developed parcels. The normal justification given for density limitations is to ensure that overall population growth is kept at a moderate pace, that new homes are of the sort that will maintain or lift average property values in the community, and that it will preserve a substantial amount of natural coverage of the land, such as woodlands, wetlands, and open areas.

The problem that immediately suggests itself is the potential perverse impacts of this approach. Consider the total fringe area of a specific community. The following simple relationship holds:

$$\underset{(A)}{\underset{\text{developed}}{\text{Total acres}}} = \underset{(NH)}{\underset{\text{new houses}}{\text{Number of}}} \times \underset{(A/NH)}{\underset{\text{per new house}}{\text{Acres used}}}$$

Field: Natural Resource
Economics — An
Introduction

V. Applied Natural
Resource Problems

14. Land Economics

© The McGraw-Hill
Companies, 2003

EXHIBIT 14-2

METHODS USED BY COMMUNITIES TO CONTROL LAND DEVELOPMENT

Throughout the United States and in other countries communities have many ways of controlling and shaping the quantity and quality of land development within their boundaries. Some of these are the following:

- **Zoning regulations:** This is the most common approach, usually supplemented with other means. Zoning can be used to restrict the amount and density of development, by specifying minimum lot sizes, maximum structure sizes, and other development features.
- **Tax relief, or public grants:** Monies for nonprofit organizations that purchase ecologically sensitive fringe lands and manage them in ways that preserve environmental values. The generic name for this type of organization is **conservation trust.**
- **Impact fees:** Fees must be paid by developers to proceed with a project. These fees are usually justified by the added costs the community will experience (such as schools and roads) as a result of the development. Impact fees have gained greater importance in some

states where traditional property taxes have been limited by law.
- **Contract zoning:** In return for rezoning a development tract, developers are required to proceed in specified ways regarding number and layout of units, road and sewer construction, and so on.
- **Public/private contracts:** These contracts are concluded between public authorities and landowners in fringe areas whereby the latter, in return for annual payments, agree to adopt environmentally sensitive land management practices.
- **Outright land acquisition by public agencies:** Objectives are to conserve sensitive natural resources. Acquisition can be the full transfer of fee simple ownership or a partial rights transfer such as purchase of development rights in cases where some private use is compatible with ecological preservation.
- **Land-use covenants:** Groups of propinquitous landowners agree to rewrite their land deeds so that they, and any future owners of the affected properties, are enjoined from engaging in certain types of land uses or management practices.

Rules that establish maximum densities in particular communities are, in effect, increasing A/NH. For a given NH, therefore, this works so as to increase A, the term on the left. When individual communities seek to limit development densities within their borders, it tends to work in the direction of increasing the total amount of land that is converted on the fringe; that is, it tends to encourage suburban sprawl.

Most of the development and density control measures undertaken on the suburban fringe in the past have been aimed at supporting property values. In essence, communities have sought to control the development process so as to ensure that **property values** have been maximized. Some conflicts have involved **natural resource preservation** issues, for example, making sure that development does not impinge on watersheds that nourish important surface or groundwater resources.

In recent years a new motive has been added to the mix, that of **preserving the habitats** of important species of plants and animals. Austin, Texas, has experienced phenomenal growth and suburban expansion in recent decades. In the early 1980s, the U.S. Fish and Wildlife Service placed on the official list of endangered species the black-capped vireo, a small bird that was once fairly extensive in the western United States but now is confined to a few small areas in Oklahoma and Texas. Planned new large housing developments in Austin had the potential of encroaching on vireo habitat situated on the (then) out-skirts of the city. After a great deal of conflict and political struggle, a plan was adopted to alter normal development processes to preserve some portions of vireo habitat. This and similar cases led the U.S. Congress in 1982 to alter the Endangered Species Act to provide for a way of trying to reconcile the incen-tives of developers and the desire for habitat preservation to protect endan-gered species.[9] The law calls for the development of **habitat conservation plans,** which basically are a vehicle for developing specific development plans that will provide some degree of protection for affected species at a moderate cost in terms of the altered plans required of developers.

Another type of land-use issue that has been at the forefront in the last few decades is the **protection of wetlands.** Wetlands, in a variety of forms, are found throughout the country. Locally, they may be called swamps, bogs, pot-holes, marshes, fens, or some other name. They provide a number of valuable hydrological and biological services, the exact nature and extent of which varies according to their location, size, and relationship to adjacent land and water areas.

LAND USE IN UNCERTAIN ENVIRONMENTS

In the example discussed above, we assumed that there were two alternative land uses (farming and a housing development) and that the annual rents flowing from each were **known with certainty.** In the real world, this is usu-ally not the case. Not only are there economic variables that cause land rents to vary from year to year (e.g., the fluctuating price of agricultural crops), but nature itself can cause rents to vary. Homes built in floodplains, or along seashores, are subject to storms and flooding; land in seismically active re-gions is subject to earthquake damage; droughts, hurricanes, and wildfires can have their impacts. The main questions here are: (1) how do uncertainties of this type affect efficient land use patterns, and (2) do normal private markets function efficiently when uncertainties of this type are important?

Suppose there is a parcel of land on which one might build a house. In an average year, the benefits of living in this house in this particular location would be, say, $1,400, and the costs (including capital costs[10] plus operating costs) would be $600. Net benefits would be $800, which, capitalized at 5 per-cent, would yield a value of $16,000. In a competitive market, the price of this parcel would be equal to these capitalized rents.

---

[9] For a discussion of this case see Charles C. Mann and Mark L. Plummer, *Noah's Choice*, Knopf, New York, 1995, pp. 175–211.

[10] Annual capital costs are the annualized amount of construction costs.

Field: Natural Resource
Economics — An
Introduction

V. Applied Natural
Resource Problems

14. Land Economics

© The McGraw–Hill
Companies, 2003

Now suppose this were actually beachfront property. This kind of property is frequently subject to storm damage, such as from the high winds and waves kicked up by hurricanes along the eastern coast of the United States. Let us assume that in this situation there is a 10 percent chance that the house will be completely destroyed. Thus, we have the following situation:

	No storm (90% chance)	Storm (10% chance)
Benefits	1,400	0
Costs (operating)	600	600
Net benefits	800	−600

Now we can calculate the expected value of **net benefits,** which is what average net benefits would be over a very long string of years, 10 percent of which have storms. The expected value of net benefits equals:

$$800 \times 0.9 + (-600) \times 0.1 = \$660$$

and the capitalized value of this at 5 percent is $13,200.

If market participants react to risk in a straightforward fashion, we would expect the market price of this property to be reduced because of the likelihood of periodic storm damage. Suppose an insurance company now steps in and offers storm insurance, at **actuarially accurate rates,** that is, at premium rates that accurately reflect annual expected losses. The insurance covers the lost benefits in the case of a storm-caused destruction of the house. Thus, the insurance company's losses will be $1,400 \times 0.1 = \$140$. Suppose this much is charged as an insurance premium to the homeowner. Their situation is now:

	Annual
Benefits	1,400
Costs (operating plus insurance premium)	740
Net benefits	660

which, again, capitalizes to a value of $13,200. The presence of the insurance, in other words, does not change land prices, but only the distribution of net benefits flowing from the use of the land.

Why, then, do people build houses right next to the San Andreas fault in California,[11] or on low-lying coastal lands in the east, or on floodplains? A major reason is simply that the benefits associated with living in these locations outweighs the costs, even when the costs include risks associated with

---

[11] The San Andreas fault runs near San Francisco, and is the source of the great San Francisco earthquake and fire early in the twentieth century. Seismologists have predicted, for a number of years now, that a new major earthquake is likely in the vicinity of this fault.

natural events. Another reason is that special public programs serve to reduce the effective costs of these events, thereby leading people to make riskier decisions. A good example of this is the program of **federally subsidized flood insurance.** For people living in areas prone to flood damage, this program provides insurance against such losses at relatively modest premium rates, rates that are below those which would prevail if they were set on the basis of real expected damages. In other words, they are sold at rates below cost, with the general taxpayer covering the difference. The impact of this is that net benefits, or land rents, will rise by an amount equal to the value of the subsidy.

Suppose, in the example above, federal flood insurance were available at a cost of only one-quarter of the actuarially sound price. Since the latter is $140, the government price is assumed to be $35 per year. Now the net benefits to the homeowner for a typical year are the following:

	Annual
Benefits	$1,400
Costs	635
Net benefits	765

and the capitalized value of a net benefit stream of this amount is $15,300. The subsidized insurance, in other words, lifts land prices, and will lead people to use land in a way that is socially inefficient.

This type of problem is an ongoing feature of publicly provided flood insurance. Of course, it is a characteristic of any public program that lowers the cost of **foreseeable risk.** Federal disaster relief is often used to lower the burden to people of natural disasters. There are powerful humanitarian motives behind this program. But if the relief serves basically to lower the cost to people of predictable disasters, it may actually lead to higher losses in the future, as people persist in making decisions that are overly risky. Only if the disaster relief is forthcoming for truly unpredictable natural events will it not tend to produce these perverse results.

MANAGING PUBLIC LANDS

So far in this chapter the major focus has been on private land markets, how they operate and how they might be managed to move toward socially efficient land-use patterns. Another important set of land-use issues in the United States, as well as many other countries of the world, revolves around how publicly owned land should be used. In the United States, 29 percent of the total land area is actually owned by the federal government. State and local governments also own a substantial amount of land. These land areas vary from spectacular natural wonders to barren wasteland, but many of them are under demand for their natural resources. Because they are publicly owned lands, however, these demands are normally not mediated through the private market, but are managed through the decisions of public agencies of various types. Thus the expression of the demands and the decisions about the uses to which public lands will be put are part of a lively political process in which groups contend for influence and try to shift the uses of the public lands in directions that are congenial to their own interests.

The number of different activities pursued by visitors to public lands is very long: hiking and camping (day, overnight, and wilderness), animal watching and sightseeing, hunting (big game, small game) and fishing, timbering, mining, snowmobiling and use of all-terrain vehicles, boating of all types, livestock grazing, scientific study, and others. Conflicts arise because these activities often are not compatible with one another. Cutting timber may interfere with sightseeing and camping, white-water boating may conflict with fishing, wilderness hiking is not compatible with all-terrain vehicles, and so on. The way public agencies typically deal with these conflicts is to specify a list of permitted activities for the areas under their management. This is usually done as part of their legislative and administrative "charter," with a certain amount of local variation tailored to the features of particular sites. Exhibit 14-3 presents information on the range of permitted activities in the areas managed by the four major federal land management agencies: the National Park Service (NPS), National Forest Service (NFS), Bureau of Land Management (BLM), and the Fish and Wildlife Service (FWS). Material relevant to the activities managed by these agencies is located in other chapters: Chapters 18 and 19 for the FWS, Chapter 17 for the NPS, and Chapter 12 for the NFS. We discuss some simple conceptual issues here.

When a range of permitted activities is specified in general enabling laws, local managers' decisions are already constrained to some extent. Significant problems can still exist, however, in terms of whether the activities that are permitted should be pursued together throughout an area or whether managers should identify separate nonintersecting portions of the land for the pursuit of each activity by itself.[12] Suppose there are two activities that might be pursued on a given land area. Should both be allowed over the whole area, or should it be divided, with one activity allowed on one part and the other on the other part? The relevant comparison would seem to be straightforward: the sum of the net benefits of the separate areas compared to the net benefits of the two activities when they are pursued together over the larger area. Two primary factors would determine the outcome of this comparison: (1) the nature of the interaction between the activities and (2) the variation in the quality of the area that makes some parts of it more suitable to one activity than to the other.

---

[12] In the policy world the doctrine of mixing uses is called **multiple use.** The idea is set out in the Multiple-Use Sustained Yield Act of 1960.

SECTION FIVE: APPLIED NATURAL RESOURCE PROBLEMS

EXHIBIT 14-3

PUBLIC LANDS MANAGED BY FEDERAL AGENCIES IN THE UNITED STATES

Four federal agencies administer most of the 657 million acres of federal land (29% of the land in the United States): the National Park Service (NPS), the Fish and Wildlife Service (FWS), and the Bureau of Land Management (BLM) in the Department of the Interior, and the Forest Service (FS) in the Department of Agriculture. The majority of the federal lands (92%) are in 12 western states, and the federal government owns more than half of the land in those states (54%, ranging from 27% in Washington to 83% in Nevada).

The National Park System

The National Park Service (NPS) manages 77 million acres in the 378 units of the National Park System (also NPS). NPS has many diverse categories for its units, with 20 different designations. The largest units are the national parks, preserves, and monuments.

National Parks. Fishing is allowed in most national parks, but hunting and resource development activities (e.g., mineral extraction and timber harvesting) generally are prohibited unless grandfathered or expressly permitted in the park's authorizing legislation.

National Preserves. Management of national preserves is generally similar to that of national parks, but typically allow not only fishing and other recreation allowed in the parks, but also hunting and mineral extraction, as long as the natural values for which the preserve was established are not jeopardized.

National Monuments. Permitted and prohibited uses in national monuments are largely the same as in the national parks: many recreation uses are allowed, although hunting may be restricted or forbidden. Wood cuffing and most commercial activities are usually curtailed (but mineral extraction may be allowed). . . .

In addition to these categories, the NPS has numerous other designations, including: national battlefields, historic sites, national seashores and lakeshores, and more. The NPS also administers 19 national recreation areas (NRAs), while 19 are administered by the FS, one by the BLM, and one by the Tennessee Valley Authority. . . . Recreation is the dominant use, but other uses may be allowed in NRAs including recovery of timber or mineral resources, livestock grazing, watershed protection, and resource preservation as long as these uses are compatible with the primary purpose for which the area was set aside.

The National Wildlife Refuge System

The Fish and Wildlife Service (FWS) manages 93 million acres in 512 national wildlife refuges, 198 waterfowl production areas, 50 wildlife coordination areas, and 114 other sites.

The National Wildife Refuge System Administration Act of 1966 and the National Wildlife Refuge System Improvement Act of 1997 direct the FWS to administer the System primarily to conserve and enhance fish and wildlife and their habitats. Only uses compatible with these gen-

---

The activities could vary from compatible to antagonistic. Limited clear-cutting of timber may be quite compatible with small-game hunting (because it creates animal-attracting edges) and not at all with big-game hunting. All-terrain vehicles may be incompatible with most other activities (except perhaps forestry and mining), so separate areas for this type of activity may be called for. Snowmobiling and cross-country skiing are likely to be antagonistic,

CHAPTER 14:   LAND ECONOMICS

EXHIBIT 14-3—*Continued*

PUBLIC LANDS MANAGED BY FEDERAL AGENCIES IN THE UNITED STATES

eral purposes, and with any specific individual purposes set out for each refuge, are permitted. For example, grazing and mineral activities are permitted in certain refuges and under certain circumstances; hunting, fishing, and other recreational uses generally are permitted in wildlife refuges.

The Public Lands [Bureau of Land Management]

The BLM administers 264 million acres concentrated in 11 western states: Alaska, Arizona, California, Colorado, Idaho, Montana, Nevada, New Mexico, Oregon, Utah, and Wyoming. . . .

BLM manages the public lands for sustained yields of multiple uses livestock grazing, outdoor recreation, wood production, water supply, wildlife and fish habitats, and wilderness; mineral extraction also is allowed. . . .

The National Forest System

The Forest Service (FS) manages the 192 million-acre National Forest System (NFS), consisting of 155 national forests, 20 national grasslands, and 112 other areas. NFS lands are concentrated in the West, but the FS manages more than half of all federal land in the East.

Congress has provided uniform, general management guidance for most NFS lands. As with the public lands, NFS lands generally are administered for sustained yields of multiple uses. . . .

Special Systems

Three special management systems have been created to protect particular features or characteristics: the National Wilderness Preservation System, the National Trails System, and the National Wild and Scenic Rivers System.

The Wilderness Act defines the purpose of wilderness as "devoted to the public purposes of recreational, scenic, scientific, educational, conservation, and historical use." The Act generally prohibits commercial activities (e.g., timber harvesting), motorized access or mechanical transport, and permanent roads, structures, and facilities in wilderness areas. . . .

National trails are administered by the FS, NPS, and BLM, many in cooperation with appropriate state and local authorities. Most recreation uses are permitted, as are other uses or facilities that do not substantially interfere with the nature and purposes of the trail. Motorized vehicles generally are prohibited on System trails.

National Wild and Scenic Rivers System. . . . To date, 155 rivers totaling 10,896 miles have been included in the National Wild and Scenic Rivers System.

The principal protection of the wild and scenic river designation is the prohibition of water resource projects which may divert or hinder the flow of the river. Management of permitted use varies with the class of the designated river.

Source: Excerpted from Ross W. Gorte, *Federal Land and Resource Management: A Primer,* Congressional Research Service, RS 20002, December 22, 1998, Washington, DC.

---

while fishing and day or overnight camping would be much less so. We are speaking here essentially of the nature and extent of external costs that different activities inflict on one another. Separate facilities are called for when the external costs of combined usage outweigh the direct benefits of the activities arising from allowing them over a wider area. Research is required if these externalities and benefits are going to be estimated with any degree of accuracy.

The other important factor affecting the desirability of mixing or separating activities is variations in the qualitative characteristics of the land itself. Some portions of a national park may clearly be better suited to sightseeing, and some to remote hiking and camping. Certain areas may lend themselves to forestry, or livestock grazing, whereas others do not. As with most other variables, the adaptability of an area to specific activities is not a yes-no situation but rather a more or less. This puts a premium on gaining knowledge about the relationships between site characteristics and the benefits that accrue to people using them for different activities.

SUMMARY

Land is the ultimate resource in the sense that it is the surface of the earth on which the activities of humans and of nonhuman organisms are concentrated. Land is an important resource in two senses: in terms of its physical properties and the ecosystem functions it supplies and in terms of its role in the spatial distribution of human activities. Efficient patterns of land use are those which maximize the net benefits of the activities distributed over its surface. Land prices are the **capitalized values** of net benefits, or land rents. Land prices will be affected both by physical and locational aspects of land parcels, and by taxes and external benefits and costs that flow among the uses to which different parcels may be put. The **land rent/price gradient** is a way of showing the structure of land prices in and around an urban area; it is useful in studying decisions involving open-space preservation and the impacts of land-use controls. Public methods to control land-use patterns include **outright purchase, eminent domain,** and the **police power;** the latter includes such approaches as **zoning, subdivision controls,** and **environmental regulations.** A major ongoing issue in the exercise of the police power to shape land use has been the **takings** issue. Public policy can also have an impact on land use by affecting the probabilities of loss and the degree of risk from such things as floods, earthquakes, and storms. The chapter concluded with a brief discussion of management issues on public lands.

KEY TERMS

Urban sprawl	Takings
Land rent	Just compensation
Land prices	Zoning
Externalities	Fee simple
Land taxes	Development rights
Land market	Rent/price gradient
Eminent domain	Leapfrogging
Police power	Uncertainty and land prices

Field: Natural Resource
Economics — An
Introduction

V. Applied Natural
Resource Problems

14. Land Economics

© The McGraw–Hill
Companies, 2003

QUESTIONS FOR FURTHER DISCUSSION

1 Suppose the town allows me to operate a small ferry from a point of land in the town to a small island not far away. My operating costs are $50,000 per year, and my total revenue is $62,000 per year on average. Is the $12,000 difference a land rent? The land in question is the site where the ferry dock is located.

2 A piece of land has a market value of $2,000 if used for agricultural purposes. A land "speculator" buys some of the land, paying $3,000 an acre. Five years later she sells it to a house builder for $7,000 an acre. The builder builds a house for $50,000 and sells it (and the land on which it sits) to a homeowner 2 years later for $68,000. Assuming the land market and housing market are both competitive and that there was no in-flation during all of this, what's the total land rent in houses, and how was that rent distributed among farmer, speculator, builder, and homeowner?

3 A community enacts a regulation that keeps people from building houses within 500 yards of the top of any hill in town. The stated purpose of the law is to protect the scenic quality of the town. Do you think this regulation amounts to an unconstitu-tional taking of private property?

4 How would the rent gradient of a city change if a new four-lane expressway were built from the middle of the city out to the next city, which is 100 miles away?

5 How do interest rate changes affect land prices?

USEFUL WEB SITES

Maps on land use, land resources, and characteristics:

- Earth Resources Observation System (EROS) of the U.S. Geological Survey (http://edcwww.cr.usgs.gov/eros-home.html)

Land-use and natural resource problems in North America and around the globe focusing on sustainability, social conflict, and political economy:

- University of Wisconsin Land Tenure Center (http://www.wisc.edu/ltc)

Using the market to accomplish land preservation:

- Nature Conservancy (http://www.tnc.org)

Public interest groups focusing especially on the use and abuse of public lands:

- Sierra Club (http://www.sierraclub.org)
- Wilderness Society (http://www.wilderness.org)
- Friends of the Earth (http://www.foe.org)

President Clinton's Council on Sustainable Development was transferred into the Department of Energy and became the U.S. Center of Excellence for Sustainable Development, with a lot of attention focused on land-use issues and the consequences of sprawl (http://www.sustainable.doe.gov).

For wetlands laws, check out the publications on this topic by the Congres-sional Research Service, available through the National Institution for the Environment (http://www.cnie.org/nle/crswet.html).

SECTION FIVE: APPLIED NATURAL RESOURCE PROBLEMS

SELECTED READINGS

Babcock, Richard F., and Charles L. Siemon: *The Zoning Game Revisited,* Oelgeschlager, Gunn and Hahn for Lincoln Institute of Land Policy, Boston, 1985.

Barlowe, Raleigh: *Land Resource Economics, The Economics of Real Estate,* 4th ed., Prentice-Hall, Englewood Cliffs, NJ, 1986.

Ellickson, Robert C.: "Suburban Growth Controls: An Economic and Legal Analysis," *Yale Law Journal,* 86, January 1977, pp. 385–511.

Epstein, Richard A.: *Takings: Private Property and the Power of Eminent Domain,* Harvard University Press, Cambridge, MA, 1985.

Fischel, William A.: *Do Growth Controls Matter?* Lincoln Institute of Land Policy, Cambridge, MA, 1990.

Fischel, William A.: *The Economics of Zoning Laws,* Johns Hopkins University Press, Baltimore, 1985.

Fischel, William A.: "Zoning and the Urban Environment," in Daniel W. Bromley (ed.), *The Handbook of Environmental Economics,* Blackwell, Cambridge, MA, 1995, pp. 61–88.

Heimlich, Ralph E. (ed.): *Land Use Transition in Urbanizing Areas,* The Farm Foundation, Washington, DC, 1989.

Miceli, Thomas J., and Kathleen Segerson: *Compensation for Regulatory Takings: An Economic Analysis with Applications,* TAI Press, Greenwich, CT, 1996.

Mills, Edwin S., and Bruce W. Hamilton: *Urban Economics,* 4th ed., Scott, Foresman, Glenview, IL, 1989.

Santos, José Manuel L.: *The Economic Valuation of Landscape Change: Theory and Policies for Land Use and Conservation,* Elgar, Cheltenham, England, and Northampton, MA, 1998.

CHAPTER **12**

FOREST ECONOMICS

Forests cover about 30 percent of the land surface of the earth.[1] These forest resources are a heterogeneous collection, ecologically, socially, institutionally, and economically. Ecologically it's customary to distinguish between tropical forests (up to about 35° north and south latitude), temperate forests (35° to between 50° and 55° north and south latitude), and boreal forests (the high-latitude forests). Within the tropic band there are rain forests, moist deciduous forests, and dryland forests. There are hardwood and softwood forests. There are expanses of natural forests (sometimes called "old growth" forests), forests modified by humans through use of various types, and human-made forests (sometimes called forest "plantations"). There are public forests and private forests, open-access forests and controlled-access forests. More than 60 percent of the world's forests are in seven countries (Brazil, Canada, China, Indonesia, Russia, United States, and Zaire); twenty-nine countries have more than half their land area in forests; forty-nine countries have less than 10 percent of their land area in forests.

Listed below are some of the major types of problems encountered in managing the world's forest resources:

1 The challenge of maintaining production of traditional forest outputs in keeping with expanding populations and economies. Recent trends in forest products consumption are discussed in Exhibit 12-1. They include wood for

---

[1] Eight thousand years ago this percentage was about 50.

CHAPTER 12: FOREST ECONOMICS

EXHIBIT 12-1

TRENDS IN CONSUMPTION OF FOREST PRODUCTS

Global consumption of wood has expanded by some 36 percent (around 900 million m³) over the past two and a half decades, reaching almost 3,400 million m³ in 1994. Broad estimates suggest the value of this consumption in 1994 to be in excess of US$ 400,000 million, with industrial usage accounting for 75 percent of this. Slightly more than half of the wood volume was used as fuelwood, and the rest was used for a variety of industrial purposes. Fuelwood consumption expanded more rapidly than industrial roundwood consumption, growing by 60 percent to 1,890 million m³ in 1994, while industrial roundwood consumption grew by 15 percent to almost 1,500 million m³, although actually declining from a high of 1,720 million m³ in 1990.

The decline in consumption from the 1990 level reflects both supply and demand conditions. A major factor was the continued dislocation of output in the Russian Federation where reported industrial roundwood removals were down substantially (around 50 percent from the 1990 level). The decline also reflected weak demand in the industrialized countries. Further, the supply of logs continued to be affected by restrictions on harvesting in North America and the main tropical Asian countries, increasingly due to environmental concerns. Some African countries also increased their restrictions on logging and export, both for forest management reasons and to encourage greater domestic processing.

World production of most individual forest products rose substantially in volume terms over the period 1970–94. Only sawnwood had a lower production in 1994 than in 1970. Output ranged from a minor fall in the production of sawnwood, to a 113 percent increase in paper and paperboard products. The slow growth for industrial roundwood masked the fact that coniferous roundwood production only increased by 1 percent, while that of non-coniferous roundwood grew by 48 percent. The main impact was post-1990, as production of both coniferous and non-coniferous roundwood had increased up to that point. Industrial roundwood and sawnwood both reached a peak in 1990 and then declined, mostly due to dislocation of output in the former USSR; recent levels have approached the 1990 high.

Growth rates for consumption of many commodities during 1980–94 have been slower than for the 1970–80 period in many regions.

The developing countries' share of total roundwood production has increased steadily from 49 percent in 1970 to 61 percent by 1994. They have increased their share of industrial roundwood from 17 percent to 33 percent.

For industrial roundwood, the most impressive changes have occurred, not for the leading consuming regions, but for the others: Africa's consumption nearly doubled to about 60 million m³ between 1970 and 1994 with its share rising from less than 3 percent to 4 percent. South American consumption also rose from 3 percent to more than 7 percent. However, it was the growth of consumption in Asia that transformed the global balance: from consuming 15 percent of world industrial roundwood in 1970, Asia came to account for 21 percent (compared to about 20 percent for Europe) in 1994. Similar shifts have occurred for other commodities. For paper and paperboard the main developments have been the sharp declines in share of consumption by North/Central America and by Europe, mostly in favour of Asia which raised its share from 15 to 30 percent.

Source: U.N. Food and Agriculture Organization, *State of the World's Forests*, Rome, Italy, 1997, p. 50.

SECTION FIVE: APPLIED NATURAL RESOURCE PROBLEMS

fuel, for manufactured products, and for the production of paper. Forests also produce many nontimber products, such as honey, nuts, oils, spices, pharmaceutical products, and cork products.

2 The shift in many developed countries from traditional types of forest uses to new forms of use, such as outdoor recreation.

3 The continued pressure, particularly in developing countries, to convert forest land to other types of land use, particularly subsistence and commercial agriculture.

4 The identification, valuation, and preservation of new types of forest services, such as biodiversity production, carbon sequestration, and ecosystem protection.

All these problems have technical aspects connected to the biological and technological factors affecting the growth of forests and their utilization. They also have important institutional and economic dimensions connected to the valuation and use of forest resources and the incentives facing those whose decisions impact the quantity and quality of forest resources. We clearly cannot deal, in a single chapter, with all the global issues in forest economics in all their specificity. But what we can do is try to lay out an analytical model with which the basic nature of these issues can be framed and analyzed.

FOREST HARVEST DECISIONS

We begin with what sounds like a very innocuous problem, but one that actually contains a perspective that can be used to analyze many of the issues involved in decisions about using forest resources. It's the problem of deciding **when to cut a tree.** Suppose there is a community that contains 1,000 acres of forest land. The objective of the community is to manage its forest land so as to maximize the sustainable value of the timber harvest. We suppose, for the moment, that there are no nontimber values involved. Whenever the community harvests a portion of its territory, it immediately replants that acreage. Assume also that the timber output of this community is small relative to the total market, so its harvest decisions do not affect the selling price of timber. How much of its acreage should it harvest each year?

A way of working into this is to focus on one representative acre of forest, which we assume to be covered with trees of roughly the same age. When should this acre be harvested? The answer lies in the combined effects of the biology and the economics of the situation. First, the biology, which in this case is wrapped up in the growth pattern of the trees. Many things affect how fast trees grow, but we will consider a generalized relationship like that shown in the numbers of Table 12-1, which are pictured in Figure 12-1. Growth rate is here related to the age of the tree. The total quantity of wood on the acre of trees grows modestly for the first several decades. In the third through fifth decades the growth rate is relatively rapid. In the sixth and later decades the rate slows down and eventually, at an age of about 100 years, be-

TABLE 12-1

TOTAL VOLUME, AVERAGE VOLUME, AND ANNUAL INCREASE IN VOLUME OF WOOD, BY DECADES, OF ONE ACRE OF FOREST

Age of trees (years)	Total volume of wood (cu ft)	Average volume (cu ft/age)	Annual increase in volume (cu ft/yr)
0	0	0.0	0.0
10	80	8.0	8.0
20	200	10.0	12.0
30	400	13.3	20.0
40	720	18.0	32.0
50	1,360	27.2	44.0
60	1,660	27.7	30.0
70	1,840	26.3	18.0
80	1,960	24.5	12.0
90	2,040	22.7	8.0
100	2,090	20.9	5.0
110	2,090	19.0	0.0
120	2,090	17.4	0.0
140	2,090	14.9	0.0

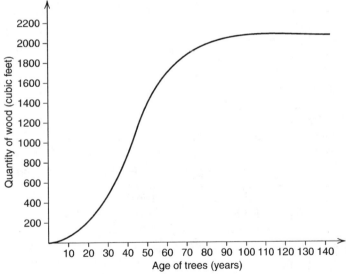

FIGURE 12-1

Total Volume of Wood by Age of Forest

comes zero. The columns of Table 12-1 show total and average volume of wood, and the yearly growth rate, in successive decades of the forest's life.[2] The average volume is simply the total volume in the forest divided by its age.

[2] Clearly the growth rates and volumes vary each year, but a table showing annual data would be too big, and we can get what we need with a table based on decades.

SECTION FIVE: APPLIED NATURAL RESOURCE PROBLEMS

It is possible to undertake various **silvicultural** steps to shift this growth function. For example, periodic thinning, or fertilizing, can increase the production of wood from a given acre of forest. It's also true that plant breeding can produce trees that grow faster. There has been enormous change through the years in the yield of timber that can be obtained from an acre of forest, in effect an increase in the volume figures shown in Table 12-1.

It is possible to make harvest decisions by reference only to the biological growth function. We might plan simply to maximize the amount of wood obtained at the time of harvest. This would imply delaying harvest until the forest achieved its maximum volume, around year 100. The problem with this is that we have to wait quite a long time to realize this harvest. Might it not be better to have a somewhat smaller harvest, in return for having it earlier in time?

One might think that it would make sense to cut at perhaps 60 years—when the average yield is the highest. Over, say, 1,000 years, this would yield about 27,666 cubic feet, as against a 100-year cycle, which would yield only 20,900 cubic feet in 1,000 years. In fact the 60-year cycle would yield the largest volume of any cycle, so it could perhaps be thought of as the **maximum sustained yield** for this forest. The question remains, however: Is this the harvest age that maximizes the net benefits of the forest to society?[3] Cutting at 50 years would produce less wood, but it would be available sooner. Thus there is a trade-off, and the solution depends as much on the values that society places on time as it does on the value of wood.

But the decision is somewhat more complicated. After the trees are cut, an acre of cleared ground will result. The optimal harvest time depends in part on what that land will be devoted to. We will assume, in keeping with the logic of the overall situation, that the land will be replanted with trees as soon as it is harvested and that this will be done each time the trees are cut, into the indefinite future. So what we are actually asking is: What is the optimal length of **timber harvest rotation** for our community? A "rotation" is a recurrent length of time, in years, between successive harvests of the same piece of land. A 40-year rotation, in other words, means that the typical acre of timber is harvested every 40 years. If we were to find, for example, that 40 years was the optimal rotation period, we would conclude that we should harvest one-fortieth of the thousand acres, or 25 acres, each year. A rotation pattern is pictured in Figure 12-2. The first harvest is made at t years from the beginning. Harvests are subsequently done at $2t$, $3t$, $4t$, and so on. Each harvest yields q cubic feet of timber. The question is: What is the socially efficient value of t?

A way of visualizing this problem is the following: Imagine that we are at the present time at the beginning of some year in the life of the trees on our acre. It doesn't matter which particular year it is. We ask the question: Should we cut the trees and send them to market this year, or should we wait and do it next

---

[3] Remember that for now we are assuming that the only thing of value is the trees for wood; we will relax this assumption later.

Field: Natural Resource
Economics — An
Introduction

V. Applied Natural
Resource Problems

12. Forest Economics

© The McGraw–Hill
Companies, 2003

CHAPTER 12: FOREST ECONOMICS

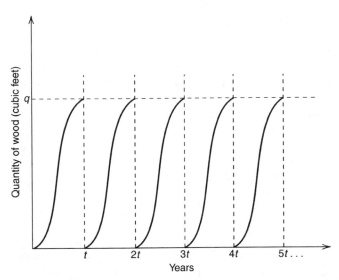

FIGURE 12-2
Typical Forest Rotation Pattern

year? This is really just a simple two-period problem, but it allows us to identify the efficient rotation period. If the decision is not to harvest this year, then next year the community will be faced with the same two-part comparison. So the community is essentially faced with a sequence of benefit-cost decisions. It compares the benefits of cutting this year with the costs, which are the returns they forgo because they won't have the trees to cut next year. In the early years of the trees' lives, the benefits of cutting are presumably less than those of waiting, because in these years the trees are growing rapidly. On the other hand, in later years when the growth rate is very low, the benefits of waiting would be very small compared to those of cutting today. At some point there will occur a tipping point, at which time the benefits of cutting are equal to, or slightly in excess of, those of waiting. This is the time to harvest the forest.

It's easier to look at this question with a little algebra. Define the following symbols.

V_0: The monetary value of the wood that would result if the forest were harvested this year

V_1: The monetary value of the wood that would be produced if harvest is delayed 1 year

$\Delta V = V_1 - V_0$: The value of the 1-year growth increment

C: Harvest costs, the monetary costs of felling the trees and getting them to market

r: Discount rate

S: The present value of all future net benefits when the forest is harvested with the optimal rotation period

The last term needs some explaining. We are actually trying to find out what the optimal rotation period is. To see the significance of S, pretend that after harvesting, the cleared land is going to be sold to somebody who is going to replant and then harvest forever at the optimal rotation period. The price the land would sell for is equal to the present value of the future stream of net benefits from following this course of action.

If the forest is harvested this year, the proceeds will be $(V_0 - C) + S$. This is the sum of $(V_0 - C)$, the net benefits of harvesting the timber, and S, the selling price of the land. If the harvest is delayed until next year, the present value of the proceeds will reflect the added growth, ΔV, and the revenue from selling the land next year. These must be discounted, giving

$$\frac{V_0 + \Delta V - C + S}{1 + r}$$

In this case both the realized yield next year and the selling price S must be discounted back one period. When the forest is young and ΔV is relatively large, the following inequality will hold:

$$\frac{(V_0 + \Delta V) - C + S}{1 + r} > (V_0 - C) + S$$

In other words, the net proceeds of waiting to harvest until next year will be greater than those of harvesting this year. But as the forest gets older, ΔV will eventually decline, and the net proceeds of harvesting this year will eventually become equal to those of waiting until next year. Thus the condition

$$\frac{(V_0 + \Delta V) - C + S}{1 + r} = (V_0 - C) + S$$

is the condition that tells when to harvest the forest.

The last expression can be reduced to the following[4]

$$\Delta V = (V_0 - C)r + Sr$$

What this amounts to is a benefit-cost type of expression. ΔV is the benefit received by waiting one more year for harvest, and $(V_0 - C)r + Sr$ is the cost of waiting. As long as the benefits of waiting exceed the costs, we put off harvest; when the benefits fall to the level of costs, it is time to harvest the trees.

---

[4] Multiplying both sides of the first expression by $1 + r$ gives: $(V_0 - C + S)(1 + r) = V_0 + \Delta V - C + S$. Isolating ΔV on the right gives $(V_0 - C + S)(1 + r) - (V_0 - C + S) = \Delta V$. Factoring gives $(V_0 - C + S)(1 + r - 1) = \Delta V$, which gives the result above.

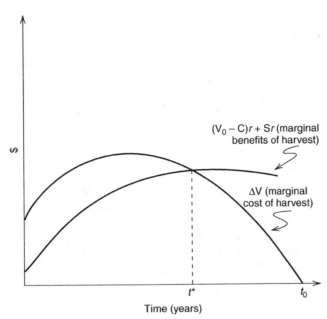

FIGURE 12-3
Depiction of the Optimal Rotation

This solution is shown in Figure 12-3. The curve labeled ΔV shows annual growth increments at varying ages. Growth is low at the beginning, increases to a maximum (which corresponds to the point on the graph of Figure 12-1 where it reaches its steepest slope), then declines to zero again when the forest reaches its maximum biomass. The other curve in Figure 12-3 shows the right side of the last equation. As the volume of wood in the forest (V_0) increases, this function also increases, up to some maximum. The optimal rotation is identified by the intersection of these two functions; it is labeled as t^* on the horizontal axis. This can be interpreted in benefit-cost terms. $(V_0 - C)r + Sr$ is benefits of harvesting this year, while ΔV is growth forgone, or the costs, if harvesting is done this year.

Portfolio Choice

We can also interpret this as a portfolio choice, that is, as a choice about the form in which the community should hold its assets. Solving the last expression for r gives

$$r = \frac{\Delta V}{S + (V_0 - C)}$$

which we can interpret as an **asset portfolio** statement. The left side is r, which can be interpreted as the rate of return obtainable on general productive assets in the community. The right side is the rate of return we could expect if we let the trees stand for another year. What the solution for the optimal rotation gives us is a rule that says: Maintain the trees as long as the rate of return from so doing exceeds the rate of return on alternative assets. When the rate of return on the growing trees falls to that of alternative assets, harvest the trees and replant.

Factors Affecting the Efficient Rotation

We can further our understanding of this by looking at some of the factors facing the forest manager that, if they change, will change the efficient length of rotation. For example, suppose that **harvesting costs** increased substantially when a nearby logging mill closed and made it necessary to ship the logs a further distance. Note that harvest costs appear in one of the functions shown in Figure 12-3 with a minus sign. The impact of the increase in C is to shift the $(V_0 - C)r + rS$ function downward, thereby lengthening the optimal rotation period. In fact if harvesting costs become expensive enough, it may be efficient to refrain from harvest altogether, that is, the efficient rotation period might get pushed right out to t_0 in Figure 12-3. One way in which the social costs of harvest could increase is through **externalities** associated with timber cutting. If flooding or soil erosion are increased as a result of harvesting the timber, as they have in many of the world's watersheds, this essentially increases the social costs of harvesting. The effect, as we have seen, is to lengthen the optimal rotation.

Consider what happens to the length of the efficient rotation when the **interest rate** changes. For example, if the interest rate were to fall in the long run, this would tend to shift the marginal cost function down, that is, $(V_0 - C)r + rS$. The intersection of marginal benefit and cost curves would shift to the right, indicating that the efficient rotation would get longer. Note that if the interest rate were actually zero, the marginal cost curve would essentially disappear, moving t^* all the way to the right where $\Delta V = 0$. A zero interest rate implies that the return on alternative assets is zero, and so it is efficient to let the forest continue to grow until the natural growth rate falls to zero.

Suppose that timber became relatively more scarce, leading to an increase in the harvested **price of timber.** In this case the outcome on the efficient rotation period is ambiguous, because higher timber prices would increase ΔV, V_0, and S, though not necessarily all in the same proportion. So the interaction of the marginal benefit and marginal cost curves could shift either to the right or to the left.

Impacts of Nontimber Forest Values

It is now time to expand the analysis to recognize that forests typically produce other social benefits beyond the commercial values of the timber they

CHAPTER 12: FOREST ECONOMICS

supply, such as habitat for valuable animal species, watershed protection, outdoor recreation, preservation of biodiversity, and carbon sequestration. Conceptually, it may be easy to understand how one of these benefit categories would affect the socially efficient rotation length. In practice it may be very complex, because different factors are likely to impact the rotation in different amounts and in different directions, so if a number of them are involved in the case of a particular forest, the overall impact may be hard to sort out.

One major service produced by forests is **animal habitat.** Obviously, there are many different animal species that rely on forest resources, from tiny insects to large carnivores, and animals that are ground-dwelling, tree-dwelling, flying, and so on. Consider a situation involving only a single species. This is approximately true in the famous case of the northern spotted owl, which lives in old-growth forests of the northwestern United States. Its required habitat, in other words, is forest that consists of relatively old trees. Suppose we had a way of valuing our acre of forest in terms of contribution to spotted owl habitat, and expressing this in monetary terms. The function relating this value to forest age might look like that in Figure 12-4. The value is essentially zero until the forest is at least 60 years old; it then increases rapidly and reaches a maximum at around 100 years, and is constant thereafter. Let us assume also that the price of timber, and of forest land, is unaffected by its owl habitat value.

It is fairly easy to see how adding this value to the forest management decision would affect the choice of efficient rotation. The habitat value function, if added to the overall timber value function shown in Figure 12-1, would give a

FIGURE 12-4
Value of Forest as Spotted Owl Habitat, Related to Forest Age

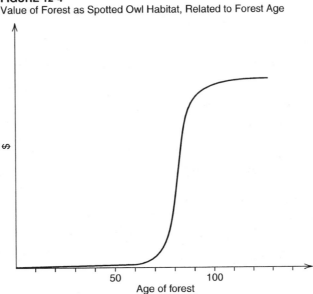

SECTION FIVE: APPLIED NATURAL RESOURCE PROBLEMS

total value function like the earlier one but now with value for the older years increased somewhat. This would have the effect of pushing out the ΔV function in Figure 12-3. Since the owls do not have a commercial value (this would change if, for example, there were ecotourist industries that sold people owl-spotting tours in the forest), and the market value of the land is unaffected by the owls, the marginal cost function, expressed as $(V_0 - C)r + Sr$, of Figure 12-3 would be unchanged. This would give a new model as in Figure 12-5. The new marginal benefit function is shown as $\Delta V + H$. The ΔV term is the same as before; it is the increment in value of timber from another year's growth. The term H is annual value of the forest as owl habitat. The effect of adding H to the model is that it increases the optimal rotation. Several new marginal bene-fit functions are shown (the dotted lines), corresponding to higher values of H. The higher is the value, the more is the optimal rotation lengthened. The first dotted curve has an optimal rotation of t_2 years; if H is somewhat higher the rotation increases to t_3, and so on. In fact, if H becomes large enough, there will be no intersection with the marginal cost curve, indicating that the opti-mal rotation is essentially infinite, that is, social efficiency implies that the trees are never to be harvested.

While it may seem easy, at least conceptually, to factor a single species like the spotted owl into the situation, it is likely to be much more difficult to do this when a number of animal species are involved, and where the ecological factors affecting them differ. Deer, for example, may be advantaged in rela-

FIGURE 12-5
Optimal Rotation When Habitat for Spotted Owl Is Included

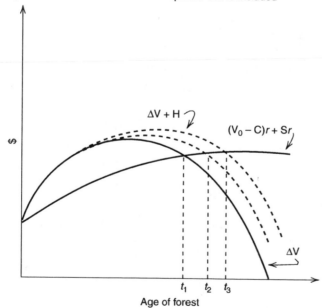

CHAPTER 12: FOREST ECONOMICS

tively young forests, where the amount of available browse is relatively high. Certain insects may be advantaged in fully mature forests where there is an abundance of decaying wood. If the full habitat value of a forest is to be added to the timber value, some way would have to be found to develop some aggregate measure of habitat value from these conflicting elements.

Another nontimber value provided by forests is **carbon sequestration.** Global emissions of carbon dioxide from the burning of fossil fuels have produced elevated levels of carbon dioxide (CO_2) in the atmosphere. The consensus among atmospheric scientists is that this will lead to a significant long-run increase in global mean surface temperatures, which in turn will have major impacts on elements of the global ecosystem and the humans who depend on it. One obvious way of trying to ameliorate this process is to reduce CO_2 emissions. Another is to manage global forest resources so as to increase their capacity to absorb atmospheric CO_2.

Trees carry out photosynthesis to produce the glucose necessary for tissue growth and maintenance. The inputs into photosynthesis are atmospheric CO_2 and water. Thus growing trees absorb CO_2 from the air and in this way help ameliorate the buildup of CO_2 in the atmosphere. To sequester more carbon, there are two courses of action: (1) convert land currently in other uses (e.g., agriculture) into forest land and (2) manage existing forest land so as to increase the amount of carbon sequestered. If a forest is left standing, it will eventually reach and maintain a maximum biomass. At that point the carbon contained in the forest will be at a maximum, and this amount of carbon can be sequestered permanently by leaving the trees standing.[5] Can this performance be improved upon? If trees are immediately burned or destroyed after harvesting (as in land clearing for agriculture, for example), the carbon is immediately released back into the atmosphere. But if the timber is harvested and converted into building materials, the carbon stays sequestered until the materials decay. Suppose these building materials did not decay at all. Then by cutting trees and converting them to building materials, we are permanently sequestering the carbon. If there were a market for carbon sequestration services, the market values of timber would reflect both its value as building material and its value for carbon storage. In effect, the addition of the carbon sequestration function simply adds to the value of the timber in proportion to the amount of wood it contains, which is essentially the same as if there were an increase in the price of building materials. In this situation we would arrive at the same conclusion we had earlier in thinking about the impact of the price of timber on the length of the efficient rotation: It could push the efficient rotation in either direction.

But building materials do not exist forever; rather they decay at fairly rapid rates, depending on their form and use. A large proportion of the lumber market is used in the construction of buildings, particularly houses. The rate at which the housing stock decays would determine the rate at which the carbon

---

[5] Of course natural events like fires and hurricanes can affect this conclusion.

SECTION FIVE: APPLIED NATURAL RESOURCE PROBLEMS

in the building materials is released into the environment. The critical factor is whether this rate is faster or slower than the growth rate of trees. If it is slower, then harvesting trees for building materials will increase the amount of carbon sequestered, relative to the quantity sequestered by leaving forests unharvested. If the decay rate is higher than the tree growth rate, the opposite conclusion holds.

One could envisage, at least theoretically, how a **carbon market** might work to motivate changes in silviculture practices and forest establishment practices that would lead to increased carbon sequestration. The market would allow forest owners to capture the value of stored carbon, thereby providing incentives for the appropriate decisions and trade-offs that would lead to efficiency in carbon sequestration. It would have to be a sophisticated market, for example, adjusting for the particular forest products into which trees are transformed if harvested. A problem with this is that the benefits of carbon storage are a massive public good, so private demanders are unlikely to materialize—which implies a program of public subsidies. Given the political context of most public subsidy programs, together with the uncertainties of the whole carbon sequestration process (see Exhibit 12-2), the likelihood that an efficient, or cost-effective, carbon sequestration subsidy program could be carried out is very small.

Optimal Clear-Cutting

Clear-cutting is the practice of harvesting all the trees in a particular area, as opposed to **selective cutting,** which means harvesting only those trees meeting certain criteria, such as species, size, or age. Clear-cutting is widely practiced in commercial forestry, and is controversial. Proponents point to harvesting cost savings and the advantages of promoting commercial forests that have trees of uniform characteristics. Opponents cite damages in terms of aesthetics, ecological integrity, watershed destruction, and reduced values for outdoor recreation.

It is relatively easy to frame the problem in conceptual terms. Suppose a company has a large forest from which it harvests timber on a 60-year rotation. On the assumption that it wishes to have a constant annual yield, in order to plan its workforce, and so on, it plans to harvest one-sixtieth of the forest each year. If the total forest contained 6,000 acres, this would mean they would harvest 100 acres each year. The harvesting pattern to be followed, in terms of clear-cutting, can vary over a wide continuum. On the one hand, it could be harvested as one large 100-acre clear-cut. At the other extreme, it could be harvested in 100 scattered 1-acre clear-cuts.[6] Or it could be harvested in any pattern between these two extremes: two 50-acre cuts, ten 10-acre cuts, and so on. Define n as the number of separate areas harvested in a year; thus $1 \leq n \leq 100$. The question is: What is the socially efficient value of n?

---

[6] We are assuming that one acre is the smallest possible harvest area.

CHAPTER 12:   FOREST ECONOMICS

EXHIBIT 12-2

FORESTS AND THE SEQUESTRATION OF CARBON

One important role that forests worldwide play is in the sequestration, or locking-up, of atmospheric carbon.

Forest management practices that can restrain the rate of increase in atmospheric CO_2 can be grouped into three categories: (i) management for carbon conservation; (ii) management for carbon sequestration and storage; and (iii) management for carbon substitution. *Conservation* practices include options such as controlling deforestation, protecting forests in reserves, changing harvesting regimes, and controlling other anthropogenic disturbances, such as fire and pest outbreaks. *Sequestration and storage* practices include expanding forest ecosystems by increasing the area and/or biomass and soil carbon density of natural and plantation forests, and increasing storage in durable wood products. *Substitution* practices aim at increasing the transfer of forest biomass carbon into products rather than using fossil fuel-based energy and products, cement-based products and other non-wood building materials.

The potential land area available for the implementation of forest management options for carbon conservation and sequestration is a function of the technical suitability of the land to grow trees and the actual availability as constrained by socioeconomic circumstances. The literature suggests that globally 700 Mha of land might be available for carbon conservation and sequestration (345 Mha for plantations and forestry, 138 Mha for slowed tropical deforestation, and 217 Mha for natural and assisted regeneration). The tropics have the potential to conserve and sequester the largest quantity of carbon (80% of the total potential), followed by the temperate (17%) and the boreal zones (3%). Natural and assisted regeneration and slowing deforestation account for more than half of the amount in the tropics. Forestation and agroforestry contribute the remaining tropical sink, and without these efforts regeneration and slowing deforestation would be highly unlikely.

Scenarios show that annual rates of carbon conservation and sequestration from all of the practices mentioned increase over time. Carbon savings from slowed deforestation and regeneration initially are the highest, but from 2020 onwards plantations sequester practically identical amounts as they reach maximum carbon accretion. On a global scale, forests turn from a global source to a sink by about 2010, as tropical deforestation is offset by carbon conserved and sequestered in all zones.

Using the mean cost of establishment or first costs for individual options by latitudinal region, the cumulative cost (undiscounted) for conserving and sequestering carbon ranges from about \$250–300 billion at an average unit cost ranging from \$3.7–4.6/t C. Average unit cost decreases with more carbon conserved by slowing deforestation and assisting regeneration, as these are the lowest cost options. Assuming an annual discount rate of 3%, these costs fall to \$77–99 billion and the average unit cost falls to \$1.2–1.4/t C. Land costs and the costs of establishing infrastructure, protective fencing, education and training are not included in these cost estimates.

While the uncertainty in the above estimates is likely to be high, the trends across options and latitudes appear to be sound. The factors causing uncertainty are the estimated land availability for forestation projects and regeneration programs, the rate at which tropical deforestation can actually be reduced, and the amount of carbon that can be conserved and sequestered in tropical forests. In summary, policies aimed at promoting mitigation efforts in the tropical zone are likely to have the largest payoff, given the significant potential for carbon conservation and sequestration in tropical forests. Those aimed at forestation in the temperate zone also will be important.

Source: Intergovernmental Panel on Climate Change, "Technologies, Policies, and Measures for Mitigating Climate Change," IPCC Technical Paper I, November 1996.

SECTION FIVE: APPLIED NATURAL RESOURCE PROBLEMS

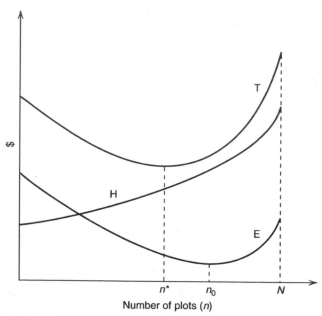

FIGURE 12-6
Efficient Clear-Cutting

In general we can identify two types of cost factors that vary with n. Harvest costs are one. As n increases, presumably the costs of harvesting timber would increase, owing to the need for the logging operation to visit an ever increasing number of scattered sites.[7] All the other costs we may lump under one category, called ecological costs. We would expect these costs to decrease as n increases, although once n gets relatively large, the costs may increase owing to the forest disruption on nonharvested acres when harvesters must visit many widely scattered cutting areas.

These relationships are pictured in Figure 12-6. Along the horizontal axis is the number of harvested plots (designated as n) varying from 1 up to some large number, say N.[8] The curve labeled H represents timber harvest costs, whereas the one labeled E shows ecological costs. The curve marked T shows total costs, and is the vertical summation of H and E. If harvesting were done simply to minimize harvesting costs, one large clear-cut would be called for, whereas if were done in such a way as to minimize ecological costs, clear-cuts of n_0 acres would be called for. The socially efficient number of acres lies between these two, at a value of n^*, where total costs are minimized.

Although it is relatively easy to discuss this on a conceptual basis, it would obviously be much harder to determine the actual number n for a specific situation. To do this, we would have to know the two cost functions H and E. It

---

[7] The spirit of this analysis is, of course, that the n areas are noncontiguous.
[8] N is the number of one-acre plots required to make up the total desired annual harvest area.

CHAPTER 12:   FOREST ECONOMICS

may not be too difficult to get the former—timber harvest companies presumably have good knowledge of their cost factors—but it is clearly a hard problem to measure ecological costs with a high degree of accuracy. Even without detailed knowledge of E, however, we can say that, as long as ecological costs are positive, the optimal clear-cut will be greater than one, the number that maximizes private profits.

INSTITUTIONAL ARRANGEMENTS FOR FORESTRY

Let us go back to the community with 1,000 acres of forest land, whose situation motivated the discussion about harvest decisions and the optimal rotation. We considered the logic of the optimal rotation when the commercial values of the timber are the only ones involved, and how the rotation decision might be affected by other factors. The next question is: How are efficiency and equity to be achieved under **alternative institutional arrangements**?

In the United States most commercial forest production is from private lands. A large part of this is from **industrial forest land,** consisting of relatively large parcels of timber land used primarily for harvesting timber. On these lands decisions are generally made with the objective of maximizing long-run net revenues. The extent to which these decisions also maximize social efficiency depends on whether unpriced outputs, on- or off-site, are taken into account by the decision makers. Some of these clearly are, because we know that private timber lands are often made available to hunters and hikers. Systematic data on these matters are not readily available, however.

Timbering is also carried out on nonindustrial timber lands. This is land held by owners who may produce some forest products, but for which timber output is not necessarily the primary goal. We can expect decisions in this case to be partially motivated by revenue considerations, but also to a large extent by the personal objectives of the landowners. Finally, some timbering is done on public lands, so that decisions on harvesting are made by public agencies. This is particularly the case in the developing world.

When an agency such as the U.S. Forest Service makes decisions about harvesting timber from national forests, its objectives and procedures are presumably dictated by its political mandate and the extent of the political/ administrative conflicts in which it finds itself embroiled. We will address this issue in the next session. In the publicly owned forests of the developing world there are several major problems: (1) the shaping of the **commercial agreements** (called "concessions") entered into with private companies to extract timber from the public forests, (2) the continued use of forest resources by local groups who rely on the resource even though they do not technically own it, and (3) the terms under which the forest land may be converted to private ownership, which determines the incentives that prospective owners have to use the land in various ways.[9]

---

[9] For a discussion of some of these issues see Chapter 21.

SECTION FIVE: APPLIED NATURAL RESOURCE PROBLEMS

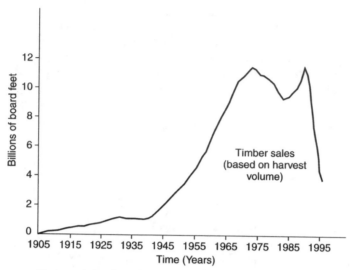

Timber sales
(based on harvest
volume)

Timber sale levels are based on rolling average
harvest volume from 1905–1996.

Conversions from cubic foot to board foot
measures are approximate.

FIGURE 12-7
Historic National Forest Timber Sale Levels (*Data Source:* USDA Forest
Service, National Forest Timber Harvest, Washington, DC, undated.

TIMBER HARVESTING FROM NATIONAL FORESTS

The national forest system of the United States was begun in the late nineteenth century and now consists of 191 million acres of land in many different sites around the country. During the first half of the twentieth century relatively little wood was harvested from national forests, but this changed after World War II. Timber sales from national forests rose steeply to a peak of about 11.5 billion board feet in the early 1970s. Since around 1990 timber sales from the national forests have dropped by about 75 percent (see Figure 12-7).

The reason for the dramatic drop in these timber sales is the perceived shift in relative valuations of the goods and services produced by national forests, in particular an increase in the demand for services such as outdoor recreation and ecosystem protection relative to the demand for harvested timber of the traditional sort. The situation is depicted in Figure 12-8. The horizontal axis indexes the annual quantity of timber produced from national forests; the demand curve labeled D represents the marginal willingness to pay for that timber, and MPC represents the costs of harvesting it. If these were the only two values involved, the efficient harvest level would be q_1. However, there are other services produced by national forests, which for the most part are competitive with timber production. These are such services as opportunities for various types of outdoor recreation, protection of biodiversity resources, sce-

CHAPTER 12: FOREST ECONOMICS

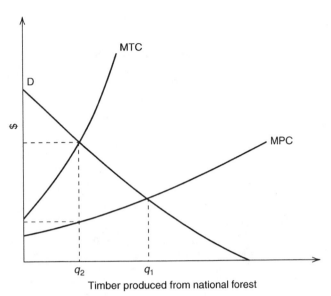

FIGURE 12-8
Efficiency with Nontimber Values

nic values, and such ecosystem protection services as flood control and soil erosion control. To a large extent these are use values, but nonuse values (e.g., existence value) are also important. On the assumption that the nontimber services diminish as the harvested timber quantity increases, they can be treated as an additional cost of timber harvesting. The curve labeled MTC in Figure 12-8 represents the total of marginal timber harvesting costs and marginal costs in the form of lost nontimber services. The difference between MTC and MPC, in other words, represents the marginal value of nontimber services being lost. According to this, full social efficiency requires that the timber harvest be reduced to q_2.

SUMMARY

This chapter first focused on the classic problem of when to harvest a tree. The decision involves a trade-off between the benefits one would receive immediately if it were harvested today, and the benefits of waiting, which are related to the rate at which the tree will grow in the next year. This basic model can also be used to look at cases where trees have value other than for timber, for example, for the provision of animal and plant habitat, a locale for outdoor recreation (e.g., hiking and hunting), and carbon sequestration. In all these cases, the optimal rotation is affected by benefit and cost values and the discount rate. We looked at a simple model that captured the major dimensions of the clear-cutting decision, and the reasons for the recent precipitous drop in sales of timber from national forests in the United States.

SECTION FIVE: APPLIED NATURAL RESOURCE PROBLEMS

KEY TERMS

Optimal rotation

Biological growth function

Portfolio choice

Habitat values

Carbon sequestration

Carbon market

Optimal clear-cutting

Timber concessions

National forests

QUESTIONS FOR FURTHER DISCUSSION

1 Derive the condition for the optimal rotation when a forest also provides species habitat services.

2 How would the optimal rotation be affected when a forest is an important supplier of outdoor recreation services, such as backpacking and hunting? How would these factors affect the size of the optimal clear-cut?

3 How would decisions about managing forests for carbon sequestration be affected by the speed at which wood building materials decay?

4 Are privately owned or publicly owned forests likely to give the best results as far as achieving efficient management of forest resources?

5 Describe what is meant by the "portfolio choice" approach to managing renewable resource stocks like forests.

6 What are the types of benefits and costs that are involved when forests that were previously open to commercial forestry are now placed in preservation status?

USEFUL WEB SITES

The primary federal forest agency in the United States is the

- U.S. Forest Service (http://www.fs.fed.us)

Forestry programs are pursued by a number of public and private agencies:

- World Resources Institute, program on forests (http://www.wri.org/biodiv/foresthm.html)
- Food and Agriculture Organization of the United Nations (http://www.fao.org)
- United Nations Intergovernmental Program on Forests (http://www.un.org/esa/ sustdev/iff.htm)
- American Forests (http://www.amfor.org)
- European Forest Institute (http://www.efi.fi)

Most other countries have public forest agencies, such as the

- Canadian Forest Service (http://www.nrcan.gc.ca/cfs)
- Japan Ministry of Agriculture, Forestry and Fisheries (http://www.maff.go.jp/eindex. htm)

CHAPTER 12: FOREST ECONOMICS

Many universities have schools of forestry, such as the

- University of Florida, School of Forest Resources and Conservation (http://www. sfrc.ufl.edu)
- Yale University, School of Forestry and Environmental Studies (http://www.yale.edu/forest/index.html)
- University of California at Berkeley (http://www.cnr.berkeley.edu/departments/espm/forestry.htm)

SELECTED READINGS

Adamowicz, W. L., et al. (eds.): *Forestry, Economics and the Environment*, CAB International, Wallingford, England, 1996.

Cubbage, Frederick W., Jay O'Laughlin, and Charles S. Bullock III: *Forest Resource Policy*, John Wiley, New York, 1993.

Ellefson, Paul V. (ed.): *Forest Resource Economics and Policy Research*, Westview Press, Boulder, CO, 1989.

Gorte, Ross W.: "Forest Service Timber Sale Practices and Procedures: Analysis of Alternative Systems," U.S. Congressional Research Service Report No. 95-1077-ENR, Washington, DC, October 30, 1995.

Hartman, Richard: "The Harvesting Decision When a Standing Forest Has Value," *Economic Inquiry*, Vol. 14, March 1976, pp. 52–58.

Newman, David H., and David N. Wear: "Production Economics of Private Forestry: A Comparison of Industrial and Nonindustrial Forest Owners," *American Journal of Agricultural Economics*, 75 (3), 1993, pp. 674–684.

Repetto, Robert, and Malcolm Gillis: *Public Policies and the Misuse of Forest Resources*, Cambridge University Press, Cambridge, England, 1988.

Sedjo, Robert A., Alberto Goetzl, and Stevenson O. Moffat: *Sustainability in Temperate Forests*, Resources for the Future, Washington, DC, 1998.

Sedjo, Roger A., R. Neil Sampson, and Joe Wisniewski (eds.): *Economics of Carbon Sequestration in Forestry*, Lewis Publishers, Boca Raton, FL, 1997.

CHAPTER **13**

MARINE RESOURCES

Oceans and inland waters cover more than two-thirds of the surface of planet Earth. This aquatic ecosystem is the source of numerous products and services of value to humans and to the ecological health of the globe. The major ones include

Commercial fishing
Recreational fishing (including aquarium fish)
Transportation services
Shore-based and offshore recreation activities
Atmospheric and climate control
Mineral supplies

In this chapter we focus on the first of these: the exploitation of fish resources by commercially oriented harvesters. On a global basis, about two-thirds of this activity is to provide food for humans. The rest is fish for industrial purposes, such as producing fish meal to use as an animal feed. Figure 13-1 shows the trend over the last few decades of the total commercial fish harvest in the world and in the United States. In both cases the overall trend has clearly been up. The fish resource looms larger in some parts of the world than in others. In North America only about 7 percent of animal protein intake comes from fish, but in Africa this proportion is 21 percent and in southeast

Field: Natural Resource
Economics — An
Introduction

V. Applied Natural
Resource Problems

13. Marine Resources

© The McGraw–Hill
Companies, 2003

CHAPTER 13: MARINE RESOURCES

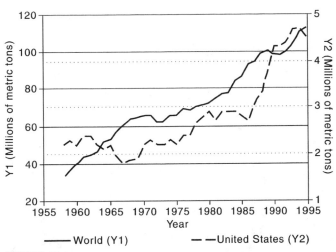

FIGURE 13-1
U.S. and World Commercial Fish Catches, 1958–1995

Asia it is 28 percent.[1] Of the total global catch, about 78 percent is saltwater-based (coastal and high seas), 7 percent is from inland fresh waters, and 15 percent is produced by aquaculture. The latter is a fast-growing segment of the total world harvest. World totals mask many changes that have taken place regionally and among different species of fish. Much of the growth in total harvest of recent years has been accounted for by lesser-valued species (sardines, pilchard) to which fishers have shifted their attention as some of the higher-valued species (cod, halibut) have become more scarce.

Within the United States, total commercial landings in 1995 were 4.5 million metric tons. This is about twice what it was 40 years ago. The total harvest has been fairly flat for the last 6 years. In 1996 the total value of commercial landings was about $3.5 billion. Just 15 years ago the Gulf of Mexico was the largest U.S. fishing region in terms of quantity of fish landed, but the largest today is the Pacific Coast/Alaska region. Table 13-1 shows the ten largest fisheries of the United States, by value.

CURRENT PROBLEMS IN MARINE FISHERIES

Major contemporary marine fisheries problems include

1 Overfishing, resulting in substantially diminished stocks of some species

[1] The data in this section come largely from the World Resources Institute, *World Resources, A Guide to the Global Environment, 1996–97*, Oxford University Press, New York, 1996; and U.S. National Marine Fisheries Service, *Fisheries of the United States, 1996*, Washington, DC, NMFS, 1997.

SECTION FIVE: APPLIED NATURAL RESOURCE PROBLEMS

TABLE 13-1
TOP TEN U.S. FISHERIES, 1996

Fishery	1996 Landings ($ million)
Gulf shrimp	401.4
Pacific salmon	368.7
American lobster	241.8
Alaska pollack	238.1
Blue crab	147.1
Pacific cod	112.0
Sea scallop	101.8
Halibut	83.5
Pacific flounder	82.0
Pacific herring	69.7

Source: National Marine Fisheries Service, *Fisheries of the United States, 1996,* NMFS, Washington, DC, 1997.

2 Overcapitalization, that is, excessive investments in national fishing fleets

3 Water pollution that threatens spawning areas vital to the health of many marine species

4 Conflicts over fishing rights; intercountry (e.g., United States and Canada), and intracountry (Native American fishing rights within the United States or Canada).

In this chapter we deal primarily with the first two of these. They are, of course, closely related; too many fishers catching too many fish relative to what is known about the current size of the various fisheries. This situation is largely the result of the **open-access** nature of marine fisheries. Until recently, anyone who wanted to buy a boat and commence fishing could do so. The result has been too many boats and a commensurate driving down of fish stocks. Historically, the opening up of new fisheries leads to a rapid influx of boats, overfishing, and, ultimately, depletion of the stocks. Figure 13-2 shows the landings profile of five historical fisheries of the United States, from 1837 to 1993. The profiles are remarkably similar and are probably representative of many other fisheries around the world.

Many countries have sought to regulate fishing to protect fish stocks, with mixed success. A major part of the problem is that public agencies have typically relied on command-and-control measures that have not adequately accounted for the incentives facing fishers. It is also true that governments have usually been very much conflicted between the desire to avoid overfishing and the even stronger desire to protect the economic livelihoods of fishing communities.

CHAPTER 13: MARINE RESOURCES

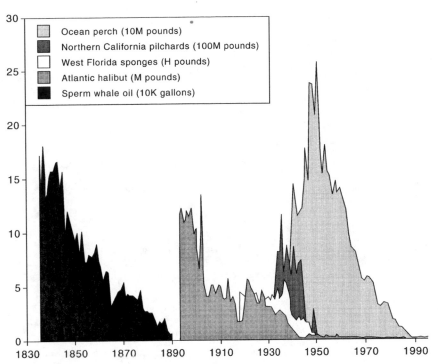

FIGURE 13-2
Profile of Landings for Five Historic Fisheries of the United States, 1837–1993 (*Source:* NMFS, *Our Living Oceans: The Economic Status of U.S. Fisheries, 1996,* U.S. Dept. of Commerce, NOAA Technical Memo NMFS F/SPO-22. Courtesy of Amy Gautam and Steve Edwards.)

U.S. FISHERIES MANAGEMENT INSTITUTIONS

The primary authority for fishery management in the United States is the **Magnuson Fishery Conservation and Management Act (MFCMA) of 1976.** Under this law, eight **Regional Fishery Management Councils** were established to pursue fishery management goals in their particular regions. The councils prepare **Fishery Management Plans** (FMPs) for the fisheries in their region that are in need of regulation. The councils, the states and other territories they include, and important species in each region, are shown in Table 13-2.

The councils are composed of public officials from the states and territories in the region, and from Washington, as well as "interested and knowledgeable members of the public," who have been, for the most part, representatives of the fish harvesting, processing, and distributing sectors. The FMPs prepared by the councils attempt to establish limits on total catches and regulations on such items as fishing gear, harvesting practices, and closure times as necessary for managing the fisheries.

SECTION FIVE: APPLIED NATURAL RESOURCE PROBLEMS

TABLE 13-2
REGIONAL FISHERIES COUNCILS

Council	States and other territories	Species
New England	Maine New Hampshire Massachusetts Rhode Island Connecticut	Atlantic groundfish, Atlantic herring, sharks, sea scallops, swordfish, redfish, billfish, hake, pollack, red crabs, and American lobster
Mid-Atlantic	New York New Jersey Pennsylvania Delaware Maryland Virginia	Surf clam and ocean quahog, Atlantic mackerel, butterfish, squid, sharks, bluefish, swordfish, scup, dogfish, billfish, other flounder, sea bass, tile fish, and sea scallops
South Atlantic	North Carolina South Carolina Georgia Florida	Billfish, coastal migratory pelagics, sharks, swordfish, corals, spiny lobster, tropical reef fish, calico scallops, sea scallops, shrimp, and coastal herring
Caribbean	Virgin Islands Puerto Rico	Spiny lobster, shallow water reef fish, swordfish, migratory pelagics, mollusks, billfish, corals, deep water reef fish, bait fishes, sharks, and rays
Gulf	Texas Louisiana Mississippi Alabama Florida	Groundfish, calico scallops, shrimp, coastal migratory pelagics, reef fish, corals, squids, spiny lobster, sharks, stone crab, sponges, billfish, coastal herring, swordfish, and tropical reef fish
Pacific	California Oregon Washington Idaho	Salmon, anchovy, groundfish, pink shrimp, billfish, and herring
North Pacific	Alaska Washington Oregon	Tanner crab, Gulf of Alaska groundfish, king crab, high sea salmon, scallops, Bering Sea groundfish, Bering Sea clam, Bering Sea herring, Bering Sea shrimp, corals, dungeness crab, shrimp, and snails
Western Pacific	Hawaii American Samoa Guam	Billfish, bottomfish, precious corals, seamount resources, and spiny lobster

Source: Lee G. Anderson, "Marine Fisheries," in Paul R. Portney (ed.), *Current Issues in Natural Resource Policy,* Johns Hopkins Press for Resources for the Future, Baltimore, 1982, p. 167.

The widely held judgment on the performance of fisheries management councils has been recently stated by the National Marine Fisheries Service.

In terms of fisheries management objectives since implementation of the MFCMA, achievement of maximum sustainable yield has been the principal goal. A patchwork of legislation and subsequent regulations, centered on complicated and some-

Field: Natural Resource
Economics — An
Introduction

V. Applied Natural
Resource Problems

13. Marine Resources

© The McGraw–Hill
Companies, 2003

times conflicting gear restrictions, quotas, trip limits, and time and area closures, has been the result. These effort control management strategies have been largely ineffective, often encouraging inefficient and excessive use of effort and capital of existing vessels, and in some cases, promoting and subsidizing further entry of new vessels. . . . These "command-and-control" measures may achieve short-run stock improvements, but in the long-run they generally are not successful at reducing effort. Despite early recognition of the potential for overfishing in the United States, the actions taken to control harvests from U.S. waters have often been ineffective from the standpoint of both biological and economic sustainability. . . .

A majority of U.S. fisheries have been 'diagnosed' by the NMFS biologists as operating at or above long-term potential yield, or maximum sustainable yield: 83% of the U.S. fishery resources which have been assessed are classified as over- or fully utilized from a biological standpoint. . . . Since most fisheries are still characterized by open-access, it seems fairly safe to suggest that the number of U.S. fisheries operating near the efficient point of effort, or harvesting using least-cost methods, is quite small.

Continuing problems with developing effective fisheries management plans led in 1996 to the passage of the **Sustainable Fisheries Act of 1996.** This law is meant to give the regional councils more authority, as well as responsibility, to develop plans that will rehabilitate fisheries deemed to be overfished. However, the law also puts a temporary moratorium on the establishment of new incentive-based management systems. To understand the impact of this, we must now focus on the basic bioeconomics of fisheries management.

MODELING A FISHERY

In this section we develop a simple **bioeconomic model** for analyzing both positive and normative questions about exploiting a fishery. A bioeconomic approach means that it combines two elements: the **biology** of fisheries growth and decline and the behavioral consequences that flow from **economic decisions** made by humans.

The Biological Growth Function

Consider a single **fishery.** By "fishery" we mean a collection of fish that inhabit a reasonably well delimited section of marine habitat. It might be fish of a single species (e.g., oysters in Chesapeake Bay) or fish of multiple, but related, species (e.g., all groundfish on Georges Bank off Cape Cod). At any given time the fishery consists of many individuals of different ages and sizes. To simplify this, we measure the total size of the fish stock in terms of **biomass,** essentially the aggregate weight of all the individuals of which the fishery is composed. The size of a fishery biomass is determined by many factors, not just the amount of fishing effort that is expended on it. Predator and prey factors, annual fecundity, ocean currents, food supply, water qualities, disease, and other factors play a role. There are few fisheries in the world where these factors are clearly understood. Fisheries biologists continue to pursue research into the complicated population dynamics of these situations.

SECTION FIVE: APPLIED NATURAL RESOURCE PROBLEMS

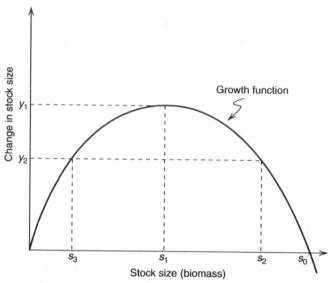

FIGURE 13-3
The Logistic Model of Population Growth for a Fishery

For the moment, however, we are going to set aside all these complex factors and focus on the all-important relationship between the **size** of the fishery biomass and the **growth** of that biomass. There are two major natural growth factors: increases in the number of individuals through processes of reproduction, and increases in the sizes (weights) of individuals through maturation. There are also two major forces working in the opposite direction: losses from predation and food scarcities and losses from natural mortality, especially old age.

At relatively small biomass levels the forces of reproduction and growth may be expected to dominate: With ecosystem abundance, high rates of reproduction are associated with rapid rates of growth of the biomass. But this obviously cannot continue indefinitely. As the size of the biomass gets relatively large, food scarcities would start to take their toll. So at some point we can expect a natural equilibrium to assert itself between the factors of growth and reduction. In this way a natural population size would be established.

This reasoning has given rise to the famous **logistic model** of population growth, first proposed by P. F. Verhulst in 1938.[2] It is pictured in Figure 13-3. The size of the biomass is indexed on the horizontal axis, and the increment, or change, in that biomass during a period of time such as a year is shown on

[2] P. F. Verhulst, "Notice sur la loi que la population suit dans son accroissement," *Correspondance Mathématique et Physique,* Vol. 10, 1938, pp. 113–121.

the vertical axis. The inverted U-shaped function starts at the origin—no fish, no increment. At higher stocks the increment is larger, reaching a maximum at a stock size of s_1. At larger stock sizes the increment is still positive but less than the maximum primarily because of the increased scarcities of food and space that the larger stocks imply. At a stock size of s_0, the different factors affecting stock size are all in balance, so that there is no increment. Stock size s_0 is thus a natural equilibrium, in the sense that this is the stock that would result if the population were left to itself and ecological factors were constant. At stock sizes above s_0, biological forces would be at work that would actually lead to negative increments, that is, to reductions in the size of the fishery biomass.

The logistic curve can be interpreted as a type of **sustained yield** curve, where by "yield" we mean a certain amount of the biomass harvested and therefore removed each year. For example, at a biomass size of s_2, the growth increment is equal to y_2 pounds, on the vertical axis. Thus if, at this stock size, y_2 pounds of fish were harvested each year, the yield would exactly match the growth increment and the size of the stock would be unchanged. This underlines an important point: There is not just one sustainable stock size in this situation. Any stock size is sustainable if the yield exactly matches the natural increment in the biomass. Note that the yield y_2 is also consistent with a stock size of s_3. But this pair, s_3 and y_2, is an unstable pair in the following sense. Suppose, with the yield kept at y_2, the stock size temporarily increased above s_3. Then the natural increment would exceed the yield, and the stock would be larger next year. So if the yield was held at y_2, the stock would slowly grow to size s_2, which is a stable situation, in the sense that short-run deviations of the stock above or below s_2 would be self-correcting.

But note also another possible outcome. Suppose, with a stock of s_3 and a yield of y_2, there was a short-run diminution in the size of the biomass, because of, say, temporary food shortages. If the yield or total catch is held at the level y_2, it will exceed the natural increment, driving the stock lower. If the yield continues at y_2, the biomass will eventually be driven to zero; the fishery will be wiped out.

From this analysis we can conclude that any yield equal to or less than y_1 is sustainable—that is, it can be continued indefinitely with a stable, sustainable stock size lying between s_1 and s_0. Any total catch over y_1 cannot be sustainable, because this would be greater than the maximum growth increment of which the fishery is capable.

The Effort-Yield Function

Now it is time to bring human behavior into the model. The "yield" referred to in the last section is actually a quantity of fish assumed to be harvested from the fishery, but this yield can come about only when human effort is given to the task. **Harvesting effort** refers to the economic resources devoted to catching fish; this includes capital goods (e.g., boats and gear), labor (captains and deckhands), and materials and energy. To simplify the graphics, we want to convert these resources to a single dimension. Perhaps the easiest way to do this is to think in terms of a standardized fishing boat, of a certain size, with a certain size crew and set of fishing gear. Then we can speak of larger or smaller amounts of human effort in terms of the number of days spent fishing by boats of the standard type. We make this assumption in order to proceed with our simple model. In the real world, of course, there can be substantial differences among boats on a fishery, in terms of size, equipment, the skills of people on them, and so on. We abstract from these differences here.

With this simplification, a typical **effort-yield curve** is depicted in Figure 13-4. It is important to keep in mind that this is a **sustained-yield** relationship. For example, an effort level of e_2 is associated with a sustained yield of y_2. This means that if effort level e_2 is applied each year on a permanent basis, the permanent (i.e., sustained) yield that will result is y_2. Yields may be different in the short run as adjustments are occurring, but eventually they will settle down to y_2.

The reasoning behind the inverted U-shape of the effort-yield relationship is because of the linkage between effort levels and the size of the stock. At a zero level of effort, the fishery will adjust to its natural size (level s_0 in Figure 13-3). As effort increases, the higher yields taken off the fishery result in the maintenance of small stock sizes; at an effort level of e_m, the sustained yield reaches its maximum point. At still higher effort levels, stock levels become re-

FIGURE 13-4
Effort-Yield Curve for a Fishery

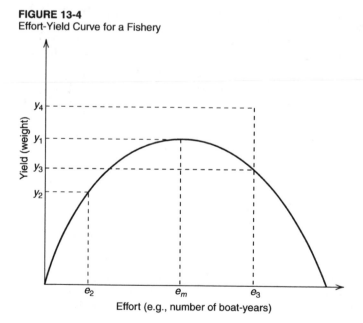

Field: Natural Resource
Economics — An
Introduction

V. Applied Natural
Resource Problems

13. Marine Resources

© The McGraw–Hill
Companies, 2003

duced (we are on the rising portion of the graph in Figure 13-3). At a very high effort level, the stock would be driven to zero.

It is again important to keep in mind that the model shows **sustained yields,** that is, yields that would result if the indicated effort level is applied **continuously** and the stock has had time to adjust to these effort levels. It is possible, in the short run, to have yields that are not on the effort-yield curve, for example a yield of y_4 at effort level e_3. But this is not sustainable. A high short-term yield like this will drive the stock down, and the yield obtainable with this effort level will fall, in the long run, to y_3.

Maximum Sustained Yield

All the yields traced out by the effort-yield curve are biologically sustainable. An effort level of e_m produces the **maximum sustained yield** (MSY) from this fishery.[3] This is the maximum quantity of harvest that can be realized in the long run, that is, on a sustainable basis. Maximum sustained yield is often regarded as the best target to aim for in exploiting renewable resources such as a fishery. Its appeal is based on the fact that this is the maximum biological yield that the fishery is capable of producing. When humans are brought in, however, this conclusion does not necessarily follow, because social efficiency, the effort level that maximizes the net benefits of the fishery, requires that the consequences of alternative effort levels be expressed in value terms.

EFFICIENT RATES OF EFFORT

To explore economic efficiency, we must determine values for both the harvested fish and the effort that goes into catching them. Let us make the assumption that the harvested fish are sold on a market, at a given and constant price, and that this price represents the full social value of the fish. We also assume that each unit of effort has a given, and constant, opportunity cost. These assumptions allow us to construct the revenue and cost functions depicted in Figure 13-5. The total revenue curve is the effort yield curve of Figure 13-4 multiplied by the unit price of the harvested fish. Thus it preserves the inverted U shape of that relationship. The total cost curve is simply a straight line starting at the origin and rising to the right at a slope that represents the opportunity costs of a unit of effort. The higher this opportunity cost, the steeper the total cost relationship. The **net income** corresponding to any effort level, which equals net social benefits in this simple model, is given by the distance between total revenue and total cost. The effort level at which this distance is maximized is e^*, and net benefits at this point are equal to

[3] Recently, the National Marine Fisheries Service (a part of the National Oceanographic and Atmospheric Administration), which is the federal agency responsible for fisheries policies, has started to call this yield the **long-term potential yield** (LTPY).

Field: Natural Resource
Economics — An
Introduction

V. Applied Natural
Resource Problems

13. Marine Resources

© The McGraw–Hill
Companies, 2003

SECTION FIVE: APPLIED NATURAL RESOURCE PROBLEMS

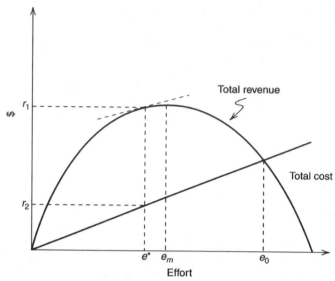

FIGURE 13-5
Efficient Harvest Level for a Fishery

$(r_1 - r_2)$.[4] It is easy to see that at any other effort level net benefits—the distance between the two curves—would be smaller than at e^*.

In particular, the net benefits produced at the point of maximum sustained yield (effort level e_m) are lower than at e_1. The reason is that, although the yields are indeed higher at e_m than at e^*, the extra costs of harvest are even greater, so the net revenues are lower. This shows that the point of maximum sustained yield in a physical, or biological, sense is not necessarily the point of maximum net social benefits in an economic sense. In fact economic efficiency implies a lower effort level, and therefore a higher permanent stock level, than does maximum sustained yield.

To explain an important point about the value of the fishery, suppose this fishery had a single owner. The annual net income of this person would be an amount equal to $r_1 - r_2$ in Figure 13-5. This value is in effect produced by the fishery; if this owner were to sell the fishery to another person, this annual net income would be the determinant of the price at which the fishery would sell. The annual return realized in this fashion is called the **annual resource rent** produced by the fishery. As we have seen before, a **natural resource rent** is the net value of a resource, prior to extraction, that is, its value **in situ.** Efficiency in natural resource use, therefore, implies using resources in such a way as to maximize their in situ value, or rent. In the case of our fishery the rent-maximizing level of effort is e^*.

---

[4] The way this is found is by drawing a line tangent to the total revenue curve with the same slope as the total cost curve. In the figure it is shown as a dotted line. The tangency point occurs at an effort level of e^*.

Field: Natural Resource
Economics — An
Introduction

V. Applied Natural
Resource Problems

13. Marine Resources

© The McGraw–Hill
Companies, 2003

CHAPTER 13:   MARINE RESOURCES

THE PROBLEM OF OPEN ACCESS

The next question to ask is whether, in the real world, effort levels on fisheries would tend to points like e^* in Figure 13-5. To answer this question we have to consider the incentive aspects of the situation, which get us into the question of how the property rights to the resource are held. In the real world, rights to ocean fisheries are typically not held by single owners or even, at least until recently, by defined groups of individuals. Rather, fisheries have historically been subject to **open-access** rules: Anybody who has wanted to buy or build a boat and go fishing essentially had the "right" to do so. To consider the incentive implications of this, suppose there is an open-access fishery in which the harvesting effort level is currently at e_1 (Figure 13-5). Consider the logic of one more fisher who is contemplating whether to get a boat and start harvesting from this fishery. Open access means that she need not get permission from anybody to do this, nor must she pay anybody for the right to engage in fishing. The only cost is the cost of buying the boat and gear, which are the standard costs reflected in the total cost curve of the model. Since effort is currently at e^*, she could be expected to compare this cost with anticipated revenues. At e^*, average revenues per unit of effort (per boat, for example) exceed average cost. Thus there are apparently profits to be made by any individual entering the fishery. Despite the fact that e^* is the efficient level of effort from the standpoint of society, there are still incentives for additional fishers to devote greater effort to harvesting from the fishery.

In fact this incentive in the open-access situation continues to exist as long as total revenue exceeds total cost (because average revenue exceeds average cost in this situation). The upshot is that entry will continue to occur until total effort has grown to e_0 in Figure 13-5. At this point total revenue equals total costs, and so the incentive for further entry has disappeared. Note also that all **resource rent** has disappeared at effort level e_0. At this level of effort the fishery is not producing positive net benefits. The resource rents have in effect been **dissipated** by excess entry and effort levels applied to the fishery.

The open-access condition of the fishery has produced substantially higher effort levels (and therefore substantially smaller stock levels) than is socially efficient. This situation is made much worse if **technological change** occurs so as to reduce the unit costs of harvesting effort. Diagrammatically, this implies a less steep total cost curve in the figure, which will make open-access levels of effort go even higher.

This is the basic incentive situation that historically has characterized most saltwater fisheries and many freshwater resources. It is accurate to say that most approaches to public fisheries management have been attempts to rectify the overharvesting implications of open access. Until recently, these management efforts were based for the most part on trying to regulate directly the performance of people harvesting particular fisheries. More recently attention has focused on changing the property rights aspects of these situations so as to alter the basic incentives facing harvesters.

Field: Natural Resource
Economics — An
Introduction

V. Applied Natural
Resource Problems

13. Marine Resources

© The McGraw-Hill
Companies, 2003

SECTION FIVE: APPLIED NATURAL RESOURCE PROBLEMS

APPROACHES TO FISHERIES MANAGEMENT

Throughout the world countries have been struggling in the last few decades to overcome the problems caused by open access in marine fisheries. Some of these efforts have already been successful, while many are still evolving in ways that may lead both to the restoration of depleted fish stocks and their efficient harvesting. A major factor has been the gradual change in attitudes, away from the long-standing notion that the ocean was a resource of unlimited abundance that ought to be freely available and toward one that recognizes the need for restraint if fisheries are to be preserved.

Fisheries regulations have, in general, progressed through a series of stages, starting first with modest regulatory moves and finally ending up, more recently, with more fundamental shifts in the property rights systems applicable to fisheries.

Restricting Access—First Steps

Open access means, very simply and in practical terms, that there are too many fishers, and fishing boats, exploiting a fishery. The natural tendency for people faced with this type of situation is to try and identify some means by which entry to the fisheries can be limited. Anthropologists and historians have found that, for centuries, localized groups of people have sought to define and defend territorial rights to fisheries, essentially by excluding outsiders from the resource. Informal territorial use rights in fisheries (**TURFs**) have been organized around particular geographical areas that make it possible to set boundaries and exclude would-be encroachers.[5] Sedentary species (clams, oysters, mussels) lend themselves relatively well to this approach because particular bays, lagoons, or coral reefs can be defended. A well-known example in a semisedentary species is the harbor gangs of Maine. These are groups of lobster fishers centered on particular bays who have pursued well-organized, but extralegal, efforts to exclude outsiders from fishing in the areas they control.[6]

But under some conditions TURFs may also be useful for migratory species. A TURF is not resource-specific as much as it is site-specific. So a species that migrated along a shoreline could be exploited by a TURF that controlled access for a certain distance along the shoreline. This might not be effective in controlling overfishing of the species because it doesn't offer control of access to the stock elsewhere in its migration journey.

The essential logic of the TURF (i.e., exclusion of outsiders) has recently been pursued worldwide at the level of the nation. As of the 1950s, most countries were claiming national jurisdiction over waters and resources that were

[5] See Francis T. Christy, Jr., "Territorial Use Rights in Marine Fisheries: Definitions and Conditions," Food and Agriculture Organization, Rome, Technical Paper No. 227, 1982.
[6] See Chapter 7.

CHAPTER 13: MARINE RESOURCES

within 3 miles (in a few cases 12 miles) from shore based on the long history of maritime custom. This meant that the majority of the productive fisheries of the world were situated on the "high seas," beyond effective political and management control. Large foreign fleets could exploit fisheries that many countries regarded as being essentially in their home waters. Attempts were made to deal with the problem through international negotiations and agreements. The International Fisheries Convention of 1946 targeted the northeastern Atlantic. The International Commission for North-West Atlantic Fisheries was established in 1949. During the 1960s a number of new regulatory bodies and conventions were formed, covering more than 80 countries and most of the world's oceans. But these international efforts were relatively ineffective at stopping overfishing, primarily because of marked differences among countries in terms of fishing technology and costs, opinions about fish stocks, and so on.

Thus the 1960s and early 1970s saw a push toward **extended jurisdiction,** essentially a state of affairs in which countries claimed and enforced offshore limits of 200 miles. This effectively nationalized, or put under the jurisdiction of national authorities of coastal countries, about 95 percent of the world's productive fisheries. In effect this might be thought of as a move toward national TURFs. But TURF will be successful only to the extent that it develops the institutional capacities with which to regulate or manage the affected fisheries within the TURF. In fact, in large countries such as the United States, the 200-mile zone is still subject to problems of open access and overfishing because of ineffective management institutions. In smaller countries, such as Iceland, authorities have been more successful at instituting effective fisheries management programs within their 200-mile exclusion zone.

Regulating Fishing Practices

The dominant approach in fishery regulation has been command-and-control types of restrictions on the fishing practices, in the hope that it could be made less productive and therefore less devastating on stocks of fish. These restraints included such measures as closing certain areas, limiting the number of days of fishing, prohibiting fine-mesh nets in order to target larger fish, restricting the size and horsepower of fishing boats, and so on.

Figure 13-6 shows a way of analyzing this approach. What regulations of this type do, essentially, is to raise the cost of fishing. By restricting certain inputs, say, the type of net that may be used, the effect is to make it more costly to catch a given quantity of fish. In our standard fisheries model, this rotates the total cost curve upward, giving it a steeper slope. If TC_1 is the original total cost curve, the new curve resulting from a regulation of this type would be something like TC_2. Now open access, instead of leading to e_0 units of effort on the fishery, would produce only e_m units of effort. This is approximately equal to the maximum sustained yield level of effort. A somewhat larger increase in costs, produced by somewhat more restrictive regulations, would shift up

SECTION FIVE: APPLIED NATURAL RESOURCE PROBLEMS

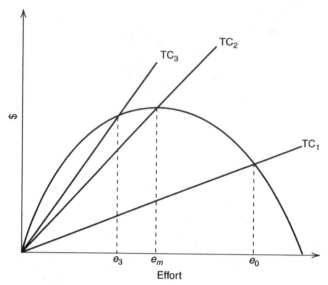

FIGURE 13-6
Effects of Fishing Regulations

total costs even more, say, to TC_3, moving the open-access level of effort to e_3, which is close to the original efficient effort level.

There are a couple of major problems with this type of approach. First and foremost is that, although it is possible to reduce effort levels and therefore increase stocks, and ultimately yields, in this way, it is being done by making fishing much more costly than it needs to be. Economic efficiency requires more than just arriving at the optimal yield and fish stock, it also requires that this yield be achieved with the minimum expenditure of scarce resources, that is, at minimum opportunity cost.

The second disadvantage of this type of direct control on fishing practices is that it can never be complete. When some parts of the fishing enterprise are constrained, fishers will attempt to expand in directions that are uncontrolled. Suppose, for example, authorities place a limit on the number of boats that may be used on a fishery. Fishers now have the incentive to build larger boats to increase their harvests. Suppose authorities step in and place an upper limit on boat length. Fishers now may shift to boats with larger engines. A limitation on horsepower may lead them to increase the number of trips they make each year. And so on.[7]

---

[7] Another potential problem, which our simple model does not illustrate, is where tighter regulations in one fishery lead fishers to shift and put added pressure on different fisheries.

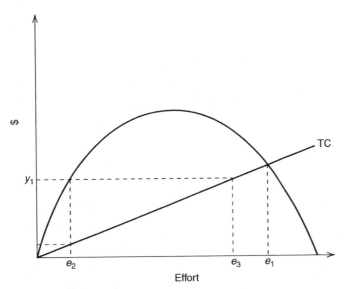

FIGURE 13-7
Catch Limits

Catch Limits

Another common regulatory approach is for authorities to establish upper limits on the quantity of fish that may be taken from particular fisheries. These are usually called TACs, for **total allowable catch** (or sometimes **total catch quotas**). TACs appear to give authorities a means of closely controlling yields. They simply establish a TAC, monitor incoming catches, and when the limit is reached, close the fishery. Apart from the difficulties in monitoring and enforcing this kind of limit, the major problem with it is shown in Figure 13-7. The open-access level of effort is e_1, which authorities regard as leading to diminished stocks. They therefore establish an upper limit on catch of y_1 (although there is a monetary scale on the vertical axis, it can readily be translated into quantity of fish by dividing by the unit price of fish). The y_1 level is below the efficient yield, but perhaps the thought is that it will be set at this level for some time to allow stocks to rejuvenate.

The minimum effort to harvest a yield of y_1 is e_2. Suppose this effort level was somehow temporarily established. At that point, there are rents being earned by fishers, and this will attract additional resources into the fishery. A common phenomenon that illustrates this is the **derby fishery.** Although the TAC has been set, no quotas have been set for individual fishers. Thus individuals will have the incentive to increase their **share** of the TAC. The advantage goes to the fishers who can get out on the fishery first with the greatest fishing power. So the effort level will get pushed to the right, as fishers do whatever it takes—bigger boats, engines, crews, and nets—to get bigger shares of the TAC before the fishery is closed down. In fact if the TAC is set permanently at y_1, the effort level will eventually increase to e_3, close to the open-access situation.

While setting catch quotas would seem to be a very specific and effective way to halt overfishing, trying to use them in fisheries where both biology and economic relationships are complex and imperfectly known can encounter a tangle of difficulties, as the excerpt in Exhibit 13-1 describes in the case of an important New England fishery.

Individual Transferable Quotas (ITQs)

The problem with these regulatory approaches is that they do not address the fundamental problem, which is that the value represented by the fishery resource is left open to capture by anybody who feels like trying. If rents are temporarily positive in a fishery, nothing stops new entrants from trying to appropriate some of them. It is this process that drives the effort level upward, eventually to e_2, and the rent to zero. Setting TACs, and then dividing them up into quotas for individual fishers, partly solves the problem, as it reduces the incentive for a "race to fish." But individual catch quotas can lock in inefficiencies and inequities stemming from the way they are originally determined. The last all-important step is to make the quotas transferable, hence the name **individual transferable quotas,** or ITQs. The approach has caught on in many fisheries around the world, as regulatory authorities seek to achieve fish harvesting levels and methods that are both efficient and sustainable.

To establish an effective ITQ, authorities must accomplish the following:

1 Establish TACs that are both economically and biologically meaningful.
2 Divide the TAC into a number of individual catch limits, or catch quotas, to be allocated to participants in the fishery.
3 Allow these individual quotas to be bought and sold, and keep track of who owns how many.
4 Enforce the catch quotas, so that fishers cannot harvest and sell quantities of fish in excess of their quota holdings.
5 Monitor the performance of the ITQ market to spot and manage problems related to concentrated ownership, community impacts, and biological uncertainties.

Step number one is easy to understand, but may be a lot harder to implement than might first be thought. Clearly some limitation on total catch is necessary if open-access conditions have led to economic and/or biological overfishing. But setting a TAC reasonably accurately requires both biological and economic information that may not be available. This is especially true if, as is normally the case, stocks fluctuate from year to year because of factors not related to fishing pressure. We discuss below some issues related to fisheries management in cases of great uncertainty.

CHAPTER 13: MARINE RESOURCES

EXHIBIT 13-1

PROBLEMS IN SETTING TACs

It is believed that there are two fairly distinct stocks of yellowtail and cod, but only one stock of haddock. The two stocks of yellowtail are thought to be located east and west of 69° west longitude, while the two stocks of cod are found in the Gulf of Maine and on Georges Bank respectively.

The fleet that harvests these three species comes mostly from New England and it also harvests other species during certain parts of the year. Because of the biological relationships between these species, as well as certain economic phenomena, this particular fishery is perhaps one of the most difficult and challenging to manage.

The plan for cod, haddock, and yellowtail was initiated in 1977 and established a total quota for each of the stocks of fish. Fishing licenses were required, but they were easily available and there was no moratorium on entry as there was in the surf clam and ocean quahog fishery. It was soon discovered that with the existing fleet and the many new entrants, the annual quota would be harvested very early in the year. This infuriated fishermen. In the following year the quota was caught early in the year but because absolute closure of the fishery would cause hardships for the industry, the council adopted a policy which effectively turned back the clock and started the fishing year and quota over again. While this may have protected employment in the short run, if continually repeated it would have serious consequences on the long-run productivity of the fishery.

Eventually the quarterly quotas were further subdivided by vessel size, and other stipulations were introduced which limited catch per boat trip. These limits were particularly wasteful of resources since boats had to return to port before they would normally have done so and hence wasted fuel and other resources. These allocation methods were not enough to subdue the loud voices heard at most council meetings concerning the perceived inequities of the plan. Larger, new boats needed substantial catches in order to pay their mortgages; smaller boats felt unable to get a fair share of the total quota since they could not fish in stormy weather. The quarterly quota allocation by vessel size did not solve either of these problems since, if the smaller boats and fixed gear vessels did not harvest their allocation, it was given to the larger boat categories rather than reserved for the following quarter. Trip limits based on the number of crew members were then instituted, presumably to allow the larger boats to catch more. The effect of doing so was predictable. Many boats increased the size of their crews in order to increase their allowable catch.

The system deteriorated still further. Toward the end of a quarter, it was possible for small boats to be forbidden to fish for yellowtail flounder west of the 69° meridian because their share of that quarterly quota was used up, but permitted to harvest them east of that line. At the same time, medium boats might be forbidden to fish for flounder on either side of the line while big boats could fish anywhere for flounder. The rules for cod and haddock, which are caught in the same nets, could be different. Vessels were subject to different rules if they fished in state waters before or after fishing beyond the 3-mile line. Since it was impossible to tell where a fish was caught, enforcement was all but impossible. Finally, complaints led to changes in both total quotas and the rules to enforce them. Neither fisherman nor regulator knew what was going on.

This excerpt explains the difficulties encountered by the New England Fisheries Council in establishing catch quotas for cod, haddock, and yellowtail flounder caught off New England.

Source: Lee G. Anderson, "Marine Fisheries," in Paul R. Portney (ed.), *Current Issues in Natural Resource Policy*, Johns Hopkins Press for Resources for the Future, Baltimore, Chapter 5, 1982, pp. 173–175. Copyright © 1982 by Johns Hopkins Press.

SECTION FIVE: APPLIED NATURAL RESOURCE PROBLEMS

The division of the total quota into individual quotas is the next step, and obviously is one that will be controversial in most cases. The quotas will eventually be valuable property rights. Every participant will prefer to have more rather than less, so some acceptable means must be found for their distribution. They might be auctioned off, or given away on some criterion, for example, past production (measured on some basis) or number of boats. Exhibit 13-2 discusses how an ITQ system was established for a fishery off the east coast of the United States and how the quotas were first distributed.

Step three is inherent in the quota system itself. But monitoring all quota transactions will require a good accounting system, especially if the number of present participants is large. In a smoothly functioning market, quotas will not

EXHIBIT 13-2

ITQs IN THE ATLANTIC SURF CLAM FISHERY

Surf clams are large, hard-shell clams harvested along coastal locations. The mid-Atlantic fishery lies off the shores of New Jersey, Maryland, Virginia, and the Carolinas. Prior to 1977 this fishery was regulated by the individual states, but there were problems in coordinating efforts. For example, the Virginia portion collapsed in the early 1970's, so fishing pressure shifted to New Jersey, prompting a closure there in 1976.

The surf clam offshore fishery was brought under federal management in 1977, when it was characterized by excessive effort levels and low yields. The first federal management effort consisted of a vessel moratorium program, an annual total catch quota, a limitation of vessel fishing hours, catch log books and vessel permits. Other measures such as minimum clam sizes were added in later years. Under the moratorium, only vessels that had fished for clams between November 1976 and November 1977 could take part in the fishery. Special provisions were added for qualifying newly constructed boats.

The moratorium program eventually became an administrative nightmare. Although the overall harvest was under reasonable control, continued efforts by fishers to expand effort led to gross inefficiencies. Allowable fishing hours were gradually reduced in response to continuous increases in vessel fishing power. By 1990 a boat was permitted to fish just six hours a week.

These conditions led the Mid-Atlantic Fishery Management Council in 1990 to shift to an ITQ system. Initial ITQ shares were issued to fishers on the basis of a formula of vessel historical catch and vessel size. Initial shares were allocated to 67 vessel owners. Most other regulations were dropped.

Within two years the number of vessels on this fishery dropped by 54 percent. The fishing time per vessel increased from 154 hours a year to 380 hours a year. The average catch per vessel increased by 96 percent in the first two years of the program. Thus the total catch increased as fishing effort declined.

ITQs are not without their problems, of course. One that has developed in this case is the concentration of quota holdings. To control the flow of their raw product supply, onshore clam processing companies have sought to expand their ownership of quota permits. It remains to be seen how important this problem becomes.

Source: Organization for Economic Cooperation and Development, *Towards Sustainable Fisheries, Economic Aspects of the Management of Living Marine Resources*, OECD, Paris, 1997, pp. 264–266.

only be bought and sold outright, but leased, or perhaps loaned, in varying amounts for varying periods of time. Step four calls on the same type of monitoring and enforcing efforts that any kind of TAC and quota system requires. As mentioned earlier, enforcement is not something that just happens automatically when a regulation is promulgated. Enforcement activities have to be designed and funded with enough resources to achieve acceptable levels of compliance. Enforcing fishery regulations is hard because fishing is done in places away from easy scrutiny, and in many cases it is fairly easy for fishers to offload "hot" fish in ways that escape surveillance. One of the major advantages of ITQs is that it can make unnecessary the kinds of detailed gear and performance restrictions that are inherently hard to monitor and enforce.

Step five is sometimes not given adequate attention. The ITQ system works by creating a new property right and a market on which that property right may be traded. It is virtually impossible to predict all of the important problems that novel institutions like this will encounter. Clear and accurate data on their operation is essential. This is especially so because one of the implications of establishing tradable quotas in a fishery is that there is no longer a tendency for the natural resource rent to be **dissipated.** This value, which is squandered under open-access conditions, will accrue, at least initially, to those who possess the fishing rights. There are many who feel that private appropriation of these values is in conflict with the fact that its source is a resource essentially supplied by nature herself. And so the issue of who ends up with the resource rents can become an important point of conflict.[8]

UNCERTAINTY AND FISHERIES MANAGEMENT

In the analyses of the previous section we implicitly assumed that the population biology of the affected fisheries was reasonably clear; regulators were assumed to have accurate knowledge of the stock-yield and effort-yield curves. A major problem with fisheries management in the real world, however, is that knowledge of these relationships is highly uncertain. One source of uncertainty is lack of complete biological and yield data, both current and historical, on the fishery, including landings and factors that would affect the stock size. Important economic information may also be missing, such as accurate data on fishing costs and likely future changes in fishing technology. Biological variability is a major problem. Natural variability in ecological variables (e.g., ocean temperature, predators) can make it difficult to identify the fish stocks accurately, not to mention the fact that the underlying biological models used for the purpose may not be accurate.

[8] In Iceland there is pressure on public authorities to tax away some of the resource rents from the rights holders: to have them pay, in a sense, for the right to fish. For the most part, this is a **distributional issue,** not an efficiency issue. If the efficient level of effort is being applied to the fishery, the resource rent could be taxed away, in part at least, without inducing a change in this effort level.

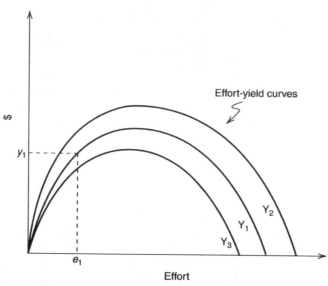

FIGURE 13-8
A Precautionary Approach in the Face of Uncertainty

When there are large uncertainties, fisheries management authorities may want to adopt rules that reflect this fact. Consider Figure 13-8. Suppose that biologists believe the most likely effort-yield curve is Y_1, but because of uncertainties in their knowledge of the fishery, there is a fairly strong probability that it could be as high as Y_2 or as low as Y_3.

Suppose the authorities establish a TAC of y_1, setting up an ITQ system so that the effort level is e_1. If the actual effort-yield curve is equal to Y_2, or anywhere else above Y_1, the fish stock will either maintain its size or even grow. But suppose the actual effort-yield curve is Y_3. In this case the harvest level y_1 is not sustainable; at effort level e_1 the sustainable harvest rate is y_2. With effort at e_1 and harvests (temporarily) at y_1, something has to give. If the effort level is maintained, stocks will decline and harvest levels will gradually diminish to the sustainable level y_2. But a more likely scenario, perhaps, is that fishers will increase effort levels as they try to maintain the permitted harvest level of y_1. If this were to happen, stocks could be driven to a precariously low level. The way out of this dilemma is for authorities to establish a lower quota level in the first place, commensurate with their uncertainty about the true bioeconomic relationships of the fishery.

SUMMARY

Ocean (and freshwater) fisheries are renewable resources, which require **bioeconomic models** for understanding and effective management. Such models combine both the biology of the resource and the economics of human behavior.

CHAPTER 13: MARINE RESOURCES

The fish biomass **growth function** shows the increment to the stock of fish as a function of the size of that stock. After converting this into an **effort-yield** curve, we were able to analyze the effects of open access on **rent dissipation** in the fishery and the effectiveness of different types of fishery regulation. In many historical situations, TURFs (territorial use rights in fisheries) have been developed in an attempt to limit access to certain individuals, but these may be ineffective in the face of rising demand and technical change in fishing. Most fishery regulations historically have been based on **command-and-control** approaches, especially gear restrictions and **catch quotas** (total allowable catch, or TACs). These regulations do nothing to solve the rent dissipation problem of the fishery. In more recent years some countries have moved in the direction of incentive-based regulations, especially **individual transferable quotas.**

KEY TERMS

Bioeconomic model

Open access

Maximum sustained yield

Effort-yield curve

Rent dissipation

Natural resource rents

TURFs (territorial use rights in fisheries)

Extended jurisdiction

Magnuson Act

TAC (total allowable catch)

ITQs (individual transferable quotas)

Derby fishery

QUESTIONS FOR FURTHER DISCUSSION

1 What would the biological growth curve look like if there exists a critical stock size below which growth rates become negative and the stock evolves to zero?

2 What would be the efficiency and equity implications of granting a fishery to one individual as a sole owner?

3 By decreasing effort, fishers can often catch more fish. Explain this.

4 Why is there a difference between the maximum sustained yield and the economically efficient sustained yield?

5 What other natural resources are like a fishery, in the sense that there are many different possible levels of steady-state stock among which one may be identified as economically efficient? (A steady state is simply one that persists over a long period of time. The optimal stock is a steady-state stock, but, as the question implies, not all steady-state stocks are efficient.)

6 What are some of the problems that might be anticipated in moving from a temporary, short-run yield to a long-run, sustainable yield?

USEFUL WEB SITES

The National Oceanic and Atmospheric Administration (NOAA) maintains a number of relevant sites:

- National Marine Fisheries Service (http://www.nmfs.gov)
- The Seagrant program in cooperation with the states (http://www.nsgo. seagrant.org)

SECTION FIVE: APPLIED NATURAL RESOURCE PROBLEMS

- Regional fisheries management councils, for example, North Pacific Fishery Management Council (http://www.fakr.noaa.gov/npfmc/default/htm) and Mid-Atlantic Fishery Management Council (http://www.mafmc.org)

Various internationally oriented agencies have fisheries programs:

- Fish Net of the World Bank Group (http://www.worldbank.org), under "development topics"
- Food and Agriculture Organization of the United Nations (http://www.fao.org)

Numerous public interest groups focus on fisheries:

- American Fisheries Society (http://www.fisheries.org)
- Sustainable Fisheries Foundation (http://www.wolfe.net/~csteward/)

SELECTED READINGS

Anderson, Lee G.: *The Economics of Fisheries Management*, revised and enlarged edition, Johns Hopkins Press, Baltimore, 1986.

Batkin, Kirsten M.: "New Zealand's Quota Management System: A Solution to the United States' Federal Fisheries Management Crisis?" *Natural Resources Journal*, 36(4), Fall 1996, pp. 855–880.

Christy, Francis T., Jr., and Anthony Scott: *The Common Wealth in Ocean Fisheries: Some Problems of Growth and Economic Allocation*, Johns Hopkins University Press, Baltimore, 1965.

Crutchfield, James A., and Giulio Pontecorvo: *The Pacific Salmon Fisheries: A Study of Irrational Conservation*, Johns Hopkins University Press, Baltimore, 1969.

Doeringer, Peter B., and David G. Terkla: *Troubled Waters: Economic Structures, Regulatory Reform, and Fisheries Trade*, University of Toronto Press, Toronto, 1996.

Gordon, H. S.: "The Economic Theory of a Common-Property Resource: The Fishery," *Journal of Political Economy*, Vol. 62, 1954, pp. 124–142.

Iudicello, Suzanne, Michael Weber, and Robert Wieland, *Fish, Markets, and Fishermen: The Economics of Overfishing*. Island Press, Washington, DC, 1999.

National Marine Fisheries Service: *Our Living Oceans, The Economic Status of U.S. Fisheries, 1996*, NMFS, Washington, DC, 1997.

National Research Council, Committee to Review Individual Fishing Quotas: *Sharing the Fish: Toward a National Policy on Individual Fishing Quotas*, National Academy Press, Washington, DC, 1999.

OECD: *Towards Sustainable Fisheries, Economic Aspects of the Management of Living Marine Resources*, OECD, Paris, 1997.

Pontecorvo, Giulio (ed.): *The New Order of the Oceans: The Advent of a Managed Environment*, Columbia University Press, New York, 1986.

Scott, Anthony: "Development of Property in the Fishery," *Marine Resource Economics*, Vol. 5, 1988, pp. 289–311.

CHAPTER **18**

THE ECONOMICS OF WILDLIFE MANAGEMENT

The various impacts of human beings on wildlife resources have become more frequent and more contentious in recent years. Continued demographic and economic growth has brought human work and dwelling places more directly into conflict with wild animals and plants. At the same time, these resources are becoming more highly valued, for preserving ecosystem integrity, for providing unconventional inputs for human societies, and as sources of direct enjoyment for an increasingly urbanized population. On a more philosophical level, preservation of wildlife has to some extent become a rallying cry for those who believe it important that modern humans seek to reestablish their roots in the workings of the natural world.

Wildlife, in its most general sense, refers to living, nonhuman organisms that have not been domesticated. The line between what is domesticated and what is not is sometimes a little fuzzy, but for present purposes we don't have to be too precise. We have dealt with several important categories of wildlife in other chapters, in particular marine, forest, and diversity resources.[1] In this chapter we deal with wildlife issues from a somewhat different perspective, in particular those cases where the value of wildlife is not solely a function of its harvested value, but rather of the contributing role it

---

[1] Each of these has wild and domesticated parts; aquaculture is the domesticated part of fisheries; commercial tree farms are the domesticated part of forestry; conventional plant breeding may be the domesticated part of diversity.

plays in various wildlife-related activities pursued by humans. This includes, for example, sport hunting and animal watching. Defined broadly, it could also include situations in which what is involved are **existence values,** that is, the values to humans of knowing that certain wildlife are present, usually in adequate numbers, in a given area.

The chapter begins with a discussion of some basic questions concerning wildlife ecology, economic institutions, and public policy. It then treats a number of important wildlife-related issues: hunting, animal watching, predator control, and the control of wildlife markets. Several other wildlife problems are treated in other chapters: land-use restrictions and habitat control in the chapter on land economics, and endangered species protection in the chapter on the economics of diversity preservation.

WILDLIFE ECOLOGY AND HUMAN INSTITUTIONS

We saw in Chapter 12 that fisheries economics and policy essentially involved bringing together the ecology of fish populations with the economic incentive of human decision makers. Wildlife economics requires the same approach. In this case, however, the interaction of the two—ecology and human institutions—may be more complicated, because of wider variations in the animals and ecological niches in which they are found, the closer physical proximity that exists between terrestrial animals and humans, and the more complicated array of human motivations that characterizes noncommercial situations.

Population Growth Curves

Regardless of what the objective of wildlife management is—hunting, ecotourism, predator control—the critical relationship is the growth dynamics of the wildlife population of interest. A population will increase, decrease, or remain constant, depending on a host of factors such as food availability, sex ratios, fecundity and mortality rates, and predation pressure. In 1942 Arthur Einarsen studied the way a population of pheasants grew after the species was introduced onto a previously uninhabited (by pheasants) island.[2] What he found is pictured in panel (a) of Figure 18-1. For the first few years population increases were modest, but then the rate of change started to get much larger. In 1941 the increment reached its maximum, and the next year it was lower. Assuming a continuance of this trend, it was expected that at some point, perhaps around 1946, the population of pheasants would meet its maximum, or the **carrying capacity** for the habitat. After that the curve would flatten out, signifying no further increase.

---

[2] Arthur S. Einarsen, "Specific Results from Ring-Necked Pheasant Studies in the Pacific Northwest," Transactions, Seventh N.A. Wildlife Conference, 1942, pp. 130–138.

SECTION FIVE: APPLIED NATURAL RESOURCE PROBLEMS

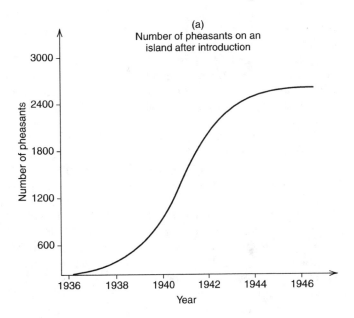

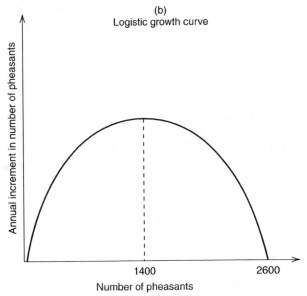

FIGURE 18-1
Growth of a Pheasant Population (*Data Source:* Arthur S. Einarsen, "Specific Results from Ring-Necked Pheasant Studies in the Pacific Northwest," Transactions, Seventh N.A. Wildlife Conference, 1942, pp. 130–138.)

CHAPTER 18:   THE ECONOMICS OF WILDLIFE MANAGEMENT

What he was seeing in this case was apparently a phenomenon following a **logistic growth curve,** a relationship we first encountered in Chapter 13. It is an inverted U curve showing how the growth increment to a population is related to the size of that population. A logistic curve is depicted in panel (b) of Figure 18-1. The annual increment of small populations is relatively low; it reaches a maximum at a population size of about 1,400 pheasants and then drops to zero at a population of about 2,600. Not all wild animals behave according to simple logistic models like this, but despite its simplicity it summarizes the basic population dynamics for many of them, as far as is known. Carrying capacity in this case is at about 2,600 animals, while 1,400 is the stock size that defines **maximum sustained yield,** the maximum quantity of the wildlife in question that could be harvested on a **sustainable** basis.

Several important points must be made here. The first is that, although 1,400 is the population level that gives the maximum sustained yield, this strictly biological point of reference is not necessarily the stock that is optimal from a social standpoint. We saw in the case of the fishery that the commercial aspects of the problem—the market values of the fish and the costs of harvest—led to an economic optimum different from the biological point of maximum sustained yield. If we consider wildlife more broadly, we have to allow for the possibility that there are other sources of value, for example, value for **recreational hunting,** or for **ecotourism** (wildlife viewing), value for purposes of **biological diversity,** or simply **existence value.** These other sources of value could make it even more difficult to identify a socially optimal wildlife stock in any particular case.

The other point to be made is about uncertainty, especially when we lack a very clear idea of what the growth curve looks like. Theoretically, if the growth function for any animal population were well known, it could be used to establish optimal harvest policies. The problem is that, in the real world, so many factors are at work that it may be very difficult, even with diligent research, to identify a simple relationship between stock size and the increment to that stock. Exhibit 18-1 illustrates this in the case of the wild turkey. The upshot is that management of many, if not most, wildlife populations will have to proceed in the face of great uncertainty about underlying growth dynamics.

Human Institutions and Values

The other side of the wildlife management and conservation issue is the array of human institutions and values that have shaped the historical development of wildlife law and management practices. Chief among the former is the institution of **property rights.** Terrestrial wildlife is just that; it exists on or close to the land surface. Property rights in land, therefore, have critical implications for the ways human beings have related to wildlife populations.

The dominant landowning tradition in the United States is private property. Landowners have the legal right to devote their land to any lawful purpose

SECTION FIVE: APPLIED NATURAL RESOURCE PROBLEMS

EXHIBIT 18-1

DIFFICULTIES IN DETERMINING WILDLIFE GROWTH RELATIONSHIPS:
THE WILD TURKEY

Hunting regulations were set cautiously after wild turkeys (*Meleagris gallopavo*) were re-established successfully in much of the United States. Weaver and Mosby (1979) analyzed the effects of varying season lengths and bag limits by comparing population data for turkey flocks in two areas of Virginia. In a study area in the Central Mountains, the turkey population was estimated at 19,600 in 1963 and 29,400 in 1976, representing a gain of 50 percent. In an area of the Eastern Piedmont, turkeys numbered 20,700 in 1963, but the population declined by more than 13 percent to 18,100 birds in 1976. The harvest generally increased in the Central Mountain population; the average kill of 1,126 birds per year for 1959–62 increased to 1,794 for 1964–1968 and reached an average of 2,271 turkeys per year for 1969–1976. Conversely, harvests in the Eastern Piedmont declined from an average of 1,075 birds for 1951–1962 to 379 turkeys per year for 1971–1976. The results show that a reduction of the harvest to levels of about 2–3 percent of the autumn population did not halt a decline of turkeys in the Eastern Piedmont. Conversely, harvests of 8 to 10 percent did not prevent steady growth in the Central Mountain population. Therefore, hunting was not a factor causing a decline or preventing an increase, respectively, in these turkey populations.

Turkey populations in good habitat may prove resilient to large reductions. Rush (1973) described the effects of live trapping and removing turkeys for stocking in other areas. No detectable decline in the resident population could be detected, even though 38 to 43 percent of the autumn population of 350 to 400 birds was removed each year during a 10-year period. Turkey numbers in Michigan have continued growing concurrently with increased harvests of gobblers.

One might ask, if turkeys can withstand heavy hunting pressure, why were they so scarce 50 years ago? Factors apart from hunting apparently play a major role in determining turkey numbers, especially habitat conditions, disease, and weather. Therefore, beyond adjusting harvest rates, a full range of ecological conditions must be addressed in the management of wild turkeys.

Source: Eric G. Bolen and William L. Robinson, *Wildlife Ecology and Management,* Prentice Hall, Englewood Cliffs, NJ, 1995, pp. 177–178. Data are from J. K. Weaver and H. S. Mosby, "Influence of Hunting Regulations on Virginia Wild Turkey Populations," *Journal of Wildlife Management,* Vol. 43, 1979, pp. 128–135, and G. Rush, "The Hen-Brood Release as a Restoration Technique," in G. C. Sanderson and H. C. Schultz (eds.), *Wild Turkey Management: Current Problems and Programs,* University of Missouri Press, 1973.

---

they wish and to exclude trespassers, that is, those who enter without permission. The law governing the wildlife resource itself has evolved in a different direction.[3] Ownership of wildlife, in the sense of having the rights and responsibilities of its management, has become vested within political bodies, especially the state governments and more recently with the federal government. Why this has happened can be seen by looking at the simple schematic in Figure 18-2. The shaded areas in the figure represent the habitat of a particular

---

[3] Numerous books deal in whole or in part with wildlife law in the United States and elsewhere. A number of these references are listed at the end of the chapter.

Field: Natural Resource
Economics — An
Introduction

V. Applied Natural
Resource Problems

18. The Economics Of
Wildlife Management

© The McGraw–Hill
Companies, 2003

CHAPTER 18:   THE ECONOMICS OF WILDLIFE MANAGEMENT

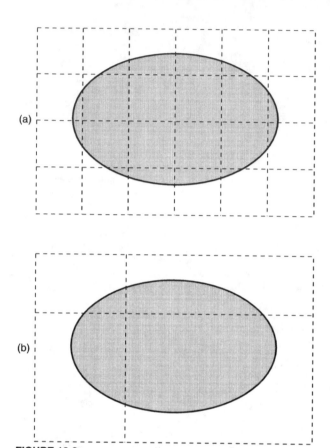

(a)

(b)

FIGURE 18-2
Schematic Representation of Wildlife Population Habitat as
Compared to Property Boundaries

population of wildlife, perhaps a certain animal, or a plant of some distinct
species. The dashed lines represent property boundaries as they have developed among the holdings of a number of private owners. Naturally, these are
highly artificial; in the real world, boundaries and habitats take on all sorts of
complicated shapes. But the simplicity will allow us to see the concept clearly.

Panel (a) depicts a situation where the habitat of this population is broken
up into many different property holdings. Put the opposite way, any one piece
of property contains only a relatively small portion of the total habitat. Panel
(b) is different in two senses. First, the number of property holdings is smaller,
in this case just four; second, just one property holding, the one in the southeast, contains the majority of the habitat. Panel (a) typifies the situation in
early America: small land holdings relative to the geographic spread of

wildlife habitats. In such situations it is useless to expect individual landowners, acting on their own, to engage in efficient wildlife conservation and management activities; each one owns such a small part of the overall habitat that uncoordinated efforts would likely be fruitless. Effective wildlife management in this case calls for one of the following alternatives:

1 Coordinated action among the landowners achieved by agreement among themselves
2 Action by some higher political body that has the power to make and enforce wildlife-related regulations

The first of these may be difficult, depending on circumstances. The costs of trying to reach and enforce an agreement among landowners are called **"transactions costs."** Factors that lead to high transactions costs in cases like this are the relatively large number of landowners, the possibility of **free riding**,[4] and the fact that not all landowners are likely to have the same views about the value and role of the wildlife in question.

In the United States, this state of affairs has led historically to two outcomes. One is that wildlife has tended to be treated as an **open-access resource**. Landowners individually had no particularly strong incentives to conserve wildlife, and so hunters and harvesters essentially had the freedom at the beginning to take the wildlife without limit. This had the predictable effects, namely overharvesting and diminution of wildlife stocks. This led to the second outcome, which is that wildlife law in America evolved historically in the direction of giving authority and responsibility over wildlife stocks to the various states. Thus, it is essentially state wildlife authorities who have primary jurisdiction over the wildlife resource. Individual landholders may take steps to exclude hunters and other harvesters from their properties, but they do not have direct jurisdiction over the wildlife on their property, in the sense of being able to enforce their own rules for hunting or otherwise harvesting it.

The historical wildlife situation in England, where much of U.S. law originated, was more like panel (b) of Figure 18-2. Private holdings were in general much bigger there, in relation to typical wildlife habitats. Thus, the transactions costs of private wildlife management were relatively modest, and for this reason wildlife law in the United Kingdom came to be based on private ownership. That is, individual landowners are also endowed with property rights over the wildlife that inhabits their property.

Public Landownership and Management

There is a third way of dealing with the landownership problem: maintain or convert the land to public ownership, and then designate a public agency to

---

[4] To review the concept of free riding see Chapter 6.

manage the wildlife resources. Chapter 14, on land economics, contains information on the extent of public lands in the United States. Table 18-1 shows the federal agencies that are heavily involved in wildlife management. State agencies also oversee wildlife resources on state-owned land.

In a very general way there are two types of public lands on which wildlife issues are important: A variety of public areas, such as national and local parks, forests, wilderness areas, and the like, have been established for a variety of purposes, of which wildlife may be one; and there are public lands, such as wildlife refuges, which have been set aside specifically for the purpose of protecting wildlife resources. At the national level the latter is the National Wildlife Refuge System, which has grown to over 92 million acres of land and water since its inception in 1924.

Despite the fact that the primary purpose of wildlife refuges is to preserve the conditions that foster the health and welfare of wildlife species, refuge management frequently confronts the same type of question that comes up on other types of public preserves: whether, and to what extent, other objectives besides wildlife preservation should be pursued within the wildlife refuges. For example, a number of refuges allow cattle grazing, which is managed by the U.S. Fish and Wildlife Service through a system of grazing permits. Many refuges allow hunting, some allow timber cutting or mining. The basic question in these cases is how much of the non-wildlife-related activity to allow on the refuges.

The relevant laws on this issue[5] state essentially that the refuges may be used for other purposes as long as these are "compatible" with the major purposes for which the refuges were established. Conflicts about what is and what is not compatible are sure to increase in the future both because people are placing higher values on wildlife preservation as a goal, because population and economic growth will increase the pressure on refuge resources, and because of underfunding of the refuge maintenance and management operations.

THE ECONOMICS OF SPORT HUNTING

In colonial America commercial harvesting of terrestrial wildlife was an important source of food and materials (like deerskins and beaver pelts). In the marine world this continues to be true. The colonials found early that, with open access to wildlife stocks, commercial exploitation of wild animals could lead very quickly to stock reductions and scarcities. Their first response was to institute closed seasons and other regulations. Eventually, the states passed laws prohibiting the commercial sale of most wild animals. But although commercial hunting declined, sport, or recreational, hunting grew as a popular pastime in the United States and elsewhere.

---

[5] Primarily the National Wildlife Refuge System Administration Act of 1966, as amended.

SECTION FIVE: APPLIED NATURAL RESOURCE PROBLEMS

TABLE 18-1
PARTIAL LISTING OF FEDERAL AGENCIES HAVING RESPONSIBILITIES
FOR WILDLIFE MANAGEMENT

Cabinet-level department	Agency name	Activities and responsibilities for wildlife
Interior*	U.S. Fish and Wildlife Service	Leading agency for conservation of migratory birds, certain mammals, and sport fishes; manages refuges and hatcheries; coordinates endangered species programs; administers federal aid to states; negotiates international agreements; works primarily from regional offices.
	National Park Service	Research and management of wildlife on national parks and monuments; coordinates Wild and Scenic Rivers System.
	Bureau of Land Management	Leading agency for managing lands in the public domain, primarily in western states; supervises multiple use, including wildlife, grazing, mining, recreation, timber, and watershed; about 55 percent of all federal lands are under Bureau of Land Management.
	Bureau of Indian Affairs	Trust for grazing, timber, water, and other resource management, including wildlife.
	Bureau of Reclamation	Leads programs for water development in western states; wildlife management and recreation considered in reclamation projects.
Agriculture†	Forest Service	Administers national forests and grasslands and wildlife thereon; research and management of all forest resources; fire protection and timber harvests are major concerns; regional experiment stations are activity centers.

In 1996 there was a total of 39.7 million participants in hunting and fishing activities in the United States (Table 18-2). The most popular activity was freshwater fishing, followed by big game hunting. Total expenditures on hunting activities in 1996 were estimated at about $72 billion. The total number of people participating in animal watching in that year was estimated at about 63 million, with $29 billion of related expenditures. Residential animal watching had three times the number of participants in nonresidential animal watching.[6]

We dealt with commercial hunting in effect, when we looked at marine resource economics in Chapter 13. The models we used there would carry over to terrestrial commercial hunting, for example, the trapping of animals for fur. The value of the harvested product in this case is established on a market, sim-

---

[6] Residential animal watching is defined as an activity that takes place within 1 mile of home.

CHAPTER 18: THE ECONOMICS OF WILDLIFE MANAGEMENT

TABLE 18-1—*Continued*
PARTIAL LISTING OF FEDERAL AGENCIES HAVING RESPONSIBILITIES
FOR WILDLIFE MANAGEMENT

Cabinet-level department	Agency name	Activities and responsibilities for wildlife
Agriculture†	Soil Conservation Service	Publishes soil surveys; provides data and technical assistance for soil and water conservation; no research activities; funds small watershed projects and assists with habitat development on private lands; works primarily with organized districts.
Commerce‡	National Marine Fisheries Service	Provides management, research, and other services for living marine resources, including mammals and invertebrates as well as marine fishes; lead agency in managing offshore development as component of National Oceanic and Atmospheric Administration.
Defense§	Army Corps of Engineers	Major responsibilities for dredging, stream stabilization, and other developments of navigable rivers and coastal wetlands; issues dredge and fill permits authorized by Section 404 of the Clean Water Act.

Source: National Wildlife Federation (1987) as reported in Eric G. Bolen and William L. Robinson, *Wildlife Ecology and Management,* 3rd ed., Prentice-Hall, Englewood Cliffs, NJ, 1995, p. 477.
*Other Department of Interior agencies in one way or another involved with wildlife management include: Bureau of Mines, U.S. Geological Survey, Office of Surface Mines, and the Office of Water Research and Technology.
†Other Department of Agriculture agencies with wildlife-related activities include Animal and Plant Health Inspection Service, Agricultural Stabilization and Conservation Service, and Economic Research Service.
‡Other Department of Commerce agencies with wildlife-related activities include the Office of Coastal Zone Management and the National Sea Grant College program; both are components of the National Oceanic and Atmospheric Administration.
§Other Department of Defense agencies (e.g., Department of the Air Force) also manage wildlife and other natural resources on military lands.

ilar to the market price of fish. Recreational hunting has the added factor that its value is related not only to the wildlife harvested, but also to the satisfaction derived from engaging in the activity itself. In fact, in many cases the greater part of the value of hunting may stem from engaging in the activity rather than in the number of wildlife harvested.

Conceptually, however, we can approach it in a similar way. In Figure 18-3, panel (a) represents the **growth relationship** of the wildlife being hunted. It has the standard U-shaped relationship between the stock level and the annual growth increment, thus s_0 is the stock level that would result in the long run if the animal (or plant) were not hunted. Any stock level lower than s_0 can be maintained indefinitely if the appropriate corresponding harvest level is correctly maintained.

SECTION FIVE: APPLIED NATURAL RESOURCE PROBLEMS

TABLE 18-2
PARTICIPATION AND EXPENDITURES IN WILDLIFE-RELATED ACTIVITIES, 1996

	Number of participants (millions)	Expenditures ($ billion)
Sport fishing		
Freshwater	29.7	
Saltwater	9.4	
Sport hunting		
Big game	11.3	
Small game	6.9	
Migratory birds	3.1	
Other	1.5	
Total fishing and hunting*	39.7	71.9
Wildlife watching		
Residential	60.8	
Nonresidential	23.7	
Total wildlife watching*	62.9	29.2

*Totals do not equal the simple sum of constituent activities because people may engage in multiple activities.
Source: U.S. Fish and Wildlife Service, National Survey of Fishing, Hunting and Wildlife Associated Recreation, 1996.

An **effort-benefits** function for **recreational hunting** is shown in panel (b) of Figure 18-3. It is drawn to reflect the fact that people obtain benefits from the activity of hunting, not solely from the number of animals taken. By contrast, the figure also shows an **effort-revenue** function that would pertain if this were a strictly commercial harvest. In that case the value is tied directly to the number of animals harvested, which is the assumption used before to model a commercial fishery.[7] Note that the effort-benefits function and the effort-revenue function have the same end points; in the long run, hunters will not get benefits from hunting if success rates are always zero. But it is skewed to the right somewhat, because benefits arise from both the catch and the activity.

Figure 18-4 shows the effort-benefits function in combination with the function representing the costs of hunting; the former is labeled EB and the latter TC. The TC function is drawn under the assumption that each hunting day has the same cost. The open-access hunting level is e_1, which is very close to the zero-catch level of e_0. The latter is the effort level that drives the stock to, or near, extinction. The reason why open access would tend to be this close to the extinction point is, to repeat, the fact that hunters get benefits from the activity itself, not just from the catch. Because of excess effort levels, no net benefits are being produced by this particular wildlife population at effort level e_1. Total costs are high enough that they exactly equal total benefits. The effort level that maximizes net benefits, on the other hand, is e^*. This is the level where the

[7] See Chapter 13.

CHAPTER 18:   THE ECONOMICS OF WILDLIFE MANAGEMENT

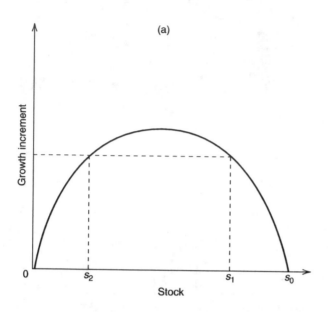

(a)

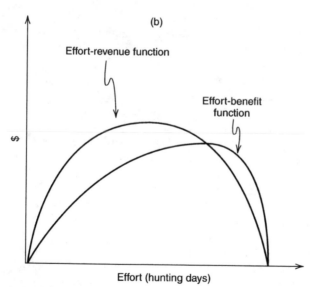

(b)

FIGURE 18-3
Stock-Growth and Effort-Benefits Functions for Recreational
Hunting

SECTION FIVE: APPLIED NATURAL RESOURCE PROBLEMS

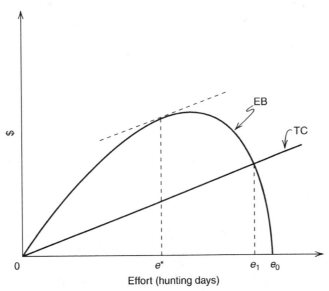

FIGURE 18-4
Efficient and Open-Access Hunting Levels

slope of the marginal cost curve (marginal cost) is equal to the slope of the EB curve (marginal benefits). Note that the efficient point involves lower levels of hunting but higher benefits than the open-access effort level.

High effort levels associated with open access suggest that some way is needed to control effort or the catch rate. Historically, authorities have tried to do this through command-and-control regulations. **Closed seasons** is one of these. The hope behind limiting the length of a hunting season, is that the number of hunting days will be reduced. How much this attains that objective, as opposed simply to compressing a given number of hunting days into a shorter time span, is an open question. In many places public authorities are using lotteries to control hunting effort. The state of Maine has a lottery to distribute moose hunting permits, as does Wyoming for distributing permits to hunt elk. Massachusetts uses a lottery to issue deer hunting permits for certain state-owned land.

Another common way of trying to reduce the impacts of open access is for public authorities to enforce **bag limits,** that is, a limitation on the number of wildlife that may be taken per trip or per year. A way of modeling this is to see it as a shift back in the effort-benefit function. By setting a bag limit, authorities attempt to reduce the benefits accruing to hunters on a typical hunting trip. In Figure 18-5, this is shown as a shift from the outer to the inner effort-benefit function (from EB_1 to EB_2). The open-access hunting level would move from e_1 to e_2. How much this changes depends on how much the effort-benefit function changes in response to the catch limitations. If the bulk of the benefits of hunting come from the activity rather than the size of the catch, the

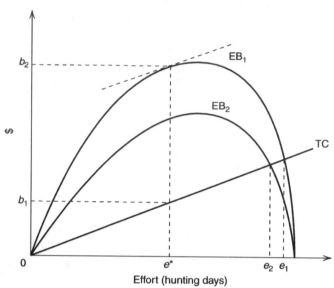

FIGURE 18-5
Policies for Controlling Hunting

relationship would not change much and the level of effort would not change much. The bag limit reduces the yield from a given number of hunting days. So though the effort level is reduced only modestly, the equilibrium size of the stock would increase. From an economic standpoint, however, the fact that there is open access, even with the bag limits, means that the effort level is still too high and net benefits are still zero. It is theoretically possible to lower the bag limit sufficient to shift the effort level back to e^*, even with open access. Net benefits would still be zero, however.

Private Ownership

Why doesn't the public wildlife management agency simply charge a price for access to the wildlife sufficiently high to shift effort levels back to e^*? State fish and game agencies typically sell hunting licenses or permits, but the prices of these are normally kept quite low for political reasons. Thus, hunting access is usually regulated through command-and-control regulations, such as bag limits, gear restrictions, and establishment of open seasons.

Private landowners, on the other hand, have the right to restrict access to their property. One possibility is to have landowners charge hunters for access and keep out those who are not willing to pay. If this could be done, and if the motives of these landowners were to maximize their net incomes, they would charge exactly the price that is needed to reduce effort to e^*. The economically efficient effort level e^* is the same effort level that would maximize the net incomes of the owners. The net income obtainable to the owners is an amount equal to $b_2 - b_1$.

SECTION FIVE: APPLIED NATURAL RESOURCE PROBLEMS

With the population and income changes of recent decades, and with diminished stocks of many wildlife populations because of open-access problems, it is not surprising that privately provided hunting has started to become popular in the United States and elsewhere. It is widespread in the Southwest as well as on commercial timberland of the southern states.[8] A market for hunting big game on private land has also developed in many states of the American West and on a number of Native American reservations in the West. In this sense, the United States is catching up with Europe, where markets in privately provided hunting and fishing opportunities have existed for some time. Privatized hunting is also growing in Africa.

One important element of these markets is a factor we discussed above, the patterns of property rights in comparison with the location of the habitat for the game animals in question. Suppose there is a pattern similar to panel (a) of Figure 18-2. Here the bulk of the habitat is divided among a large number of landowners, each of whom owns only a small part of the total area. To privatize the hunting would require all the landowners to get together and agree on goals, procedures, and especially on how the total revenues would be shared among themselves. The transactions costs of doing this may simply be too high to overcome, especially if the projected revenues are not particularly great. If there is only a modest number of landowners, however, transactions cost may not be excessive. In some parts of the world new businesses have appeared whose specialty is contracting with a sufficient number of contiguous landowners to put together a large hunting territory, then managing the territory as a private hunting preserve.

The reservation of land for market-regulated hunting of wild, free-ranging animals blends into what can be called **game ranching,** where active management steps are undertaken to enhance the value of the wildlife stock. Such management practices as supplementary feeding, selective culling, and predator control may be used to increase the value of the stock of game animals. Of course to do these things effectively, it is important that the firms or agencies doing the managing have control over most of the habitat of the target wildlife.

The models used above are extremely simple and unrealistic in many ways. We use them simply to explore some of the basic aspects of recreational hunting. One factor that is common in the real world, but overlooked here, is that there will usually be other wildlife species, both plant and animal, that interact with the species being hunted. These other species may also be hunted, or perhaps are valuable in other ways, say, for habitat control or animal watching. The relevant effort-benefits function now becomes much more complex, because a relationship that contained all social benefits associated with hunting this species would have to take into account all these other impacts. This can be a problem in both publicly and privately provided hunting arrangements.

[8] Robert K. Davis, "A New Paradigm in Wildlife Conservation: Using Markets to Produce Big Game Hunting," in Terry L. Anderson and Peter J. Hill (eds.), *Wildlife in the Marketplace*, Rowmand and Littlefield Publishers, 1995, pp. 109–125.

CHAPTER 18:   THE ECONOMICS OF WILDLIFE MANAGEMENT

WILDLIFE IN SUBURBAN AREAS

In most parts of the world urban areas are growing both demographically and in terms of area. For the most part it is a process of **suburbanization,** in which growth occurs on the fringes of expanding urban areas, to satisfy peoples' demands for single-family dwellings with an attached amount of surrounding space. Thus the common phenomenon of low-density housing developments spreading slowly, or sometimes rapidly, into lands that were previously uninhabited or used for farms. One effect of this has been to bring people into contact with the wildlife that were living on the suburban fringe. Coupled with this is the fact that in some parts of the country, such as the Northeast, changes in rural landscapes (e.g., the abandonment of farms) has allowed the reestablishment of some species in areas from which they previously had been pushed out. This has added to the likelihood of human/animal contacts as suburban development spreads.

There are two major dimensions of this phenomenon: (1) the biology, ecology, and population dynamics of the particular animal species at issue and (2) the human demography and attitudes that determine the social benefits and costs of animal populations in the suburbs. In extremely simple terms, we have pictured these two dimensions in Figure 18-6. Panel (a) shows the standard model of population growth. It says essentially that if nothing is done with respect to managing the particular animal in question, its population will settle at something around k_0. Population levels lower than this can be realized, but only if some amount of harvesting or stock reduction is pursued. To keep the population at a level of k^*, for example, would require that Δk^* of the animals be removed each year.

The population level k^* is chosen for a reason, as we can see by looking at panel (b) of the figure. This schematic presents the marginal benefits (marginal willingness to pay) by suburbanites at different stock levels and also the marginal costs associated with different population levels of the animal in question. The benefit function (labeled MWTP) summarizes peoples' attitudes about wildlife. It shows that they place a high initial value on this animal and that the value of a marginal animal declines as the animal population gets larger. This value is based on such factors as **existence value, hunting value,** or **viewing value.** The relationship—its height and shape—clearly will depend on the particular animal involved (deer vs. skunks, for example) and the size and characteristics of the human population involved.[9]

---

[9] For any species there may be indirect sources of value. These are animals (and it could also apply to plants) that are not particularly valuable to humans in themselves, but either support or diminish other species that are so valued. Mice may not be particularly desirable themselves, but they may be highly valued because they support other animals, such as foxes and hawks. In such cases the social value that is inherent in marginal willingness to pay is a **derived value.** The social value of the species is derived from the social value of the supported species that is essentially transmitted through the biological linkages connecting the different species in a particular ecosystem.

SECTION FIVE: APPLIED NATURAL RESOURCE PROBLEMS

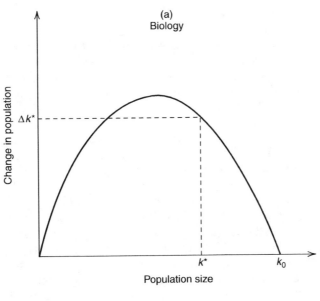

(a)
Biology

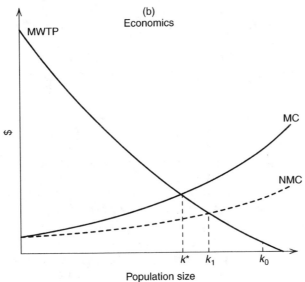

(b)
Economics

FIGURE 18-6
Wildlife in Suburban Areas

The marginal cost curve (labeled MC) shows the social costs of this stock of wildlife. Costs could arise from several factors. The animals could bring about changes in the ecosystem sufficient to produce costs for humans. A case of this, for example, is changes to a surface water system produced by beaver dams. Health costs may occur in some cases, such as threats of lyme disease from tick-carrying deer and rabbits. A major cause of damage in some regions is collisions between animals and automobiles. Physical threats to pets and children may be at issue, or perhaps damage to agricultural crops. Whatever the source of the costs, the MC curve is meant to encompass all the relevant ones present in the case at issue. On the basis of the marginal benefit and marginal cost curves indicated, the efficient animal population size is k^*. This is substantially below the nonintervention level of k_0, but in different circumstances and with different animals, of course, the relationship of these two stock levels could be quite different.

As it stands, the analysis says nothing about the actual costs of managing the animal stock, of removing a portion of the animal population if that is what is called for. This can be a contentious issue in itself, because many people and groups are committed to their views of humane treatment of animals, which may rule out certain approaches to animal removal. One way of modeling this is by deducting removal costs from the MC curve pictured. As a community moves to a lower population size, it does not experience a savings in cost indicated by the original MC curve, but by this amount minus the control costs. This would yield a **net MC curve** (labeled NMC), which is sketched in the figure as a dashed line under the MC curve. The new dashed marginal cost curve intersects the MWTP curve at k_1, which is to the right of k^*, indicating that when control costs are included, the efficient population size of the animal would be somewhat larger than when these costs are not taken into account. Exactly what these removal costs are is open to question. Certainly they include the opportunity costs of reducing the stock size. Exhibit 18-2 contains a newspaper account of a company organized to reduce the size of deer herds in suburban communities.

DISTRIBUTIONAL ISSUES IN RESTORATION AND PREDATOR CONTROL

In the analysis of the previous section we were assuming that members of a particular suburban community were both recipients of benefits and the bearers of costs associated with wildlife control. In many wildlife management programs, however, there is a major difference between groups of interested people: some groups being primarily beneficiaries and others being primarily bearers of cost.

In Minnesota the reestablishment of the gray wolf has been quite successful; as of 1998 there were well over 2,000 individuals in the state, and steps were being taken to delist the animal as an endangered species. This program is quite similar in concept to many other wildlife restoration programs. It confers existence value benefits on a widely dispersed group of people, both inside and outside of the state. And it leads to substantial costs for a relatively small group, in this case ranchers and farmers who experience depredation of their domestic livestock. Many cases involving the endangered species fit this type of pattern: diffuse benefits, concentrated costs.

The basic structure of the problem is depicted in Figure 18-7. The horizontal axis measures the stock size of an animal in a particular community, while the vertical axis contains a monetary scale. People who receive benefits from this stock are divided into two groups, a local group and everybody else. The local

SECTION FIVE: APPLIED NATURAL RESOURCE PROBLEMS

EXHIBIT 18-2

SHARPSHOOTER AND ASSOCIATE KILL 50 DEER IN TOWN CULL

Don Ward

DUNE ACRES, Ind.—A professional sharpshooter and his associate killed 50 deer over the past week in the state's first municipal deer cull.

But additional deer kills probably will be considered necessary in future years to control the size of the herd, reduce vegetation damage and improve drivers' safety.

"We barely made a dent in our deer population, but at least we got through it. And maybe we set a precedent for other towns in Indiana, so they won't have to go through the legal expense of sorting it all out in court," said Town Council President Yolanda Stemer.

So far, no other towns have approached the Indiana Department of Natural Resources about conducting a deer kill, said spokesman Stephen Sellers.

The privately owned Hayes Arboretum in Richmond conducts an annual deer kill to protect the 179 plant species in the 355-acre nature preserve. And in 1994, Northern Indiana Public Service Co. employed the same sharpshooter used by Dune Acres, Anthony DiNicola of White Buffalo Inc., to thin the deer herd at a generating station in Wheatfield.

And the Department of Natural Resources itself has used supervised hunts in recent years to thin the deer population at several Indiana state parks.

Sellers said natural resources agency studies have shown a significant reduction in deer populations at those parks.

"We want a balance to be able to see deer and to hunt deer, but also to minimize the damage to crops and vegetation, and to reduce the number of accidents with vehicles," Sellers said.

Dune Acres might be breaking ground in Indiana, but it is hardly the nation's first city or town to do so.

For instance, DiNicola recently returned from Eden Prairie, Minn., an affluent Minneapolis suburb, where he killed 160 deer in two weeks.

The Pittsburgh suburb of Fox Chapel, meanwhile, has been using bow hunters to thin its deer herd because of the community's dense population.

But after killing 300 deer in three years, the town still had made only a small dent in its deer population. Despite protest, town officials planned to continue the program for at least six more years.

In nearby Illinois, some Chicago suburbs have been conducting their own deer culls for years using their own trained shooters, most of whom use guns and spotlights.

Officials in DuPage County, Ill., however, started killing deer in 1992 using a controversial method: catching deer with a net and then killing them with a bolt gun. After much opposition by animal rights groups, the county resorted to guns and spotlights.

"After five years of culling deer, we're just now getting the numbers down to where we want," said DuPage County Board member Patricia Bellock. "You have to stay at it for several years until a faster method comes along, especially because of the fact the deer give birth to two or three fawns at a time."

At Dune Acres, working without the aid of gun silencers and spotlights, DiNicola and an associate used .223-caliber bolt-action rifles and military-style night vision scopes to spot and kill deer. Accompanied at all times by Department of Natural Resources officials, the two fired from the back of a truck as it stopped at a dozen sites previously baited with corn.

The method was considered the best—and the quickest—by Town Council members.

"There's no sport or hunt in this," said Stemer. "It's the most efficient, humane solution to the problem."

Source: The Indianapolis Star, March 2, 1998. Reprinted by permission.

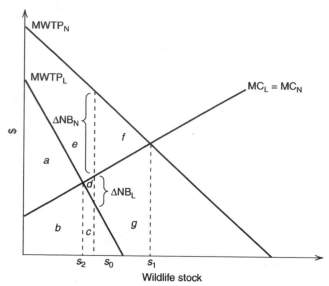

FIGURE 18-7
Wildlife Restoration

group consists of people who live in the vicinity of the animal community; $MWTP_L$ depicts the benefits this group receives from this wildlife. It could be expected to contain both market-type benefits (stemming from, for example, net revenues from animal spotting businesses) and nonmarket benefits. Ranchers in Florida whose livestock may be threatened by the Florida panther also appear to gain some satisfaction from knowing that panthers inhabit their lands.[10]

$MWTP_N$ represents the valuation of this animal by all nonlocals. We would suppose that this is primarily existence value, though some will be viewing value also by people who visit the area. Both MWTP curves are of traditional shape, that is, downward-sloping to the right.

The curve labeled $MC_L = MC_N$ represents two marginal cost curves—the marginal cost curve for the locals is assumed to be the same as for the nonlocals. Remember these are aggregate marginal cost curves for the two groups. Thus, although the damage per person is undoubtedly higher among the local group, there are fewer of them. And although the costs per person (e.g., in terms, say, of lost hunting values) are much lower for outsiders, there are far more of them than there are locals. Thus, the two marginal cost curves have been drawn as the same. The reason for this is to keep the graph relatively uncluttered.

The model shows a substantial discrepancy between the stock levels that are efficient from the standpoint of the local community and from the standpoint of the nonlocal group. These are, respectively, s_2 and s_1. The overall social efficiency level would lie between these two points. If current stock levels

[10] David S. Maehr, *The Florida Panther, Life and Death of a Vanishing Carnivore*, Island Press, Washington, DC, 1997.

were to the left of s_2 or to the right of s_1, there would be agreement between locals and nonlocals for building up the stock with a restoration program in the first case, and for reducing the stock in the second case.

But there would be conflicts for any stock level between s_2 and s_1. Suppose the actual stock level was s_0. Locals would be improved (i.e., their net benefits would increase) by a move to the left, whereas nonlocals would be improved by a move to the right. It's possible to determine the gains and losses from the diagram. For a small increase in the stock at s_0, nonlocals would experience a gain equal to the distance between $MWTP_N$ and MC_N, shown as the distance ΔNB_N (for change in net benefits to the nonlocal group). Locals would experience a reduction in net benefits equal to ΔNB_L. Since $\Delta NB_N > \Delta NB_L$, overall social efficiency would call for an increase in the stock size. As the stock size increases, ΔNB_N would diminish and ΔNB_L would increase, and at some stock size they would come into balance. This would identify the socially efficient size of the animal population.

How different s_0 and s_1 are, and how much adjustment of the actual stock would be required, and how much difference there is between net benefits to the two different groups, obviously depends, at least conceptually, on the shapes and slopes of the different curves. Even though we don't know them exactly, they can still be used to help us think about cases of wildlife management. In Alaska in recent years, state officials planned a wolf control project to reduce depredation of the state elk herds. In effect, their planning was done in accordance with the $MWTP_L$ and MC_L curves, as depicted in the figure, with little recognition that there might be a $MWTP_N$ curve well to the right, representing the values of people in the rest of the country for the existence of wolves in Alaska. After a notable political backlash from this nonlocal group, the Alaskan authorities were essentially forced to return to the drawing board and develop new plans.

Another idea that presents itself just from the logic of the diagram is the possibility of compensation. Suppose the initial population is at s_0. For a small increase in the stock size, $\Delta NB_N > \Delta NB_L$, implying that compensation could be paid by the nonlocals to the locals to cover their loss in net benefits and still leave positive net benefits for the nonlocals. In fact, compensation could be used to reduce the political opposition that locals might express for the program. In the Minnesota restoration program, for example, compensation is paid to ranchers for livestock killed by the wolves.

These are abstract notions, however, until they can be filled in with actual numbers from surveys or other types of economic analyses. An illustration is available from a recent national survey to assess the net benefits stemming from the reestablishment of wolves in Yellowstone National Park.[11] The researchers surveyed 335 local people (defined as people who lived in the three-

---

[11] See John W. Duffield and Chris J. Neher, "Economics of Wolf Recovery in Yellowstone National Park," Transactions of the Sixty-First North American Wildlife and Natural Resource Conference, 1996, pp. 285–292.

CHAPTER 18:   THE ECONOMICS OF WILDLIFE MANAGEMENT

TABLE 18-3

BENEFITS AND COSTS TO LOCAL AND NONLOCAL PEOPLE FROM WOLF RESTORATION IN YELLOWSTONE NATIONAL PARK

	Local	Nonlocal	Total
Mean WTP* of supporters	$20.50	$8.92	
Mean WTP of nonsupporters	$10.80	$1.52	
Estimated number of supporters	391,204	50,152,416	50,543,620
Estimated number of nonsupporters	340,522	25,774,280	26,114,802
Total WTP of supporters†	$160,553	$8,956,130	$9,116,683
Total WTP of nonsupporters†	$68,718	$784,322	$853,040
Net benefits	$91,835	$8,171,808	$8,263,643

*WTP = willingness to pay.

†These numbers are calculated by assuming a perpetual income stream, discounted at 7 percent, that gave a present value equal to the one-time payments that respondents indicated as their willingness to pay. They are also adjusted to reflect an estimate that **actual willingness to pay** is only 28.6 percent of **stated willingness to pay;** this is based on the researchers' previous work on the relationship between stated and actual WTP.

Source: John W. Duffield and Chris J. Neher, "Economics of Wolf Recovery in Yellowstone National Park," Transactions of the Sixty-First North American Wildlife and Natural Resource Conference, 1996, pp. 285-292.

state region of Wyoming, Montana, and Idaho) and 313 nonlocal individuals, asking them willingness-to-pay–type questions for wolf restoration in Yellowstone. The mean response levels of the surveyed individuals were then blown up to regional and national dimensions by using state and national population numbers. The results are shown in Table 18-3.

The respondents were broken into supporters and nonsupporters of the wolf restoration. If we assume that the willingness to pay by supporters represents benefits, and willingness to pay by nonsupporters[12] represents costs,[13] then we can interpret these numbers in terms of the areas shown in Figure 18-7. Benefits to locals ($a + b + c$ in the diagram) are $160,553, and their costs ($b + c + d$) are $68,718, leaving net benefits of $91,835. For nonlocals, benefits ($a + b + c + d + e + f + g$) equal $8,956,130, while costs ($b + c + d + g$) are $784,322, leaving a net of $8,171,808. Note, again, how much more the net benefits are for nonlocals as compared to locals. The reason for this is that the total number of nonlocals essentially swamps the number of locals, and so the net benefits to nonlocals is the most important determinant of overall net benefits. Note further, however, that net benefits to nonlocals are at least positive.

PUBLIC POLICY AND WILDLIFE MARKETS

The harvesting of wildlife, as well as much of the nonconsumptive appreciation of wildlife, is usually governed by, or influenced by, what happens in

[12] This is the willingness to pay by nonsupporters to have the restoration stopped or abandoned.

[13] This basically assumes that no individuals will experience both benefits and costs from the restoration.

markets. This is clearly true of commercial harvesting. But it is increasingly true of noncommercial activities. The commercial packaging of sport hunting and fishing on private lands is a growing activity, as is ecotourism. What is more, illegal markets often thrive in places where conservation regulations cannot be enforced with vigor. This means in many cases that we must look to the operation of those legal and illegal markets for an understanding of the forces that are pushing toward or away from conservation. An understanding of these markets can give us valuable perspective on how best to conserve wildlife resources in ways that are efficient and equitable.

To illustrate this let us look at two elements of African wildlife, the elephant and the black rhinoceros.[14] Several decades ago these animals were widely hunted for elephant ivory and rhino horn, which had high value in world markets. But growing scarcities of the animals led to concern about their long-run survival prospects. Conservation groups such as the World Wildlife Fund and the International Union for the Conservation of Nature were instrumental in getting a ban on rhino horn (1977) and later on elephant ivory (1989). The bans were carried out under the Convention on International Trade in Endangered Species.

The reason for the market ban was to take away the incentives for hunters to kill these animals for their horn and ivory. In fact, the ban on ivory has been quite successful, leading to substantial increases in elephant numbers and greatly reduced concern for their long-run survival.[15] The rhino horn ban, however, has been a disaster for the black rhino. Illegal rhino hunting ("poaching") has continued and even grown in intensity, enforcement has been insufficient, and black rhino populations have continued a precipitous decline.

The question is: Why the difference? Why has the ban worked with one animal and not with the other? The reason is that there are big differences between the factors affecting the supply and demand for ivory and those affecting rhino horn. The differences can be seen in Figure 18-8. Panel (a) shows very generally the situation in the ivory market, and panel (b) illustrates the horn market. Each model contains two supply (marginal cost) curves and two demand (marginal willingness-to-pay) curves. In each case, D_1 is the demand curve prior to the ban and D_2 is the demand curve after the ban. The bans, in other words, have the effect of reducing the demand for the products in world trade. Accompanying the bans are laws making it illegal to hunt the animals in question. This has the effect of raising the harvest marginal cost curves in the two cases, from the lower one, which is applicable before the ban, to the upper one, labeled S (poachers). The regulations against hunting, in other words, do not end the activity; they just make it somewhat more expensive be-

---

[14] The inspiration for this example comes from Gardner Brown and David Layton, "Saving Rhinos," paper given at the meetings of the Association of Environmental and Resource Economists, Annapolis, MD, June 1997.

[15] This is a judgment from the standpoint of the international community; from that of the African communities who might see elephants more as a potential source of economic wealth the judgment might be different.

CHAPTER 18: THE ECONOMICS OF WILDLIFE MANAGEMENT

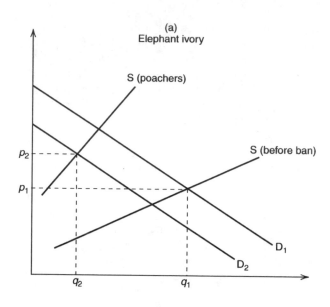

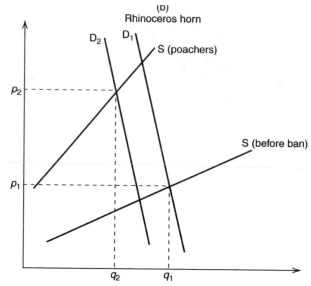

FIGURE 18-8
The Markets for Elephant Ivory and Rhinoceros Horn

cause of the possible costs of getting caught and punished; in effect, they shift up the supply functions.

The major underlying difference between the two markets is the slopes of the demand curves. In the ivory market it is relatively flat, whereas in the horn market it is quite steep. The basic reason for this is that there are relatively good substitutes for elephant ivory, but not for rhino horn. Ivory is used primarily for tourist carvings and for such specialty items as piano keys. These items have relatively good substitutes; in fact, an environmental group was instrumental in helping develop a plastic substitute for ivory piano keys. Good substitutes mean that the ivory demand curve will be relatively flat, because modest price increases will cause many consumers of ivory to shift to substitute materials. The major result that follows from this is that when the ivory ban is put in place, demand shifts back and supply shifts upward; the overall increase in market price is modest, but there is a large dropoff in quantity bought and sold. The ban, in other words, produces a substantial drop in quantity at a relatively small increase in price.

The rhino market is different. The demand for rhino horn comes mainly from its supposed medicinal value. In some Asian countries there are many medicinal recipes for which rhino horn is an essential ingredient; in effect it has no ready substitutes. The impact of this is that the market demand curve for rhino horn is quite steep. Increased prices do not lead to substantial decreases in quantity demanded. Thus, the ban on rhino horn will have a very different impact from the one on ivory. The rhino horn demand curve shifts back because of the ban, and the supply function shifts upward to the illegal poachers supply. There is a large increase in price for rhino horn, and a relatively small drop in quantity sold and bought. The ban does little, then, for reducing the quantities of rhino horn traded, so the rhino remains threatened by high rates of harvest.

The major lesson to get from this discussion is that simple attempts by regulators to intervene and change the way a market operates can have very different impacts, depending on the basic structure of supply and demand factors in those markets. This should be a cautionary note that market intervention, if it is to be at all successful, has to be done with good knowledge of the parameters of the markets affected, not only the primary market in which intervention is carried out, but also of markets for closely related goods and services.

SUMMARY

Wildlife management issues have become much more prominent in recent years. Increasing population growth has brought about greater contacts between humans and wildlife, and value changes among wealthier populations giving wildlife a higher priority in public decisions. To manage wildlife efficiently and effectively requires information from wildlife biologists combined with that from economics and other social perspectives. **Wildlife law** has developed in ways consistent with other dimensions of social change. In the United States, wildlife has been regarded as essentially an **open-access resource,** available to whoever gets there first. Open access, coupled with habitat loss, have led to substantial declines in many species of wildlife. This has led, among other things, to an expanded system of **wildlife refuges** here and elsewhere. It has also led to the growth of **private provision** of wildlife access, for hunting or viewing. The management of wildlife in **suburban** areas is becoming an increasing problem. **Wildlife restoration** and **predator control** programs have important distributional characteristics, usually consisting of benefits that are spread widely among a population and costs that are borne by a relatively small subgroup of the population. An investigation of several African wildlife restoration programs highlighted how important it is to have knowledge about the markets that one is trying to manage.

KEY TERMS

Wildlife biology	Suburbanization
Open-access resources	Recreational hunting
Private provision of wildlife benefits	Closed seasons
Distributional impacts of wildlife management programs	Bag limits
	Game ranching
Management of suburban wildlife	Existence, hunting, and viewing values

QUESTIONS FOR FURTHER DISCUSSION

1 If access to a hunting area is rationed by price, we can be sure that the level of visitation that results will maximize the social net benefits of the activity. If the same activity level is determined by lottery, however, we cannot be sure of this. Explain why not.

2 The bioeconomic models used in wildlife economics are based on biological growth processes. How would the basic model change in a case like recreational trout fishing where the replenishment process is one of stocking by humans?

3 In determining the optimal stock levels for suburban wildlife, whose preferences should count, everybody's or just the people living in the particular suburb under analysis?

4 Suppose an elk herd is to be managed for the benefits it produces for hunters. Would you expect that management decisions would be different if a public agency is in charge of the operation as compared to a private firm?

5 Apply the concept of price elasticity of demand, as discussed in Chapter 17, to the two elements of African wildlife, the elephant and the black rhinoceros.

6 For the situation depicted in Figure 18-4, the state is going to use a lottery to choose e^* hunters who will each be allowed to hunt one day. If the state wishes to maximize the amount of revenue it can obtain from this system, what price should it set for each permit?

USEFUL WEB SITES

The primary federal agency for wildlife resources:

• U.S. Fish and Wildlife Service in the Department of Interior (http://www.fws.gov)

Virtually all states have wildlife agencies, e.g.,

• Montana: Department of Fish, Wildlife, and Parks (http://www.fwp.state.mt)

SECTION FIVE: APPLIED NATURAL RESOURCE PROBLEMS

- California: Department of Fish and Game (http://www.dfg.ca.gov)
- North Carolina: Wildlife Resources Commission (http://www.wildlife. state.nc)

Public interest groups provide useful information on policy issues and a wide range of wildlife populations:

- National Audubon Society (especially for birds) (http://www.audubon.org)
- World Wildlife Fund (http://www.wwf.org)
- National Fish and Wildlife Foundation (http://www.nfwf.org)

A number of organizations are devoted to specific species or populations, for example:

- Ducks Unlimited (http://www.ducks.org)

SELECTED READINGS

Anderson, Terry L., and Peter J. Hill (eds.): *Wildlife in the Marketplace,* Rowmand and Littlefield, Lanham, MD, 1995.

Brown, Gardner: "Wildlife in Developing Countries," in Partha Dasgupta and Karl-Göran Mäler, *The Environment and Emerging Development Issues,* Vol. 2, Clarendon Press, Oxford, England, 1997, pp. 555–573.

Decker, Daniel, and Gary Goff: *Valuing Wildlife: Economic and Social Perspectives,* Westview Press, Boulder, CO, 1987.

Dixon, John, and Paul Sherman: *Economics of Protected Areas: A New Look at Benefits and Costs,* Island Press, Washington, DC, 1990.

Eltringham, S. K.: *Wildlife Resources and Economic Development,* John Wiley, New York, 1984.

Hammack, Judd, and Gardner Brown: *Waterfowl and Wetlands: Toward Bioeconomic Analysis,* Johns Hopkins Press, Baltimore, 1974.

Jewell, Peter A., and Sidney Holt: *Problems in Management of Locally Abundant Wild Mammals,* Academic Press, New York, 1981.

McCullough, Dale R. (ed.): *Metapopulations and Wildlife Conservation,* Island Press, Covelo, CA, 1996.

Porter, Douglas R., and David A. Salvesen (eds.): *Collaborative Planning for Wetlands and Wildlife: Issues and Examples,* Island Press, Covelo, CA, 1995.

Tober, James A.: *Who Owns the Wildlife, The Political Economy of Wildlife in Nineteenth Century America,* Greenwood Press, Westport, CT, 1981.

Tober, James A.: *Wildlife and the Public Interest,* Praeger, New York, 1989.

Frank–Bernanke:
Principles of
Microeconomics, Second
Edition

Back Matter

Glossary

© The McGraw-Hill
Companies, 2004

GLOSSARY

A

Absolute advantage. One person has an absolute advantage over another if he or she takes fewer hours to perform a task than the other person.

Accounting profit. The difference between a firm's total revenue and its explicit costs.

Adverse selection. The pattern in which insurance tends to be purchased disproportionately by those who are most costly for companies to insure.

Allocative function of price. Changes in prices direct resources away from overcrowded markets and toward markets that are underserved.

Asymmetric information. Situations in which buyers and sellers are not equally well informed about the characteristics of goods and services for sale in the marketplace.

Attainable point. Any combination of goods that can be produced using currently available resources.

Autarky. A situation in which a country is economically self-sufficient.

Average benefit. Total benefit of undertaking n units of an activity divided by n.

Average cost. Total cost of undertaking n units of an activity divided by n.

Average total cost (ATC). Total cost divided by total output.

Average variable cost (AVC). Variable cost divided by total output.

B

Barrier to entry. Any force that prevents firms from entering a new market.

Basic elements of a game. The players, the strategies available to each player, and the payoffs each player receives for each possible combination of strategies.

Better-than-fair gamble. A gamble whose expected value is positive.

Breakeven income level. Under a negative income tax, the level of before-tax income at which a family's tax liability exactly offsets its initial tax credit.

Buyer's reservation price. The largest dollar amount the buyer would be willing to pay for a good.

Buyer's surplus. The difference between the buyer's reservation price and the price he or she actually pays.

C

Cartel. A coalition of firms that agrees to restrict output for the purpose of earning an economic profit.

Cash on the table. Economic metaphor for unexploited gains from exchange.

Change in demand. A shift of the entire demand curve.

Change in supply. A shift of the entire supply curve.

Change in the quantity demanded. A movement along the demand curve that occurs in response to a change in price.

Change in the quantity supplied. A movement along the supply curve that occurs in response to a change in price.

Coase theorem. If at no cost people can negotiate the purchase and sale of the right to perform activities that cause externalities, they can always arrive at efficient solutions to the problems caused by externalities.

Collective good. A good or service that, to at least some degree, is nonrival but excludable.

Commitment device. A way of changing incentives so as to make otherwise empty threats or promises credible.

Commitment problem. A situation in which people cannot achieve their goals because of an inability to make credible threats or promises.

Comparative advantage. One person has a comparative advantage over another if his or her opportunity cost of performing a task is lower than the other person's opportunity cost.

Compensating wage differential. A difference in the wage rate—negative or positive—that reflects the attractiveness of a job's working conditions.

Complements. Two goods are complements in consumption if an increase in the price of one causes a leftward shift in the demand curve for the other.

Constant (or parameter). A quantity that is fixed in value.

Constant returns to scale. A production process is said to have constant returns to scale if, when all inputs are changed by a given proportion, output changes by the same proportion.

Consumer surplus. The economic surplus gained by the buyers of a product as measured by the cumulative difference between their respective reservation prices and the price they actually paid.

Consumption possibilities. The combination of goods and services that a country's citizens might feasibly consume.

Costly-to-fake principle. To communicate information credibly to a potential rival, a signal must be costly or difficult to fake.

Cost-plus regulation. A method of regulation under which the regulated firm is permitted to charge a price equal to its explicit costs of production plus a markup to cover the opportunity cost of resources provided by the firm's owners.

Credible promise. A promise to take an action that is in the promiser's interest to keep.

Frank–Bernanke:
Principles of
Microeconomics, Second
Edition

Back Matter

Glossary

© The McGraw–Hill
Companies, 2004

GLOSSARY

Credible threat. A threat to take an action that is in the threatener's interest to carry out.

Cross-price elasticity of demand. The percentage by which the quantity demanded of the first good changes in response to a 1 percent change in the price of the second.

Crowding out. Government borrowing that leads private firms to cancel planned investment projects because of higher interest rates.

Customer discrimination. The willingness of consumers to pay more for a product produced by members of a favored group, even if the quality of the product is unaffected.

D

Deadweight loss. The deadweight loss caused by a policy is the reduction in economic surplus that results from adoption of that policy.

Decision tree (or game tree). A diagram that describes the possible moves in a game in sequence and lists the payoffs that correspond to each possible combination of moves.

Demand curve. A curve or schedule showing the total quantity of a good that buyers wish to buy at each price.

Dependent variable. A variable in an equation whose value is determined by the value taken by another variable in the equation.

Disappearing political discourse. The theory that people who support a position may remain silent, because speaking out would create a risk of being misunderstood.

Dominant strategy. One that yields a higher payoff no matter what the other players in a game choose.

Dominated strategy. Any other strategy available to a player who has a dominant strategy.

E

Earned-income tax credit (EITC). A policy under which low-income workers receive credits on their federal income tax.

Economic loss. An economic profit that is less than zero.

Economic profit. The difference between a firm's total revenue and the sum of its explicit and implicit costs; also called *excess profit*.

Economic rent. That part of the payment for a factor of production that exceeds the owner's reservation price, the price below which the owner would not supply the factor.

Economic surplus. The economic surplus from taking any action is the benefit of taking the action minus its cost.

Economics. The study of how people make choices under conditions of scarcity and of the results of those choices for society.

Efficiency or economic efficiency. Condition that occurs when all goods and services are produced and consumed at their respective socially optimal levels.

Efficient (or Pareto-efficient). A situation is efficient if no change is possible that will help some people without harming others.

Efficient markets hypothesis. The theory that the current price of stock in a corporation reflects all relevant information about its current and future earnings prospects.

Efficient point. Any combination of goods for which currently available resources do not allow an increase in the production of one good without a reduction in the production of the other.

Efficient quantity. The efficient quantity of any good is the quantity that maximizes the economic surplus that results from producing and consuming the good.

Elastic. The demand for a good is elastic with respect to price if its price elasticity of demand is greater than 1.

Employer discrimination. An arbitrary preference by an employer for one group of workers over another.

Equation. A mathematical expression that describes the relationship between two or more variables.

Equilibrium. A stable, balanced, or unchanging situation in which all forces at work within a system are canceled by others.

Equilibrium price and equilibrium quantity. The price and quantity of a good at the intersection of the supply and demand curves for the good.

Excess demand (or shortage). The difference between the quantity supplied and the quantity demanded when the price of a good lies below the equilibrium price; buyers are dissatisfied when there is excess demand.

Excess supply (or surplus). The difference between the quantity supplied and the quantity demanded when the price of a good exceeds the equilibrium price; sellers are dissatisfied when there is excess supply.

Expected value of a gamble. The sum of the possible outcomes of the gamble multiplied by their respective probabilities.

Explicit costs. The actual payments a firm makes to its factors of production and other suppliers.

External benefit (or positive externality). A benefit of an activity received by people other than those who pursue the activity.

External cost (or negative externality). A cost of an activity that falls on people other than those who pursue the activity.

Externality. An external cost or benefit of an activity.

F

Factor of production. An input used in the production of a good or service.

Fair gamble. A gamble whose expected value is zero.

First-dollar insurance coverage. Insurance that pays all expenses generated by the insured activity.

Fixed cost. A cost that does not vary with the level of an activity.

Fixed factor of production. An input whose quantity cannot be altered in the short run.

Free-rider problem. An incentive problem in which too little of a good or service is produced because nonpayers cannot be excluded from using it.

G

Game tree. *See* **Decision tree.**

H

Head tax. A tax that collects the same amount from every taxpayer.

Frank–Bernanke:
Principles of
Microeconomics, Second
Edition

Back Matter

Glossary

© The McGraw–Hill
Companies, 2004

Health maintenance organization (HMO). A group of physicians that provides health services to individuals and families for a fixed annual fee.

Human capital. An amalgam of factors such as education, training, experience, intelligence, energy, work habits, trustworthiness, initiative, and others that affect the value of a worker's marginal product.

Human capital theory. A theory of pay determination that says a worker's wage will be proportional to his or her stock of human capital.

Hurdle method of price discrimination. The practice by which a seller offers a discount to all buyers who overcome some obstacle.

I

Imperfectly competitive firm. A firm that has at least some control over the market price of its product.

Implicit costs. All the firm's opportunity costs of the resources supplied by the firm's owners.

Income effect. The change in the quantity demanded of a good that results because a change in the price of a good changes the buyer's purchasing power.

Income elasticity of demand. The percentage by which a good's quantity demanded changes in response to a 1 percent change in income.

Increasing returns to scale. A production process is said to have increasing returns to scale if, when all inputs are changed by a given proportion, output changes by more than that proportion; also called *economies of scale*.

Independent variable. A variable in an equation whose value determines the value taken by another variable in the equation.

Inefficient point. Any combination of goods for which currently available resources enable an increase in the production of one good without a reduction in the production of the other.

Inelastic. The demand for a good is inelastic with respect to price if its price elasticity of demand is less than 1.

Inferior good. A good whose demand curve shifts leftward when the incomes of buyers increase.

In-kind transfer. A payment made not in the form of cash but in the form of a good or service.

Invisible hand theory. A theory stating that the actions of independent, self-interested buyers and sellers will often result in the most efficient allocation of resources.

L

Labor union. A group of workers who bargain collectively with employers for better wages and working conditions.

Law of diminishing marginal utility. The tendency for the additional utility gained from consuming an additional unit of a good to diminish as consumption increases beyond some point.

Law of diminishing returns. A property of the relationship between the amount of a good or service produced and the amount of a variable factor required to produce it; the law says that when some factors of production are fixed, increased production of the good eventually requires ever larger increases in the variable factor.

Lemons model. George Akerlof's explanation of how asymmetric information tends to reduce the average quality of goods offered for sale.

Logrolling. The practice whereby legislators support one another's legislative proposals.

Long run. A period of time of sufficient length that all the firm's factors of production are variable.

M

Macroeconomics. The study of the performance of national economies and the policies that governments use to try to improve that performance.

Marginal benefit. The marginal benefit of an activity is the increase in total benefit that results from carrying out one additional unit of the activity.

Marginal cost. The marginal cost of an activity is the increase in total cost that results from carrying out one additional unit of the activity.

Marginal labor cost. The amount by which a monopsonist's total wage bill goes up if it hires an extra worker.

Marginal product of labor (MP). The additional output a firm gets by employing one additional unit of labor.

Marginal revenue. The change in a firm's total revenue that results from a one-unit change in output.

Marginal utility. The additional utility gained from consuming an additional unit of a good.

Market. The market for any good consists of all buyers or sellers of that good.

Market equilibrium. Occurs when all buyers and sellers are satisfied with their respective quantities at the market price.

Market power. A firm's ability to raise the price of a good without losing all its sales.

Means-tested. A benefit program is means-tested if its benefit level declines as the recipient earns additional income.

Microeconomics. The study of individual choice under scarcity and its implications for the behavior of prices and quantities in individual markets.

Monopolistically competitive firm. One of a large number of firms that produce slightly differentiated products that are reasonably close substitutes for one another.

Monopsony. A market with only a single buyer.

Moral hazard. The tendency of people to expend less effort protecting those goods that are insured against theft or damage.

N

Nash equilibrium. Any combination of strategies in which each player's strategy is his or her best choice, given the other players' strategies.

Natural monopoly. A monopoly that results from economies of scale (increasing returns to scale).

Negative externality. *See* External cost.

Negative income tax. A system under which the government would grant every citizen a cash payment each year, financed by an additional tax on earned income.

Nominal price. Absolute price of a good in dollar terms.

Nonexcludable good. A good that is difficult, or costly, to exclude nonpayers from consuming.

GLOSSARY

Nonrival good. A good whose consumption by one person does not diminish its availability for others.

Normal good. A good whose demand curve shifts rightward when the incomes of buyers increase.

Normal profit. The opportunity cost of the resources supplied by the firm's owners; Normal profit = Accounting profit − Economic profit.

O

Oligopolist. A firm that produces a product for which only a few rival firms produce close substitutes.

Opportunity cost. The opportunity cost of an activity is the value of the next-best alternative that must be forgone to undertake the activity.

Optimal combination of goods. The affordable combination that yields the highest total utility.

P

Parameter. *See* **Constant.**

Pareto-efficient. *See* **Efficient.**

Payoff matrix. A table that describes the payoffs in a game for each possible combination of strategies.

Perfect hurdle. One that completely segregates buyers whose reservation prices lie above some threshold from others whose reservation prices lie below it, imposing no cost on those who jump the hurdle.

Perfectly competitive market. A market in which no individual supplier has significant influence on the market price of the product.

Perfectly discriminating monopolist. A firm that charges each buyer exactly his or her reservation price.

Perfectly elastic demand. The demand for a good is perfectly elastic with respect to price if its price elasticity of demand is infinite.

Perfectly elastic supply curve. A supply curve whose elasticity with respect to price is infinite.

Perfectly inelastic demand. The demand for a good is perfectly inelastic with respect to price if its price elasticity of demand is zero.

Perfectly inelastic supply curve. A supply curve whose elasticity with respect to price is zero.

Personal Responsibility Act. The 1996 federal law that transferred responsibility for welfare programs from the federal level to the state level and placed a five-year lifetime limit on payment of AFDC benefits to any given recipient.

Pork barrel spending. A public expenditure that is larger than the total benefit it creates but that is favored by a legislator because his or her constituents benefit from the expenditure by more than their share of the resulting extra taxes.

Positional arms control agreement. An agreement in which contestants attempt to limit mutually offsetting investments in performance enhancement.

Positional arms race. A series of mutually offsetting investments in performance enhancement that is stimulated by a positional externality.

Positional externality. Occurs when an increase in one person's performance reduces the expected reward of another's in situations in which reward depends on relative performance.

Positive externality. *See* **External benefit.**

Poverty threshold. The level of income below which the federal government classifies a family as poor.

Present value. When the annual interest rate is r, the present value (PV) of a payment M to be received T years from now is the amount that would have to be deposited today at an annual interest rate r to generate a balance of M after T years: $PV = M/(1 + r)^T$.

Price ceiling. A maximum allowable price, specified by law.

Price discrimination. The practice of charging different buyers different prices for essentially the same good or service.

Price elasticity of demand. The percentage change in the quantity demanded of a good or service that results from a 1 percent change in its price.

Price elasticity of supply. The percentage change in the quantity supplied that will occur in response to a 1 percent change in the price of a good or service.

Price floor. A law or regulation that guarantees that suppliers will receive at least a specified amount for their product.

Price setter. A firm with at least some latitude to set its own price.

Price taker. A firm that has no influence over the price at which it sells its product.

Prisoner's dilemma. A game in which each player has a dominant strategy, and when each plays it, the resulting payoffs are smaller than if each had played a dominated strategy.

Producer surplus. The economic surplus gained by the sellers of a product as measured by the cumulative difference between the price received and their respective reservation prices.

Production possibilities curve. A graph that describes the maximum amount of one good that can be produced for every possible level of production of the other good.

Profit. The total revenue a firm receives from the sale of its product minus all costs—explicit and implicit—incurred in producing it.

Profit-maximizing firm. A firm whose primary goal is to maximize the difference between its total revenues and total costs.

Profitable firm. A firm whose total revenue exceeds its total cost.

Progressive tax. One in which the proportion of income paid in taxes rises as income rises.

Proportional income tax. One under which all taxpayers pay the same proportion of their incomes in taxes.

Public good. A good or service that, to at least some degree, is both nonrival and nonexcludable.

Pure commons good. One for which nonpayers cannot easily be excluded and for which each unit consumed by one person means one less unit available for others.

Pure monopoly. The only supplier of a unique product with no close substitutes.

Pure private good. One for which nonpayers can easily be excluded and for which each unit consumed by one person means one less unit available for others.

Pure public good. A good or service that, to a high degree, is both nonrival and nonexcludable.

Frank–Bernanke:
Principles of
Microeconomics, Second
Edition

Back Matter

Glossary

© The McGraw–Hill
Companies, 2004

Q

Quota. A legal limit on the quantity of a good that may be imported.

R

Rational person. Someone with well-defined goals who tries to fulfill those goals as best he or she can.

Rationing function of price. Changes in prices that distribute scarce goods to those consumers who value them most highly.

Real price. Dollar price of a good relative to the average dollar price of all other goods and services.

Regressive tax. A tax under which the proportion of income paid in taxes declines as income rises.

Rent-seeking. The socially unproductive efforts of people or firms to win a prize.

Repeated prisoner's dilemma. A standard prisoner's dilemma that confronts the same players repeatedly.

Reservation price. The highest price someone is willing to pay to obtain any good or service, or the lowest payment someone would accept for giving up a good or performing a service.

Risk-averse person. Someone who would refuse any fair gamble.

Risk-neutral person. Someone who would accept any gamble that is fair or better.

Run. *See* **Slope.**

S

Seller's reservation price. The smallest dollar amount for which a seller would be willing to sell an additional unit, generally equal to marginal cost.

Seller's surplus. The difference between the price received by the seller and his or her reservation price.

Short run. A period of time sufficiently short that at least some of the firm's factors of production are fixed.

Shortage. *See* **Excess demand.**

Slope. In a straight line, the ratio of the vertical distance the straight line travels between any two points (*rise*) to the corresponding horizontal distance (*run*).

Socially optimal quantity. The quantity of a good that results in the maximum possible economic surplus from producing and consuming the good.

Statistical discrimination. The practice of making judgments about the quality of people, goods, or services based on the characteristics of the groups to which they belong.

Substitutes. Two goods are substitutes in consumption if an increase in the price of one causes a rightward shift in the demand curve for the other.

Substitution effect. The change in the quantity demanded of a good that results because buyers switch to or from substitutes when the price of the good changes.

Sunk cost. A cost that is beyond recovery at the moment a decision must be made.

Supply curve. A curve or schedule showing the total quantity of a good that sellers wish to sell at each price.

Surplus. *See* **Excess supply.**

T

Tariff. A tax imposed on an imported good.

Time value of money. The fact that a given dollar amount today is equivalent to a larger dollar amount in the future, because the money can be invested in an interest-bearing account in the meantime.

Tit-for-tat. A strategy for the repeated prisoner's dilemma in which players cooperate on the first move, then mimic their partner's last move on each successive move.

Total cost. The sum of all payments made to the firm's fixed and variable factors of production.

Total economic surplus. The sum of all the individual economic surpluses gained by buyers and sellers who participate in the market.

Total expenditure = Total revenue. The dollar amount consumers spend on a product is equal to the dollar amount sellers receive.

Total revenue. *See* **Total expenditure.**

Total surplus. The difference between the buyer's reservation price and the seller's reservation price.

Tragedy of the commons. The tendency for a resource that has no price to be used until its marginal benefit falls to zero.

U

Ultimatum bargaining game. One in which the first player has the power to confront the second player with a take-it-or-leave-it offer.

Unattainable point. Any combination of goods that cannot be produced using currently available resources.

Unit elastic. The demand for a good is unit elastic with respect to price if its price elasticity of demand is equal to 1.

Utilitarianism. A moral theory in which the right course of action is the one that results in the highest total utility.

V

Value of marginal product of labor. The dollar value of the additional output a firm gets by employing one additional unit of labor.

Variable. A quantity that is free to take a range of different values.

Variable cost. A cost that varies with the level of an activity.

Variable factor of production. An input whose quantity can be altered in the short run.

Vertical intercept. The value taken by the dependent variable when the independent variable equals zero.

W

Winner-take-all labor market. One in which small differences in human capital translate into large differences in pay.

Workers' compensation. A government insurance system that provides benefits to workers who are injured on the job.

World price. The price at which a good or service is traded on international markets.